Alan Rogers

FRANCE
2004

Quality Camping and Caravanning Sites

INSPECTED
CAMPSITES
& SELECTED

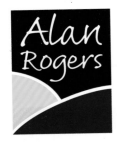

Compiled by: Alan Rogers Guides Ltd

Cover design: Paul Effenberg, Vine Cottage

Maps created by Customised Mapping (01769 560101)
contain background data provided by GisDATA Ltd

Maps are © Alan Rogers Guides and Gis DATA Ltd 2003

© Alan Rogers Guides Ltd 2003

Published by: Alan Rogers Guides Ltd, Burton Bradstock, Bridport, Dorset DT6 4QA

British Library Cataloguing-in-Publication Data:
A catalogue record for this book is available from the British Library.

ISBN: 0 901586 93 5

Printed in Great Britain by J H Haynes & Co Ltd

Contents

4   Introduction

6   How to use this Guide

8   Alan Rogers TRAVEL SERVICE

28   Brittany

65   Normandy

80   Northern France

89   Paris & Ile de France

95   Eastern France

108 Vendée & Charente

140 Loire Valley

161 Burgundy

172 Franche Comté

178 Savoy & Dauphiny Alps

190 Atlantic Coast

214 Dordogne & Averyron

244 Limousin & Auvergne

257 Rhône Valley

271 Provence

282 Midi-Pyrénées

294 Mediterranean West

326 Mediterranean East

348 Corsica

355 Naturist Sites

357 Open All Year

357 No Dogs

358 Bicycle Hire

359 Fishing

361 Riding, Golf

385 Maps

402 Town and Village Index

405 Campsite Index by Number

410 Campsite Index by Region

the Alan Rogers
approach

IT IS 36 YEARS SINCE ALAN ROGERS PUBLISHED THE FIRST CAMPSITE GUIDE THAT BORE HIS NAME. SINCE THEN THE RANGE OF TITLES HAS EXPANDED, WITH NEW GUIDES TO ITALY AND SPAIN & PORTUGAL BEING PUBLISHED FOR 2004. WHAT'S MORE THE ALAN ROGERS GUIDES ARE FAST BECOMING A FORCE TO BE RECKONED WITH IN THE NETHERLANDS TOO: IN 2004 ALL SIX TITLES WILL BE AVAILABLE FOR THE FIRST TIME, STOCKED BY WELL OVER 90% OF ALL DUTCH BOOKSHOPS.

There are over 11,000 campsites in France of varying quality: this guide contains impartially written reports on over 550, including some of the very finest, each being individually inspected and selected. All the usual maps and indexes are also included, designed to help you find the choice of campsite that's right for you. We hope you enjoy some happy and safe travels – and some pleasurable 'armchair touring' in the meantime!

INDEPENDENT AND HONEST

Whilst the content and scope of the guides have expanded considerably since the early editions, our selection of campsites still employs exactly the same philosophy and criteria as defined by Alan Rogers 36 years ago.

'warts and all'

Firstly, and most importantly, our selection is based entirely on our own rigorous and independent inspection and selection process. Campsites cannot buy their way into our guides – indeed the extensive Site Report which is written by us, not by the site owner, is provided free of charge so we are free to say what we think and to provide an honest, 'warts and all' description. This is written in plain English and without the use of confusing icons or symbols.

" ...the campsites included in this book have been chosen entirely on merit, and no payment of any sort is made by them for their inclusion."
Alan Rogers, 1968

INSPECTED
SINCE 1968
& SELECTED

A question of quality

The criteria which we use when inspecting and selecting sites are numerous, but the most important by far is the question of good quality. People want different things from their choice of campsite so we try to include a range of campsite 'styles' to cater for a wide variety of preferences: from those seeking a small peaceful campsite in the heart of the countryside, to visitors looking for an 'all singing, all dancing' site in a popular seaside resort. Those with more specific needs, such as sports facilities, cultural or historical attractions, are also catered for.

The size of the site, whether it's part of a campsite chain or privately owned, makes no difference in terms of it being required to meet our exacting standards regarding its quality and it being 'fit for purpose'. In other words, irrespective of the size of the site, or the number of facilities offered, the essentials (the welcome, the pitches, the sanitary facilities, the cleanliness and the general maintenance) must all be of a high standard.

Expert opinions

We rely on our dedicated team of Site Assessors, all of whom are experienced campers, caravanners or motorcaravanners, to visit and recommend sites. Each year they travel some 100,000 miles around Europe inspecting new sites and re-inspecting old ones. Our thanks are due to them for their enthusiastic efforts, their diligence and integrity and their commitment to the philosophy of the Alan Rogers Guides.

We also appreciate the feedback we receive from many of our readers, and we always make a point of following up complaints, suggestions or recommendations for possible new sites. Of course we get a few grumbles too – but it really is a few, and those we do receive usually arrive at the end of the high season and relate mainly to overcrowding or to poor maintenance during the peak school holiday period.

Please bear in mind that although we are interested to hear about any complaints we have no contractual relationship with the sites featured in our guides and are therefore not in a position to intervene in any dispute between a reader and a campsite. If you have a complaint about a campsite featured in our guides the first step should be to take the matter up with the site owner or manager.

Widely regarded as the 'Bible' by site owners and readers alike, there is no better guide when it comes to forming an independent view of a campsite's quality. When you need to be confident in your choice of campsite, you need the Alan Rogers Guide.

- ☑ Sites only included on merit
- ☑ Sites cannot pay to be included
- ☑ Independently inspected, rigorously assessed
- ☑ Impartial reviews
- ☑ 36 years of expertise

Being written in plain English, our guides are exceptionally easy to use, but a few words of explanation regarding the layout and content may be helpful. Regular readers will see that our site reports are grouped into 19 'tourist regions' and then by the various départements in each of these regions in numerical order.

Regions and départements

For administrative purposes France is actually divided into 23 official regions covering the 95 départements (similar to our counties). However, these do not always coincide with the needs of tourists. For example the area we think of as the Dordogne is split between two of the official regions. We have, therefore, opted to feature our campsites within unofficial 'tourist regions', and the relevant départements are stated in our introduction to each region with their official number (eg. the département of Manche is number 50) is included. We use these département numbers as the first two digits of our campsite numbers, so any campsite in the Manche département will start with the number 50.

Indexes

Our three indexes allow you to find sites by site number and name, by region and site name or by the town or village where the site is situated.

Campsite Maps

The maps relate to our tourist regions and will help you to identify the approximate position of each campsite.

Region

The Site Reports – *Example of an entry*

Number **Campsite Name**

Postal Address (including département)

A description of the site in which we try to give an idea its general features – its size, its situation, its strengths and its weaknesses. This column should provide a picture of the site itself with reference to the facilities that are provided and if they impact on its appearance or character. We include details on pitch numbers, electricity (with amperage), hardstandings etc. in this section as pitch design, planning and terracing affects the site's overall appearance. Similarly we continue to include reference to pitches used for caravan holiday homes, chalets, and the like. Importantly at the end of this column we indicate if there are any restrictions, e.g. no tents, dogs.

Facilities

Lists more specific information on the site's facilities, as well as certain off site activities.

At a glance			
Welcome & Ambience ✓✓✓✓✓	Location	✓✓✓✓✓
Quality of Pitches ✓✓✓✓✓	Range of Facilities ✓✓✓✓✓

Directions

Separated from the main text in order that they may be read and assimilated more easily by a navigator en-route. Bear in mind that road improvement schemes can result in some road numbers being altered. Websites like **www.mappy.com** and others give detailed route plans.

Charges 2003

Reservations including contact details

Open

Facilities

Toilet blocks: We assume that toilet blocks will be equipped with at least some British style WCs, washbasins with hot and cold water and hot showers with dividers or curtains, and will have all necessary shelves, hooks, plugs and mirrors. We also assume that there will be an identified chemical toilet disposal point, and that the campsite will provide water and waste water points and bin areas. If not the case, we comment. We continue to mention certain features that some readers find important: washbasins in cubicles, facilities for babies, facilities for those with disabilities and motorcaravan service points. Readers with disabilities are advised to contact the site of their choice to ensure that facilities are appropriate to their needs.

Shop: Basic or fully supplied, and opening dates.

Bars, restaurants, takeaway facilities and entertainment: We try hard to supply opening and closing dates (if other than the campsite opening dates) and to identify if there are discos or other noisy entertainment.

Children's play areas: Fenced and with safety surface (e.g. sand, bark or pea-gravel).

Swimming pools: If particularly special, we cover in detail in the first column but reference is always included in the second column. Opening dates, charges and levels of supervision are provided where we have been notified.

Leisure facilities: For example, playing fields, bicycle hire, organised activities and entertainment.

Dogs: If dogs are not accepted or restrictions apply, we state it here. Check the quick reference list on page 357.

Off site: This briefly covers leisure facilities, tourist attractions, restaurants etc nearby. Geographical tourist information is more likely to be in the first column.

At A Glance: All Alan Rogers sites have been inspected and selected – they must meet stringent quality criteria. A campsite may have all the boxes ticked when it comes to listing facilities but if it's not inherently a 'good site' then it will not be in the guide.

These 'at a glance' ratings are a unique indication of certain key criteria that may be important when making your decision. Quite deliberately they are subjective and, modesty aside, are based on our inspectors' own expert opinions at the time of their inspection.

Charges: These are the latest provided by the parks. In those few cases where 2003 or 2004 prices are not given, we try to give a general guide.

Telephone numbers: All numbers assume that you are phoning from within France. To phone France from outside that country, prefix the number shown with the relevant International Code (00 33) and drop the first 0, shown as (0) in the numbers indicated.

Opening dates: Are those advised to us during the early autumn of the previous year – parks can, and sometimes do, alter these dates before the start of the following season, often for good reasons. If you intend to visit shortly after a published opening date, or shortly before the closing date, it is wise to check that it will actually be open at the time required. Similarly some parks operate a restricted service during the low season, only opening some of their facilities (e.g. swimming pools) during the main season; where we know about this, and have the relevant dates, we indicate it – again if you are at all doubtful it is wise to check.

Reservations: Necessary for high season (roughly mid-July to mid-August) in popular holiday areas (ie beach areas). You can reserve via our own Alan Rogers Travel Service or through tour operators (see adverts). Or be wholly independent and contact the campsite(s) of your choice direct, using the phone, fax or e-mail numbers shown in the site reports, but please bear in mind that many sites are closed all winter.

Points to bear in mind

Some French site owners are very laid back when it comes to opening and closing dates. They may not be fully ready by their opening date – grass and hedges may not all be cut or perhaps only limited sanitary facilities open. At the end of the season they also tend to close down some facilities and generally wind down prior to the closing date. Bear this in mind if you are travelling early or late in the season – it is worth phoning ahead.

The Camping Cheque low season touring system goes some way to addressing this in that participating campsites are advised to have all facilities open and running by the opening date and to remain fully operational until the closing date.

Another area which has caused readers problems is the regulations which exist in some regions whereby Bermuda shorts may not be worn in swimming pools (for health reasons). It is worth ensuring that you do take 'proper' swimming trunks with you.

Whether you're an 'old hand' in terms of camping and caravanning or are contemplating your first trip, a regular reader of our Guides or a new 'convert', we wish you well in your travels and hope we have been able to help in some way. We are, of course, also out and about ourselves, visiting parks, talking to owners and readers, and generally checking on standards and new developments.

We wish all our readers thoroughly enjoyable Camping and Caravanning in 2004 – favoured by good weather of course!

service
and value

The Alan Rogers Travel Service was started three years ago in response to unrelenting requests from readers. We had so many requests asking us to take away the hassle of booking pitches on overseas campsites that we gave in. The Alan Rogers Travel Service was set up to provide a low cost booking service for readers: the next logical step to producing the guide books, allowing readers to browse through the guides, make a choice of campsite, then simply ask us to arrange everything.

Of course, with our contacts and relation-ships we can offer the pick of Europe's finest campsites. And, because we organise so many holidays, we can negotiate unbeatable ferry deals too. In fact the rates we get are so low that the ferry companies do not normally allow us to sell ferry crossings alone.

the travel service

TO BOOK THIS SITE

0870 405 4055

Expert Advice & Special Offers

Unbeatable
Ferry Deals

WE ARE ALWAYS NEGOTIATING NEW OFFERS ON CHANNEL CROSS-INGS. MAKE SURE YOU ASK US ABOUT OUR FAMOUS DEALS!

- ☑ CARAVANS GO FREE
- ☑ TRAILERS GO FREE
- ☑ MOTORHOMES PRICED AS CARS

At the Alan Rogers Travel Service we're always keen to find the best deals and keenest prices. There's always great savings on offer, and we're constantly negotiating new ferry rates and money-saving offers, so just call us on

0870 405 4055

and ask about the latest deals.

or visit
www.alanrogersdirect.com

THE AIMS OF THE TRAVEL SERVICE ARE SIMPLE.

- To provide convenience - when booking a campsite yourself can be anything but convenient.
- To provide peace of mind - when you need it most.
- To provide a friendly, knowledgeable, efficient service - when this can be hard to find.
- To provide a low cost means of organising your holiday – when prices can be so complicated.

HOW IT WORKS

1 Choose your campsite(s)

2 Choose your dates

3 Choose your ferry crossing

Then just call us for an instant quote

0870 405 4055
or visit
www.alanrogersdirect.com

For full details see our **FREE** 2004 brochure

0870 405 4055

Ask about our incredible Ferry Deals:

- ☑ **Caravans GO** FREE
- ☑ **Motorhomes Priced as Cars**

Let us book your pitch and ferry for you

don't miss out·
book early

Because so many of our best campsites are booked well in advance by those in the know, we do advise early action. We make it as simple as possible, and it's risk-free. A £100 deposit is all it takes to confirm those important campsite dates and secure the vital ferry crossing. The balance is not due until 10 weeks before departure, leaving you plenty of time to relax knowing that next year's holiday is 'in the bag'. Each year we unfortunately have to disappoint a number of would-be travellers who have left it just too late for the high summer dates (and ferry crossings) – please don't allow yourself to be one of them.

extra nights
FREE

Booking with The Alan Rogers Travel Service always means great value and real peace of mind. Now we've negotiated new special offers for 2004 – all designed to save you more money.

These are generally extra nights **FREE** of charge, subject to certain conditions and availability. Examples might be 7 nights for 6 or 12 nights for 10. Qualifying dates are usually in the off-peak period.

Ask for details or see our 2004 brochure (above).

WE ACT AS AGENTS FOR ALL THE CAMPSITES AND FERRY OPERATORS FEATURED IN THE TRAVEL SERVICE. AS SUCH, WE CAN BOOK ALL YOUR TRAVEL ARRANGEMENTS WITH THE MINIMUM OF FUSS AND AT THE BEST POSSIBLE PRICES. THE BASE PRICES BELOW INCLUDE 12 NIGHTS PITCH FEES AND RETURN FERRY CROSSING.

First night on site	Base Price 2 adults + car 12 nights	extra adult	child (0-13)	extra/fewer nights
Before 18 May	£294	£25	FREE	£12
18 May – 18 June	£314	£25	FREE	£12
19 June - 2 July	£345	£25	FREE	£12
3 July – 13 August	£415	£25	FREE	£12
14 August – 23 August	£375	£25	FREE	£12
From 24 August	£314	£25	FREE	£12

The base price of your holiday includes 12 nights pitch fees and a mid-week return ferry crossing from Dover to Calais with P&O Ferries for a car and five passengers (outward sailing times must be between 14:01 and 06:59. Inward sailing times must be between 20:01 and 14:59). Additional supplements are payable for caravans, trailers and motorhomes at all times and for cars at weekends and times outside those given above. There will also usually be a campsite supplement payable (see opposite). Call us on **0870 405 4055** for details and a quote.

If your holiday is longer or shorter than 12 nights, simply add or subtract £12 per night. Holidays must be for a minimum of 3 nights, with ferry (many sites have a minimum stay requirement). For holidays longer than 21 nights please call for a quotation. You may stay on as many sites as you wish, subject to individual site requirements, with a one-off £10 multi-site fee.

LOW £100 DEPOSIT
A special low deposit of just £100 secures your holiday
(full payment is required at the time of booking for travel within 10 weeks)

12 nights pitch fees + ferry for car and passengers	from **£294** DOVER - CALAIS
12 nights pitch fees + ferry for motorhome and passengers	from **£310** PORTSMOUTH - LE HAVRE/ CHERBOURG
12 nights pitch fees + ferry for car and caravan and passengers	from **£294** DOVER - CALAIS

* *Special Offers: Look for our famous money-saving deals: Caravans Go Free, Motorhomes Priced as Car. Ask us for details.*

Motorhomes

Priced

as Cars

Caravans and Trailers

GO FREE

Site Supplements

All sites operate their own independent pricing structure, and in order to reflect the differences in cost from one site to another, we will add a nightly 'site supplement' to the Base Prices indicated above. Although some sites in our brochure have very low supplements (eg 80060 Val de Trie: 2 adults and car/ caravan/ motorhome carries no supplement all season), others may carry much higher supplements. These reflect their location and amenities (eg 83020 Esterel Caravaning: 2 adults and car/caravan/motorhome = £28 supplement per night in high season).

Additional supplements can often apply for electricity, water and drainage or special pitches.

The simplest next step is to just call us for an immediate price quotation for your chosen site and all the available options, as well as any other important information, such as any minimum stay requirements.

CALL US NOW **0870 405 4055** FOR AN INSTANT QUOTE

OR VISIT **www.alanrogersdirect.com**

Leave The Hassle To Us

- All site fees paid in advance – you won't need to take extra currency with you.
- Your pitch is reserved for you – travel with peace of mind.
- No endless overseas phone calls or correspondence with foreign site owners.
- No need to pay foreign currency deposits and booking fees.
- Take advantage of our expert advice and experience of camping in Europe.

Already Booked Your Ferry?

We're confident that our ferry inclusive booking service offers unbeatable value. However, if you have already booked your ferry then we can still make a pitch-only reservation for you. Your booking must be for a minimum of 10 nights, and since our prices are based on our ferry inclusive service, you need to be aware that a non-ferry booking will always result in somewhat higher prices than if you were to book direct with the site.

You still benefit from:

- Hassle-free booking with no booking fees and foreign currency deposits.
- Comprehensive Travel Pack.
- Peace of mind: site fees paid in advance, with your pitch reserved for you.

FULL DETAILS IN OUR 64 PAGE 2004 COLOUR BROCHURE CALL

0870 405 4055

book
on-line
and save money

NEW for 2004 **www.alanrogersdirect.com** is a brand new website designed to give you everything you need to know when it comes to booking your Alan Rogers inspected and selected campsite, and your low cost ferry.

Our glossy brochure gives you all the info you need but it is only printed once a year. And our friendly, expert reservations team is always happy to help on **0870 405 4055** – but they do go home sometimes!

Visit www.alanrogersdirect.com and you'll find constantly updated information, latest ferry deals, special offers from campsites and much more. And you can visit it at any time of day or night!

alan rogers direct.com

book on-line and save

Campsite Information

- ☑ Details of all Travel Service campsites - **instantly**
- ☑ Find latest special offers on campsites - **instantly**
- ☑ Check campsite availability - **instantly**

Ferry Information

- ☑ Check ferry availability - **instantly**
- ☑ Find latest ferry deals - **instantly**
- ☑ Book your ferry online - **instantly**
- ☑ Save money - **instantly**

Save Money!

BOOK YOUR CAMPSITE AND FERRY - INSTANTLY

NEW Perfect Match
Find the campsite that's right for you

With so many sites to choose from it can be difficult to find a short-list. With the unique Alan Rogers Perfect Match system you can quickly find a campsite that meets your requirements. This powerful and searchable database of top campsites, all Alan Rogers inspected and selected, means you can quickly find an ideal site, book it on-line and relax in the knowledge that your holiday is safely reserved.

Ferry Deals On-line

FOR 2004 WE HAVE ARRANGED SOME EXCEPTIONAL OFFERS ON KEY CROSS-CHANNEL ROUTES. THESE ARE CERTAIN TO MAKE YOU WANT TO THINK ABOUT YOUR HOLIDAY NOW AND NOT RISK MISSING OUT.

Caravans Go FREE
Trailers Go FREE
Motorhomes Priced as Cars

Dover – Calais
Portsmouth – Cherbourg
Portsmouth – Le Havre

P&O Ferries

Portsmouth – Caen
Poole – Cherbourg

Conditions apply – ask for details or see page 26.

Brittany Ferries

Don't delay – this offer is strictly subject to availability and will be first come, first served.

TO BOOK THIS SITE

0870 405 4055

Expert Advice &
Special Offers

IN ESTABLISHING OUR PROGRAMME, WE HAVE ENSURED A SELECTION OF SITES IN EVERY CORNER OF FRANCE AND, AS WELL AS OFFERING SITES IN WELL KNOWN AREAS AND WELL ESTABLISHED RESORTS, WE HAVE ALSO SOUGHT TO INCLUDE SOME SMALLER SITES IN LITTLE KNOWN AREAS, BUT WHICH ARE WELL WORTH A VISIT. THIS IS A SELECTION OF THE SITES WE CAN BOOK FOR YOU, WITH FERRY, IN 2004.

(M) Mobile   (C) Chalet   (P) Pitch   (T) Ready erected tents

Brittany

22090 (P)
Château de Galinée
St Cast le Guido

Well kept family run site with excellent pool complex, a few kilometres back from St Cast.

22100 (P)
L'Abri Côtier
Etables-sur-Mer

Small, tranquil family site 500m from superb sandy beach

22130 (M) (P)
Port l'Epine
Trélévern

Small, friendly site on pretty promontory with pool and with beach access.

22140 (P)
Port la Chaîne
Pleubian

Set in a beautiful location, this friendly family run site has direct access to the sea.

29000 (M) (P)
Les Mouettes
Carantec

Sheltered site with excellent pool complex in attractive bay, near to Roscoff ferry port.

29010 (M) (P)
Le Ty-Nadan
Arzano

Well organised country site beside the River Ellé, with good swimming pools.

29050 (M) (P)
L'Orangerie de Lanniron
Quimper

Beautiful, quiet site in mature grounds of riverside estate, 15 km from the sea.

29080 (P)
Le Panoramic
Telgruc-sur-Mer

Family site in West Brittany near Châteaulin, quite close to good beach.

29090 (M) (P)
Le Raguenès Plage
Névez

Well regulated, attractive and popular site in small seaside village, with beach access.

29110 (P)
Village la Plage
Le Guilvinec

This spacious site is located beside a long sandy beach, ideal for fishing and sandcastles.

29120 (P)
Le Manoir de Kerlut
Plobannalec

This modern site is set in the grounds of an old manor house near Pont l'Abbe.

29130 (P)
Les Abers
Landéda

Attractively situated, family run site in tranquil western Brittany.

29140 (P)
Domaine de Kerlann
Pont-Aven

Good complex of indoor and outdoor pools and a range of entertainment and activities.

29170 (P)
La Piscine
Beg-Meil

Attractive family site with relaxed atmosphere and a warm welcome.

29240 (P)
Kéranterec
La Forêt-Fouesnant

Well established family run site with access to small beach and the coastal pathway.

29280 (P)	29290 (T)(M)(P)	35000 (P)	35020 (P)
La Pointe Superbe **St Coulitz**	**Village le Grand Large** **Mousterlin**	**Le Vieux Chêne** **Dol-de-Bretagne**	**Domaine des Ormes** **Epiniac**
This friendly site, based just outside the market town Châteaulin, is 15k from the beach.	Good family site with pool and waterslides adjacent to excellent sandy beach.	Attractive, family owned site between St Malo and Mont St Michel.	Impressive site on an estate of wooded park-land and lakes, with 18 hole golf course.

35040 (M)(P)	350600 (P)	44040 (P)	44090 (P)
Sunêlia Le P'tit Bois **St Malo**	**La Touesse** **Dinard**	**Parc Sainte-Brigitte** **La Turballe**	**Le Château du Deffay** **Pontchâteau**
Busy, well kept site near ferry port and yachting centre of St Malo.	Family campsite close to Dinard and only 300 metres from the beach.	Well established site in grounds of manor house, 3km from beaches.	Naturally landscaped to encourage wildlife, this site blends well with its rural surrounds.

44100 (M)(P)	56040 (P)	56050 (P)	56110 (P)
Sunêlia Le Patisseau **Pornic**	**Le Penboch** **Arradon**	**Kervilor** **La-Trinité-sur-Mer**	**Le Moustoir** **Carnac**
Friendly, busy site with its own pool, near fishing port of Pornic.	Quietly situated site with good facilities on the pretty Golfe du Morbihan.	Quieter, more spacious site, close to stylish resort.	Family-friendly site, with good pool complex and relaxed atmosphere. Beach 3 km.

56120 (P)	29350 (M)(P)	56180 (P)	**Normandy**
Les Iles **Pénestin**	**Sunêlia l'Atlantique** **Beg Meil**	**Le Cénic** **Pénestin-sur-Mer**	
Friendly, family run site with direct access to beach.	A well organised site amid picturesque countryside and close to a superb beach.	This attractive site meets all tastes with a fantastic pool complex, fishing lake and sports activities.	

14030 (P)	14090 (P)	50030 (C)(P)	50050 (P)
Château de Martragny **Martragny**	**Le Brèvedent** **Pont l'Evêque**	**Lez Eaux** **Granville**	**Le Cormoran** **Ravenôville**
Attractive site in parkland setting adjoining chateau and close to D-Day beaches.	Well established traditional site, with own swimming pool and fishing lake.	Family site with swimming pools set back from the sea on the Cotentin coast.	Neat seaside site on eastern Cotentin coast, 5 km north of Utah beach.

50060 Ⓜ Ⓟ
Le Grand Large
Les Pieux

Established family site
with direct access to a
long sandy beach, 20 km
south of Cherbourg.

50070 Ⓟ
L'Anse du Brick
Maupertus-sur-Mer

Friendly, family run
coastal site with attractive
pool complex, 8 km east
of Cherbourg Port.

02030 Ⓟ
La Croix du Vieux
Pont
Berny Rivière

Handy for Paris, with
outstanding amenities,
in an attractive location.

02000 Ⓟ
Le Vivier aux Carpes
Séraucourt-le-Grand

This small and friendly
site is just two hours
from Calais and is won-
derfully convenient.

62010 Ⓟ
La Bien Assise
Guines

Mature, quality site with
pools, close to cross
Channel links.

62030 Ⓜ Ⓟ
Château de Gandspette
Eperlecques

Friendly, comfortable,
family run site with
swimming pools in
grounds of château.

80010 Ⓟ
Château de Drancourt
St Valéry sur Somme

Popular site with pools
and other amenities,
between Boulogne
and Dieppe.

80060 Ⓜ Ⓟ
Le Val de Trie
Bouillancourt

Natural countryside tour-
ing site, in a woodland
location,
near small village.

80070 Ⓟ
La Ferme des Aulnes
Fresne-sur-Authie

This pretty site has been
developed on the grassy
meadows of a small 17th
century farm.

17210 Ⓒ Ⓟ
Interlude
Ile de Ré

This well managed site
offers first class facilities
and has direct access to
a beach.

17110 Ⓟ
Monplaisir
Les Mathes

Small, quiet site with garden atmosphere
and swimming pool,
close to town.

17140 Ⓜ Ⓟ
Séquoia Parc
Saint-Just Luzac

Top class site in grounds
of a chateau, with
pool complex.

17160 Ⓟ
Le Clos Fleuri
Médis

Pretty, family site amid
fields with friendly
atmosphere and bar.
Royan's beaches 5 km.

17170 Ⓜ Ⓟ
Les Charmilles
Fouras

Site close to quieter
resort, with good pool
and other amenities.

17180 Ⓟ
La Pignade
Ronce-les-Bains

Lively site with good pool
and entertainment. Ideal
for families.

85020 Ⓟ
Camping du Jard
La-Tranche-sur-Mer

Well maintained, wel-
coming site, between La
Rochelle and Les Sables
d'Olonne.

85040 Ⓟ
La Garangeoire
St Julien-des-Landes

Rurally situated site
in the grounds of
château, 15km from
the Atlantic coast.

85440 Ⓜ Ⓟ
Les Brunelles
Longeville

A friendly site with
good facilities and entertainment in
high season.

85080 (M) (P)
La Puerta del Sol
St Hilaire de Riez

Good quality site a short distance away from the lively coast.

85090 (P)
L'Abri des Pins
St Jean-de-Monts

A pleasant 15 minute walk through pine woods takes you to a lovely sandy beach.

85430 (P)
Bolée d'Air
St Vincent sur Jard

This friendly, well managed site is ideal for families, with high season entertainment.

85130 (P)
Camping Pong
Landevieille

Pleasant, traditional site, just 5km from the long sandy beaches at Brétignolles.

85150 (M) (P)
La Yole
St Jean de Monts

Attractive, popular, well run site, very close to a fine sandy beach.

17190 (P)
Logis du Breuil
St Augustin

Spacious, parkland setting, handy for the beach and good for families.

85210 (P)
Les Ecureuils
Jard-sur-Mer

Attractive, wooded site in quieter part of Southern Vendée.

85240 (P)
Jarny Océan
Longeville-sur-Mer

Popular site in wooded area and within walking distance to beach.

85260 (P)
La Guyonnière
St Julien-des-Landes

Spacious, rural site, away from the lively coast with attractive pool.

85270 (P)
L'Océano d'Or
Jard-sur-Mer

Busy holiday site with many facilities, 900 metres from beach.

85280 (T) (M) (P)
Les Places Dorées
St Jean de Monts

Modern site with excellent pool complex and waterslides just north of St Jean.

85310 (P)
La Trévillière
Brétignolles sur Mer

Relaxed, leafy site with good range of activities and amenities. Sandy beach 2 km.

85470 (M) (P)
Les Pirons
Château d'Olonne

A modern site, close to the beach with an impressive swimming pool complex.

85330 (P)
Cap Natur
St Hilaire de Riez

This family campsite for naturists is in an area of undulating sand dunes and pine trees.

85350 (P)
La Ningle
St Hilaire de Riez

Well established, family run campsite in a popular tourist area.

Paris/Ile De France

60010 (P)
Campix
St-Leu-d'Esserent

In a former sandstone quarry, this informal site has a peaceful environment.

77040 (C) (P)
Les Quatre Vents
Crèvecoeur en Brie

Peaceful site in countryside location, within easy reach of Disneyland Paris.

77070 (M) (P)
La Belle Etoile
Melun

Friendly, family-run site set beside the Seine, ideal for Paris.

78010 (M) (P)
Camping International
Maisons-Laffitte

Busy all year site on the banks of the Seine convenient for central Paris.

37010 Ⓟ
La Mignardière
Ballan-Miré

Ideal for relaxing on-site or exploring the city of Tours and many of the Loire châteaux nearby.

41030 Ⓒ Ⓜ Ⓟ
Parc des Alicourts
Pierrefitte sur Sauldre

Secluded, quality site in the heart of the forest, with many excellent facilities.

41040 Ⓟ
Château des Marais
Chambord

Impressive family site with excellent facilities, near famous château.

41060 Ⓟ
Camping de Dugny
Onzain

A mature and well organised campsite surrounded by many acres of rural farmland.

45010 Ⓒ Ⓜ Ⓟ
Les Bois du Bardelet
Gien

Attractive, lively family run site with lake and pool complex, in eastern Loire.

49020 Ⓜ Ⓟ
Chantepie
St Hilaire-St Florent

Pleasant site with swimming pools, close to Saumur with lovely views over the Loire.

37030 Ⓣ Ⓟ
Moulin Fort
Chenonceaux

A pretty riverside site enhanced with a variety of shrubs and trees and a restored old mill.

49060 Ⓟ
L'Européen
Coutures

Elegant, spacious site, ideal for exploring the Saumur and Angers area.

49080 Ⓜ Ⓟ
Ile d'Offard
Saumur

Set on an island overlooked by the château. Great stopover, great base for exploring.

49090 Ⓟ
Isle Verte
Montsoreau

This friendly, natural site overlooks the Loire and offers excellent facilities for fishermen.

72030 Ⓟ
Château de Chanteloup
Sillé-le-Philippe

A peaceful, pleasant and friendly site, situated in the park of a 19th century château.

86030 Ⓟ
Relais du Miel
Châtellerault

A beautiful site situated in the grounds of a grand Napoleonic house beside the river Vienne.

86040 Ⓟ
Le Futuriste
St Georges Baillargeaux

Purpose built convenient site on hill overlooking Futurscope, open all year.

49040 Ⓟ
Camping de l'Etang
Brissac

Originally a farm, this site offers comfort with pleasant views.

88080 Ⓟ
Domaine des Bans
Corcieux

A well organised site situated in the heart of the Vosges mountains on the edge of a National Park.

51020M Ⓟ
Camping Municipal
Chalons-en Champagne

Ideally situated for exploring this famous region of France with its vineyards.

52020 Ⓟ
La Forge de Ste Marie
Thonnance-les Moulins

Attractive site with indoor pool and varied activities programme, in pleasant country.

88040 Ⓟ
Lac de Bouzey
Sanchey

Pleasant all year site with heated pool, overlooking the lake

52030 Ⓟ
Lac de la Liez
Langres

A newly renovated lake-side site with beautiful views and excellent facilities.

25030 Ⓟ
Bois de Reveuge
Huanne-Montmartin

Set in lovely countryside leading down to two lakes, this pretty site is ideal for watersports.

39040 Ⓜ Ⓟ
Sunêlia La Pergola
Marigny

A neat and tidy site set amongst rolling hills, overlooking the sparkling waters of Lac de Chalain.

39010 Ⓟ
La Plage Blanche
Ounans

Situated on the banks of the river Loue with direct access to a river-side beach.

08040 Ⓟ
La Samaritaine
Buzancy

A delightful site set in the heart of the Ardennes with a nearby lake.

Burgundy

21000 Ⓟ
Lac de Panthier
Vandenesse-en-Auxois

Attractively situated lake-side site in Burgundy countryside.

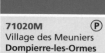

58010 Ⓟ
Les Bains
St Honoré les Bains

This attractive, family run site is ideally situated for exploring the Morvan area.

58030 Ⓒ Ⓟ
Manoir de Bezolle
St Péreuse-en-Morvan

Well situated for exploring the Morvan National Park and the Nivernais area.

71020M Ⓟ
Village des Meuniers
Dompierre-les-Ormes

Stunning panoramic views can be enjoyed from this superbly landscaped, well run site.

71070 Ⓟ
Château de l'Epervière
Gigny-sur-Saône

Friendly and popular, enthusiastically run rural site in the grounds of a château.

71080 Ⓜ Ⓟ
Etang Neuf
Issy l'Evêque

A friendly tranquil site with a forest on one side, a château on another overlooking a lake.

Alps

38010 Ⓒ Ⓟ
Le Coin Tranquille
Les Abrets

Family run site with swimming pool and restaurant with peaceful surroundings.

38040 Ⓒ Ⓟ
La Rencontre du Soleil
Bourg d'Oisans

Small, friendly site amid spectacular Alpine scenery with high quality amenities.

74040 Ⓟ
La Ravoire
Doussard

Quality site in a pleasant location overlooking Lake Annecy, with a good pool and waterslide.

74060 Ⓟ
La Colombière
Neydens

Neat and tidy small site with pool, within easy reach of Geneva.

74070 Ⓟ
L'Escale
Le Grand Bornand

Friendly, family site in magnificent mountain setting, open all year.

Atlantic Coast

33080 Ⓟ
Domaine de la Barbanne
St Emilion

Pleasant, friendly, family-owned site in heart of celebrated wine region. Just outside St Emilion.

33210 (M) (P)
Sunêlia Pointe du Médoc
Le Verdon

A modern site set near the tip of the Medoc peninsula just 1km from a sandy beach.

33110 (M) (P)
La Côte d'Argent
Hourtin Plage

Large, family run Médoc site with easy access to the vast white sandy beaches.

40030 (P)
Les Pins du Soleil
St Paul lès Dax

Family oriented site with swimming pool close to spa town of Dax.

33220 (M) (P)
Sunêlia Petit Nice
Pyla-sur-Mer

A friendly traditional seaside site with direct access to a lovely sandy beach.

40050 (M) (P)
Sunêlia Le Col Vert
Vielle-Saint-Girons

Familiy holiday centre with long frontage to lake, 5 km from Atlantic beaches.

40100 (M) (P)
Domaine de la Rive
Biscarosse

Landes site in superb beach-side location on Lac de Sanguinet.

40110 (P)
Sen Yan
Mezos

Superb family site with tropical ambience set in the Landes forest area.

40140 (M) (P)
Lou P'tit Poun
St Martin de Seignanx

Friendly, family run site in a quiet setting with swimming pool.

40170 (P)
La Réserve
Parentis-en-Born

High quality site by large lake with indoor and outdoor pools.

40180 (T) (M) (P)
Le Vieux Port
Messanges

A popular site with excellent facilities for all the family. Short walk to the beach.

64070 (P)
Le Ruisseau
Bidart

Pleasant, busy site with excellent swimming pool, set back from the sea.

64080 (P)
Tamaris Plage
St Jean-de-Luz

Pleasant well tended site with individual pitches, close to a lovely sandy beach.

64110 (P)
Col d'Ibardin
Urrugne

Friendly family owned site with swimming pool at foot of Basque Pyrenees.

64140 (M) (P)
Sunêlia Bérrua
Bidart

Set only one kilometre from the sea, this site is ideal for visiting the beaches.

Dordogne/Aveyron

12170 (M) (P)
Sunêlia Le Caussanel
Canet-en-Salars

A pretty site near a lake, surrounded by beautiful countryside, ideal for swimming.

12020 (P)
Les Rivages
Millau

Large site on town outskirts close to Tarn Gorges with good range of sporting facilities.

12040 (M) (P)
Les Tours
St Amans des Cots

Attractive, friendly and efficiently run site on shores of Lac de la Selves.

12080 (P)
Les Genêts
Salles Curan

Fantastic family holiday and watersports facilities are available on this friendly, family run site.

16020 (P)
Gorges du Chambon
Eymouthiers

Family site tucked away in pretty, rolling Perigord Vert countryside.

24010 Ⓟ
Château le Verdoyer
Champs Romain

Respected Dutch owned site set in the grounds of restored Château Le Verdoyer.

24040 Ⓣ Ⓜ Ⓟ
Moulin du Roch
Sarlat

Family run site midway between Sarlat and Les Eyzies with activities to suit everyone.

24080 Ⓟ
Moulin de David
Monpazier

Secluded valley site with pool, on southwest of the Dordogne. Lovely towns and countryside.

24180 Ⓟ
Saint Avit Loisirs
Le Bugue

Well appointed site with impressive pool complex close to Dordogne attractions.

24100 Ⓜ Ⓟ
Sunêlia Le Moulinal
Biron

This is a lakeside site with a wide range of activities with extensive wooded grounds to explore.

46010 Ⓟ
La Paille Basse
Souillac

High quality site in rural situation with panoramic views.

47010 Ⓟ
Moulin du Perié
Sauveterre-la-Lemance

Pretty, family run site set in wooded country away from much of the tourist bustle.

24110 Ⓜ Ⓟ
Aqua Viva
Carsac

This friendly site with many activities on-site and interesting places to visit nearby.

24170 Ⓟ
Port de Limeuil
Limeuil

A delightful family site set opposite the picturesque village of Limeuil.

46030 Ⓟ
Les Pins
Payrac-en-Quercy

Impressive views can be enjoyed from this well equipped family site. The pine forest offers shade.

19060 Ⓟ
Mialaret
Neuvic

This pretty site is set in the grounds of a 19th century château, where wildlife is in abundance.

24330 Ⓟ
Etang Bleu
Vieux-Mareuil

A countryside site set in mature woodland between Perigueux and Angoulême.

Limousin/ Auvergne

87020 Ⓟ
Château de Leychoisier
Bonnac la Côte

Impressive site in the grounds of a château, 10km north of Limoges.

03010 Ⓟ
La Filature
Ebreuil

Developed on the site of a spinning mill, this rural setting is ideal for cycling and walking.

23010 Ⓟ
Château de Poinsouze
Boussac-Bourg

Well designed, high quality site, set in beautiful château parkland.

Rhone Valley

07020 Ⓟ
L'Ardèchois
St Sauveur-de-Montagut

In a spectacular setting, this site offers unspoilt countryside and a large range of amenities.

07030 Ⓜ Ⓟ
Soleil Vivarais
Sampzon

Large, quality site bordering the River Ardèche complete with sandy beach. Ideal for families.

07070 Ⓟ
Les Ranchisses
Chassiers

Friendly, family site in an attractive peaceful location on the Route de Valgorge.

Jan & Sophie

Roppeman

F. Verslmysstraat 6

8 310   BRUGES

050 | 35. 85. 19

26030 Ⓜ Ⓟ
Sunêlia Le Grand Lierne
Valence

Conveniently and attractively situated family site on the route south.

69010 Ⓟ
Camping International
Lyon

Neat site with good amenities, popular for overnight stops.

07050 Ⓜ Ⓟ
Sunêlia Ranc Davaine
Ruoms

This large family oriented site offers activities and entertainment in high season.

07090 Ⓒ Ⓟ
Domaine des Plantas
Les Ollières

A good quality site in a spectacular setting, considerably less crowded than sites further south.

Provence

04010 Ⓜ Ⓟ
Sunêlia L'Hippocampe
Volonne

Friendly site with good pool complex and lots of activities.

84080 Ⓟ
Simioune
Bollène

Set amongst tall pines on sandy ground, this rural site is ideal for horse and pony lovers.

84070 Ⓟ
Carpe Diem
Vaison la Romaine

Superbly located site with marvellous views and impressive main pool.

Midi-Pyrenees

09020 Ⓟ
L'Arize
La Bastide-de-Sérou

This friendly site sits in a delightful, tranquil valley among the foothills of the Pyrenees.

32010 Ⓜ Ⓟ
Camp de Florence
La Romieu

Attractive site on the edge of historic village in pleasantly undulating Gers countryside.

65030 Ⓜ Ⓟ
Airotel Pyrénées
Luz St-Sauveur

Spectacular views of the Pyrenees surround this site and everything you need is within easy reach.

65060 Ⓜ Ⓟ
Pyrénées Natura
Estaing

Small friendly site, with the emphasis on enjoying the countryside.

63060 Ⓟ
Le Clos Auroy
Orcet

A warm welcome is guaranteed at this pretty site with superb facilities and good walking.

09060 Ⓟ
Le Pré Lombard
Tarascon-sur-Ariège

Well managed riverside site in popular area and just 800m from an interesting town.

65020 Ⓜ Ⓟ
Sunêlia les Trois Vallées
Argelès-Gazost

A friendly, well organised site located in the heart of the Pyrenees amid beautiful countryside.

Mediterranean

06010 Ⓟ
Domaine Sainte Madeleine
Sospel

Attractive, peaceful site, with swimming pool, in spectacular mountain scenery.

06050 Ⓟ
La Vieille Ferme
Villenêuve Loubet

Family owned site with good facilities, open all year, in popular resort area.

06080 Ⓜ Ⓟ
Les Cigales
Mandelieu la Napoule

Quiet haven with good pool in centre of Mandelieu. Open all year.

11070 (P)
Les Mimosas
Narbonne

Lively site on Mediterranean Littoral, close to beaches at Narbonne and Gruissan.

11080 (T) (P)
La Nautique
Narbonne

Family site with lots of space and excellent windsurfing facilities on adjacent lake.

30140 (P)
La Soubeyranne
Remoulins

Medium sized campsite near Pont du Gard and beautiful Avignon.

34070 (P)
Le Sérignan Plage
Sérignan

Unusual well equipped, family run site - superb indoor pool and direct access to sandy beach.

34090 (P)
Domaine de la Yole
Valras Plage

Large family site with a very relaxed atmosphere. Good facilities and pool complex.

34140 (P)
La Carabasse
Vias-sur-Mer

Popular Mediterranean site with two pool complexes and its own beach club.

66190 (M) (P)
Sunêlia Les Tropiques
Torreilles

This attractive site has a good range of activities and is just 400m from a sandy beach.

66200 (P)
Les Marsouins
Argelès

A well organised large site situated just 1km from a beach – ideal for watersports enthusiasts.

34200 (M) (P)
Californie Plage
Vias

This site has a good range of excellent facilities and has direct access to a sandy cove.

66020 (M) (P)
Club Ma Prairie
Canet Plage

Excellent site 3 km back from sea among the vineyards, with various amenities.

34230 (M) (P)
Sunêlia Plein Air de Chênes, **Clapiers**

This site boasts an amazing pool complex and excellent facilities with villages nearby.

66050 (P)
Le Haras
Palau del Vidre

Delightful and imaginative family site with good facilities, set back from the coast.

66170 (T) (M) (P)
Mar I Sol
Torreilles

A large site with an extensive entertainment programme, children's club and beach.

83020 (P)
Esterel Caravaning
Agay

Attractive, good site for caravans only, in hills east of St Raphael, 3.5 km from sea.

83060 (P)
La Baume/La Palmeraie
Fréjus

Busy, large site back from the sea with excellent pool complex and other amenities.

83070 (P)
L'Etoile d'Argens
St Aygulf

Large, well equipped site near beach, with good pool complex, suitable for families.

83130 (P)
Le Beau Vézé
Carqueiranne

Quiet site, with pool, a little way inland from the lively resort of Hyeres.

83200 (M) (P)
Les Pêcheurs
Roquebrune

Friendly family run site beside river at foot of Roquebrune Mountain. Beaches 7 miles.

83250 (M) (P)
Sunêlia Douce Quiétude
St Raphaël

This attractive site offers a wide range of services and facilities complete with pool complex.

83260 (P)
Château de l'Eouvière
Montmeyan

A quieter site set in the grounds of an 18th century château with magnificent views.

Crossing the Channel

One of the great advantages of booking with the Alan Rogers Travel Service is the tremendous value we offer. A package of 12 nights on site and return ferry costs from just £294 – check current public ferry fares and you'll see what incredible value this represents. As agents for all the cross-Channel operators we can book all your travel arrangements with the minimum of fuss and at the best possible rates.

Just call us for an instant quote

0870 405 4055

or visit

www.alanrogersdirect.com
Book on-line AND SAVE

Short Sea Routes

Hop across the Channel in the shortest possible time and you can be on your way. We offer all main routes at great prices (when you book a pitch + ferry 'package' through us). And why not take advantage of our Ferry Deals? Caravans and trailers can go **FREE** on Dover – Calais with P&O Ferries.

Caravans can even go **FREE** with **Eurotunnel** - ask for detals.

SEAFRANCE
DOVER-CALAIS FERRIES

P&O Ferries
Dover - Calais

hoverspeed
Dover – Calais
Newhaven - Dieppe

EURO TUNNEL

Folkestone – Calais

Stena Line
Harwich – Hook of Holland

Special offers £

Caravans Go **FREE**
Trailers Go **FREE**

Dover - Calais
Qualifying Dates   **P&O Ferries**

Travel can be all year long between 1 January 2004 – 31 Oct 2004 (excluding 16/7 to 31/8 outward and 24/7 to 5/9 inward).

Midweek crossings only (excludes Friday, Saturday outward, Saturday, Sunday inward).

Low prices available on other sailings - ask for details.

Don't delay – this offer is strictly subject to availability and will be first come, first served.

Just call us for an instant quote

0870 405 4055

or visit www.alanrogersdirect.com
BOOK ON-LINE AND SAVE

Longer Routes

Sometimes it pays to take a longer crossing: a more leisurely journey perhaps. Or a chance to enjoy dinner on board ship, followed by a night in a comfortable cabin, awaking refreshed and ready for the onward drive. Either way there are still savings to be had with our super Ferry Deals.

Brittany Ferries

P&O Ferries

Condor *ferries*

Portsmouth – St Malo/
Caen/Cherbourg
Plymouth – Roscoff/Santander
Poole – Cherbourg

Portsmouth – Le Havre/
Cherbourg/Bilbao
Hull - Rotterdam/Zeebrugge

Poole – St Malo

Special offers

Caravans Go **FREE**
Trailers Go **FREE**
Motorhomes Priced as Cars

Portsmouth – Cherbourg
Portsmouth – Le Havre

P&O Ferries

Portsmouth – Caen
Portsmouth – Cherbourg
Poole – Cherbourg

Brittany Ferries

Qualifying Dates

Travel can be all summer long between 1 May 2004 - 31 October 2004. Midweek crossings only (excludes Friday, Saturday outward, Saturday, Sunday inward).

Low prices available on other sailings - ask for details.

1st time abroad?

PREPARATIONS FOR THAT FIRST TRIP CAN DE DAUNTING. BUT DON'T WORRY - WE'RE WITH YOU ALL THE WAY.

Don't delay – this offer is strictly subject to availability and will be first come, first served.

Just call us for an instant quote
0870 405 4055

or visit **www.alanrogersdirect.com**
BOOK ON-LINE AND SAVE

Vendée

let yourself go...

NANTES ○

CHOLET ○

ST-JEAN-DE-MONTS ○

LA ROCHE-SUR-YON ○

LES SABLES-D'OLONNE ○   FONTENAY-LE-COMTE ○

JARD-SUR-MER ○

LA ROCHELLE ○

the travel service

the travel service

Vendée extra 2004

VENDÉE TOURISME

Call today for your FREE brochure

0870 405 4055

☀ Long sandy shores, clear blue skies, brilliant sunshine and historical towns. With an enviable sunshine record, watersports galore and the warm Atlantic waves, it's easy to see why the Vendée is one of the most popular areas of France for couples and families alike.

☀ Beach lovers will discover 140 kilometres of sandy shores backed by fragrant pine forests running alongside and, as a change, Le Puy du Fou spectacle is a must.

☀ You'll find excellent mobile homes in a superb selection of campsites, all Alan Rogers inspected and selected.

Why not let yourself go?

alanrogersdirect.com

book on-line and save

Map 1

Brittany

Rolling sandy beaches, hidden coves, pretty villages and a picturesque coastline all combine to make Brittany a very popular holiday destination. Full of Celtic culture steeped in myths and legends, Brittany is one of the most distinctive regions of France.

Départements: 22 Côtes d'Armor, 29 Finistère, 35 Ille-et-Vilaine, 56 Morbihan, 44 Loire Atlantique

Major cities: Rennes and Brest

Brittany offers 800 miles of rocky coastline with numerous bays, busy little fishing villages and broad sandy beaches dotted with charming seaside resorts. The coastline to the north of Brittany is rugged with a maze of rocky coves, while to the south, the shore is flatter with long sandy beaches. Inland you'll find wooded valleys, rolling fields, moors and giant granite boulders, but most impressive is the wealth of prehistoric sites, notably the Carnac standing stones.

Breton culture offers a rich history of menhirs, dolmens, crosses, cathedrals and castles. Strong Celtic roots provide this region with its own distinctive traditions, evident in the local Breton costume and music, the traditional religious festivals and the cuisine, featuring crêpes and cider. Many castles and manor houses, countless chapels and old towns and villages provide evidence of Brittany's eventful history and wealth of traditions. The abbey fortress of Mont-St-Michel on the north coast should not be missed and Concarneau in the south is a lovely walled town enclosed by granite rocks.

Cuisine of the region

Fish and shellfish are commonplace; traditional *crêperies* abound and welcome visitors with a cup of local cider

Agneau de pré-salé: leg of lamb from animals pastured in the salt marshes and meadows

Beurre blanc: sauce for fish dishes made with shallots, wine vinegar and butter

Cotriade: fish soup with potatoes, onions, garlic and butter

Crêpes Bretonnes: the thinnest of pancakes with a variety of sweet fillings

Galette: can be a biscuit, cake or pancake; with sweet or savoury fillings

Gâteau Breton: rich cake

Poulet blanc Breton: free-range, quality, white Breton chicken

Places of interest

Cancale: small fishing port famous for oysters

Carnac: 3,000 standing stones (menhirs)

Concarneau: fishing port, old walled town

Dinan: historical walled town

La Baule: resort with lovely, sandy bay and beach

Le Croisic: fishing port, Naval museum

Guérande: historic walled town

Perros-Guirec: leading resort of the 'Pink Granite Coast'

Quiberon: boat service to three islands: Belle Ile (largest of the Breton islands), Houat, Hoedic

Rennes: capital of Brittany, medieval streets, half timbered houses; Brittany Museum

St Malo: historical walled city, fishing port

Alan Rogers tip

FOR A TASTE OF LOCAL CULTURE THE INTER-CELTIC FESTIVAL IN LORIENT, HELD IN AUGUST, IS A CELEBRATION OF TRADIONAL BRETON MUSIC, POETRY AND DANCE.

FR22050 Camping Le Vieux Moulin

14 rue des Moulins, 22430 Erquy (Côtes d'Armor)

Le Vieux Moulin is a well established and busy site, open from 1 May and which becomes full with much activity in July and August. It is situated about 1 km. from a beach of sand and shingle, accessed by an unmade track which can get dusty. There is, however, a good pool complex on site with a children's pool and water slides. There are 173 pitches, of which 150 have electricity and 87 have electricity, water and waste water. A further newer section of 39 pitches is arranged around a pond. Most pitches are of a fair size in square boxes with trees giving shade. Discos are arranged in high season, which finish at midnight so expect some noise. This is a good site for children of all ages. About 60 tour operator pitches add to the busy atmosphere.

Facilities

Two good quality toilet blocks have mostly British toilets and plenty of individual basins, facilities for disabled people and for babies. A further small block provides toilets and dishwashing only. Washing machines and dryer. Motorcaravan service point. Shop. Smart pizzeria and takeaway. Attractive bar and terrace overlooking the heated pool complex. Two playgrounds, with carousel roundabout. Free tennis, free fitness gym. TV room (with satellite) and games room with table tennis. Off site: Bicycle hire 1 km, fishing 1.2 km, riding 9 km, golf 7 km.

At a glance

Welcome & Ambience	✓✓✓✓	Location	✓✓✓✓
Quality of Pitches	✓✓✓✓	Range of Facilities	✓✓✓✓✓

Directions

Site is 2 km. east of Erquy. Take minor road towards Les Hôpitaux and site is signed from junction of D786 and D34 roads.

Charges 2003

Per person	€ 3.90 - € 4.90
child (under 7 yrs)	€ 2.80 - € 3.90
pitch with electricity (6-9A)	€ 12.40 - € 15.50

Reservations

Made for a min. of 1 week. Tel: 02 96 72 34 23. Email: camp.vieux.moulin@wanadoo.fr

Open

1 May - 7 September.

FR22090 Camping Château de Galinée

La Galinée, 22380 St Cast-le-Guildo (Côtes d'Armor)

Situated a few kilometers back from St Cast and owned and managed by the Vervel family, Galinée is in a parkland setting on level grass with numerous and varied mature trees. It has 273 pitches, all with electricity, water and drainage and separated by many mature shrubs and bushes. The top section is mostly for mobile homes. An attractive pool complex has swimming and paddling pools, two new pools with a water slide and a 'magic stream'. Entertainment is organised during peak season featuring traditional Breton music at times or weekly discos. The gate is locked 23.00-07.00 hrs. Used by tour operators (30 pitches).

Facilities

The main tiled, modern sanitary block includes washbasins in private cabins, facilities for babies and a good unit for disabled people. Dishwashing. Laundry room. Shop for basics, bar and excellent takeaway menu (both 1/7-30/8). Attractive, heated pool complex (26/5-2/9) with swimming and paddling pools, two new pools with water slide and 'magic stream'. Three tennis courts. Fishing. Play area and field for ball games. Off site: Riding 6 km, golf 3.5 km.

At a glance

Welcome & Ambience	✓✓✓✓	Location	✓✓✓✓
Quality of Pitches	✓✓✓✓	Range of Facilities	✓✓✓✓✓

Directions

From D168 Ploubalay-Plancoet road turn onto D786 towards Matignon and St Cast. Site is very well signed 1 km. after leaving Notre Dame de Guildo.

Latest charges

Per adult	€ 3.85 - € 5.30
child (under 7 yrs)	€ 2.30 - € 3.60
pitch incl. water and drainage	€ 8.40 - € 5.50
electricity (10A)	€ 4.20

Camping Cheques accepted.

Reservations

Made with deposit (€ 31) and fee (€ 15.24); min. 1 week July/Aug. Tel: 02 96 41 10 56. Email: chateaugalinee@wanadoo.fr

Open

15 May - 8 September.

FR22200 Camping Le Bocage

Rue du Bocage, 22270 Jugon-les-Lacs (Côtes d'Armor)

This well kept former municipal site is on the edge of the village beside a lake, 25 km. from the sea. It offers 180 good size pitches, all with electrical connections, set on gently sloping grass and divided by shrubs and bushes, with mature trees providing shade. Some 40 wooden chalets and mobile homes are intermingled with the touring pitches. On-site facilities include a good pool with children's section and sunbathing patio.

Facilities

Two main sanitary blocks include facilities for disabled visitors, British and Turkish style WCs and some washbasins in cabins. Washing machine. Small shop (1/7-10/9). Bar (1/7-31/8). Swimming pool (15/6-10/9). Table tennis, tennis, football. Play area. Activity programmes July/Aug. Fishing. Bicycle hire. Off site: Supermarket in village (1 km). River 1 km.

At a glance

Welcome & Ambience	✓✓✓✓	Location	✓✓✓
Quality of Pitches	✓✓✓✓	Range of Facilities	✓✓✓

Directions

From N176 (E401) Lamballe - Dinan road, approx. 15 km. from Lamballe take turning for Jugon-les-Lacs. Site is signed shortly after.

Charges 2003

Per person	€ 4.50 - € 5.50
child (2-10 yrs)	€ 2.00 - € 2.50
pitch	€ 4.50 - € 5.50
electricity (5A)	€ 2.00 - € 3.00

Reservations

Contact site. Tel: 02 96 31 60 16.
Email: camping-le-bocage@wanadoo.fr

Open

1 May - 30 September.

FR2203 Camping Nautic International

Route de Beau-Rivage, 22530 Caurel (Côtes d'Armor)

This friendly family site is on the north shore of the Lac de Guerledan. The lake is popular for all manner of watersports and there are some pleasant walks around the shores and through the surrounding Breton countryside and forests. The site is terraced down to the lake shore and offers 100 large pitches, all with electrical connections. A number of 'super pitches' (160 - 200 sq.m) are also available. There is an imaginatively designed swimming pool and smaller childrens' pool, both of which are heated by a wood burning stove (open from June). Small boats can be launched from the site, and other boating activities are available on the lake. Mobile homes available for rent. A member of 'Sites et Paysages'.

Facilities

Washing and drying machines. Small shop (1/7- 31/8). Swimming pools. Gym. Sauna. Giant chess. Play area. Fishing. Tennis. Table tennis. Games room. Off site: Watersports. Riding. Canal from Nantes to Brest. Seaside 50 minutes by car.

At a glance

Welcome & Ambience	✓✓✓✓	Location	✓✓✓
Quality of Pitches	✓✓✓	Range of Facilities	✓✓✓✓

Directions

From N164 Rennes - Brest road, turn off between Mur-de-Bretagne and Gouarec to the village of Caurel. Site is well signed from here.

Charges 2003

Per adult	€ 3.30 - € 4.60
child (2-10 yrs)	€ 1.90 - € 3.10
pitch	€ 5.40 - € 6.90
electricity (10A)	€ 4.00

Reservations

Contact site. Tel: 02 96 28 57 94.
Email: contact@campingnautic.fr.st

Open

15 May - 25 September

FR22040 Camping Le Châtelet

Rue des Nouettes, 22380 St Cast-le-Guildo (Côtes d'Armor)

Carefully developed over the years from a former quarry, Le Châtelet is pleasantly and quietly situated with lovely views over the estuary from many pitches. It is well laid out, mainly in terraces with fairly narrow access roads. There are 216 good-sized pitches separated by hedges, all with electricity and 70 with water and drainage. Some pitches are around a little lake (unfenced) which can be used for fishing. A 'green' walking area is a nice feature around the lower edge of the site and a path leads from the site directly down to a beach (about 150 m. but including steps). St Cast, 1 km. away to the centre, has a very long beach with many opportunities for sail-boarding and other watersports. Used by three different tour operators (73 pitches).

Facilities

Four toilet blocks with access at different levels include plentiful washbasins in cabins and small toilets and showers for children. Three small, attractive new toilet blocks have been added for the lower terraces. Some facilities may be closed outside July/Aug. Motorcaravan services. Heated swimming pool and children's pool. Shop for basics, takeaway service, bar lounge and general room with satellite TV and pool table. Games room with table tennis, amusement machines. Small play area. Organised games and activities for all the family in season. Dancing weekly in June, July and Aug. Off site: Bicycle hire, riding and golf within 1.5 km.

At a glance

Welcome & Ambience	✓✓✓✓✓	Location	✓✓✓✓✓
Quality of Pitches	✓✓✓✓	Range of Facilities	✓✓✓✓

Directions

Best approach is to turn off D786 road at Matignon towards St Cast; just inside St Cast limits turn left at sign for 'campings' and follow camp signs on C90.

Charges 2003

Per person	€ 3.80 - € 5.50
child (under 7 yrs)	€ 2.30 - € 3.80
pitch with electricity (6/10A)	€ 14.80 - € 22.50
animal	€ 2.50 - € 3.40

Reservations

Necessary for July/Aug. and made (min. 1 week) with deposit (€ 60) and booking fee (€ 20).
Tel: 02 96 41 96 33. Email: chateletcp@aol.com

Open

1 May - 8 September.

LE CHÂTELET
CAMPING-CARAVANING ★ ★ ★ ★
Rue des Nouettes
22380 Saint-Cast-Le-Guildo
Tel: 0033 296.41.96.33
Fax: 0033 296.41.97.99
E-mail: chateletcp@aol.com
Website: www.lechatelet.com
CÔTE D'EMERAUDE

FR22060M Camping Municipal La Hallerais

6 Bourg de Taden, 22100 Taden (Côtes d'Armor)

As well as being an attractive old medieval town, Dinan is quite a short run from the resorts of the Côte d'Armor. This useful municipal site, open for a long season, is just outside Dinan, beyond and above the little harbour on the Rance estuary. There is a pleasant riverside walk where the site slopes down towards the Rance. The 226 pitches, all with electricity and most with water and drainaway, are mainly on level, shallow terraces connected by tarmac roads, with trees and hedges giving a park-like atmosphere. This is a clean efficiently run and well organised site.

Facilities

Three traditional toilet blocks, of good quality and heated in cool seasons, have some private cabins with shower and washbasin. Unit for disabled people. Laundry room. Shop. Attractive bar/restaurant with outside terrace and takeaway (all season). Swimming pool and children's pool (20/5-15/9). Tennis courts, minigolf, games room with table tennis and TV room. Playground. Fishing. Chalets for disabled visitors. Off site: Riding 2 km. Boating 15 km.

At a glance

Welcome & Ambience	✓✓✓✓	Location	✓✓✓✓
Quality of Pitches	✓✓✓✓	Range of Facilities	✓✓✓✓

Directions

Taden is northeast of Dinan; on leaving Dinan on D766, turn right to Taden and site before reaching large bridge and N176 junction. From N176 take Taden/Dinan exit and follow Taden signs to pick up signs for site.

Charges 2003

Per person	€ 3.00 - € 3.60
child (under 7 yrs)	€ 1.25 - € 1.55
pitch incl. electricity (6A)	€ 8.50 - € 11.20

Reservations

Made for high season only (min. 1 week) with deposit.
Tel: 02 96 39 15 93.
Email: camping.la.hallerais@wanadoo.fr

Open

15 March - 31 October.

FR22100 Camping L'Abri Côtier

Ville Es Rouxel, 22680 Etables-sur-Mer (Côtes d'Armor)

L'Abri Cotier is a well-cared-for, family run site 500 m. from a sandy beach. Small and tranquil, it is arranged in two sections separated by a lane. The pitches are marked out on part level, part sloping grass, divided by mature trees and shrubs with some in a charming walled area with a quaint, old-world atmosphere. The second section has an orchard type setting. Tim Lee and his French wife are busy with ideas to improve this very popular, friendly site. In total there are 140 pitches, all with electrical connections (6/10A, long leads useful) and 60 fully serviced. Beach within walking distance. Restaurants in the village.

Facilities

Good clean sanitary facilities, heated in low season, include some washbasins in cabins, two units for disabled visitors (shower, washbasin and toilet) and a baby bath/shower. Dishwashing under cover. Laundry room. Well stocked shop, set menu and simple takeaway service. Bar (with TV) and outdoor terrace area. Sheltered, heated swimming pool with children's pool and outdoor jacuzzi. Playground. Games room with billiards, darts, pinball and table tennis. Some entertainment in peak season. Gates locked at 11 pm. Off site: Beach within walking distance. Restaurants and indoor pool in the village. Fishing 2 km, bicycle hire 1 km, riding 1 km, golf 12 km.

At a glance

Welcome & Ambience	✓✓✓✓	Location	✓✓✓✓
Quality of Pitches	✓✓✓✓	Range of Facilities	✓✓✓✓

Directions

From N12 after St Brieuc take D786; site is well signed before St Quay Portrieux.

Charges 2003

Per person	€ 4.50
child (under 7 yrs)	€ 3.00
pitch	€ 7.00
serviced pitch	€ 8.00
local tax	€ 0.15

Reservations

Advised in season; made with deposit (€ 40, sterling cheque acceptable £25). Tel: 02 96 70 61 57. Email: camping.abricotier@wanadoo.fr

Open

12 April - 15 September.

FR22160 Camping Le Neptune

Kerguistin, 22580 Lanloup (Côtes d'Armor)

Situated on the Côte de Goëlo at Lanloup, Le Neptune offers a peaceful, rural retreat for families. This neat, well kept site has 84 level, grass pitches, 65 available for touring units. Trimmed hedges separate them, allowing for privacy and all have electricity (6A). There are also 13 mobile homes to rent. The friendly owners, M. & Mme. Schira, keep the site neat and tidy. A heated swimming pool has a retractable roof so can be open for a long season. Within walking distance is the local village, with a restaurant and shop, and sandy beaches. The site is also a good base for cycling and walking.

Facilities

The modern toilet block is of a good standard, clean and well maintained. Laundry room with washing machine and dryer. No restaurant but good takeaway (open all season). Small shop well stocked for basic needs. Bar with indoor and outdoor seating. Heated swimming pool (Easter - end Oct). Petanque. Volleyball. Table tennis. Table football. Minigolf. Animation in season. Off site: Fishing 2 km. Golf 8 km. Riding 8 km. Tennis courts 300 m. Beach 2 km. Restaurant and shop within walking distance.

At a glance

Welcome & Ambience	✓✓✓✓✓	Location	✓✓✓✓✓
Quality of Pitches	✓✓✓✓	Range of Facilities	✓✓✓✓

Directions

From St Brieuc (N12) take D786 Paimpol (par la Côte). After 28 km. on approaching Lanloup, site is well signed.

Charges 2003

Per person	€ 4.25
child (under 7 yrs)	€ 2.75
pitch	€ 7.30
electricity (6A)	€ 3.00
dog	€ 1.70

Camping Cheques accepted.

Reservations

Less 10% for second week. Tel: 02 96 22 33 35. Email: contact@leneptune.com

Open

Easter - end October.

FR22080 Yelloh! Village Le Ranolien

Ploumanach, 22700 Perros Guirec (Côtes d'Armor)

Le Ranolien has been attractively developed around a former Breton farm – everything here is either made from, or placed on or around the often massive pink rocks. The original buildings are sympathetically converted into site facilities and there is an imaginative pool complex with terraces and water toboggans, water cascading over boulders into smaller pools and a covered, heated pool which can be opened. It is all quite impressive and is over looked by the bar terrace. The site is on the coast, with beaches and coves within walking distance and there are spectacular views from many pitches. The 540 pitches are of a variety of sizes and types, mostly large and flat but some are quite small. Some are formally arranged in rows with hedge separators, but most are either on open ground or under trees, amongst large boulders. With many holiday caravans and tour operator tents around the site (318 pitches), there are 70 pitches for tourists, most with electricity and some with water and drainage also. Reservation is recommended for high season. This site can be noisy in high season and is not for those seeking a calm and peaceful holiday.

Facilities

The main toilet block, heated in cool weather, is supplemented by several more open type blocks around the site. Washbasins in cabins, mostly British WCs and good showers. Dishwashing facilities are mainly in the open. Laundry. Motorcaravan service point. Supermarket and gift shop (1/5-18/9). Restaurant, crêperie and bar (all open over a long season). Disco some nights in high season. Minigolf. Tennis. Table tennis. Games room. Play area. Cinema. Gym and steam room. Mobile homes for hire.

At a glance

Welcome & Ambience	✓✓✓✓	Location	✓✓✓✓✓
Quality of Pitches	✓✓✓	Range of Facilities	✓✓✓✓✓

Directions

From Lannion take D788 to Perros Guirec. Follow signs to 'Centre Ville' past main harbour area and then signs to Ploumanach, La Clarté. Pass through village of La Clarté and around sharp left hand bend. Site is immediately on the right.

Charges 2003

Per unit incl. 2 persons and electricity	€ 15.00 - € 34.00
with water and drainage	€ 20.00 - € 37.00
extra person	€ 3.00 - € 5.00
child (2-7 yrs)	free - € 4.00
animal	€ 2.00

Reservations

Contact site. Tel: 02 96 91 65 65.
Email: leranolien@wanadoo.fr

Open

3 April - 18 September.

FR22130 Camping de Port L'Epine

Venelle de Pors Garo, 22660 Trélévern (Côtes d'Armor)

Port L'Epine is a pretty little site in a unique situation on a promontory. There is access to the sea, therefore, on the south side of the site, with views across to Perros Guirec, and just outside the entrance on the north side is a further sandy bay with little boats moored and facing out to an archipelago of seven small islands. It is charming – you can sail or swim from both sides. However, in spite of this, the site has its own small heated pool. The area covered by the site is not large but there are 160 grass pitches, all with 16A electricity, which are divided by pretty hedging and trees, some of which are used for mobile homes. Access is a little tight in parts. This site is ideal for families with young children (probably not for teenagers). The site is used by tour operators (17 pitches).

Facilities

The original toilet block is well equipped and a second block has been refurbished in modern style, including facilities for disabled visitors. Unusual dishwashing sinks in open air stone units. Shop and bar/restaurant with takeaway facility (both 1/7-31/8). Small heated swimming pool and paddling pool. Fenced children's play area near exit road. Table tennis and video games. Bicycle hire. Site's own beach has rock pools and a jetty and slipway for small boats or fishing. Barrier closed 23.00-07.00 hrs. Off site: Riding or golf 15 km. Useful small supermarket up-hill from the site. Many coastal paths to enjoy.

At a glance

Welcome & Ambience	✓✓✓✓✓	Location	✓✓✓✓✓
Quality of Pitches	✓✓✓✓	Range of Facilities	✓✓✓✓

Directions

From roundabout south of Perros Guirec take D6 towards Tréguier. After passing through Louannec, take left turn at crossroads for Trélévern. Go through village following camp signs - Port L'Epine is clearly marked as distinct from the municipal site.

Charges 2003

Per pitch incl. 2 persons and electricity	€ 14.50 - € 25.00
serviced pitch	€ 2.30
extra person	€ 5.00
child (2-7 yrs)	€ 2.50
animal	€ 2.50
Camping Cheques accepted.	

Reservations

Made with deposit (€ 90, or € 45 for stay of less than
3 nights). Tel: 02 96 23 71 94.
Email: camping-de-port-lepine@wanadoo.fr

Open

1 April - 30 September.

the travel service
TO BOOK THIS SITE
0870 405 4055
Expert Advice & Special Offers

FR22140 Camping de Port La Chaine

22610 Pleubian (Côtes d'Armor)

The Palvadeau family have worked hard to establish Camping de Port La Chaîne as a comfortable, quiet, family site. In a beautiful location on the 'Untamed Peninsula' between Paimpol and Perros Guirec, attractive trees and shrubs provide a balance of sun and shade, edging the central roadway and grassy bays or fields which branch off on the gradual decline towards the bay and the sea (a sandy bay with rocks). To the right are mostly French mobile homes, quite discreet, with the left side for independent units. Most of the bays have a slight slope, so those with motorcaravans will need to choose their pitch carefully. More open, level pitches nearer the sea are useful for tents. In all there are 200 pitches with electricity said to be available everywhere (a long lead may be useful). There are good opportunities for walking and cycling, with a way-marked footpath running along the coast to the Sillon du Talbert that juts out into the sea opposite the Island of Bréhat.

Facilities

Two traditional style toilet blocks are comfortable and fully equipped, both completely renovated. There are washbasins in cabins, British and Turkish style toilets. Cabins for families or disabled visitors. Plentiful dishwashing sinks (H&C). Laundry sinks with cold water only. Washing machines and dryer. Bar and terrace (1/7-1/9) overlooking a heated pool (2/6-15/9), play area and petanque pitch. Children's entertainer in July/Aug. Off site: Village 2 km. for tennis, market, shops and restaurants. Good fishing and diving.

At a glance

Welcome & Ambience	✓✓✓✓✓	Location	✓✓✓✓✓
Quality of Pitches	✓✓✓✓	Range of Facilities	✓✓✓✓

Directions

Leave D786 between Lézardrieux and Tréguier to go north to the village of Pleubian (approx. 8 km). Continue on D20 towards Larmor Pleubian and site signed on left, approx. 2 km. from Pleubian.

Charges 2003

Per person	€ 5.00
child (under 7 yrs)	€ 3.20
pitch	€ 8.50
electricity (6A)	€ 3.50
dog	€ 2.00
Less 10-20% in low seasons.	

Reservations

Contact site. Tel: 02 96 22 92 38.
Email: info@portlachaine.com

Open

1 May - 15 September.

FR22010 Camping Les Capucines

Kervourdon, 22300 Tredrez-Locquémeau (Côtes d'Armor)

A warm welcome awaits at Les Capucines which is quietly situated 1 km. from the village of St Michel with its good, sandy beach and also very near Locquémeau, a pretty fishing village. This attractive, family run site has 100 pitches on flat or slightly sloping ground. All are well marked out by hedges, with mature trees and with more recently planted. There are 70 with electricity, water and drainage, including 10 for larger units. All the amenities are open all season. A good value restaurant/crêperie is at Trédrez, others at St Michel. A 'Sites et Paysages member'.

Facilities

Two modern toilet blocks include washbasins mainly in cabins, facilities for babies and disabled people. Laundry with washing machines and dryer. Small shop for essentials (bread to order). Takeaway, bar with TV and a general room with table tennis and table football. Swimming and paddling pools. Playground. Tennis. Minigolf. Dogs are not accepted. Off site: Fishing 1 km, riding 2 km, golf 15 km.

At a glance

Welcome & Ambience	✓✓✓✓✓	Location	✓✓✓✓
Quality of Pitches	✓✓✓✓	Range of Facilities	✓✓✓✓

Directions

Turn off main D786 road northeast of St Michel where site is signed, and 1 km. to site.

Charges 2004

Per person	€ 3.60 - € 5.00
child	free - € 3.26
caravan pitch with	
water and drainage	€ 17.40 - € 24.50
tent pitch	€ 13.00 - € 18.40
electricity (4/7A)	free
local tax (over 18 yrs)	€ 0.31

Reservations

Advised for high season and made for any length with deposit (€ 70). Tel: 02 96 35 72 28.
Email: les.capucines@wanadoo.fr

Open

1 May - 11 September.

FR29000 Camping Les Mouettes

La Grande Grève, 29660 Carantec (Finistère)

Les Mouettes is less than 15 km. from the Roscoff ferry port, so is well situated when heading to or from home, although it also provides many facilities for a longer family holiday. For those who do not want to drive too far, the area has plenty to offer with beautiful bays and many places of interest within easy reach. Les Mouettes is a sheltered site on the edge of an attractive bay with access to the sea at the front of the site. In a wooded setting with many attractive trees and shrubs, the 273 pitches include just 70 for touring units, the remainder being taken by tour operators and around 60 site-owned mobile homes and tents (located together at the top of the site). The touring pitches, mostly arranged in hedged areas in the lower areas of the site, are of a good size and all have electricity connections. The focal point of the site is an impressive heated swimming pool complex comprising three water slides, 'tropical river', swimming pool, children's pool, a jacuzzi and sauna.

Facilities

Three clean unisex sanitary blocks include washbasins in cabins, mainly British toilets and baby bathrooms. Facilities for disabled people. Laundry facilities. Motorcaravan services. Shop 19/5-12/9, limited hours outside the main season). Takeaway. Centrally located bar (15/5-12/9) overlooking pool complex. Games and TV rooms. Play area. Volleyball, two half-courts for tennis and minigolf (in peak season). Table tennis. Discos and other entertainment organised in main season. Off site: Bicycle hire 10 km. Riding 6 km. Golf 2 km.

At a glance

Welcome & Ambience	✓✓✓✓✓	Location	✓✓✓✓
Quality of Pitches	✓✓✓✓	Range of Facilities	✓✓✓✓✓

Directions

From D58 Roscoff - Morlaix road, turn to Carantec on D173. Site is approx. 4 km. from here on the outskirts of the village, signed to the left at roundabout immediately after passing supermarket on right.

Charges 2003

Per person	€ 3.50 - € 6.10
pitch with electricity (6A)	€ 12.90 - € 21.60
Camping Cheques accepted.	

Reservations

Write to site with deposit (€ 46) and fee (€ 18.29). Tel: 02 98 67 02 46.
Email: camping@les-mouettes.com

Open

1 May - 12 September.

FR29210M Camping Municipal Bois de la Palud

29250 Plougoulm (Finistère)

This delightful, small municipal site is on the edge of the little village of Plougoulm, about 10 km. southwest of Roscoff. It sits on the brow of a hill with lovely views across the Guillec valley and the sandy bay and estuary to which there is access by footpath. There are 34 reasonably level, numbered pitches grouped in small hedged bays and most have access to 6A electricity (although long leads may be necessary). A small building near the entrance houses reception and sanitary facilities. The season is short – only 15 June - 15 September.

Facilities

All necessary toilet facilities are provided. Play area. Off site: Fishing, bicycle hire, riding and golf, all within 4 km.

At a glance

Welcome & Ambience	✓✓✓	Location	✓✓✓✓
Quality of Pitches	✓✓✓	Range of Facilities	✓✓

Directions

On leaving Roscoff, follow signs for Morlaix. After 6 km. take D10 (westward) signed Plouescat and after 3 km. watch for clear camp signs in the village of Plougoulm.

Charges 2003

Per adult	€ 3.00
pitch with electricity	€ 6.00
No credit cards.	

Reservations

Advised in high season. Tel: 02 98 29 81 82.
When closed contact the Mairie: Tel: 02 98 29 90 76.

Open

15 June - 15 September.

FR29130 **Camping des Abers**

Dunes de Ste Marguerite, 29870 Landéda (Finistère)

This delightful 12 acre site is beautifully situated almost at the tip of the Ste Marguerite peninsula on the north-western shores of Brittany in a wide bay formed between the mouths (abers) of two rivers, L'Aber Wrac'h and L'Aber Benoit. With soft, white sandy beaches and rocky outcrops and islands at high tide, the setting is ideal for those with younger children and this quiet, rural area provides a wonderful, tranquil escape from the busier areas of France, even in high season. Camping des Abers is set just back from the beach, the lower pitches sheltered from the wind by high hedges or with panoramic views of the bay from the higher places. There are 180 pitches arranged in distinct areas, partly shaded and sheltered by mature hedges, trees and flowering shrubs, all planted and carefully tended over 30 years by the Le Cuff family. Landscaping and terracing where appropriate on the different levels avoids any regimentation or crowding. Easily accessed by good internal roads, electricity is available to all (long leads may be needed). Speaking several languages, the family who own and run this site with 'TLC' will make you very welcome.

Facilities

Three toilet blocks (one part of the reception building and all recently refurbished) are very clean, providing washbasins in cubicles and roomy showers (token from reception). Good new facilities for disabled visitors and babies have been added at the reception block. Dishwashing sinks. Fully equipped laundry. Motorcaravan service point. Mini-market stocks essentials (8/6-8/9). Simple takeaway dishes (1/7-31/8). Pizzeria and restaurant next door. Table tennis. Good play area (on sand). Games room. Live music, Breton dancing and Breton cooking classes, and guided walks arranged. Splendid beach reached direct from the site with good bathing (best at high tide), fishing, windsurfing and other watersports. Miles of superb coastal walks. Torch useful. Gates locked 22.30-07.00 hrs. Off site: Tennis and riding close. The nearby town of L'Aber Wrac'h, a well known yachting centre, has many memorable restaurants.

Directions

From Roscoff (D10, then D13), cross river bridge (L'Aber Wrac'h) to Lannilis. Go through town taking road to Landéda and from there signs for Dunes de Ste Marguerite, 'camping' and des Abers.

Charges 2003

Per person	€ 3.10
child (-17 yrs)	€ 1.70
pitch	€ 4.70
car	€ 1.40
electricity (5A)	€ 2.20
dog	€ 1.50

Less 20% until 15 June and Sept. Camping Cheques accepted.

Reservations

Write to site. Tel: 02 98 04 93 35. Email: camping-des-abers@wanadoo.fr

Open

1 May - 26 September.

At a glance

Welcome & Ambience	✓✓✓✓✓	Location	✓✓✓✓✓
Quality of Pitches	✓✓✓✓	Range of Facilities	✓✓✓✓

BRETAGNE - FINISTÈRE

CAMPING DES ABERS

★ ★ ★

Situated in an exceptional tourist region with marvellous views of the sea
10 terraced acres equipped with all necessary facilities, next to safe sandy beach
Sea Angling - Walking - Swimming
Windsurfing - Horse riding
Mobile homes to rent

Camping des Abers
29870 LANDEDA - France
Tel: 0033 298 04 93 35
Fax: 0033 298 04 84 35
http://www.abers-tourisme.com

Camping Cheque

FR29080 Camping Le Panoramic

Route de la Plage-Penker, 29560 Telgruc-sur-Mer (Finistère)

This medium sized, traditional style site is situated on quite a steep, ten acre hillside, with fine views along the coast. It is well tended and personally run by M. Jacq and his family who all speak good English. The site is in two parts, divided by a fairly quiet road leading to a good beach. The main upper site is where most of the facilities are situated, with the swimming pool, terrace and a playground located with the lower pitches across the road. Some up-and-down walking is therefore necessary, but this is a small price to pay for such pleasant and comfortable surroundings. The 220 pitches are arranged on flat, shady terraces, mostly in small groups with hedges and flowering shrubs and 20 pitches are fully serivced. A good area for lovely coastal footpaths. A 'Sites et Paysages' member.

Facilities

The main site has two well kept toilet blocks with another very good block opened for main season across the road. All three blocks include British and Turkish style WCs, washbasins in cubicles, facilities for disabled people, baby baths, dishwashing, plus washing machines and dryers. Motorcaravan services. Small shop (1/7-31/8). Bar/restaurant with good value takeaway (1/7-31/8). Barbecue area. Heated swimming pool, paddling pool and jacuzzi (all 15/5-7/9). Playground. Games and TV rooms. Children's club in season. Sports ground with tennis courts, volleyball. Bicycle hire. Off site: Fishing 700 m, riding 6 km, golf 14 km. Sailing school nearby. Good sandy beach 700 m. downhill by road, bit less on foot.

At a glance

Welcome & Ambience	✓✓✓✓✓	Location	✓✓✓✓
Quality of Pitches	✓✓✓	Range of Facilities	✓✓✓✓

Directions

Site is just south of Telgruc-sur-Mer. On D887 pass through Ste Marie du Ménez Horn. In 11 km. turn left on D208 signed Telgruc-sur-Mer. Continue straight on through the town and site is on right within 1 km.

Charges 2004

Per person	€ 5.00
child (under 7 yrs)	€ 3.00
pitch with electricity (6-10A)	€ 13.10 - € 14.50
water and drainage connection	€ 2.50
Less 20% outside July/Aug.	

Reservations

Made for any period; contact site. Tel: 02 98 27 78 41. Email: info@camping-panoramic.com

Open

1 June - 15 September.

Camping **LE PANORAMIC** ★★★★ *BRITTANY*

On the Crozon penninsular and the Bay of Douarnenez, this is a family campsite bordering the sea, where english is spoken and everything is well-maintened. There are many holiday activities available, including a swimming pool, childrens'play area, tennis, bathing, sailing, mountain biking etc., and a further choice of cultural activities in the Armorique Regional Park - the coast, the local ports, museums and of course the richness of the Breton culture itself.

Mr et Mme JACQ
29560 Telgruc-sur-Mer - France
Tel. 0033 298 27 78 41 - Fax: 0033 298 27 36 10
Email : info@camping-panoramic.com / www.camping-panoramic.com

FR29280 La Pointe Superbe Camping

Route de St Coulitz, 29150 Châteaulin (Finistère)

La Pointe, just outside Châteaulin, has been lovingly and impressively brought back to life by its delightful English owners Colin Grewer and Sue Dodds. Châteaulin is a bustling market town, 15 km. from the beach at Pentrez and within easy reach of Quimper, mediaeval Locronan and the Crozon peninsula. Although not endowed with a great deal in terms of amenities, this very tranquil site does boast particularly large, grassy pitches in a quiet valley leading down to the River Aulne, which makes up part of the Nantes - Brest canal. The 60 pitches all have electricity with water close by. This small site is well suited to those who like peace and quiet.

Facilities

The first-class toilet block, kept very clean at all times, has many washbasins in cubicles. Shower cubicles are somewhat small but have full adjustable hot and cold taps. Large room with facilities for disabled visitors. Baby bathroom. Motorcaravan service point. Play area. Table tennis, volleyball and large activity room with basketball, badminton and children's corner. Off site: Châteaulin has a wide range of shops (700 m), as well as plenty of restaurants and bars. Riding and tennis nearby. Woodland walks and fishing possible in the Aulne (permit needed).

At a glance

Welcome & Ambience	✓✓✓✓✓	Location	✓✓✓✓
Quality of Pitches	✓✓✓✓	Range of Facilities	✓✓✓

Directions

Site is just southeast of Châteaulin. From the bridge over the river in town centre follow signs for St Coulitz and Quimper. Shortly turn left signed St Coulitz. Site is signed at this point and is 100 m. on the right.

Charges 2003

Per unit incl. 2 persons	€ 10.00 - € 12.00
electricity (10A)	€ 2.00 - € 3.00
No credit cards.	

Reservations

Advised for high season and made with deposit (€ 15.24). Tel: 02 98 86 51 53.

Open

15 March - 31 October.

FR29110 Yelloh! Village La Plage

Rue de Men-Meur BP 9, 29730 Le Guilvinec (Finistère)

La Plage is a friendly site located beside a long sandy beach between the fishing town of Le Guilvinec and the watersports beaches of Penmarc'h on the southwest tip of Brittany. It is spacious and surrounded by tall trees, which provide shelter, and is made up of several flat, sandy meadows. The 410 pitches (100 for touring units) are arranged on either side of sandy access roads, mostly not separated but all numbered. There is less shade in the newer areas. Electricity is available on most pitches (6 or 10A). Like all beach-side sites, the facilities receive heavy usage. There is plenty to occupy one at this friendly site but the bustling fishing harbour at Le Guilvinec and the watersports of Penmarc'h and Pointe de la Torche are within easy travelling distance. Used by tour operators (176 pitches). A Yelloh Village member.

Facilities

Five sanitary blocks are of differing designs but all provide modern, bright facilities including washbasins in cabins, good facilities for children and toilets for disabled people. Laundry facilities. Motorcaravan service point. Shop with gas supplies. Bright, airy well furnished bar, crêperie and takeaway. Heated swimming pool with paddling pool and water slide. Sauna. Play area. TV room. Tennis courts. Volleyball, basketball, minigolf, badminton, petanque, table tennis, giant chess/draughts. Bicycle hire. Off site: Fishing and watersports near. Riding 5 km. Golf 20 km.

At a glance

Welcome & Ambience	✓✓✓✓	Location	✓✓✓✓✓
Quality of Pitches	✓✓✓	Range of Facilities	✓✓✓✓✓

Directions

Site is west of Guilvinec. From Pont l'Abbé, take the D785 road towards Penmarc'h. In Plomeur, turn left on D57 signed Guilvinec. On entering Guilvinec fork right signed Port and camping. Follow road along coast to site on left.

Charges 2004

Per unit incl. 2 persons and 5A electricity	€ 15.00 - € 36.00
extra person	€ 4.00 - € 6.00
child (under 10 yrs)	free - € 4.00
electricity (10A)	free - € 1.00
dog	€ 2.50 - € 3.50
local tax (over 16 yrs)	€ 0.16 - € 0.40

Reservations

Advised and accepted until 15/6 with deposit (25%) and fee (€ 19). Tel: 02 98 58 61 90. Email: info@campingsbretagnesud.com

Open

15 May - 11 September, with all facilities.

FR29120 Yelloh! Village Le Manoir de Kerlut

29740 Plobannalec-Lesconil (Finistère)

Le Manoir de Kerlut is a comfortable site in the grounds of a manor house on a river estuary near Pont l'Abbe. The old 'manoir' is not open to the public, but is used occasionally for weddings and private functions. Opened in '89, the campsite has neat, modern buildings and is laid out on flat grass providing 240 pitches (90 for touring units). All have electricity connections, some also have water and drainage and around ten pitches have hardstanding. One area is rather open with separating hedges planted, the other part being amongst more mature bushes and some trees which provide shade. Site amenities are of good quality. Used by tour operators (18 pitches). A 'Yelloh Village' member.

Facilities

Toilet facilities in two good blocks, each with several rooms (not all open outside July/Aug), include washbasins all in cabins, and facilities for babies and disabled people. Laundry. Small shop. Takeaway. Large modern bar with TV (satellite) and entertainment all season. Bar in the Manoir. Two heated swimming pools, children's pool and water slide. Sauna, solarium and small gym. Play area. Tennis, volleyball, badminton and petanque. Games room. Bicycle hire. Gates closed 22.30 - 7.30 hrs. Off site: Fishing 2 km, riding 5 km, golf 15 km.

At a glance

Welcome & Ambience	✓✓✓✓	Location	✓✓✓✓
Quality of Pitches	✓✓✓✓	Range of Facilities	✓✓✓✓✓

Directions

From Pont l'Abbé, on D785, take D102 road towards Lesconil. Site is signed on the left, shortly after the village of Plobannalec.

Charges 2003

Per unit incl. 2 persons and 5A electricity	€ 15.00 - € 36.00
extra person	€ 4.00 - € 6.00
child (under 7 yrs)	free - € 4.00
electricity (10A)	free - € 1.00
dog	€ 2.50 - € 3.50
local tax (over 16 yrs)	€ 0.15

Reservations

Write to site with deposit (€ 45) and fee (€ 19). Tel: 02 98 82 23 89. Email: info@campingsbretagnesud.com

Open

15 May - 11 September, with all services.

FR29060 Camping Caravaning Le Pil–Koad

Route de Douarnenez, Poullan-sur-Mer, 29100 Douarnenez (Finistère)

Pil Koad is an attractive, family run site just back from the sea near Douarnenez in Finistère. It has 190 pitches on fairly flat ground, marked out by separating hedges and of quite good quality, though varying size and shape. The site also has a number of mobile homes and chalets. Nearly all pitches have electrical connections and original trees provide shade in some areas. A large room, the 'Woodpecker Bar', is used for entertainment with discos and cabaret in July/Aug. The gates are closed 10.30 - 07.00 hrs. A variety of beaches is within easy reach, with the coast offering some wonderful scenery and good for walking.

Facilities

Two main toilet blocks in modern style include mainly British style WCs and washbasins mostly in cabins. Laundry facilities. Motorcaravan service point. Gas supplies. Small shop for basics (15/6-11/9). Takeaway (25/6-4/9). Heated swimming pool and paddling pool (no bermuda-style shorts). Tennis court. Table tennis, minigolf and volleyball. Fishing. Bicycle hire. Playground. Weekly outings and clubs for children (30/6-30/8) with charge included in tariff. Off site: Riding 4 km. Restaurants in village 500 m. Nearest sandy beach 4 km. Douarnenez 6 km.

At a glance

Welcome & Ambience	✓✓✓✓	Location	✓✓✓✓
Quality of Pitches	✓✓✓✓	Range of Facilities	✓✓✓✓

Directions

Site is 500 m. east from the centre of Poullan on D7 road towards Douarnenez. From Douarnenez take circular bypass route towards Audierne; if you see road for Poullan sign at roundabout, take it, otherwise there is camping sign at turning to Poullan from the D765 road.

Charges 2003

Per person	€ 3.00 - € 4.50
child (under 7 yrs)	€ 1.50 - € 3.00
pitch	€ 6.20 - € 13.00
electricity (10A)	€ 3.50
dog	€ 2.00 - € 3.00
local tax (over 16 yrs from 1/7-31/8)	€ 0.15

Camping Cheques accepted.

Reservations

Made for min. 1 week with 25% deposit and fee (€ 19). Tel: 02 98 74 26 39. Email: camping.pil.koad@wanadoo.fr

Open

15 May - 15 September.

FR29050 Castel Camping L'Orangerie de Lanniron

Château de Lanniron, 29336 Quimper (Finistère)

L'Orangerie is a beautiful and peaceful, family site in 10 acres of a XVIIth century, 42 acre country estate on the banks of the Odet river. It is just to the south of Quimper and about 15 km. from the sea and beaches at Bénodet. The family have a five year programme to restore and rehabilitate the park, the original canal, fountains, ornamental Lake of Neptune, the boat-house and the gardens and avenues. The original outbuildings have been attractively converted around a walled courtyard. The site has 200 grassy pitches, 146 for touring units, of three types (varying in size and services) on fairly flat ground laid out in rows alongside access roads. All have electricity and 88 have all three services, with shrubs and bushes providing pleasant pitches. The restaurant in the beautiful XVIIth century Orangerie, and the Gardens are both open to the public and in Spring the rhododendrons and azaleas are magnificent, with lovely walks within the grounds. Used by tour operators (34 pitches).

Facilities

The main heated block in the courtyard has been totally refurbished and is excellent. A second modern block serves the newer pitches at the top of the site and includes facilities for disabled people and babies. Washing machines and dryers. Motorcaravan service point. Shop (15/5-9/9), Gas supplies. Bar, snacks and takeaway, plus restaurant (open daily from 25/5-9/9, reasonably priced with children's menu). Heated swimming pool (144 sq.m.) with children's pool. New pool planned. Small play area. Tennis. Minigolf, attractively set among mature trees. Table tennis. Fishing. Archery. Bicycle hire. General reading, games and billiards rooms. TV/video room (cable and satellite). Karaoke. Animation provided including outdoor activities with large room for indoor activities. Off site: Sea 15 km. Historic town of Quimper under 3 km. Two hypermarkets 1 km.

At a glance

Welcome & Ambience	✓✓✓✓✓	Location		✓✓✓✓
Quality of Pitches	✓✓✓✓	Range of Facilities		✓✓✓✓

Directions

From Quimper follow 'Quimper Sud' signs, then 'Toutes Directions' and general camping signs, finally signs for Lanniron.

Charges 2003

Per adult	€ 6.00
child (2-7 yrs)	€ 4.00
pitch (100 sq.m.)	€ 14.00
with electricity (10A)	€ 18.00
special pitch (120/150 sq.m.)	
with water and electricity	€ 21.00
animal	€ 3.50

Less 15% outside July/Aug.
Camping Cheques accepted.

Reservations

Made with deposit (€ 70) and fee (€ 20).
Tel: 02 98 90 62 02. Email: camping@lanniron.com

Open

15 May - 15 September (with all facilities).

FR29030 Camping du Letty

29950 Bénodet (Finistère)

Built around their former farm, the Guyader family have ensured that this excellent and attractive site, with direct beach access, has plenty to offer for all the family. The site on the outskirts of the popular resort of Bénodet spreads over 22 acres with 493 pitches, all for touring units. Groups of eight to ten pitches are set in cul-de-sacs with mature hedging and trees to divide each cul-de-sac. Markers indicate the limits of each pitch which are slightly smaller than average (none more than about 80 sq.m), although they do not feel too small since they are not hedged or fenced. Most pitches have electricity (up to 10A), fresh and waste water connections. At the attractive floral entrance, former farm buildings provide a host of facilities including an extensively equipped fitness room. There is also a modern, purpose built nightclub and bar providing high quality live entertainment most evenings (situated well away from most pitches to avoid disturbance). Although there is no swimming pool here, the site has direct access to a small sandy beach, and has provided a floating pontoon with diving platform and water slides into the sea (safe bathing depends on the tides).

Facilities

Six well placed toilet blocks are of good quality and include mixed style WCs, washbasins in large cabins and controllable hot showers (charged). One refurbished block includes a separate laundry and dog washing enclosures. Four well equipped baby rooms. Separate facility for disabled visitors. Launderette. Hairdressing room. Motorcaravan service points. Well stocked mini-market. Extensive snack bar and takeaway (22/6-30/8). Bar with games room and night club. Library/reading room. Games lounge with billiard and card tables and entertainment room with satellite TV. Fitness centre (no charge). Saunas, jacuzzis and solarium (all on payment). Table tennis. Two tennis and two squash courts (charged). Boules, volleyball, basketball and archery. Well equipped play area. In July/Aug. entertainment and activities organised for the whole family.

Directions

From N165 take D70 Concarneau exit. At first roundabout take D44 to Fouesnant. Turn right at T junction. After about 2 km. turn left to Fouesnant (still D44). Continue through La Forêt Fouesnant and Fouesnant, picking up signs for Bénodet. Shortly before Benodet at roundabout turn left (signed Le Letty). Turn right at next mini roundabout and site is 500 m. on left.

Charges 2003

Per adult	€ 4.50
child (under 7 yrs)	€ 2.25
pitch with electricity (1-10A)	€ 8.50 - € 11.00
car or motorcaravan	€ 1.70

Reservations

Not made. Tel: 02 98 57 04 69.
Email: reception@campingduletty.com

Open

15 June - 6 September.

At a glance

Welcome & Ambience	✓✓✓✓	Location	✓✓✓✓✓
Quality of Pitches	✓✓✓	Range of Facilities	✓✓✓✓

FR29240 Camping de Kéranterec

Route de Port la Forêt, 29940 La Forêt Fouesnant (Finistère)

The area around La Forêt Fouesnant is very much picture postcard Brittany – plenty of enticing crêperies and seafood restaurants, enchanting mediaeval villages and towns and delightful hidden coves. For these and many other reasons, there are plenty of campsites to choose from and Camping de Keranterec is well worth considering. A well established, family run site with a very French ambience (unlike some of the neighbouring sites which have a much higher UK presence), Keranterec has 265 grassy pitches in two distinct areas. The upper part of the site is more open and has little shade, and is largely taken up by private mobile homes. The lower, more mature area is predominantly for tourers, with terraced pitches set in a former orchard (the trees still provide fruit for the cider produced on site, which we can highly recommend!). Some of these pitches have shade from the trees on this part of the site, and some also overlook the little cove at the rear of the site. Spacious and divided by mature hedging, all have electricty (25 m. cable advised) and most also offer water and drainage. At the rear of the site a gate leads to a small beach and the coastal footpath to Concarneau (8 km).

Facilities

Two modern, fully equipped toilet blocks kept very clean include washbasins in cubicles, baby baths and facilities for disabled visitors. Washing machines, dryers and ironing boards. Small shop and bar (15/6-7/9) and takeaway (1/7-31/8). TV room with satellite. Heated swimming pool (15/5-7/9) with paddling pool, jacuzzi and three new water slides. Tennis court, boules, volleyball and basketball, table tennis (some indoors). Play area. In July/Aug. organised daily events and activities for all the family, and a free children's club. Off site: Attractive sandy beach of Kerleven 10 minutes walk. Golf 1 km. Riding 3 km.

Directions

From N165 take D70 Concarneau exit. At first roundabout take D44 signed Fouesnant. After 2.5 km. turn right at T junction, and follow for 2.5 km. and turn left (Port La Forêt - take care, 200 m. before junction a sign implies Port La Forêt is straight on - it isn't). Continue to roundabout and take second exit (straight ahead), signed Port La Forêt. After 1 km. turn left (site signed), then in 400 m. left to site on left.

Latest charges

Per person	€ 4.50 - € 5.80
child (under 7 yrs)	€ 2.10 - € 2.90
pitch with electricity	€ 8.55 - € 10.50

Reservations

Advised in high season and made with deposit (€ 77) and fee (€ 22). Tel: 02 98 56 98 11.
Email: info@camping-keranterec.com

Open

5 April - 21 September.

At a glance

Welcome & Ambience	✓✓✓✓✓	Location	✓✓✓✓✓
Quality of Pitches	✓✓✓✓	Range of Facilities	✓✓✓✓

travel service
TO BOOK THIS SITE
0870 405 4055
Expert Advice & Special Offers

(41)

FR29020 Camping Club du St Laurent

Kerleven, 29940 La Forêt-Fouesnant (Finistère)

Saint-Laurent is a well established site, situated on a sheltered wooded slope bordering one of the many attractive little inlets that typify the Brittany coastline. There is direct access from the site to two small sandy bays, which empty at low tide to reveal rockpools and the site is on the coastal footpath that leads from Kerleven to Concarneau. The 260 pitches are on level terraces, under tall trees. All pitches are divided by hedging, have electricity and are of average size (100 sq.m). Pitches with the best sea views tend to be adjacent to the cliff edge, and may not be suitable for families with young children. Access to some pitches can also be a little difficult, but the friendly site owners ensure that this is not a problem by offering to site any caravan using their own 4 x 4 vehicle. The pool (complete with paddling pool and two water slides) is overlooked by the bar terrace. With organised activities and entertainment in high season, this site is an ideal choice for a lively family holiday, particularly for older children. Around 50% of the pitches are occupied by tour operators or site owned mobile homes.

Facilities

Two sanitary blocks provide combined shower and washbasin cubicles, separate washbasin cubicles, baby changing and facilities for disabled people. Laundry and dishwashing sinks. Washing machines, dryers and ironing facilities in newly refurbished room. Small shop at reception provides essentials. Bar, snack bar and takeaway (all 12/5-10/9). Swimming pools. Gym and sauna. Canoe hire. Basketball, two tennis courts (no charge), and table tennis. Play area. During July and August daily children's clubs and adult entertainments are organised (in English as well as in French), with discos in the bar each evening.

At a glance

Welcome & Ambience	✓✓✓✓	Location	✓✓✓✓✓
Quality of Pitches	✓✓✓✓	Range of Facilities	✓✓✓✓

Directions

From N165, D70 Concarneau exit, at roundabout take first exit D44 (Fouesnant). After 2.5 km. turn right at T junction, follow for 2.5 km, then turn left (Port La Forêt). Continue to roundabout, straight ahead and after 1 km. turn left to site.

Charges 2003

Per unit incl. 1 or 2 persons, electricity (6A) and water	€ 20.00 - € 30.00
child (2-7 yrs)	€ 1.80 - € 3.50

Reservations

Advised for July/Aug. and made with deposit (€ 77) and fee (€ 22.87). Tel: 02 98 56 97 65. Email: info@ camping-du-saint-laurent.fr

Open

3 May - 13 September.

FR29220M Camping Municipal de Kerisole

Kerisole, 29390 Scaer (Finistère)

Within walking distance of the pleasant little town, Kerisole is an attractive and well kept site, ideal for exploring inland Brittany and yet only 32 km. from the coast. There are 83 mostly level, grass pitches, not hedged, but individually numbered. Most have electricity. All season the site in conjunction with the local council organises walks, local visits and various activities (even how to make genuine Breton crêpes!), many of which are free of charge. With its delightful park-like setting, reasonable charges, and proximity to both town facilities and countryside walks, this site makes an ideal base.

Facilities

Central, clean and tidy sanitary blocks include washbasins in cubicles and separate men's and ladies' facilities for disabled people. Laundry and dishwashing sinks. Bread to order. Adjacent play area in large grassy field. Off site: Nearby tennis, basketball and petanque courts, and indoor swimming pool (free entry for campers). Shops, bars and restaurants a few minutes walk away in the centre of Scaër.

At a glance

Welcome & Ambience	✓✓✓✓	Location	✓✓✓✓
Quality of Pitches	✓✓✓✓	Range of Facilities	✓✓✓

Directions

From N165 take D70 to Rosporden, then D782 to Scaër. Drive through town following signs for Faouet, and site is on left at traffic lights on leaving town.

Charges 2003

Per adult	€ 2.05
pitch with electricity (10A)	€ 4.80 - € 6.15

Reservations

Contact site. Tel: 02 98 57 60 91. Email: mairie@ville-scaer.fr

Open

15 June - 15 September.

FR29190 Camping Les Prés Verts

Kernous-Plage, 29900 Concarneau (Finistère)

What sets this family site apart from the many others in this region are its more unusual features – its stylish pool complex with Romanesque style columns and statue, and its plants and flower tubs. The 150 pitches are mostly arranged on long, open, grassy areas either side of main access roads. Specimen trees, shrubs or hedges divide the site into smaller areas. There are a few individual pitches and an area towards the rear of the site where the pitches have sea views. Concarneau is just 2.5 km. and there are numerous marked coastal walks to enjoy in the area, plus watersports or boat and fishing trips available nearby. A 'Sites et Paysages' member.

Facilities

Two toilet blocks provide unisex WCs, but separate washing facilities for ladies and men. Pre-set hot showers and washbasins in cabins for ladies, both closed 21.00 - 08.00 hrs. Some child size toilets. Dishwashing and laundry sinks, washing machine and dryer. Pizza service twice weekly. Swimming pool (1/6-31/8) and children's pool. Playground (0-5 yrs only). Minigolf. Path to sandy/rocky beach (300 m.) and coastal path. Off site: Supermarket 2 km. Riding 1 km, bicycle hire 3 km, golf 5 km.

At a glance

Welcome & Ambience	✓✓✓	Location	✓✓✓✓✓
Quality of Pitches	✓✓✓✓	Range of Facilities	✓✓✓

Directions

Turn off C7 road, 2.5 km. north of Concarneau, where site is signed. Take third left after Hotel de l'Océan.

Charges 2003

Per unit incl. 2 adults	€ 16.48 - € 20.60
child (2-7 yrs)	€ 3.12 - € 3.90
dog	€ 1.16 - € 1.45
electricity (2-6A)	€ 2.90 - € 4.43
local tax	€ 0.30

Reservations

Contact site for details. Tel: 02 98 97 09 74.
Email: info@pres-verts.com

Open

1 May - 22 September.

FR29350 Sunêlia L'Atlantique

Mousterlin, 29170 Fouesnant (Finistère)

L'Atlantique is quietly situated just outside Beg-Meil and is a superb site for families and those looking for a beach holiday. The sandy beach faces the Glénan Islands and is a pleasant 400 m. walk away through a nature reserve. The 432 pitches are of a good size and all have electricity (over 130 are used for mobile homes and chalets). Level and grassy, they are separated by an attractive variety of low shrubs, with apple orchards used for cider production also on the site. All the facilities are grouped together at the centre of the site including an innovative play area and excellent pool complex with water slides and a paddling pool. Coastal paths await exploration and Concarneau, Pont-Aven and La Pointe du Raz are all nearby. The site is used by a number of tour operators.

Facilities

Clean, modern, fully equipped toilet blocks incude facilities for disabled visitors. Shop. Bar. Snack bar with takeaway meals and pizza. Heated outdoor pool, water complex with slides (all 18/5-8/9). Tennis. TV room. Billiards, table tennis. Minigolf. Sports ground. Play area. Children's club (4-12 yrs, July/Aug). Evening entertainment (July/Aug). Off site: Windsurf hire 1 km. Boat hire 3 or 5 km. Fishing 300 m. Riding 3 km. Golf 8 km.

At a glance

Welcome & Ambience	✓✓✓✓	Location	✓✓✓✓
Quality of Pitches	✓✓✓✓	Range of Facilities	✓✓✓✓✓

Directions

From Fouesnant follow directions for Mousterlin for 4.5 km. Site is signed.

Charges 2003

Per unit incl. 2 persons	€ 21.00 - € 36.00
extra person	€ 2.70 - € 6.00
child (0-10 yrs)	€ 1.30 - € 3.00

Reservations

Contact site. Tel: 02 98 56 14 44.
Email: information@camping-atlantique.fr

Open

28 April - 14 September.

FR29310 Camping La Roche Percée

Hent Kerveltrec, Beg-Meil, 29170 Fouesnant (Finistère)

Close to the beautiful Brittany coastline, La Roche Percée combines a tranquil setting with a friendly and active family environment, only 400 metres from the beach. The site is English/French owned with 123 pitches, of which 80 are available for touring units, the rest being for privately owned or site owned mobile homes. Pitches are arranged in cul-de-sacs off a central area, and are of good size, grassy and flat, all with electrical connections (some may require a long lead). All pitches are separated by mature hedging, and some benefit from the shade of the variety of trees planted around the site. The bar terrace overlooks the swimming and paddling pools, and there is a waterslide into the main pool. During high season the owners organise a variety of entertainment activities, including boules, table tennis, pool and darts tournaments, barbecues, and live music in the bar.

Facilities

The clean, tidy central toilet block includes mostly British style toilets, washbasins in cubicles, dishwashing and laundry sinks. Baby bath and changing area. Wheelchair access provided on request. Motorcaravan service point. Small shop, snack bar and bar, open 15/5 - 15/9, with bread to order outside these dates (dates can be flexible if busy). Swimming pools (all season). Two play areas for children. Football and volleyball. Large trampoline (parental supervision essential!) Bicycle hire. Off site: Sailing school, golf and riding nearby.

At a glance

Welcome & Ambience	✓✓✓✓	Location	✓✓✓✓✓
Quality of Pitches	✓✓✓✓	Range of Facilities	✓✓✓✓

Directions

From N165 take D70 Concarneau exit. At roundabout exit on D44 (Fouesnant and Benodet). Following D44, turn right at T junction, after 2 km turn left and follow through Forêt Fouesnant. 2 km. after village go straight over first roundabout, and left at second on D45 to Beg Meil. After 3 km. site is signed on left.

Charges 2003

Per person	€ 3.00 - € 4.50
pitch with electricity (6/10A)	€ 11.50 - € 14.50

Reservations

Accepted with deposit and fee. Tel: 02 98 94 94 15. Email: info@campingbrittany.com

Open

17 April - 28 September.

Over 40% reductions on low season mobile homes prices.
12 km of varied beaches to discover nearby. All styles of local entertainments : fetes, festivals, concerts, markets. A very popular holiday destination for all sports and pastimes.
Many return again and again to this friendly family campsite.

BEG-MEIL
29170 Fouesnant
Sounth Brittany

info@campingbrittany.com
www.campingbrittany.com

FR29170 Camping de la Piscine

Kerleya B.P.12, Beg-Meil, 29170 Fouesnant (Finistère)

There are many campsites in this area but La Piscine is notable for the care and attention to detail that contributes to the well-being of its guests. Created by the Caradec family from an apple orchard, the 185 level, grass pitches are of generous size and are separated by an interesting variety of hedges and trees. Water, waste and electricity points are provided, normally one stand between two pitches. The nearby towns of Beg-Meil and Fouesnant, and (a little further) Quimper, are well worth a visit if only to taste the local cider and crêpes which are specialities of the area. A quiet site, set back from the sea, La Piscine will appeal to families looking for good quality without too many on site activities.

Facilities

Two refurbished toilet units of differing design and size include British and Turkish style toilets and washbasins in cabins. Facilities for disabled people. Dishwashing and laundry sinks, washing machines and dryers. Motorcaravan service point. Shop (1/7-15/9). Takeaway (high season). Swimming pool with waterfall and separate flume (from 1/6, no bermuda style shorts), sauna and solarium. Play area. BMX track. Football pitch, volleyball, half-court tennis and table tennis. TV room. Entertainment organised in high season. Caravan storage. Off site: Bicycle hire, fishing and riding within 4 km. Golf 7 km. The sea is 15 minutes walk.

At a glance

Welcome & Ambience	✓✓✓✓✓	Location	✓✓✓✓
Quality of Pitches	✓✓✓✓✓	Range of Facilities	✓✓✓✓

Directions

Site is 5 km. south of Fouesnant. Turn off N165 at Coat Conq (Concarnau, Fouesnant). At Fouesnant join D45 signed Beg Meil and shortly turn left on D145 to Mousterlin. In 1 km. turn left and follow signs to site.

Charges 2004

Per person	€ 3.50 - € 5.00
pitch with electricity (3-10A)	€ 9.85 - € 14.20

Reservations

Made with 25% deposit and € 19 fee. Tel: 02 98 56 56 06. Email: contact@campingdelapiscine.com

Open

Easter - 28 September.

FR29290 Yelloh! Village le Grand Large

48 route du Grand Large, Mousterlin, 29170 Fouesnant (Finistère)

Le Grand Large is a beach-side site situated on the Pointe de Mousterlin in natural surroundings. The site is separated from the beach by the road that follows the coast around the point. It is also protected from the wind by an earth bank with trees and a fence. The beach itself looks over the bay towards the Isles de Glénan. There are 300 level grass pitches of average size and rather sandy in places with some shrubs and mature trees. Tour operators take 25 places and the site itself has 96 tents and mobile homes to rent. Electricity is available everywhere (long leads useful) and some pitches have drainage. A small river runs through the site but it is fenced. Benodet (7 km.) and Fouesnant (5 km) are near in different directions and the sandy beach is just up the steps and across the road. A family site, would also suit walkers and nature lovers in the low seasons as it is next to a large tract of protected land, Marais de Mousterlin, ideal for walking, cycling and birdwatching.

Facilities

Two neat, new sanitary blocks include plenty of washbasins in cabins (warm water only). Two baby baths in the larger block with children's shower and toilet and facilities for disabled people in both blocks. Two washing machines, two dryers and plenty of laundry and washing up sinks (hot water only). Bar overlooks the sea with attractive terrace and a crêperie/grill restaurant that also provides takeaway food. Swimming pool with paddling pool, water slides in a separate pool. Tennis court and multi-sport court where it is possible to play 5-a-side football, badminton, volleyball, handball or basketball. Small play area. TV room and games room with table tennis and billiards.

At a glance

Welcome & Ambience	✓✓✓	Location	✓✓✓
Quality of Pitches	✓✓✓	Range of Facilities	✓✓✓✓✓

Directions

Site is 7 km. south of Fouesnant. Turn off N165 expressway at Coat Conq, signed Concarneau and Fouesnant. At Fouesnant take A45 signed Beg Meil, then follow signs to Mousterlin. In Mousterlin turn left and follow camping signs.

Charges 2004

Per unit incl. 2 persons and 5A electricity	€ 15.00 - € 36.00
extra person	€ 4.00 - € 6.00
child (under 10 yrs)	free - € 4.00
electricity (10A)	free - € 1.00
dog	€ 2.50 - € 3.50
local tax (over 16 yrs)	€ 0.16 - € 0.40

Reservations

Made with deposit (€ 45) and non-refundable fee (€ 19). Tel: 02 98 56 04 06. Email: info@campingsbretagnesud.com

Open

15 May - 11 September (with all services).

FR29250 Camping Bois des Ecureuils

29300 Guilligomarc'h (Finistère)

Situated in beautiful countryside between the rivers Scorff and Elle, this two star site provides camping 'au natural' for those seeking an ideal base from which to explore southern and central Brittany. The site is set in 5 acres of natural woodland, with oak, chestnut, birch and beech trees providing shade for many of the 40 pitches. Of reasonable size, marked by shrubs and trees, and although not all pitches are officially provided with electrical connections, the owners say that 'electricity is possible everywhere'. Those pitching tents may find a bit of manoeuvring necessary in order to avoid protruding tree roots, etc. The British owners, David and Barbara Reed, are knowledgeable about the area, and can provide a wealth of advice and information on places to visit and things to do, including walking, cycling, canoeing and fishing. Although by no means a luxurious site, the tranquillity and peacefulness of this rural setting, combined with the friendly reception make it ideal for anyone seeking a 'back to nature' style holiday.

Facilities

Small toilet block with hot showers, washbasins, British and Turkish style WCs, dishwashing and laundry sinks. Reception also provides basic groceries and bread to order. Small playground for children. Large grass area with boules pitch, table tennis, badminton net and TV tent. Bicycle hire.

At a glance

Welcome & Ambience	✓✓✓✓✓	Location	✓✓✓✓
Quality of Pitches	✓✓✓	Range of Facilities	✓✓✓

Directions

From south on N165 take D765 Quimperlé exit. Before entering Quimperlé turn right on D22 to Arzano. On leaving Arzano turn left on D222 to Guilligomarc'h. After 3 km. turn right and follow road into village (site signed). Once in the village follow one way system around the church and take C2 to Meslan. Site is 3 km. on right. From north take D769 Carhaix-Plouguer - Lorient road and, 39 km. past Carhaix-Plouguer turn right on D6 to Arzano, then left on C2 to Guilligomarc'h to site 3 km on left.

Charges 2003

Per person	€ 2.40
child (under 7 yrs)	€ 1.30
pitch with electricity (5A)	€ 6.20

No credit cards.

Reservations

Made with deposit (€ 15 or £10); contact site. Tel: 02 98 71 70 98. Email: price.reed@wanadoo.fr

Open

15 May - 15 September.

FR29140 Haven Camping Domaine de Kerlann

Land Rosted, 29930 Pont-Aven (Finistère)

Starting with a small original site, Haven Europe have, with careful and imaginative planning, ensured that mobile homes blend naturally into the environment. The remaining 20% of around 140 touring pitches (some 80 sq.m, some 120 sq.m) have been left in a more natural situation on rough grass with a small stream flowing through and with some of the mature trees providing shade. Electricity is available to all pitches. Land drainage may be poor due to the park being situated on low lying ground. The 'piece de resistance' of the site is the amazing pool complex comprising three outdoor pools with separate toboggan, attractively landscaped with sunbathing terraces, and an indoor tropical style complex complete with jacuzzi and its own toboggan. Much evening holiday camp style entertainment (with a French flavour) takes place on the bar terrace with its stage overlooking the complex.

Facilities

The main large toilet block on the edge of the mobile home area offers a good provision including washbasins in cubicles, outside dishwashing and laundry sinks. Good laundry. A second block in the touring section opens in high season. Mini supermarket. French style restaurant, snack restaurant, takeaway and bar. Impressive pool complex including indoor and outdoor pools with lifeguards. Well equipped play areas. All weather multi-sports court, tennis courts, minigolf. Video games room, pool tables and satellite TV in the bar. Three children's clubs for different age groups. Gas barbecues are not permitted. Off site: Pont-Aven with its Gauguin connection, art galleries and museums. Safe beaches and small ports are near.

At a glance

Welcome & Ambience	✓✓✓✓	Location	✓✓✓✓
Quality of Pitches	✓✓✓✓	Range of Facilities	✓✓✓✓✓

Directions

From Tregunc - Pont-Aven road, turn south towards Névez and site is on right.

Charges 2003

Per pitch incl. up to 2 persons
with electricity   € 11.00 - € 29.00
extra person   € 2.00 - € 5.00
extra vehicle   € 1.00 - € 3.00

Reservations

Accepted at any time for min. 4 days; no booking fee. Contact site or Haven Europe in the UK on Tel: 0870 242 7777 for information or reservation. Tel: 02 98 06 01 77. Email: kerlann@haven.fr

Open

2 April - 29 October.

FR29160 Camping Les Genets d'Or

Kermerour, Pont Kereon, 29380 Bannalec (Finistère)

A jewel of a small site, Les Genets d'Or is situated in a tiny country hamlet at the end of a road from Bannalec, 12 km. from Pont-Aven in Finistère. The spacious surroundings offer a safe haven for young children and a rural, tranquil environment for adults. The gently sloping, grassy site is edged with mature trees and divided into hedged glades with the odd apple tree providing shade. There are only 52 pitches (46 for touring units), all of a good size – some of over 100 sq.m. – and most pitches have electricity (6A), each glade having a water point. Alan and Judy, the English owners, ensure a warm friendly welcome and are justifiably proud of their site which they have improved over the last few years and keep in pristine condition. There are plans for a play area and pond.

Facilities

The good quality toilet block provides all the necessary amenities and washing facilities, including a shower for disabled campers. Small bar/drinks service. Bread delivered in season. Reception has a small library and an indoor room provides snooker and table tennis. Bicycle hire. Caravan storage. Off site: Riding 3 km. The village is 15 minutes walk with bars, shop, baker, etc.

At a glance

Welcome & Ambience	✓✓✓✓✓	Location	✓✓✓✓
Quality of Pitches	✓✓✓✓✓	Range of Facilities	✓✓✓✓

Directions

Take exit D4 from N165 (Bannalec). In town turn right into Rue Lorec (Quimperlé) and follow signs for 1 km.

Charges 2003

Per person   € 2.00 -   € 3.00
pitch   € 5.50
electricity (6A)   € 3.00

Reservations

Contact site. Tel: 02 98 39 54 35. Email: Enquiries@holidaybrittany.com

Open

Easter/1 April - 30 September.

FR29090 Camping Le Raguénès-Plage

19 rue des Iles, Raguénéz, 29920 Névez (Finistère)

Mme Guyader and her family will ensure you receive a warm welcome on arrival at this well kept and pleasant site. Although the entrance could best be described as more functional than beautiful, once you have passed the reception block you find yourself in an attractive and well laid out campsite with many shrubs and trees. The 287 pitches are a good size, flat and grassy, separated by trees and hedges. All have electricity, water and drainage. The site is used by one tour operator (63 pitches), and has 27 mobile homes of its own. A new pool complex complete with a water toboggan has recently been built. From the far end of the campsite a five minute walk along a path takes you down to a pleasant, sandy beach.

Facilities

Three clean, well maintained sanitary blocks include mixed style toilets, washbasins in cabins, baby baths and facilities for disabled visitors. Laundry and dishwashing sinks. Laundry room. Motorcaravan service point. Small shop (from 15/5). Bar and restaurant (from 1/6) with outside terrace and takeaway. Reading and TV room, internet access point. Heated pool with sun terrace and children's pool. Sauna (charged). Play areas, table tennis, games room and volleyball. Various activities are organised in July/Aug. Currency and traveller's cheques can be exchanged at reception. Off site: Supermarket 3 km. Fishing and watersports 300 m. Riding 4 km.

At a glance

Welcome & Ambience	✓✓✓✓✓	Location	✓✓✓✓✓
Quality of Pitches	✓✓✓✓	Range of Facilities	✓✓✓✓✓

Directions

From N165 take D24 Kerampaou exit. After 3 km turn right towards Nizon and bear right at church in village following signs to Névez (D77). Continue straight over roundabout through Névez, following signs to Raguénès. Continue for about 3 km. to site entrance on left (take care - entrance is quite small and easy to miss).

Charges 2003

Per unit incl. 2 persons	€ 14.40 - € 24.00
extra person	€ 3.80 - € 5.30
child (under 7 yrs)	€ 2.20 - € 3.00
electricity (2/6A)	€ 2.50 - € 3.20
local tax (over 18 yrs)	€ 0.40

Reservations

Advised for high season, min. 7 days preferred for July/Aug. Write with deposit (€ 100).
Tel: 02 98 06 80 69.
Email: info@camping-le.raguenes-plage.com

Open

10 April - 1 October.

FR29010 Camping Ty-Nadan

Route d'Arzano, 29310 Locunolé (Finistère)

Ty Nadan is a well organised site set amongst wooded countryside along the bank of the River Elle. The 183 pitches for touring units are grassy, many with shade and 152 with electricity. An exciting and varied programme of activities is offered throughout the season – canoeing, rock climbing, mountain biking, aqua-gym, riding or walking – all supervised by qualified staff. A full programme of entertainment for all ages is provided in high season including concerts, Breton evenings with pig roasts, dancing, etc. (be warned, you will be actively encouraged to join in!) Recent developments include a new toilet block and extensions to the shop and bar. The pool complex with its slides and paddling pool is very popular and now has an attractive viewing platform. A large indoor pool complex is planned for 2004. Several tour operators use the site (90 pitches).

Facilities

Two older, split-level toilet blocks are of fair quality and unusual design. They include washbasins in cabins, and baby rooms. An impressively equipped block was opened in 2002 which provides easier access for disabled people. Dishwashing facilities in two attractive gazebo style units. Laundry room with washing machines and dryers. Good sized restaurant, takeaway, bar and well stocked shop (all open all season). Heated swimming pool (17 x 8 m), pool with water slides and paddling pool. Small beach on the river (unfenced). Tennis courts, table tennis, pool tables, archery and trampolines. Exciting adventure play park. Riding. Small roller skating rink. Bicycle hire. Skateboards, roller skates and boat hire. Fishing. Canoe expeditions. High season entertainment.

At a glance

Welcome & Ambience	✓✓✓✓	Location	✓✓✓✓
Quality of Pitches	✓✓✓✓	Range of Facilities	✓✓✓✓✓

Directions

Make for Arzano which is northeast of Quimperlé on the Pontivy road and turn off D22 just west of village at camp sign. Site is approx. 3 km.

Charges 2003

Per person	€ 4.96 - € 6.20
child (under 7 yrs)	€ 3.12 - € 3.90
pitch	€ 10.40 - € 13.00
electricity (10A)	€ 3.92 - € 4.90
animal	€ 2.64 - € 3.30

Less 15-20% outside July/Aug.
Camping Cheques accepted.

Reservations

Made for exact dates with deposit (€ 50) and fee (€ 25). Tel: 02 98 71 75 47.
Email: TY-NADAN@wanadoo.fr

Open

15 May - 5 September.

Camping "Le Ty Nadan" ★★★★

the only campsite where you can do this...

New for 2004 : Indoor swimming pool complex

www.camping-ty-nadan.fr

i comme... 33(2) 98 10 19 20

FR29180 Camping Les Embruns

Rue du Philosophe Alain, Le Pouldu, 29360 Clohars-Carnoët (Finistère)

This site is unusual in that it is located in the heart of a village, yet is only 250 metres from a sandy cove. It is also close to beautiful countryside and the Carnoët Forest. The entrance with its card operated barrier and superb floral displays, is the first indication that this is a well tended and well organised site, and the owners have won numerous regional and national awards for its superb presentation. The 180 pitches (100 occupied by mobile homes) are separated by trees, shrubs and bushes, and most have electricity, water and waste water facilities. There is a covered, heated swimming pool, a circular paddling pool, and a water play pool. It is only a short walk to the village centre, with all its attractions and services.

Facilities

Two modern sanitary blocks (decorated in the floral and nautical theme that pervades the whole site), include mainly British style toilets, some washbasins in cubicles, baby baths and good facilities for the disabled. Dishwashing and laundry sinks under cover. Washing, drying and ironing facilities. Motorcaravan service point. Small shop (3/4-15/9). Bar and terrace (1/7-31/8) overlooking a covered, heated swimming pool (3/4-15/9) and paddling pool. Takeaway (20/6-5/9). Large games hall with pinball machines and table tennis. Play area. Football field, volleyball and minigolf. Communal barbecue area. Daily activities for children and adults organised in July/Aug. Off site: Nearby sea and river fishing and watersports. Bicycle hire 50 m, riding 2 km. Good cycling in the surrounding countryside.

At a glance

Welcome & Ambience	✓✓✓✓	Location	✓✓✓✓
Quality of Pitches	✓✓✓✓	Range of Facilities	✓✓✓✓✓

Directions

From N165 take either 'Kervidanou, Quimperlé Ouest' exit or 'Kergostiou, Quimperlé Centre, Clohars Carnoët' exit and follow the D16 to Clohars Carnoët. Then take the D24 for Le Pouldu and follow site signs in village.

Charges 2003

Per unit incl. 2 persons	€ 9.90 - € 20.50
fully serviced pitch	€ 14.00 - € 24.50
extra person	€ 3.50 - € 4.60
child (under 7 yrs)	€ 2.30 - € 2.80
electricity on ordinary pitch (3/5A)	€ 3.00
animal	free - € 1.00
local tax (June-Sept)	€ 0.30

Less in low seasons. Use of motorcaravan services € 1.83.

Reservations

Advised for high season. Tel: 02 98 39 91 07. Email: camping-les-embruns@wanadoo.fr

Open

3 April - 15 September.

FR35040 Sunêlia Le P'tit Bois

St Jouan-des-Guerets, 35430 St Malo (Ille-et-Vilaine)

On the outskirts of St Malo, this neat, family oriented site is very popular with British visitors, being ideal for one night stops or for longer stays in this interesting area. Le P'tit Bois is a busy site providing 274 large level pitches (around 140 for touring units) which are divided into groups by mature hedges and trees, separated by shrubs and flowers and with access from tarmac roads. Nearly all have electrical hook-ups and over half have water taps. Behind reception, an attractive, sheltered terraced area around the pools provides a focus during the day with the bar and snack bar. There are site-owned mobile homes and chalets but this does mean that the facilities are open over a long season (but possibly for limited hours).

Facilities

Two fully equipped toilet blocks, one in the newer area across the lane, include washbasins in cabins, baby baths and laundry facilities. Simple facilities for disabled people. Motorcaravan service point. Small shop (from 15/5). Bar where entertainment and discos are organised (July-Aug). Snack bar with takeaway, small bar, TV room (large screen for sports events) and games rooms. Swimming pool complex with standard pool, paddling pool and two water slides (from 15/5). Indoor pool with jacuzzi and turkish bath. Playground and multi-sports court. Tennis court, minigolf, table tennis, and outdoor chess. Charcoal barbecues are not permitted. Card operated security gates (deposit). Off site: Fishing 1.5 km, bicycle hire or riding 5 km, golf 7 km.

At a glance

Welcome & Ambience	✓✓✓✓	Location	✓✓✓✓
Quality of Pitches	✓✓✓✓✓	Range of Facilities	✓✓✓✓✓

Directions

St Jouan is west off the St Malo - Rennes road (N137) just outside St Malo. Site is signed from the N137 (exit St Jouan or Quelmer).

Charges 2003

Per person	€ 7.00
child (under 7 yrs)	€ 4.00
pitch incl. electricity (6A)	€ 14.00 - € 22.00
water and drainage (min 7 nights)	€ 3.00
dog	€ 4.00

Reservations

Made on receipt of 25% of total cost, plus fee (€ 30) from 19 June - 4 September. Tel: 02 99 21 14 30. Email: camping.ptitbois@wanadoo.fr

Open

15 May - 11 September.

FR35000 Camping Le Vieux Chêne

Baguer-Pican, 35120 Dol-de-Bretagne (Ille-et-Vilaine)

This attractive, family owned site is situated between St Malo and Mont St Michel. Developed in the grounds of a country farmhouse dating from 1638, its young and enthusiastic new owner has created a really pleasant, traditional atmosphere. It offers 200 good sized pitches, most with electricity, water tap and light, in spacious rural surroundings on gently sloping grass. They are separated by bushes and flowers, with mature trees for shade. A very attractive tenting area (without electricity) is in the orchard. There are three lakes in the grounds and centrally located leisure facilities include an attractive pool complex. Some entertainment is provided in high season, free for children. Used by a Dutch tour operator (10 pitches).

Facilities

Three very good, unisex toilet blocks include washbasins in cabins, a baby room and facilities for disabled people. All recently been refurbished and can be heated. Small laundry with washing machine, dryer and iron. Motorcaravan services. Shop. Takeaway. Café with terrace (all season). Medium sized, heated pool, children's pool, slides, etc. (17/5-14/9; lifeguard July/Aug). TV room (satellite) and games room. Tennis court, minigolf, giant chess. Play area. Riding in July/Aug. Fishing is possible in two of the three lakes. Off site: Supermarket in Dol (3 km). Golf 12 km.

At a glance

Welcome & Ambience	✓✓✓✓✓	Location	✓✓✓✓
Quality of Pitches	✓✓✓✓	Range of Facilities	✓✓✓✓✓

Directions

Site is by the D576 Dol-de-Bretagne - Pontorson road, just east of Baguer-Pican. It can be reached from the new N176 taking exit for Dol-Est and Baguer-Pican.

Charges 2003

Per person	€ 5.00
child (under 10 yrs)	€ 3.00
pitch incl. electricity (5A)	€ 9.50 - € 18.00

Reservations

Made with deposit (€ 30) and fee (€ 15). Tel: 02 99 48 09 55. Email: vieux.chene@wanadoo.fr

Open

1 April - 1 October.

FR35020 Castel Camping des Ormes

Epiniac, 35120 Dol-de-Bretagne (Ille-et-Vilaine)

This impressive site is in the northern part of Brittany, about 30 kilometres from the old town of St Malo, in the grounds of the Château des Ormes. In an estate of wooded parkland and lakes it has a pleasant atmosphere, busy in high season, almost a holiday village, but peaceful at other times, with a wide range of facilities. The 800 pitches, of which only 150 are for touring units, are divided into a series of different sections, each with its own distinctive character. They offer a choice of terrain – flat or gently sloping, wooded or open – and mixed with the range of tour operator units. There are electrical connections on 200 pitches. A marvellous 'Aqua Park' with pink stone and palms and a variety of pools, toboggans, waterfalls and jacuzzi (free) is set just above the small lake with pedaloes and canoes for hire. A pleasant bar and terrace overlooks the pools and a grass sunbathing area surrounds them – almost a touch of the Caribbean! The original pools are sheltered by the restaurant building, parts of which are developed from the 600 year old water-mill. A particular feature is an 18 hole golf course; also a golf practice range and a beginners 5 hole course. A restaurant and hotel with pool is part of the complex. A popular site with British visitors, with some 80% of the pitches occupied by tour operators and seasonal units and consequently very busy with much organised entertainment.

Facilities

Sanitary installations are of fair standard, including washbasins in cabins and ample facilities for disabled people. Motorcaravan services. Shop, bar, restaurant, pizzeria and takeaway. Games room, bar and disco. Two traditional heated swimming pools and Aqua park. New adventure play area. Golf. Bicycle hire. Fishing. Riding. Minigolf, two tennis courts, sports ground with volleyball, etc, paintball, archery and a cricket club.

At a glance

Welcome & Ambience	✓✓✓✓	Location	✓✓✓✓✓
Quality of Pitches	✓✓✓✓	Range of Facilities	✓✓✓✓✓

Directions

Access road leads off main D795 about 7 km. south of Dol-de-Bretagne, north of Combourg.

Charges 2004

Per person	€ 6.50 - € 7.20
child (under 7 yrs)	€ 3.75 - € 4.10
pitch incl. vehicle	€ 19.00 - € 21.00
electricity (3/6A)	€ 3.70 - € 4.10

Less 10% outside July/Aug.
Camping Cheques accepted.

Reservations

Made for min. 3 nights; details from site.
Tel: 02 99 73 53 00. Email: info@lesormes.com

Open

22 May - 12 September, with all services.

FR35060 Camping La Touesse

35800 St Lunaire (Ille-et-Vilaine)

This family campsite was purpose built and has been developed since 1987 by Alain Clement who is keen to welcome more British visitors. Set just back from the coast road, 300 m. from a sandy beach it is in a semi-residential area. It is, nevertheless, an attractive sheltered site with a range of trees and shrubs. The 142 level, grass pitches in bays (95 for touring units) have electricity and are accessed by circular tarmac roads. The plus factor of this site, besides its proximity to Dinard, is the fine sandy beach which is sheltered – so useful in early season – and safe for children. The owners speak English.

Facilities

The central toilet block is well maintained, heated in low season and provides all modern facilities. Part of it may not be open outside July/Aug. Baby bath and toilet for disabled people. Dishwashing and laundry sinks, and two washing machines and a dryer. Motorcaravan service point. Shop for basics (1/4-15/9). Pleasant bar/restaurant (or clubhouse as it is called) with TV. Volleyball, table tennis and video games for children. Sauna. Off site: Many amenities near. Bicycle hire 1 km. Fishing 300 m. Riding 500 m. Golf 2 km. Sandy beach 4 minutes walk.

At a glance

Welcome & Ambience	✓✓✓✓	Location	✓✓✓✓✓
Quality of Pitches	✓✓✓✓	Range of Facilities	✓✓✓✓

Directions

From Dinard take D786 coast road towards St Lunaire; watch for site signs to the left.

Charges 2003

Per person	€ 3.40 - € 4.40
child (under 7 yrs)	€ 1.90 - € 2.40
pitch	€ 4.20 - € 5.70
car	€ 2.40 - € 2.90
electricity (5/10A)	€ 2.90 - € 3.10
dog	€ 1.20 - € 1.20
local tax	€ 0.10 - € 0.25

No credit cards.

Reservations

Tel: 02 99 46 61 13.
Email: camping.la.touesse@wanadoo.fr

Open

1 April - 30 September.

FR44040 Camping Parc Sainte-Brigitte

Domaine de Bréhet, 44420 La Turballe (Loire-Atlantique)

Sainte-Brigitte is a well established site in the grounds of a manor house, three kilometres from the beaches. It is a spacious site with 150 pitches, 106 with electricity and 25 also with water and waste water. Some are in a circular, park-like setting near the entrance, others are in wooded areas under tall trees and the rest are on more open grass in an unmarked area near the pool. One can walk around many of the areas of the estate not used for camping, there are farm animals to see and a fishing lake is very popular. A quiet place to stay outside the main season, with few facilities open; in high season, however, it is mainly used by families with its full share of British visitors and it can become very busy. Used by a tour operator (20 pitches).

Facilities
The main toilet block is of fair quality, supplemented by second block next to it. They include washbasins in cabins, with bidets for women, and two bathrooms. Washing machines and dryer (no washing to be hung out on pitches, lines provided). Motorcaravan services. Small shop for basics, bread available (baker calls). Nice little restaurant/bar with takeaway (both 15/5-15/9). Heated swimming pool and children's pool open all season, Playground. Bicycle hire. Boules, volleyball, pool and 'baby-foot' and table tennis room. TV room and traditional 'salle de reunion' in renovated outbuildings of the manor house. Off site: Nearest beach 3 km. Riding 2 km, golf 15 km.

At a glance
| Welcome & Ambience | ✓✓✓✓ | Location | ✓✓✓✓ |
| Quality of Pitches | ✓✓✓✓ | Range of Facilities | ✓✓✓✓ |

Directions
Entrance is off the busy La Turballe-Guérande D99 road, 3 km. east of La Turballe. A one-way system operates - in one lane, out via another.

Charges 2004
Per person	€ 5.00
child (under 7 yrs)	€ 3.30
pitch incl. water and electricity (6A)	€ 10.50

No credit cards.

Reservations
Made for any length with exact dates and recommended for July/Aug, with deposit (€ 77) plus fee (€ 15.24). Tel: 02 40 24 88 91.

Open
1 April - 1 October.

PARC SAINTE-BRIGITTE ★★★★ N.N. De Luxe Camping Site

HEATED SWIMMING POOL
Close to the fishing village of La Turballe and neighbouring beaches. 10 km from the well-known resort of La Baule. The charm of the countryside with the pleasures of the seaside. Sanitary facilities as in a first class hotel. Heated and covered swimming pool (approximately 200 m² water and 200 m² covered terrace around it). The cover can be retracted during warm weather. Children's pool.
campingsaintebrigitte@wanadoo.fr
www.campingsaintebrigitte.com

FR44030 Castel Camping Le Pré du Château de Careil

33 rue du Château, Careil, 44350 Guérande (Loire-Atlantique)

This site is totally different from the more usual Castel sites. It is the smallest site in the group and has few of the facilities or activities usually associated with these sites. It has a quiet atmosphere and is very popular with couples, retired people and those with young children (it is not really recommended for families with older children or teenagers). In the grounds of the Château de Careil, a building dating from the 14th century which may be visited, this small site, shaded by mature trees, contains just 50 good sized pitches. All are equipped with electricity (6/10A) and water, some also have drainage.

Facilities
The main refurbished toilet facilities in the main building are fully equipped, including four unisex shower and washbasin rooms. En-suite facilities for disabled people, baby room and washing machine. In season (15/6-5/9) some emergency provisions are kept and bread can be ordered. Small swimming pool (11 x 5 m. open 15/6-5/9). Playground. TV room. Volleyball and table tennis. Archery occasionally. Off site: Supermarket near. Fishing or golf 10 km, bicycle hire 2 km, riding 5 km. In July and August, tours of the Château are possible (€ 4.57), also by candlelight (€ 5.34).

At a glance
| Welcome & Ambience | ✓✓✓✓ | Location | ✓✓✓✓ |
| Quality of Pitches | ✓✓✓ | Range of Facilities | ✓✓✓ |

Directions
Take D92 from Guérande to La Baule and turn east to Careil before the town. From D99 Guérande - St Nazaire road, turn onto D92, following signs to 'Intermarche' and for Château de Careil. The gate is fairly narrow and between two bends.

Latest charges
Per unit incl. 2 persons, electricity	€ 17.00 - € 20.00
child (under 10 yrs)	€ 3.00

No credit cards.

Reservations
Contact site. Tel: 02 40 60 22 99. Email: chateau.careil@free.fr

Open
1 May - 30 September.

FR44020M Camping Municipal du Moulin

Route de Nantes, 44190 Clisson (Loire-Atlantique)

This good value, small site is conveniently located on one of the main north – south routes on the edge of the interesting old town of Clisson. A typical municipal site, it is useful for short stays. The site has 47 good sized, marked and level pitches with electricity and divided by hedges and trees giving a good degree of privacy; also an unmarked area for small tents. A barbecue and camp fire area (with free wood) is to the rear of the site above the river where one can fish or canoe (via a steep path). The warden lives on site in high season. The attractive old town is within walking distance.

Facilities

The fully equipped unisex toilet block includes some washbasins in cabins and others in a separate large room, with hot and cold water. Unit for disabled people. Dishwashing and laundry sinks. Cleaning can be a bit haphazard at times. Bread delivered daily. Table tennis, volleyball, and small playground. No double axle or commercial vehicles accepted. Off site: Supermarket with cheap fuel just across the road.

At a glance

| Welcome & Ambience | ✓✓✓✓ | Location | ✓✓✓✓ |
| Quality of Pitches | ✓✓✓✓ | Range of Facilities | ✓✓✓ |

Directions

Entering Clisson from the north on N249 (Nantes - Poitiers) road, turn right at roundabout after passing Leclerc supermarket on your left. Site access is directly off roundabout.

Charges 2003

| Per unit incl. 1 adult, 6A electricity | € 8.30 - € 8.47 |

Reservations

Contact site. Tel: 02 40 54 44 48.

Open

Easter - mid October.

FR44100 Sunêlia Le Patisseau

29 rue du Patisseau, 44210 Pornic (Loire-Atlantique)

Le Patisseau is situated 2.5 km. from the sea. It is a relaxed site which can be very busy and even a little noisy in high season due to its popularity with young families and teenagers from the large number of mobile homes and chalets. On the left of the campsite there are some attractive touring pitches, all with electrical connections and water supply near. On the field area at the bottom of the site, pitches are close to the site's mobile homes and tend to be noisier. The pitches are connected by mostly unmade roads which can become quite muddy in wet weather. A railway line runs along the bottom half of the site with trains two or three times a day, but they do finish at 22.30 hrs and the noise is minimal. The site's restaurant and bar overlook the indoor pool. This is a busy site and the Morice family work very hard to maintain a friendly atmosphere, but don't expect it to be too neat and tidy with everything run like clockwork. They plan to convert all the touring pitches to hard accommodation in the future and are not spending money on maintaining the toilet blocks.

Facilities

There are three sanitary blocks, one of reasonable quality, but the other two dating from the '80s are very poor. They include washbasins in private cabins, child-size toilets, baby baths, fully equipped laundry rooms and dishwashing facilities. Maintenance can be variable so do not expect too much. Shop (main season). New bar and restaurant (3/4-12/9). Takeaway (1/7-31/8). Indoor heated pool with sauna, jacuzzi and spa (all season). Outdoor pools with water slides (1/5-12/9). Play area. Volleyball and table tennis. Bicycle hire. Off site: Fishing 1.5 km, golf 5 km.

At a glance

| Welcome & Ambience | ✓✓✓✓ | Location | ✓✓✓ |
| Quality of Pitches | ✓✓✓ | Range of Facilities | ✓✓✓✓✓ |

Directions

Site signed at roundabout junction of D751 (Pornic - Nantes) road, and from the town centre.

Charges 2004

| Per unit incl. 2 persons electricity (4/10A) | € 19.00 - € 29.00 |
| | € 4.00 |

Camping Cheques accepted.

Reservations

Made with deposit (€ 46.15) and fee (€ 15.38); contact site by letter, phone or fax. Tel: 02 40 82 10 39. Email: contact@lepatisseau.com

Open

3 April - 12 September.

FR44140M Camping Municipal Henri Dubourg

Route de Rennes, 44170 Nozay (Loire-Atlantique)

This good, small site is ideal for short stays or as an overnight stop, being situated in the northern outskirts of Nozay with easy access from the N137 Rennes - Nantes road. There are 25 well hedged, level, grassy pitches with electricity and a more open area at the rear of the site. Tourist information and an ice pack service are available at reception, there is a barbecue area and a baker calls each morning. Reception opens 07.30-09.00 and 18.00-20.30 hrs.

Facilities

A neat, modern and very clean toilet block has plenty of hot water, roomy showers and includes an odd Turkish style toilet. Facilities for disabled visitors. Dishwashing area under cover, laundry sinks inside. Off site: Small lake with playground and minigolf within 5 minutes walk. Fishing or golf 400 m. Two supermarkets in Nozay.

At a glance

| Welcome & Ambience | ✓✓✓✓ | Location | ✓✓✓✓✓ |
| Quality of Pitches | ✓✓✓✓ | Range of Facilities | ✓✓✓✓ |

Directions

From N137 take N171 Chateaubriant exit, then first right D121 for Nozay. Site is on right after the lake.

Charges 2003

| Per unit incl. 2 persons, 6A electricity | € 7.50 |

Reservations

Contact site. Tel: 02 40 87 94 33. Email: mairie@nozay.fr

Open

15 May - 15 September.

FR44090 Castel Camping Château du Deffay

B.P. 18, Le Deffay, St Reine de Bretagne, 44160 Pontchâteau (Loire-Atlantique)

A family managed site, Château de Deffay is a refreshing departure from the usual Castel formula in that it is not over organised or supervised and has no tour operator units. The landscape is natural right down to the molehills, and the site blends well with the rural environment of the estate, lake and farmland which surround it. For these reasons it is enjoyed by many. However, with the temptation of free pedaloes and the fairly deep, unfenced lake, parents should ensure that children are supervised. The 120 good sized, fairly level pitches have pleasant views and are either on open grass, on shallow terraces divided by hedges, or informally arranged in a central, slightly sloping wooded area. Most have electricity. The facilities are situated within the old courtyard area of the smaller château (that dates from before 1400). The larger château (built 1880) and another lake stand away from this area providing pleasant walking. The reception has been built separately to contain the camping area. Alpine type chalets overlook the lake and fit well with the environment.

Facilities

The main sanitary unit, housed in a converted barn, is well equipped including washbasins in cabins, provision for disabled people and a baby bathroom. Washing machines, and dryer. Maintenance can be variable and, with the boiler located at one end of the block, hot water can take time to reach the other in low season. Extra facilities are in the courtyard area where the well stocked shop, bar, small restaurant with takeaway and solar heated swimming pool and paddling pool are located (all 15/5-15/9). Play area. TV in the bar, separate room for table tennis. English language animation in season including children's mini club. Torches useful. Off site: Golf 5 km. Close to the Brière Regional Park, the Guérande Peninsula, and La Baule with its magnificent beach.

At a glance

Welcome & Ambience	✓✓✓✓✓	Location	✓✓✓✓
Quality of Pitches	✓✓✓✓	Range of Facilities	✓✓✓✓

Directions

Site is signed from D33 Pontchâteau - Herbignac road near St Reine. Also signed from the D773 and N165.

Charges 2003

Per person	€ 2.67 - € 4.33
child (2-12 yrs)	€ 1.85 - € 2.84
pitch	€ 6.41 - € 9.74
with electricity (4A)	€ 9.89 - € 13.24
with 3 services	€ 11.33 - € 14.88

Camping Cheques accepted.

Reservations

Accepted with deposit (€ 10 per day) and fee (€ 16). Tel: 02 40 88 00 57.
Email: info@camping-le-deffay.com

Open

1 May - 21 September.

EASON & SON LTD
O'CONNELL STREET
Vat No.: IE 8148114D
Please Retain Your Receipt
For Refunds

29-04-04 16.06   SALE 11 5617   100
PRODUCT   EURO   VAT

FRANCE CARAVANING   1   16.40 1

    TOTAL   1   16.40
    VISA CARD   16.40
    TOTAL TENDERED   16.40
    CHANGE   0.00

Tax Summary   Goods   Tax
1=VAT 0.00   16.40   0.00

THANK YOU FOR SHOPPING WITH
EASON & SON LTD
VISIT OUR WEBSITE AT

FR44130 Camping L'Hermitage

36 ave du Paradis, 44290 Guemene-Penfao (Loire-Atlantique)

L'Hermitage is a pretty wooded site, useful for en-route or longer stays. The enthusiastic staff, even though their English is a little limited, provide a warm welcome and maintain this reasonably priced site to high standards. There are 110 pitches of which 80 are a good size for touring and camping. Some are formally arranged on open, level grass pitches, whereas others are informal amongst light woodland. Electricity (6A) is available to all (a long lead may be useful).

Facilities

A clean, old style and well serviced toilet block includes some washbasins in cabins with warm water. Laundry and dishwashing sinks under cover (cold water but a hot tap is provided). Smallish pool and paddling pool nicely maintained and carefully fenced. Small play area. Table tennis, petanque and games room with video games. Off site: Leisure complex with an indoor pool opposite. Village 1 km. for all facilities. Fishing 500 m. Riding 2 km. Many walking trails.

At a glance

Welcome & Ambience	✓✓✓✓	Location	✓✓✓
Quality of Pitches	✓✓✓	Range of Facilities	✓✓✓

Directions

Exit N137 at Derval (signed Châteaubriant) but take D775 for Redon. Guémené-Penfao is approx. 13 km. Watch for site signs before village centre. Site is in the outskirts in a semi-residential area to the northeast.

Charges 2004

Per unit incl. 2 adults	€ 8.20 - € 9.60
child (under 10 yrs)	€ 1.90
electricity	€ 2.40
dog	€ 1.20

Reservations

Contact site. Tel: 02 40 79 23 48.
Email: contact@campinglhermitage.com

Open

1 April - 30 September.

CAMPING • GÎTE D'ÉTAPE
L'HERMITAGE
★★★

Sun, calm and uncovered

New 2004: water slide

36 avenue du Paradis
44290 GUÉMENÉ-PENFAO
Tél. : 02 40 79 23 48
Fax : 02 40 51 11 87
contact@campinglhermitage.com
www.campinglhermitage.com

FR44150 Camping La Tabardière

44770 La Plaine-Sur-Mer (Loire-Atlantique)

Owned and managed by the Barre family, this campsite lies next to the family farm. Pleasant, peaceful and immaculate, this site will suit those who want to enjoy the local coast and towns but return to an 'oasis' for relaxation. It still, however, provides activities and fun for those with energy remaining. The pitches are mostly terraced either side of a narrow valley and care needs to be taken in manoeuvring caravans into position – although the effort is well worth it. Most pitches have access to electricity (3/6A) and water taps are conveniently situated. Whilst this is a rural site, its amenities are excellent with a swimming pool, paddling pool and water toboggan slide, table tennis, volleyball, tennis, boules and a very challenging 18 hole minigolf to keep you occupied, plus a friendly bar. The beautiful beaches are 3 km distant, with the fishing harbour town, Pomic, some 5 km, ideal for cafes, restaurants and the evening strolls.

Facilities

The good, clean sanitary block is well equipped and includes laundry facilities. Bar. Shop. Snacks and takeaway. Good sized swimming pool, paddling pool and slides (supervised). Playground. Minigolf. Table tennis. Volleyball. asketball. Half size tennis courts. Boules. Motorcaravan service point. Overnight area for motorcaravans (€ 9 per night). Off site: Sea fishing, golf, riding all 5 km. Beach 3 km.

At a glance

Welcome & Ambience	✓✓✓✓✓	Location	✓✓✓✓✓
Quality of Pitches	✓✓✓✓	Range of Facilities	✓✓✓✓

Directions

Site is well signed, situated inland off the D13 Pornic - La Plaine sur Mer road.

Charges 2003

Per unit incl. 2 persons	€ 11.00 - € 18.00
child (2-10 yrs)	€ 2.40 - € 3.40
dog	€ 2.50
electricity (3/6A)	€ 2.60 - € 3.50

Reservations

Made with 20% deposit and € 13 fee.
Tel: 02 40 21 58 83.
Email: info@camping-la-tabardiere.com

Open

1 April - 30 September.

FR44160 Camping Armor-Héol

Route de Guérande, 44420 Piriac-sur-Mer (Loire-Atlantique)

Situated only 700 metres from Piriac town and beach and 14 km. from Guérande this campsite makes an ideal base for a beach holiday or for touring the beautiful Breton countryside and coastline. With considerable recent investment, the site now offers excellent facilities for visitors of all ages. There are 250 good sized (120 sq.m) level pitches all with 5A electricity. Although site owned mobiles and chalets take 160 pitches, they do not feel intrusive to the camper and caravanner. In 2002 a new facility was completed providing an outdoor swimming pool, a paddling pool and 70 m. of exciting water slides, together with a bar and restaurant with a large terrace. In 2003 a new indoor pool was added with water movement where you swim and stay stationary! This is a friendly site with English speaking reception staff and good amenities.

Facilities

Two clean and well maintained toilet blocks include washbasins in cabins, baby rooms, family rooms, dishwashing and laundries. Dishwashing, washing machines and dryers. Super bar and restaurant (1/6-15/9). Most activities are in one part of the site with heated pools and water slides ((1/6-15/9). Multi sports area, tennis courts, volleyball. Playground. Off site: Beach and town, fishing, boat launching, surfing and bicycle hire 700 m. Golf 2 km.

At a glance

Welcome & Ambience	✓✓✓✓	Location	✓✓✓✓
Quality of Pitches	✓✓✓✓	Range of Facilities	✓✓✓✓

Directions

From N165 Vannes - Nantes road, take D774 southwest at Guérande. Follow D333 signed Piriac sur Mer. Site is on left 0.5 km. before Piriac sur Mer, 4 km. from Guérande.

Charges 2004

Per unit incl. 2 persons	€ 13.00 - € 28.60
child (under 4 yrs)	€ 2.10 - € 4.40
electricity	€ 3.05 - € 3.35

Reservations

Tel: 02 40 23 57 80. Email: armor.heol@wanadoo.fr

Open

3 April - 26 September.

FR44170 Camping Les Ajoncs d'Or

Chemin du Rocher, 44500 La Baule (Loire-Atlantique)

This site is situated in pine woods, 1.5 km. on the inland side of La Baule and its beautiful bay. It can be difficult to find an informal campsite close to an exciting seaside resort that retains its touring and camping identity. Les Ajoncs d'Or does this. A well maintained, natural woodland setting provides a wide variety of pitch types, some level and bordered with hedges and tall trees to provide shade and many others that maintain the natural characteristics of the woodland. Most pitches have electricity and water nearby and are usually of a larger size. A central building provides a shop and friendly bar that serve snacks and takeaway. The English speaking Bazillails family (the owners) who live on site are justifiably proud of their site and will welcome you. There are only just over 200 pitches, so large areas of woodland have been retained for quiet and recreational purposes and are safe for children to roam. Enjoy the gentle breezes off the sea that constantly rustle the trees.

Facilities

Two good quality sanitary blocks are clean and well maintained providing plenty of facilities including a baby room. Washing machines and dryers. Shop and bar (July/Aug). Good size swimming pool and paddling pool (1/6-5/9). Sports and playground areas. Bicycle hire. Reception with security barrier (closed 22.30 - 7.30 hrs). Off site: Everything for an enjoyable holiday can be found in nearby La Baule. Fishing and riding 1.5 km. Golf 3 km.

At a glance

Welcome & Ambience	✓✓✓✓	Location	✓✓✓✓
Quality of Pitches	✓✓✓✓	Range of Facilities	✓✓✓✓

Directions

From N171 take exit for La Baule les Pins. Follow signs for 'La Baule Centre', then left at roundabout in front of Champion supermarket and follow site signs.

Charges 2003

Per unit incl. 2 persons, 6A electricity	€ 21.00
child (2-7 yrs)	€ 3.00
Less 15-25% outside July/Aug.	

Reservations

Tel: 02 40 60 33 29. Email: contact@ajoncs.com

Open

1 April - 30 September.

FR44180 Camping de la Boutinardière

Rue de la Plage de la Boutinardière, 44210 Pornic (Loire-Atlantique)

This campsite has it all – 2 km. from the beautiful harbour town of Pornic and 200 m. from the sea, together with the very best of amenities and facilities (unusually all open and functioning 1/5 - 22/9). This is a holiday site to suit all the family whatever their age. The site has 250 individual good sized pitches, 100-120 sq.m. in size, many bordered by three metre high, well maintained hedges for shade and privacy. All pitches have electricity available. This is a family owned site and English is spoken by the helpful reception staff. Across the road is a new complex of indoor and outdoor swimming pools, paddling pool and a twin water slide. Facing the water complex, the bar, restaurant and terraces are also new and serve excellent food. On site there are also sports and entertainment areas.

Facilities

Toilet facilities are in three good blocks, one large and centrally situated and two supporting blocks. Whilst the blocks are of traditional build the quality, maintenance and cleanliness are amongst the best. Washbasins are in cabins, dishwashing is under cover. Laundry room with sinks, washing machines and dryers. Excellent shop (15/6-15/9). New complex of bar, restaurant, terraces (1/4-22/9). Three heated swimming pools, one indoor, a paddling pool and water slides (15/5-22/9). Games room. Sports and activity area. Playground. Minigolf. Table tennis. Off site: Sandy cove 200 m. Golf, riding, sea fishing, restaurants, fishing harbour, boat trips, sailing and windsurfing, all within 5 km.

Directions

From north or south on D213, take Nantes D751 exit. At roundabout (with McDonalds) take D13 signed Bemarie-en-Retz. After 4 km. site is signed to right. Note: do NOT exit from D213 at Pornic Ouest or Centre.

Latest charges

Per unit incl. 2 persons	€ 11.00 - € 21.00
child (2-10 yrs)	€ 2.00 - € 4.00
electricity (3-10A)	€ 2.50 - € 5.00

Reservations

Made with deposit (€ 60) and fee (€ 15). Tel: 02 40 82 05 68. Email: info@laboutinardiere.com

Open

30 March - 29 September.

At a glance

Welcome & Ambience	✓✓✓✓✓	Location	✓✓✓✓✓
Quality of Pitches	✓✓✓✓	Range of Facilities	✓✓✓✓

FR56020 Camping de la Plage

Plage de Kervilaine, 56470 La Trinité-sur-Mer (Morbihan)

The area of Carnac/La Trinité is popular with holiday makers and the two La Trinité sites of La Plage and La Baie have the great advantage of direct access to a good sandy beach. Both sites are owned by the same family, and each is very well maintained, both having a small (12 m.) heated pool with a slide. The grassy pitches, which have electricity and water (70% with drainage also), are separated by hedges and shrubs and at La Plage there are attractive flower beds. Situated on a low cliff, the terrace with its views across the bay is a very popular place for a meal or a drink. Reception areas are welcoming and friendly with tourist information on display. Both sites have a number of tour operator pitches.

Facilities

Toilet blocks have washbasins in cubicles and facilities for disabled people and small children. Washing machines and dryers. Well stocked shop with bakery. Bar, restaurant, crêperie, takeaway. Swimming pools with new water slides, etc. Good play areas including ball pool. Tennis, basketball, minigolf, table tennis. Large TV screen. Lively entertainment programme in high season for all ages. Bicycle hire. Guided tours on foot or bicycle. Internet access. Small communal barbecue areas (only gas ones permitted on pitches). Off site: The village of La Trinité is 20 minutes walk along the cliff path and 10 minutes (approx) by car.

Directions

Site is signed in different places from the D186 coast road running from La Trinité to Carnac-Plage.

Charges 2003

Per unit incl. 2 persons	€ 16.40 - € 31.10
child (2-18 yrs)	€ 2.80 - € 3.00
electricity (6/10A)	€ 2.00 - € 3.70

Reservations

Contact site. Tel: 02 97 55 73 28. Email: laplage@club-internet.fr

Open

7 May - 17 September.

At a glance

Welcome & Ambience	✓✓✓	Location	✓✓✓✓✓
Quality of Pitches	✓✓✓✓	Range of Facilities	✓✓✓✓

FR56010 Camping La Grande Métairie

Route des Alignements de Kermario, B.P. 85, 56342 Carnac Cedex (Morbihan)

La Grande Métairie is a good quality site quietly situated a little back from the sea, close to the impressive rows of the famous 'menhirs' (giant prehistoric standing stones). It has a great deal to offer on site and is lively and busy over a long season. There is a feeling of spaciousness with a wide entrance and access road, with 574 individual pitches (129 for touring units), surrounded by hedges and trees. All have electricity (30 m. cables are needed in parts). Paddocks with ponds are home for ducks, goats and ponies to watch and feed. A super swimming pool complex comprises heated pools, water slides and toboggans, a flowing river, jacuzzi and a covered pool. The site, although large and not cheap, is well known and popular. Services are limited before late May. It has many British visitors with 358 pitches taken by several tour operators, plus site-owned mobile homes and touring caravanners and campers.

Facilities

Three large toilet blocks are good and well maintained, with washbasins in cabins, and facilities for babies and disabled people. Laundry room in each block. Motorcaravan service points. Shop and boutique. Restaurant, good takeaway. Bar lounge and terrace, and adjoining TV and games rooms. Pool complex with poolside bar and terrace. Two playgrounds and large playing field with football posts. Two tennis courts. Volleyball and basketball. Minigolf. BMX track. Bicycle hire. Table tennis. Fishing (on permit). Pony rides around the site. Outside amphitheatre for musical evenings and barbecues. Organised events daytime and evening. Occasional dances (pitches near these facilities may be noisy late at night - the bar closes at midnight). American motorhomes accepted up to 27 ft. Dogs and other pets only accepted by arrangement. Off site: Riding 1 km, golf 12 km. Nearest beach 3 km. by road. Local market at Carnac on Wednesdays and Sundays.

At a glance

Welcome & Ambience	✓✓✓✓	Location	✓✓✓✓
Quality of Pitches	✓✓✓✓✓	Range of Facilities	✓✓✓✓✓

Directions

From N165 take Quiberon/Carnac exit onto the D768. After 5 km. turn left on D119 towards Carnac and after 4 km. turn left onto D196 to the site.

Charges 2003

Per person	€ 3.90 - € 6.50
child (under 7 yrs)	€ 2.80 - € 4.70
pitch incl. car	€ 14.10 - € 23.50
with 6A electricity	€ 16.20 - € 27.00
water and drainage	€ 3.50
local tax	€ 0.61

Less 20% 22/5-29/6 and after 1/9.

Reservations

Made (min. 1 week) with deposit € 120. English is spoken - office open from 2 Jan. Tel: 02 97 52 24 01. Email: info@lagrandemetairie.com

Open

3 April - 11 September (all services from 24/5).

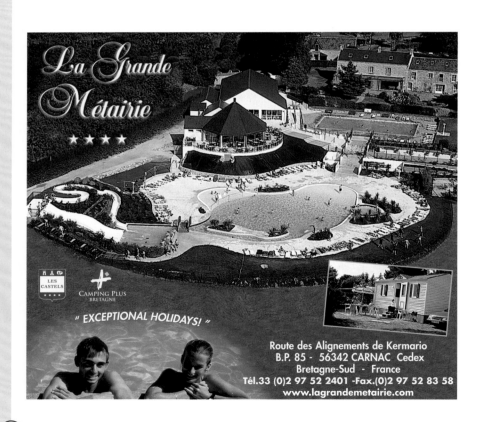

FR56110 Camping du Moustoir

Route du Moustoir, 56340 Carnac (Morbihan)

Camping du Moustoir is a friendly, family run site situated about three kilometres inland from the many beaches of the area and close to the famous 'alignments' of standing stones. Pitches are grassy and separated by shrubs and hedges, with several shaded by tall pine trees. There is a popular pool area with slides, a separate swimming pool and a paddling pool with 'mushroom' fountain. The bar and terrace adjoining the pool become the social centre of the site in the evenings. A high season programme includes family entertainment and a daily 'Kid's club' which attracts children of several nationalities. Several small tour operators use the site.

Facilities

The substantial, traditional style toilet block is well maintained and clean (outside peak season some sections may be closed). Motorcaravan service facilities. Shop, bar and takeaway (all from 20/5, hours vary). Heated swimming pool (21 x 8 m), water slides with landing pool, and paddling pool (from 15/5). Adventure style playground. Tennis. Boules. Volleyball, football and basketball. Table tennis and pool table. Kids Club' daily in high season. Off site: Easy access to water sports at Carnac Plage. Fishing, bicycle hire or riding 2 km, golf 5 km.

At a glance

Welcome & Ambience	✓✓✓✓✓	Location		✓✓✓✓
Quality of Pitches	✓✓✓✓	Range of Facilities	✓✓✓✓✓

Directions

From N165, take exit to D768 (Carnac and Quiberon). At second crossroads after 5 km. turn left D119) towards Carnac. After 3 km. turn left (oblique turning) after a hotel, and site is 500 m. on your left.

Charges 2004

Per person (over 2 yrs)	€ 4.10
pitch	€ 5.00 - € 14.00
electricity	€ 3.10
animal	€ 1.50
local tax	€ 0.35

Camping Cheques accepted.

Reservations

Made with deposit (€ 75). Tel: 02 97 52 16 18. Email: info@lemoustoir.com

Open

1 May - 10 September.

FR56090 Camping Moulin de Kermaux

56340 Carnac (Morbihan)

Only 100 metres from the famous Carnac megaliths, Le Moulin de Kermaux is an excellent base from which to see these ancient stones as they portray their ever changing mood, colour and profile. The family run site has 150 pitches (120 with electricity) and its compact nature offers a safe environment for parents and children alike. The 70 pitches for touring units are mostly separated by hedges and numerous mature trees offer welcome shade. Keen distance walkers and families with young children alike, will enjoy the numerous footpaths in the area. Carnac town provides an assortment of boutiques, crêperies, restaurants and night clubs. Used by tour operators (11 pitches).

Facilities

The fully equipped toilet block has high standards of cleanliness and washbasins in cabins. Toilets are a mix of (mainly) British and (a few) Turkish types. Facilities for disabled visitors. Baby bath. Laundry and dishwashing sinks. Washing machine and dryer - washing line provided. Motorcaravan service point. Well stocked shop (20/5-7/9). Bar (20/5-7/9) evenings in low season, all day in high season. Swimming pool and paddling pool. Sauna and jacuzzi. Challenging adventure playground. Volleyball and basketball, minigolf and table tennis. Organised activities in July/Aug. including a variety of competitions during the day and a weekly disco and karaoke in the evening. Off site: Fishing, bicycle hire and riding within 2 km. Sandy beaches and rocky coves within 3 km. Large supermarkets 3 km.

At a glance

Welcome & Ambience	✓✓✓✓	Location		✓✓✓✓
Quality of Pitches	✓✓✓✓	Range of Facilities	✓✓✓✓✓

Directions

From N165 take Quiberon/Carnac exit onto D768. After 5 km. turn left on D781 to Carnac and following camp signs, turn left at traffic lights to site.

Charges 2003

Per person	€ 4.00
child (under 7 yrs)	€ 3.00
pitch and car	€ 13.00
electricity 3A/6A	€ 3.00
dog	€ 2.00
local tax	€ 0.61

Less 10-40% outside high season.

Reservations

Contact site. Tel: 02 97 52 15 90.

Open

30 March - 15 September.

FR56040 Camping de Penboch

9 chemin de Penboch, 56610 Arradon (Morbihan)

Penboch is 200 metres by footpath from the shores of the Golfe du Morbihan with its many islands, where there is plenty to do including watersports, fishing and boat trips. There are also old towns with weekly markets nearby and it is 30 minutes walk to Arradon which has a good range of shops and restaurants. The site in a peaceful, rural area is divided into two parts — one in woodland with lots of shade and used mainly for mobile homes and youth groups (which can be very noisy at times) and the other main part, across a minor road on more open ground with hedges and young trees. Penboch offers 175 pitches on flat grass, mostly divided into groups; electricity is available on most pitches (6/10A) and there are plenty of water points. British tour operator (12 pitches). A 'Sites et Paysages' member.

Facilities

Three fully equipped toilet blocks, two on the main part of the site and one on the annex, include washbasins in cabins. Facilities can be under considerable pressure in peak season. Washing machines and dryers. Motorcaravan service point. Friendly bar with satellite TV, snacks and takeaway, where basic food supplies kept (all 20/5-11/9) and further TV room. Heated swimming pool with water slide, toboggan and children's pool with mushroom fountain (15/5-19/9). Good playground, visible from reception, with interesting play equipment. Games room. Caravan storage. American motorhomes accepted in low season. Off site: Fishing 200 m, bicycle hire 6 km, golf or riding 6 km. Sailing and windsurfing 2 km.

Directions

From N165 at Auray or Vannes, take D101 along northern shores of the Golfe du Morbihan; or leave N165 at D127 signed Ploeren and Arradon. Take turn to Arradon and site is signed.

Charges 2004

Per unit incl. 2 persons	€ 9.95 - € 28.10
child (2-7 yrs)	€ 2.50 - € 3.60
electricity 6/10A	€ 3.00 - € 4.00
dog	free - € 2.00
local tax	€ 0.45

Reservations

Advised for high season (min. 7 days 10/7-18/8).
Tel: 02 97 44 71 29.
Email: camping.penboch@wanadoo.fr

Open

3 April - 25 September.

At a glance

Welcome & Ambience	✓✓✓✓✓	Location	✓✓✓✓✓
Quality of Pitches	✓✓✓✓	Range of Facilities	✓✓✓✓✓

FR56080M Camping Municipal Le Pâtis

3 chemin du Pâtis, 56130 La Roche Bernard (Morbihan)

This is another of those excellent municipal sites one comes across in France. Situated beside the River Vilaine, just below the very attractive old town of La Roche Bernard and beside the port and marina, it provides 60 level grass, part-hedged pitches in bays of four, with electricity and water. Next door is a sailing school, boats to hire, fishing, tennis, archery, etc. A restaurant and bar are on the quay-side, with others uphill in the town.

Facilities

There are two fully equipped sanitary blocks, one new and very modern, the other fully refurbished. Laundry room with washing machine and dryer. Small play area. Off site: Bicycle hire 500 m, riding 5 km, golf 15 km.

Directions

Go into town centre and follow signs for the Port around a one-way system and then a sharp turn down hill.

Latest charges

Per person	€ 2.44
child (under 9 yrs)	€ 1.22
pitch incl. electricity (10A)	€ 5.18
vehicle	€ 1.06

No credit cards.

Reservations

Contact site. Tel: 02 99 90 60 13.

Open

Easter/April - 30 September.

At a glance

Welcome & Ambience	✓✓✓✓	Location	✓✓✓✓
Quality of Pitches	✓✓✓✓	Range of Facilities	✓✓✓

FR56050 Camping de Kervilor

56470 La Trinité-sur-Mer (Morbihan)

Kervilor may be a good alternative for those who find the beach-side sites in La Trinité too busy and lively. In a village on the outskirts of the town, it has 230 pitches on flat grass and is attractively land-scaped with trees (silver birches) and flowers. The pitches are in groups divided by hedges, separated by shrubs and trees and 200 have electricity. There is a medium sized swimming pool, paddling pool and new water slides. The site has a feeling of spaciousness. Used by tour operators (39 pitches).

Facilities

Two modern toilet blocks are of a good standard with further facilities in an older block by the entrance (all very clean when seen). They include many washbasins in cabins, facilities for disabled people and babies. Dishwashing under cover. Small laundry. Small shop for basics and takeaway in season. Bar with terrace (20/5-9/9). Swimming pool. Play area. Minigolf, pétanque, tennis and volleyball. Table tennis. Bicycle hire. Off site: Fishing or riding 2 km, golf 12 km. Sandy beach 2 km. Town facilities 1.5 km by car.

At a glance

Welcome & Ambience	✓✓✓	Location	✓✓✓✓
Quality of Pitches	✓✓✓✓	Range of Facilities	✓✓✓✓✓

Directions

Site is north of La Trinité-sur-Mer and is signed in the town centre. From Auray take D186 Quiberon road; turn left at camp sign at Kergroix on D186 to La Trinité-sur-Mer, and left again at outskirts of town.

Charges 2003

Per person	€ 4.50
child (under 7 yrs)	€ 3.00
pitch incl. electricity (3-10A)	€ 16.40 - € 17.80

Reservations

Made with deposit (€ 46) and fee (€ 18.30). Tel: 02 97 55 76 75. Email: ebideau@camping-kervilor.com

Open

9 May - 15 September.

FR56100 Camping de Moulin Neuf

56220 Rochefort en Terre (Morbihan)

This quiet family site is in wooded countryside, 600 m. from the small medieval town. Ian and Norma Hetherington have worked hard over the last few years to develop Moulin Neuf into a neat, tidy and organised site. There are 72 pitches (60 for tourers, 44 with electricity) of a good size (120 sq.m.) on neat grass, laid out on two levels. The top level, with a limited number of electrical hook-ups, is flat and pitches are divided by young shrubs. The entrance to the site is here and reception is located just beyond the security gate. The lower level is partly sloping but offers mature trees, shade and electricity on all the pitches. Rochefort en Terre itself is a marvellous medieval town, beautifully preserved and only ten minutes walk from the site, with a wealth of art and craft workshops, antique shops and art galleries.

Facilities

The modern heated sanitary block is on the lower level but convenient for both. Facilities are kept very clean and include large, comfortable showers, cabins with washbasins and British and Turkish style WCs. Provision for disabled people. Baby changing room. Dishwashing area and laundry room with sinks. Washing machine, dryer and washing lines. Bread delivered each morning. Heated swimming pool (15/6-31/8). Tennis court, table tennis, basketball, football area. Two play areas. Off site: Shop 600 m. Riding and golf locally. Lake within 500 m. with watersports. Vannes is a 30 minute drive and the beaches of Golfe du Morbihan.

At a glance

Welcome & Ambience	✓✓✓✓	Location	✓✓✓✓
Quality of Pitches	✓✓✓✓	Range of Facilities	✓✓✓

Directions

From Redon take D775 Vannes road west for 25 km. Branch north on D774 signed Rochefort en Terre. Follow road past the lake on left, in 800 m. Turn left and follow sign to site.

Charges 2003

Per person	€ 4.30 - € 5.00
child (under 8 yrs)	€ 2.60 - € 3.50
pitch incl. electricity (10A)	€ 11.40 - € 12.40
local tax	€ 0.30 - € 2.00

Reservations

Made with deposit (€ 90) and fee (€ 10); contact site for booking form. Tel: 02 97 43 37 52.

Open

15 May - 16 September.

FR56200 Camping La Ferme de Lann Hoedic

56370 Sarzeau (Morbihan)

Whilst still maintaining the character of 'Camping a la Ferme', the welcoming owners, Mireille and Timothy Prouten have upgraded this site to a good standard, and have attractively landscaped the site with many flowering shrubs and trees. The 108 pitches, all with electricity are large and mostly level, with maturing trees which are beginning to offer some shade. There are new toilet facilities and an excellent children's play area. Families are welcome to visit the working farm which produces cereal crops and raises sheep. Located in the countryside on the Rhuys Peninsula, Golfe du Morbihan, it is an ideal base for cycling, walking and water based activities.

Facilities

Two new, high quality toilet blocks with facilities for disabled people and bathing babies. Washing machines and dyers. Playground with modern well designed equipment. Volleyball and petanque. Bread delivery (high season). Ice creams and soft drinks available at reception. Takeaway meals and traditional Breton 'soirées' (high season). Off site: Beach 800 m. Riding 2 km. Bicycle hire 2 km. Boating 800 m.

At a glance

| Welcome & Ambience | ✓✓✓✓✓ | Location | ✓✓✓✓ |
| Quality of Pitches | ✓✓✓ | Range of Facilities | ✓✓✓✓ |

Directions

East of Vannes, on the N165, join the D780 in direction of Sarzeau. Exit D780 at the 'Super U' roundabout south of Sarzeau, following signs for Le Roaliguen. Campsite is signed.

Charges 2003

Per pitch incl electricity (10A)	€ 8.55 - € 9.50
per person (over 7 yrs)	€ 3.60 - € 4.00
child (under 7 yrs)	€ 1.80 - € 2.00

Reservations

Made with deposit (€ 45). Tel: 02 97 48 01 73. Email: contact@camping-lannhodic.fr

Open

1 April - 31 October.

La Ferme de Lann Hoëdic

SOUTHERN BRITTANY

Only 2 hours south of St Malo, discover the beautiful Gulf of Morbihan from our peaceful and spacious 3 star site. 800 meters from sandy beaches, we offer brand new facilities and a warm welcome waiting just for you.

Open from 01/04 to 31/10

Route du Roaliguen   56370 Sarzeau
Tel : +33 297 48 01 73
Fax : +33 297 41 72 87
contact@camping-lannhoedic.fr

The comfort of a 3-star campsite, the charm of a country setting

FR56140M Camping Municipal du Bas de la Lande

56120 Guégon-Josselin (Morbihan)

Bas de la Lande is a top quality municipal site, ideally located for overnight stops or for discovering the delights of inland Brittany, not least Josselin with its superb fortified 15th century château. Attractive discounts are offered for longer stays. The Oust river, which makes up part of the Nantes - Brest canal, runs opposite the site and provides good fishing (permit needed). Bas de la Lande has 60 pitches, 49 of which have electricity (6/10A). The pitches are on a number of flat terraces and are large, grassy and lightly shaded. As the site is situated close to the N24, a busy dual-carriageway, road noise can be audible in all parts of the site.

Facilities

The principal toilet block just behind reception is of a very high standard, and well equipped with washbasins in cabins and large showers. Unit for disabled people (with shower, washbasin and toilet). Washing machine and dryer. A second, much older block is only used at peak periods. Motorcaravan service point. Play area. Fishing. Off site: Table tennis, minigolf (opposite site - free to campers). Bar/crêperie adjacent to site entrance (1/7-31/8). Nearest shops are in Josselin (2 km), where there is also bicycle hire and tennis.

At a glance

| Welcome & Ambience | ✓✓✓ | Location | ✓✓✓✓ |
| Quality of Pitches | ✓✓✓✓ | Range of Facilities | ✓✓ |

Directions

Leave N24 Rennes - Lorient road to west of Josselin following signs to Guégon, then Josselin. Site is clearly signed from this point.

Charges 2003

Per adult	€ 2.50 - € 3.00
child (under 7 yrs)	€ 1.30 - € 1.50
pitch incl. electricity (5A)	€ 5.20 - € 6.10
car or motorcaravan	€ 1.60 - € 2.00

Less 5% for stays over 5 nights, 10% for over 7 days. No credit cards.

Reservations

Unlikely to be necessary but can be made by contacting Tel: 02 97 22 22 20. Email: campingbasdelalande@wanadoo.fr

Open

1 April - 31 October.

FR56120 Camping Les Iles

La Pointe du Bile, 56760 Penestin-sur-Mer (Morbihan)

You are assured of a warm and friendly welcome at this family run campsite where the owners, M. and Mme. Communal, encourage everyone to make the most of this beautiful region. The 124 pitches are mostly of a reasonable size (although larger caravans and American motorhomes are advised to book) and all have electricity. All services are fully open 14/5-16/9, with a limited service at other times. There is direct access from the site to cliff-top walks and local beaches (you can even walk to small off-shore islands at low tide). Used by one tour operator (20 pitches).

Facilities

The large central toilet block has mostly British style WCs and washbasins in cabins (with hairdryers for ladies). Dishwashing and laundry sinks. Facilities for disabled people and two baby baths. Motorcaravan service point across the road at 'Parc des Iles', in the mobile home section of the site. Shop selling groceries and other goods. Bar with takeaway overlooking swimming and paddling pools (14/5-16/9). Modern multi-sports pitch for football, basketball and volleyball. Tennis court across the road. Bicycle hire. Riding. Full range of activities and entertainment for adults and children in July/Aug. Off site: Windsurfing (500 m.), sailing school 3 km.

At a glance

Welcome & Ambience	✓✓✓✓✓	Location	✓✓✓✓✓
Quality of Pitches	✓✓✓✓	Range of Facilities	✓✓✓✓✓

Directions

From Pénestin take D201 south, taking a right fork to Pointe du Bile after 2 km. Turn right at crossroads just before beach and site is on left. Take care on arrival - the barrier is fairly close to the entrance, but there is some parking along the road outside.

Charges 2003

Per unit incl. 2 adults	€ 19.00 - € 28.50
extra person (over 10 yrs)	€ 3.00 - € 4.00
child (2-10 yrs)	€ 1.50 - € 2.00
pet	€ 1.80 - € 2.30
electricity (6A)	€ 2.80

Reservations

Made with deposit (€ 92) and fee (€ 18.9).
Tel: 02 99 90 30 24.
Email: contact@camping-des-iles.fr

Open

1 April - 4 October.

CAMPING & PARC
DES ILES

LES ILES
La Pointe du Bile
B.P.4
56760 PENESTIN
Tél. 02 99 90 30 24
Fax 02 99 90 44 55
www.camping-des-iles.fr
E mail : contact@camping-des-iles.fr

Camping Qualité

CAMPSITE INSPECTIONS

Every campsite in this guide has been inspected and selected by one our seasonal campsite inspection teams.

Our teams are required to visit typically between 30 and 50 sites and submit detailed reports on each site visited.

We now have a number of vacancies for campsite Inspectors and would be interested to hear from candidates with a good knowledge of camping and caravanning.
A fee is paid for each inspection, as well as travel expenses.

For applications for these posts and further information, please contact:

Rod Wheat
Alan Rogers Guides Ltd, 96 High Street, Tunbridge Wells TN1 1YF
Fax: 01892 51 00 55   Email: contact@alanrogers.com

INSPECTED CAMPSITES & SELECTED

FR56130 Camping Mané Guernehué

56870 Baden (Morbihan)

Located close to the Morbihan Gulf, Mané Guernehué is a smart, modern site offering a variety of pitches. Some are terraced beneath pine trees, others in a former orchard with delightful views of the surrounding countryside. The 277 pitches are generally large, 65 being occupied by mobile homes and chalets. All pitches have electricity and a few are also equipped with water and drainage. Many are level but others, particularly those in the centre of the site, slope to varying degrees. There are plenty of excellent amenities. A fitness track runs through the site, with a well stocked fishing lake on the edge. Used by tour operators (around 45 pitches).

Facilities

Three modern toilet blocks include washbasins in cabins. In high season the maintenance of the blocks does seem to be under some pressure. Facilities for disabled visitors. Washing machines and dryers. Small shop, bar and takeaway. Heated swimming pool, waterslide, jacuzzi and gym. Fishing. Teenagers' room with table tennis, pool, billiards and TV. Childrens' play area. Varied entertainment programme in high season, based around a large purpose built hall.
Off site: Beach 3 km. Golf 3 km.

At a glance

Welcome & Ambience	✓✓✓✓	Location	✓✓✓✓
Quality of Pitches	✓✓✓✓	Range of Facilities	✓✓✓✓✓

Directions

From Auray or Vannes use the D101 to Baden and watch for signs to site.

Charges 2004

Per person	€ 3.10 - € 5.80
child (2-7 yrs)	€ 2.00 - € 4.20
pitch	€ 10.50 - € 16.00
electricity (6/10A)	€ 4.20
dog	€ 1.60 - € 3.40

Camping Cheques accepted.

Reservations

Advised for high season and made with deposit (€ 70) and fee (€ 20). Tel: 02 97 57 02 06.
Email: mane-guernehue@wanadoo.fr

Open

Easter - 30 September.

FR56180 Camping Le Cénic

56760 Pénestin-sur-Mer (Morbihan)

Le Cénic is attractively set amidst trees and flowers, providing activities for all tastes. An attractive covered aquatic complex has water slides, bridges, rivers and a jacuzzi, whilst the outdoor pool comes complete with water slide, 'magic mushroom' fountain and sunbathing areas. You may fish in the pretty lake or use inflatables, watched by the peacock and the geese and turkeys. Unusually there is also a covered sports hall for ball games. A range of accommodation is on offer from pitches for tents and caravans to static caravans and chalets and bungalows to rent. There are 90 pitches in total with electricity available. The area has much to offer from the beaches of La Mine d' Or, the harbour at Trébiguier-Pénestin, the Golf du Morbihan with its numerous islands, La Baule with its magnificent beach and the medieval city of Guérande to the unique Brière nature reserve.

Facilities

Fully equipped toilet facilities include laundry and dishwashing sinks. Washing machines and dryers. Bar, restaurant, shop, TV and games room. Indoor and outdoor swimming pools. Play area. Indoor ball area. Fishing.

At a glance

Welcome & Ambience	✓✓✓✓	Location	✓✓✓✓
Quality of Pitches	✓✓✓✓	Range of Facilities	✓✓✓✓✓

Directions

Site is 300 m. from the D34, and 1 km. from the town, to the southwest.

Charges 2003

Per person	€ 4.00 - € 5.50
child (under 7 yrs.)	€ 2.00 - € 3.00
pitch	€ 5.00 - € 8.50
electricity (6A)	€ 3.00
dog	€ 1.50
local tax	€ 0.30

Reservations

Necessary for high season. Tel: 02 99 90 33 14.

Open

1 May - 30 September.

Map 2

A striking area whose beauty lies not only in the landscape. Famed for its seafood and Celtic tradition, certain areas of Normandy remain untouched and wonderfully old fashioned.

Départements: 14 Calvados, 27 Eure, 50 Manche, 61 Orme, 76 Seine Maritime

Major cities: Caen and Rouen

Normandy is a rich landscape full of variety. From the wild craggy granite coastline of the northern Cotentine to the long sandy beaches and chalk cliffs of the south. It also boasts a superb coast line including the Cotentin Peninsula, cliffs of the Côte d'Albâtre and the fine beaches and fashionable resorts of the Côte Fleurie. Plus a wealth of quiet villages and unspoilt countryside for leisurely exploration.

The history of Normandy is closely linked with our own. The famous Bayeux Tapestry chronicles the exploits of the battle of Hastings and there are lots of museums, exhibitions, sites and monuments, including the Caen Memorial Museum, which commemorate operations that took place during the D-Day Landings of 1944.

Known as the dairy of France you'll also find plenty of fresh fish, rich cream, butter, and fine cheeses such as Camembert and Pont l'Evêque. The many apple orchards are used in producing cider and the well known Calvados, Normandy's apple brandy.

Cuisine of the region

Andouillette de Vire: small chitterling (tripe) sausage

Barbue au cidre: brill cooked in cider and Calvados

Douillons de pommes à la Normande: baked apples in pastry

Escalope (Vallée d'Auge): veal sautéed and flamed in Calvados and served with cream and apples

Ficelle Normande: pancake with ham, mushrooms and cheese

Marnite Dieppoisse: fish soup

Poulet (Vallée d'Auge): chicken cooked in the same way as Escalope Vallée d'Auge

Tripes à la Mode de Caen: stewed beef tripe with onions, carrots, leeks, garlic, cider and Calvados

Places of interest

Bayeux: home to the famous tapestry; 15th-18th century houses, cathedral, museums

Caen: feudal castle, Museum of Normandy, Museum for Peace

Omaha Beach: D-Day beaches, Landing site monuments, American Cemetery

Deauville: seaside resort, horse racing centre

Giverny: home of impressionist painter Claude Monet, Monet Museum

Honfleur: picturesque port city with old town

Lisieux: pilgrimage site, shrine of Ste Thérèse

Mont St Michel: world famous abbey on island

Rouen: Joan of Arc Museum; Gothic churches, cathedrals, abbey, clock tower

tip

FOR A REAL TASTE OF WHAT NORMANDY HAS TO OFFER. FOLLOW THE WELL-TRODDEN CIDER AND CHEESE ROUTES AND STOCK UP ON ALL THOSE GOODIES!

FR14020M Camping Municipal du Bayeux

Boulevard Eindhoven, 14400 Bayeux (Calvados)

Whether or not you want to see the tapestry, this site makes a very useful night stop on the way to or from Cherbourg, and in addition it is only a few kilometres from the coast and the landing beaches. Pleasantly laid out with grassy lawns and bushes, its neat, cared for appearance make a good impression. The 140 pitches are in two areas (many are on hardstanding), and are well marked, generally of good size and with electricity. The site is busy over a long season – early arrival is advised as reservations are not taken. There is a full time site warden from 15/6-15/9, otherwise reception is open from 08.00-10.00 and 17.00-19.00 hrs. There may be some road noise on one side of the site.

Facilities

The two good quality toilet blocks have British and Turkish style WCs, washbasins in cabins in the main block, and units for disabled people. Motorcaravan service point. Laundry room. Takeaway food and snacks. Two children's playgrounds. Volleyball. Reading room with TV. Games room. Off site: Large public indoor swimming pool adjoins site with children's pool and jacuzzi. Large supermarket very close (closes 8 pm). Bicycle hire 1 km, riding 5 km, golf or fishing 8 km.

At a glance

Welcome & Ambience	✓✓✓✓	Location	✓✓✓✓
Quality of Pitches	✓✓✓✓	Range of Facilities	✓✓✓

Directions

Site is on the south side of northern ring road (D613) to town, and just west of the junction with the D516 to autoroute.

Charges 2003

Per person	€ 2.91
child (under 7 yrs)	€ 1.56
pitch and car	€ 3.60
electricity	€ 2.90

Less 10% for stay over 5 days.

Reservations

Not made. Tel: 02 31 92 08 43.

Open

1 May - 30 September.

FR14030 Camping Le Château de Martragny

14740 Martragny (Calvados)

Martragny is an attractive site in a parkland setting adjoining the château and close to D-Day beaches. It is a particularly convenient location for both the ports of Caen and Cherbourg, and has the facilities and charm to encourage both long stays and stopovers. The pleasant lawns that surround and approach the château take 160 units, with electricity connections for 140. The majority of the pitches are divided by either a small hedge or a couple of trees, only a few not marked out. Bed and breakfast (en-suite) are available in the château all year (reservation essential). Madame de Chassey takes great pride in the site and takes care that the peace and quiet is preserved. This is a perfect place for a quiet relaxing holiday yet only 12 km. from the sea, the wartime landing beaches, the excellent museum at Arromanche, the Bayeux tapestry or the Calvados 'Cider Route'.

Facilities

Two recently modernised sanitary blocks include washbasins in cabins, sinks for dishes and clothes and two baby baths. Disabled people are well catered for. Good laundry. Well stocked shop and takeaway (15/5-15/9). Bar. Swimming pool (20 x 6 m.) and children's paddling pool heated in poor weather. Play areas, one new. Tennis courts. Minigolf, games and TV room, table tennis and billiards. Fishing. Bicycle and buggy hire. Off site: Riding 1 km, golf 20 km.

At a glance

Welcome & Ambience	✓✓✓✓	Location	✓✓✓✓
Quality of Pitches	✓✓✓✓	Range of Facilities	✓✓✓✓

Directions

Site is off N13, 8 km. southeast of Bayeux. Take Martragny exit from dual carriageway.

Charges 2003

Per person	€ 3.90 - € 4.50
child (under 7 yrs)	€ 2.30 - € 2.70
pitch for caravan or motorcaravan	€ 8.30 - € 9.80
tent pitch	€ 7.70 - € 9.20
electricity (6A)	€ 2.50 - € 2.80
local tax	€ 0.15

Less 15% outside 1/7-31/8.
Camping Cheques accepted.

Reservations

Made for min. 3 nights; deposit and small fee required. Tel: 02 31 80 21 40.
Email: chateau.martragny@wanadoo.fr

Open

1 May - 15 September.

FR14060 Camping Les Hautes Coutures

Route de Ouistreham, 14970 Bénouville (Calvados)

Les Hautes Coutures is a useful site near the Caen-Portsmouth ferry terminal suitable for overnight stays. It is beside the Caen ship canal, 2 km. from the sea (and ferry port) and 10 km. from Caen – the site gates are opened at 6 am. for early ferries and there can be movement on site late into the evening. There are 110 grass touring pitches of 100 sq.m, marked by mature hedges with tarmac roads. All pitches have electrical connections. An area close to the canal is being developed to provide further pitches. There are also over 150 mobile homes on the site. Ouistreham is within walking distance along the canal and the Pegasus Bridge Airborne Division Museum. A pedestrian gate leads on to the towpath (a code is needed for re-entry).

Facilities

Two toilet blocks include showers, washbasins in cabins (warm water only). Facilities can be under pressure at peak times and the hot water supply can be variable. Dishwashing and laundry facilities with washing machine and dryer. Motorcaravan service point. Small shop keeps basic items. Bar and takeaway. Small heated swimming pool (from May) which is kept locked - ask for access. Small lounge/TV area and games room. Play area on sand. Two tennis courts. Volleyball. Minigolf. Boules. Table tennis. Off site: Golf 4 km. Riding 2 km. Beach 2 km.

At a glance

Welcome & Ambience	✓✓✓	Location	✓✓✓✓
Quality of Pitches	✓✓✓	Range of Facilities	✓✓✓

Directions

Site is just off the D514 dual-carriageway, north of Benouville. From Caen, follow Ouistreham car ferry signs and take first exit from D514 after Benouville.

Charges 2003

Per person	€ 6.50
child (under 7 yrs)	€ 4.50
pitch	€ 7.20
electricity (2/10A)	€ 3.80 - € 7.50

Reservations

Tel: 02 31 44 73 08.
Email: camping-hautes-coutures@wanadoo.fr

Open

1 April - 30 September.

FR14070 Camping de la Vallée

88 rue de la Vallée, 14510 Houlgate (Calvados)

Camping de la Vallée is an attractive site with good, well maintained facilities. Situated on a grassy hillside overlooking Houlgate, the 355 pitches (98 for touring units) are large and open. Hedges have been planted and all have electricity. Part of the site is sloping, the rest level, with gravel or tarmac roads. An old farmhouse has been converted to house a new bar and comfortable TV lounge and billiards room. English is spoken in season. Used by tour operators (87 pitches). Very busy in high season, maintenance and cleaning could be variable at that time. There are 130 mobile homes on site and around 40 seasonal units are also taken.

Facilities

Three good toilet blocks include washbasins in cabins, mainly British style toilets, facilities for disabled people and baby bathroom. Dishwashing, laundry with machines, dryers and ironing boards (no washing lines allowed). Motorcaravan services. Shop (from 1/5). Bar. Small snack bar with takeaway in season (from 15/5). Heated swimming pool (from 15/5; no shorts). Games room. Playground. Bicycle hire. Volleyball, football field, tennis, petanque, and table tennis. Organised entertainment in Jul/Aug. Off site: Beach 1 km, town 1 km. Fishing 1 km. Riding 500 m. Championship golf course 2 km

At a glance

Welcome & Ambience	✓✓✓✓	Location	✓✓✓✓
Quality of Pitches	✓✓✓✓	Range of Facilities	✓✓✓✓

Directions

From A13 take exit for Cabourg and follow signs for Dives/Houlgate going straight on at roundabout. Follow road straight on at next roundabout, and then four sets of traffic lights. Turn left along seafront. After 1 km. at lights turn right, carry on for about 1 km. and over mini-roundabout - look for site sign and flag poles on right.

Charges 2003

Per unit incl. 2 persons and electricity	€ 18.50 - € 25.00
extra adult	€ 4.00 - € 6.00
child (under 7 yrs)	€ 3.00 - € 4.00
dog	€ 3.00

Credit card minimum € 35. Barrier card deposit € 20. Camping Cheques accepted.

Reservations

Made with deposit and fee. Tel: 02 31 24 40 69.
Email: camping.lavallee@wanadoo.fr

Open

1 April - 30 September.

FR14080 Camping Le Puits

La Groudière, 14350 St Martin des Besaces (Calvados)

This traditional little site in the heart of historic Normandy is becoming very popular. Situated on the edge of the village, it only has 40 pitches in two areas, either individual ones divided by flowers and shrubs, or marked out on an open grassy field. All have electricity (6A) and are slightly sloping. The Ashworth family are gradually upgrading the facilities on what was originally an 'á la ferme' site. The site has its own newsletter to keep guests informed and a comprehensive stock of tourist information in reception. A museum with a difference is close to the site featuring a unique account of the Battle of Normandy with displays, sound and light presentations, artefacts and personal memorabilia (some belonging to regular visitors to the campsite).

Facilities

Simple, basic toilet facilities at the rear of the farmhouse are being upgraded with additional toilets and showers. Sinks for dishwashing and laundry, plus washing machine and dryer. Motorcaravan services. In renovated barns are a small shop, bar with a snack bar serving pizzas, chips and quiches to order with a café style eating area outside. Bread, croissants or breakfast can be ordered. One barn provides a function room and games room. Minigolf, table tennis, billiards, volleyball and fishing in pond. Small playground. Activities organised or available in the area in season - barbecues, murder mysteries, quizzes and visits to local cider makers - even bungee jumping! Off site: Bicycle hire 5 km, riding 10 km. Market in St Martin des Besaces Saturday morning.

At a glance

Welcome & Ambience	✓✓✓✓	Location	✓✓✓✓
Quality of Pitches	✓✓✓✓	Range of Facilities	✓✓✓✓

Directions

From Caen take A84 at Porte de Bretagne towards Rennes to St Martin des Besaces (exit 41). Follow signs to village on D53. At lights turn right on D675 and site is signed to left at far end of village. From Cherbourg follow N13 and after Carentan (approx. 50 km) take N174 signed St Lô. In St Lô follow signs for Vire, then Torigni-sur-Vire. After Torigni in 9 km. take D675 (not A84) turn left towards St Martin des Besaces and site is signed to right at entrance to village.

Charges 2003

Per adult	€ 3.00
child (3-9 yrs)	€ 1.50
pitch	€ 6.00
small tent and bicycle	€ 3.00
electricity (6A)	€ 3.00

Credit cards are accepted with a 20% surcharge.

Reservations

Advised in season and made with deposit of 1 nights fees. Tel: 02 31 67 80 02.
Email: camping.le.puits@wanadoo.fr

Open

1 February - 31 October.

FR14090 Castel Camping du Brévedent

Le Brévedent, 14130 Pont-l'Evêque (Calvados)

Le Brévedent is a well established, traditional site with 140 pitches (100 for tourists) set in the grounds of an elegant 18th century hunting pavilion. Level pitches are set around the fishing lake or in the lower gardens, others are in the old orchard. All have electricity (10A). Reception provides a vast amount of tourist information, with organised tours in the main season to Paris, Disney, a cider farm and a local distillery. The site is used by a tour operator (40 pitches). This is an excellent holiday destination within easy reach of the Channel ports. The church bells ring out every morning at 0700, but the otherwise peaceful, friendly environment makes it ideal for mature campers or families with younger children (note the lake is unfenced). Particularly popular are the Saturday evening talks, the Sunday countryside rambles and the evening family meal.

Facilities

Three sanitary units of varying ages (one new), include washbasins in cubicles, dishwashing and laundry sinks, and new facilities for babies and disabled people. Good motorcaravan service point. Laundries. Well stocked shop. Baker calls each morning. Small bar in the hunting lodge itself, open each evening (1/5-26/9). Restaurant including snacks and tradtional Normandy cuisine (24/5-19/9). Takeaway (1/5-26/9). Clubroom with TV and library. Swimming pool and children's pool (unsupervised) are heated and in separate enclosures. Playground. Table tennis, minigolf, boules, volleyball, games room with games machines, and a pool table. Fishing is free (but put the fish back). Rowing boats (with lifejackets). Bicycle and buggy hire. Organised activities for children including pony lessons. Dogs are not accepted. Off site: Riding 1 km. (with discounts). The nearby golf club and tennis on the local court. Attractions in the area include cheese factories, Pont L'Evêque (14 km.) and its market (Sunday and Monday) and the Château de Betteville with its motor museum. Market days in Cormeilles (Friday), Lisieux and Honfleur (Thursday).

At a glance

Welcome & Ambience	✓✓✓✓	Location	✓✓✓✓
Quality of Pitches	✓✓✓✓	Range of Facilities	✓✓✓✓

Directions

From Pont L'Eveque take D579 toward Lisieux for 4 km. then D51 towards Moyaux. At Blangy le Chateau turn right (still on D51) to Le Brevendent.

Charges 2003

Per adult	€ 5.50
child 1-6 yrs	€ 2.30
child 7-12 yrs	€ 3.80
pitch	€ 8.00
electricity	€ 3.00

Camping Cheques accepted.

Reservations

Advised for the main season; contact site.
Tel: 02 31 64 72 88.
Email: castelcamp.lebrevedent@mageos.com

Open

12 May - 20 September.

FR14100M Camping Municipal du Château

3 Rue du Val d'Ante, 14700 Falaise (Calvados)

The location of this site is really quite spectacular, lying in the shadow of the Château de Falaise, in the old part of the town, in the 'coeur de Normandie'. The site itself is small, with only 66 pitches (all with electricity). It has a rather intimate 'up-market' feel about it, rather different from the average municipal site. With good shade, tarmac roads and easy access, it was well recommended by the British campers we met there. Whatever this site lacks in size and facilities it makes up for in its situation, close to the town centre, the tennis club and near to the river for fishing. The charges are reasonable and the reception friendly.

Facilities

The sanitary facilities could be insufficient in terms of quantity when the site is full - perhaps it never is and campers we met felt they were adequate. The quality is good and they are clean. Unit for disabled visitors (shower room and separate WC). Access to showers, laundry and dishwashing closed 22.00-07.30. Playground. Table tennis. TV room. Off site: Tennis courts adjacent.

At a glance

Welcome & Ambience	✓✓✓✓	Location	✓✓✓✓
Quality of Pitches	✓✓✓✓	Range of Facilities	✓✓✓

Directions

Site is on western side of town, well signed from the ring road. From N158 heading south take first roundabout into Falaise (site signed), then pass through residential suburb to site.

Charges 2003

Per adult	€ 3.00
child (under 10 yrs)	€ 2.00
pitch	€ 2.50
dog	€ 1.00
electricity (5A)	€ 2.50

No credit cards.

Reservations

Advised for July/Aug. Tel: 02 31 90 16 55.
Email: camping@falaise.fr

Open

1 May - 30 September.

FR14120 Camping Les Ammonites

Auberville, Route de la Corniche, 14640 Villers-sur-Mer (Calvados)

Les Ammonites is a friendly, family owned site with a total of 140 pitches in a location that slopes gently downwards towards the coast. On entering the site you pass through an area with about 100 mobile homes, 60 privately owned, and 40 to rent. The 40 tourist pitches are at the far end of the site with the most wonderful panoramic views over the Channel. All on grass with electric hook-ups, most are slightly sloping, although the views do compensate for the inconvenience. The heated swimming pool with sunbathing terrace and a shallow area for children, is next to the reception building. On the other side of the road, opposite reception, is a parking area, the bar/brasserie and takeaway. Also on this side are a basic children's playground, giant chess, table tennis, basketball net, two tennis courts (on payment), and some more pitches. The main site is unsuitable for large units and American RVs, although the pitches by the tennis courts may be accessible.

Facilities

The single sanitary unit is positioned mid-way on the site, with separate facilities for men and women at the front, some unisex facilities including well refitted showers, and a dishwashing room at the rear. Laundry with washing machines and dryer, plus facilities for disabled people are at one end. Motorcaravan service point. Reception has a small shop with basic essentials. Bar/brasserie and takeaway. Swimming pool (15m x 8 m). Playground. Small games room. Animation in July/August. Off site: Houlgate (4 km) and Villers-sur-Mer (3 km) both have good sandy beaches. The fashionable resort of Deauville is 11 km. and within easy day trip distance are Caen and picturesque Honfleur.

At a glance

Welcome & Ambience	✓✓✓✓	Location	✓✓✓✓✓
Quality of Pitches	✓✓✓✓	Range of Facilities	✓✓✓✓

Directions

Auberville is mid-way between Houlgate and Villers-sur-Mer. From Deauville take D513 southwest, through Villers-sur-Mer, and after 3 km. turn right (staggered cross-roads) towards coast on D163 signed Auberville. Site entrance is 500 m. on right.

Charges 2003

Per unit incl. 2 persons	€ 20.00
extra person	€ 3.00
electricity (10A)	€ 3.00
local tax	€ 0.50

Reservations

Advisable for peak season. Made with deposit of 50% of total fees. Tel: 02 31 87 06 06.
Email: camping-lesammonites@wanadoo.fr

Open

1 April - 31 October.

FR14130M Camping Le Fanal

Rue de Fanal, 14230 Isigny-sur-Mer (Calvados)

A useful informal spacious site, Le Fanal is on the outskirts of a fairly typical small town. There are 97 generally unmarked touring pitches, all on grass with around 42 electric hook-ups, arranged in several large bays, surrounded by mature trees. Some areas could be a little soft in inclement weather, so the site is not really suitable for American RVs. The small, fenced swimming pool (8 x 4 m) may look like a child's pool, but is in fact between one and two metres deep – only supervised children are permitted (open mid-June until Sept, ask for key). The town is noted for its dairy products, with visits possible to factories producing cheese, butter, cream, and caramels.

Facilities

The main sanitary unit provides washbasins in cubicles, pre-set hot showers, plus facilities for disabled people. Motorcaravan service point. The reception building has a dining room with a microwave and soft drink dispensing machines, a lounge with TV, a laundry with washing machine, dryer and ironing facility, plus more toilets and washbasins. Small swimming pool. Playground. Tennis, table tennis, volleyball, boules. Off site: Fishing and boating are possible in the adjacent lake, with a fitness course in the surrounding parkland. Site is close to the D-day landing beaches. Isigny market on Wednesday, small market Saturday a.m.

At a glance

Welcome & Ambience	✓✓✓✓	Location	✓✓✓✓
Quality of Pitches	✓✓✓	Range of Facilities	✓✓✓

Directions

Isigny-sur-Mer is just off N13/E46, mid-way between Cherbourg and Caen, (10 km. east of Carentan). Site is west of town centre off D917A, and is well signed.

Charges 2003

Per pitch	€ 3.05 - € 4.57
adult	€ 3.05 - € 3.35
child under 16 yrs (third free)	€ 1.52
electricity (16A)	€ 3.05
dog	€ 0.76
No credit cards.	

Reservations

Contact site. Tel: 02 31 21 33 20.

Open

1 April - 15 October.

FR14140 Camping Municipal Pont Farcy

14380 Pont Farcy (Calvados)

This well tended, riverside site is in a tranquil location within easy walking distance of the small village, with a warden who lives on site. You can cycle or walk along the 'chemin de halage' (towpath) along-side the River Vire all the way to Carentan (65 km.). Reception can also provide maps of local walks and cycle routes. Activities available either on-site or at the adjacent 'base plein air' include tennis, minigolf, volleyball, petanque, table tennis, canoe/kayak, pedalos and cycle hire, walking and fishing. Swimming is not permitted and the river is well fenced with access gates for anglers. The 60 numbered pitches are on grass, some separated by small hedges, with electricity available to all (some long leads may be needed). This site is also within easy driving distance of Cherbourg or Caen and is just off the A84 motorway.

Facilities

A rather stylish modern building houses all the facilities, including some washbasins in cubicles and a suite for disabled campers. First floor 'salle' with dining tables for campers, table tennis and other games (ask the warden). There is a lift from the ground floor. Adventure style playground (5-12 yrs). Off site: Garage with a small shop, bakery, butcher, post office and bar/hotel in the village. Nearby attractions include the Gorges de la Vire and opportunities in the area for riding, climbing and parachuting.

At a glance

Welcome & Ambience	✓✓✓✓	Location	✓✓✓✓✓
Quality of Pitches	✓✓✓✓	Range of Facilities	✓✓✓✓

Directions

Pont-Farcy is about 25 km. due south of St Lo. From A84, exit 39, take D21 south for 1 km. and site is om left at entrance to village.

Charges 2003

Per unit incl. 1 or 2 persons	€ 8.74
extra person	€ 2.13
child (under 7 yrs)	€ 1.97
electricity (5A)	€ 1.83

Reservations

Contact site. Tel: 02 31 68 32 06.

Open

1 April - 30 September.

FR27020 Camping du Domaine Catinière

Route de Honfleur, 27210 Fiquefleur-Equainville (Eure)

A peaceful, friendly site, convenient for Le Havre ferries, this is a developing site with owners who are intent on improving this countryside site which lies in the middle of a very long village. The site is steadily achieving a modern look, whilst retaining its original French flavour. There are 12 rental and 30 privately owned mobile homes, but there should be around 75 pitches for tourists including a large open field for tents and units not needing electricity. Caravan pitches are separated, some with shade, others are more open and all have electricity hook-ups. The site is divided by well fenced streams, popular with young anglers. It is a good base for visiting this part of Normandy, with the pretty harbour town of Honfleur less than 5 km., and the nearby Vallée de la Risle. It is only a short distance from the ferry terminal, and makes every effort to meet the demands of ferry users.

Facilities

Already modernised, the toilet facilities include some washbasins in cubicles, and facilities for disabled people and babies. Dishwashing sinks. Washing machine and dryer. Reception with shop. Small bar/restaurant with regional dishes and snacks. Heated swimming pool (mid-June - end Aug). Two playgrounds, trampoline. Table tennis. Boules. New barrier (card deposit). Off site: Large supermarket is also close to the southern end of the bridge. Smaller supermarket in Beuzeville - 7 km.

At a glance

Welcome & Ambience	✓✓✓✓	Location	✓✓✓✓
Quality of Pitches	✓✓✓✓	Range of Facilities	✓✓✓✓

Directions

From Le Havre ferry terminal and the north, follow signs to Pont de Normandie crossing (toll € 5 in 2003). Take first exit on leaving the bridge (exit 3, A29) signed Honfleur. At roundabout turn left under the motorway in the direction of Le Mans and Alencon. Take the second exit on the right after about 1.5 miles, signed Beuzeville. The site is on the right after about 0.5 mile.

Charges 2003

Per adult	€ 4.20
child (under 7 yrs)	€ 2.50
pitch incl. electricity (4/10A)	€ 8.50 - € 9.50

No credit cards.

Reservations

Advisable for high season, made with deposit of 50% of total amount due. Tel: 02 32 57 63 51. Email: info@camping-catiniere.com

Open

3 April - 30 September.

Route d'Honfleur D22 - 27210 FIQUEFLEUR EQUAINVILLE   Tel: 0033 232 576 351 - Fax: 0033 232 421 257
info@camping-catiniere.com - www.camping-catiniere.com

FR27050 Camping Municipal Saint Paul

2 Route de St Paul, 27480 Lyons la Foret (Eure)

The village of Lyons-La-Foret, with its medieval covered market and magnificently preserved half-timbered buildings is regarded as one of the most beautiful in France. Within walking distance (900 m) its quiet municipal campsite provides a pleasant respite. Next to the stadium and public swimming pool, the site has 100 level grass, numbered pitches of which 45 are available for tourists. Each has access to electricity, water and drainage. They are separated by mature trees providing shade. The site is edged by fast flowing shallow (unfenced) streams.

Facilities

Two well maintained toilet blocks include facilities for people with disabilities. Laundry and dishwashing sinks. Washing machine. Drying lines. Play area. Separate tent area. Off site: All facilities in nearby village. Many walking and cycling routes.

At a glance

Welcome & Ambience	✓✓✓	Location	✓✓✓✓
Quality of Pitches	✓✓✓✓	Range of Facilities	✓✓✓

Directions

Site is north of Lyons-La-Foret on the D921 road.

Charges 2003

Per adult	€ 3.70
child (4-13 yrs)	€ 2.20
pitch incl. electricity (6A)	€ 4.75 - € 8.10

Reservations

Contact site. Tel: 02 32 49 42 02.

Open

1 April - 1 November.

FR27030M Camping Municipal Saint Nicolas

27800 Le Bec-Hellouin (Eure)

This lovely, sheltered, floral site with resident wardens is located on a forested hillside above the interesting and attractive small town of Le Bec-Hellouin. There are 90 marked grassy pitches, 30 used for seasonal units, leaving about 60 for tourists all with hook-ups and some with water taps. There is some shade from mature trees. A rather steep footpath leads down to the town and the imposing Abbey of Bec. This is still a working monastery, which was founded in 1034, at the time of William the Conqueror, and has links to the archbishops of Canterbury. It is well worth a visit. The town itself is quite photogenic, has the usual tourist shops, several bars and restaurants and horse drawn carriage rides. The surrounding area is very popular with artists and photographers.

Facilities

A modern heated unit has good showers, British style WCs, open and cubicled washbasins, and a dishwashing area which overlooks the good playground via an attractive large window. Extra facilities in the old unit by reception, where you will find the laundry with washing machine and dryer. Reception keeps soft drinks and ices, and the baker calls each morning. Playing field and tennis courts. Off site: Le Bec-Hellouin and its Abbey 1.5 km. Swimming pool at Brionne, 6 km. Fishing 1.5 km. Riding 2 km. Golf 20 km.

At a glance

Welcome & Ambience	✓✓✓✓	Location	✓✓✓✓
Quality of Pitches	✓✓✓✓	Range of Facilities	✓✓✓

Directions

Le Bec-Hellouin is about 30 km. southwest of Rouen, 24 km. southeast of Pont Audemer. From Pont Audemer take D130 southeast for 20 km to Pont Authou. Turn left onto D39 to Le Bec-Hellouin, pass slowly through town and at far end of one-way system, turn left on minor road (site signed). Continue for about 1 km. then take left hand fork, and carry on for about 500 m. to site entrance on right.

Charges 2003

Per unit incl. 2 persons	€ 7.00
child under 7 yrs	€ 1.30
electricity (10A)	€ 2.60
first animal free, extra animal	€ 0.80
No credit cards.	

Reservations

Contact site. Tel: 02 32 44 83 55.

Open

1 April - 30 September.

FR50030 Camping Lez-Eaux

St Aubin des Préaux, 50380 St Pair-sur-Mer (Manche)

Set in the spacious grounds of a château, Lez Eaux lies in a rural situation just off the main route south, under two hours from Cherbourg. It is a very pleasant situation from which to explore this corner of the Cotentin peninsula, with swimming pools on site and beaches nearby. However, because of its location Lez Eaux receives much en-route trade, both from tour operator clients and independent campers on their way further south and at times this can put heavy pressure on the facilities (it is a good idea to book for peak season visits, or for single nights arrive early). There are 229 pitches (100 are fully serviced), with nearly 50% taken by British and several Dutch tour operators. Most pitches are of a very good size, partly separated by trees and shrubs on either flat or very slightly sloping, grassy ground overlooking Normandy farmland and on either side of a small lake (with carp and other fish). All pitches have electrical connections and some have drainage.

Facilities

Three modern toilet blocks (cleaned several times a day) include washbasins in cabins, good facilities for children and babies, and full provision for disabled people. Shop, small bar, snacks and takeaway with set meal each night to order in advance (all from 15/5). Small heated swimming pool (12 x 6 m.) and attractive, indoor tropical style fun pool with slides and a glass roof (from 15/5, no T-shirts or Bermuda style shorts). Adventure play area. Good tennis court. Football, volleyball. Games room with table tennis, and TV room. Bicycle hire. Lake fishing. Torches required at night. Only one dog per pitch is accepted. Note: facilities not fully open until 15/5. Off site: Riding 5 km, golf 7 km. Nearest beach is 3 km, St Pair is 4 km. and Granville 7 km.

At a glance

Welcome & Ambience	✓✓✓✓	Location	✓✓✓✓
Quality of Pitches	✓✓✓✓	Range of Facilities	✓✓✓✓✓

Directions

Site access is signed west about 7 km. southeast of Granville on main D973 road to Avranches.

Charges 2004

Per pitch incl. 2 persons	€ 15.00 - € 28.00
extra person	€ 7.00
child (under 7 yrs)	€ 5.00
electricity (5A)	€ 6.00
all services	€ 9.00

Reservations

Advisable for high season and made with 25% deposit. Tel: 02 33 51 66 09. Email: lez.eaux@wanadoo.fr

Open

1 May - 15 September.

FR50000 Camping L'Etang des Haizes

43 Rue Cauticotte, La Haye du Puits, 50250 St Symphorien-le-Valois (Manche)

This already appealing and friendly site has added a new swimming pool complex with four lane slides, jacuzzi and a paddling pool. L'Etang des Haizes provides 98 good size pitches, of which 60 are for touring units, on fairly level ground and all with electricity. They are set in a mixture of conifers, orchard and shrubbery, with some very attractive slightly smaller pitches overlooking the lake and 34 mobile homes inconspicuously sited. The fenced lake offers good coarse fishing for huge carp (we are told!), pedaloes, a small beach, ducks and, believe it or not, a turtle can sometimes be seen on a fine day! The gate is locked 22.00 - 07.00 hrs.

Facilities

Two well kept toilet blocks are of modern construction, open plan and unisex. They have washbasins in cabins and units for disabled people. Dishwashing under cover, small laundry. Motorcaravan services. Milk, bread and takeaway snacks are available on site (no gas). Restaurant/Bar with TV and terrace overlooking the lake and pool complex (all 25/5-5/9). Two play areas. Bicycle hire. Table tennis, pool table, petanque and volleyball. Entertainment and activities organised for all ages, including treasure hunts, archery and food tasting (10/7-25/8). Off site: La Haye-du-Puits (1 km) has two supermarkets, good restaurants and a market on Wednesdays. Good sandy beach 8 km. Normandy landing beaches 25 km.

At a glance

Welcome & Ambience	✓✓✓✓✓	Location	✓✓✓✓
Quality of Pitches	✓✓✓✓	Range of Facilities	✓✓✓✓✓

Directions

From Cherbourg follow N13 (Mont St Michel) road as far as Valognes, then the D2 to St Sauveur-le-Vicomte. Continue on the D900 for La Haye-du-Puits, go straight on at new roundabout on outskirts of town and site is signed almost immediately on the right.

Charges 2003

Per unit incl. 2 adults	€ 7.00 - € 12.00
with electricity (6/10A)	€ 15.00 - € 28.00
extra person over 3 yrs	€ 3.00 - € 6.00
dog	€ 1.00 - € 2.00
Camping Cheques accepted.	

Reservations

Made with 25% deposit. Tel: 02 33 46 01 16.
Email: etang.des.haizes@wanadoo.fr

Open

1 April - 15 October.

FR50050 Camping Le Cormoran

Ravenoville-Plage, 50480 Sainte Mère Eglise (Manche)

Set in a flat and open landscape and only separated from the beach by the coast road, Le Cormoran is ideal for a holiday or short break quite near to Cherbourg (33 km), with the Landing Beaches close by. Holiday mobile homes, many privately owned, take 136 places and there are 40 for rent. The remaining 80 pitches for touring units are sheltered from the wind by neat hedges and have electricity available. With a narrow frontage, decorated with flags and a fountain, it is a fairly long site with most of the amenities at the entrance. This is a well run, family managed site with many regular visitors, which gets full in peak season. A 'Sites et Paysages' member.

Facilities

Four toilet blocks are of varying styles and ages. Washbasins are in cabins. Dishwashing sinks. Washing machines and dryers. The smallest block is of the mobile type and serves 15 extra large pitches (150 sq.m.) at the back of the site. Small shop, bar with snacks (all season) and takeaway. Swimming pool (heated 1/5-15/9, unsupervised). Small play areas. Tennis court. Boules pitch. Entertainment and games room. Bicycle and shrimp net hire. Communal barbecue. Off site: Archery, riding and day trips to the Channel Islands can be organised. Golf 5 km. Utah Beach 5 km. Sports field and storage for up to 60 boats adjacent to the site.

At a glance

Welcome & Ambience	✓✓✓✓	Location	✓✓✓✓
Quality of Pitches	✓✓✓✓	Range of Facilities	✓✓✓✓

Directions

From N13 take Ste Mère Eglise exit. In centre of town take road to Ravenoville (6 km), then Ravenoville-Plage (3 km). Just before beach turn right and site is 500 m.

Charges 2004

Per unit incl. 1 or 2 persons	€ 15.75 - € 22.00
child (3- 7 yrs)	€ 1.70 - € 2.10
electricity (6A)	€ 3.80

Local tax included. Camping Cheques accepted.

Reservations

Essential for July/Aug. and made with 25% deposit. Tel: 02 33 41 33 94. Email: lecormoran@wanadoo.fr

Open

2 April - 26 September.

FR50070 Castel Camping Caravaning L'Anse du Brick

Route du Val de Saire, 50330 Maupertus-sur-Mer (Manche)

A friendly, family site, L'Anse du Brick overlooks a picturesque bay on the northern tip of the Contentin peninsula, 8 km. east of Cherbourg Port. This quality site makes a pleasant night halt, or an ideal longer stay destination for those not wishing to travel too far. Its pleasing location offers access to a small sandy beach, also to a woodland walk where only the noise of a cascading stream disturbs the peace. Beyond the site lies miles of walking tracks through the gorse-covered hills which, together with a stark rock face, cluster around the site and make it a sheltered sun-trap. This is a mature, terraced site with magnificent sea and hill views from certain pitches. Tarmac roads climb gradually to the pitches which are level, separated and mostly well shaded by the many trees, bushes and shrubs.

Facilities

Two sanitary blocks, although not ultra-modern, are kept spotlessly clean and are maintained to a satisfactory standard. They include provision for disabled visitors, laundry and dishwashing areas and a motorcaravan service point. Swimming pool complex. Restaurant and popular bar/pizzeria with an extensive menu. Tennis court. Play area. Organised entertainment in season. Mini-club for children (6-12 yrs). Bicycle and kayak hire. Off site: Fishing 100 m. Golf 10 km. Riding 10 km.

At a glance

Welcome & Ambience	✓✓✓✓✓	Location	✓✓✓✓
Quality of Pitches	✓✓✓	Range of Facilities	✓✓✓✓

Directions

From Cherbourg follow directions for Caen/Rennes. After third roundabout, turn left at lights towards Bretteville (D116). Continue for 8 km; site signed right.

Charges 2004

Per person	€ 3.80 - € 5.10
child (3-10 yrs)	€ 2.60 - € 3.50
pitch incl. electricity (10A)	€ 12.00 - € 15.30

Camping Cheques accepted.

Reservations

Advised for July/Aug. Tel: 02 33 54 33 57. Email: welcome@anse-du-brick.com

Open

1 April - 30 September.

Beach at 100 m

L'Anse du Brick ★★★★

50330 MAUPERTUS/MER
Tel : 33 (0) 233 543 357
Fax :33 (0) 233 544 966
Internet : www.anse-du-brick.com
Mail : welcome@anse-du-brick.com

Mobil home and chalets to rent

FR50060 Camping Le Grand Large

50340 Les Pieux (Manche)

Le Grand Large is a well established, quality family site with direct access to a long sandy beach and within a 20 km. drive of Cherbourg. A neat, tidy site with both touring and mobile home pitches which are divided and separated by hedging, which gives an orderly well laid out appearance. At the entrance, alongside the security barrier, stands the modern reception area. Decorating the forecourt are low brick walls with sunken flower beds, the toilet blocks also having their share of flower troughs. To the rear of the site and laid out in the sand-hills is an excellent play area for children, with swings, slides and climbing frame. However, the sandy beach is the big attraction. Roads around the site are tarmac and there are pleasant views across the bay to the tip of the Cherbourg peninsula.

Facilities

The two toilet blocks are well maintained, the main one modern and colourful including washbasins in cubicles and some family rooms. WCs are mostly to the outside of the building. Provision for people with disabilities is good. Baby bathroom, dishwashing sinks, laundry area, and motorcaravan services. Shop for basic groceries. Bar/café and takeaway (snacks 15/6-31/8). Swimming pool and children's pool. Play area. Tennis, table tennis, volleyball and boules. TV room. Animation in July/Aug. Off site: Bicycle hire or riding 5 km, golf 15 km.

At a glance

Welcome & Ambience	✓✓✓✓	Location	✓✓✓✓
Quality of Pitches	✓✓✓✓	Range of Facilities	✓✓✓✓✓

Directions

From Cherbourg port take N13 south for approx. 2 km. Branch right on D650 road (previously D904) signed Cartaret. Continue for 18 km to Les Pieux. Take D4 in town and turn left just after Super 'U' supermarket and follow camp signs via D117/517.

Charges 2003

Per unit incl. 2 persons	€ 22.00
extra person	€ 5.00
child (under 7 yrs)	€ 3.00
electricity (6A)	€ 3.50

Less 20% in low seasons (excl. electricity). Motorcaravan services € 6,10 - € 7,62 (free to guests). Camping Cheques accepted.

Reservations

Made with deposit (€ 80). Tel: 02 33 52 40 75. Email: le-grand-large@wanadoo.fr

Open

5 April - 21 September.

FR50080 Camping Haliotis

Chemin des Soupirs, 50170 Pontorson (Manche)

In the past year the Duchesne family have achieved a remarkable transformation of this former municiple site. Situated on the edge of the little town of Pontorson and next to the river Couesnon, Haliotis is within walking, cycling and canoeing distance of Le Mont Saint-Michel. The site has 110 pitches, including 95 for tourers, and there are plans to extend the site for 2004. Most pitches have electricity. A new swimming pool with jacuzzi has been built, and the large, comfortable reception area developed to incorporate a bar and restaurant.

Facilities

Very clean, renovated and well-equipped wash block. Bar and restaurant. No shop or takeaway on site, facilities available in nearby town. Swimming pool with jacuzzi, separate paddling pool. Good fenced play area. Large games room. Free tennis court. Free fishing in the River Couesnon. Off site: Local services in Pontorson within walking distance. Riding 5 km, golf 18 km. Bicycle hire 1 km.

At a glance

Welcome & Ambience	✓✓✓✓✓	Location	✓✓✓✓
Quality of Pitches	✓✓✓✓	Range of Facilities	✓✓✓✓

Directions

Site is 300 m. from the town centre, west of D976, alongside the river, and is well signed from the town.

Charges 2003

Per adult	€ 4.20
child (under 7 yrs)	€ 1.95
caravan and car	€ 3.80
tent and car	€ 3.50
motorcaravan	€ 3.00
electricity (8-16A)	€ 2.50
dog	€ 0.50
local tax	€ 0.20

No credit cards. Camping Cheques accepted.

Reservations

Contact site. Tel: 02 33 68 11 59. Email: info@camping-haliotis-mont-saint-michel.com

Open

1 May - 31 October.

Great on-line holiday deals *alanrogersdirect*.com

FR50090 Camping La Gerfleur

Rue Guillaume Le Conquérant, 50270 Barneville Carteret (Manche)

La Gerfleur is a very pleasant little site with a warm welcome from the owners, a heated pool, a fishing lake and reasonable sanitary facilities. There are 26 mobile homes, but these are separated from 55 individual tourist pitches. On grass with small dividing hedges, these all have electric hook-ups and some shade from mature trees. A few are in a newly created, more open area next to the lake, and will need more time to fully mature. The outdoor, heated pool has a separate paddling pool. An excellent long ramp gives access for disabled people, with toilet facilities next to the pool. La Gerfleur makes a good holiday base, being an easy cycle ride from the large sandy beach at Barneville Plage, or from the harbour and the smaller cove at Carteret (both only 1.5 km).

Facilities

Clean facilities include British style WCs, chain operated showers and some washbasins, all in modern cubicles, units for disabled visitors, laundry and dishwashing sinks. Washing machine and dryer in own building by reception. Basic motorcaravan service point. Swimming pool (6.5 x 14 m). Fishing lake. Table tennis, boules, games room with snooker and table football. Enclosed small playground. In July/Aug. bar, a visit by a 'frites' van and a daily visit from the baker. Off site: Barneville town centre 550 m, sandy beach at Barneville Plage (1.5 km). Golf 4 km. Riding 7 km.

At a glance			
Welcome & Ambience	✓✓✓✓	Location	✓✓✓✓
Quality of Pitches	✓✓✓✓	Range of Facilities	✓✓✓

Directions

Barneville-Carteret is 37 km. SSW of Cherbourg. From north on D904 turn off Barneville-Carteret by-pass, and use the old road to town. After 1 km. at roundabout, continue on D903E towards town centre, and site entrance is immediately on your right.

Charges 2004

Per adult	€ 4.30
pitch incl. electricity (6A)	€ 8.70

Reservations

Advisable for July/August and made with deposit (€ 76). Tel: 02 33 04 38 41. Email: alabouriau@aol.com

Open

1 April - 31 October.

FR50100M Camping Municipal Le Pont-Roulland

50370 Brécey (Manche)

Comfortable and good value, this little site is set in an old orchard of apple and cherry trees. The 50 numbered tourist pitches are on lush grass, with electric hook-ups for all, although some may need long leads. The entire site has a slight slope, so motorcaravans may need levelling blocks. There is good site lighting and tarmac roads. The guardienne lives on site and reception is open 17.00-22.00 hrs daily – just choose your pitch and pay later if you arrive outside these hours. The usual small country town bustle and swimming pool noise during the day gives way to quiet nights after 8 pm.

Facilities

A traditional Normandy stone building houses toilet facilities with modern fittings including spacious hot showers, some basins in cubicles, dishwashing and laundry sinks, and a washing machine, but no dedicated facilities for disabled persons. Table tennis. Playground for young children. Off site: Town centre and shops 1 km. Reception issues vouchers for free admission to adjacent municipal pool (June 16.30-19.00, July/Aug 14.00-19.00) and tennis (balls and rackets for hire). Small park with free paddling pool also adjacent. River fishing nearby. Beaches 25 km.

At a glance			
Welcome & Ambience	✓✓✓✓	Location	✓✓✓✓
Quality of Pitches	✓✓✓✓	Range of Facilities	✓✓✓✓

Directions

Brécey is 16 km. northeast of Avranches. Site is 1 km. east of town centre just off D911. Turn south on D79 towards Les Cresnays (site isigned).

Charges 2003

Per person	€ 2.35
pitch incl electricity (6A)	€ 4.20
No credit cards.	

Reservations

Contact site. Tel: 02 33 48 60 60. Email: tourisme-brecey@wanadoo.fr

Open

1 April - 30 September.

FR61040M Camping Municipal du Champ Passais

61700 Domfront (Orne)

Situated on the edge of the old fortified town of Domfront, this small site has 34 individual pitches on a series of level terraces and a separate open grassy area for tents. The nine pitches nearest the entrance are all hardstandings separated by grass with a 10A electricity connection. Grass pitches on the lower levels, divided by well tended shrubs and hedges, have a 5A electricity connection.

Facilities

Excellent toilet facilities in a modern building, include some washbasins in cubicles, facilities for disabled people, dishwashing and laundry sinks plus a washing machine. No separate chemical disposal point, but a notice tells visitors where to empty toilets. Boules. Play area. Double axle caravans are not accepted; American RVs can be accommodated. Off site: Fishing 1 km. Supermarket, with cheap fuel 800 m. Sports centre adjacent to site.

At a glance			
Welcome & Ambience	✓✓✓✓✓	Location	✓✓✓✓✓
Quality of Pitches	✓✓✓✓✓	Range of Facilities	✓✓✓

Directions

Site is well signed from the town.

Charges 2003

Per unit incl. 1 adult	€ 3.70
extra adult	€ 2.00
electricity (5/10A)	€ 1.80 - € 3.00
No credit cards.	

Reservations

Not normally necessary. Tel: 02 33 37 37 66.

Open

1 April - 30 September.

FR61010M **Camping La Campière**

Bvd. du Docteur Dentu, 61120 Vimoutiers (Orne)

This small, well kept site is situated in a valley to the north of the town, which is on both the Normandy Cheese and Cider routes. Indeed the town is famous for its cheese and has a Camembert Museum, five minutes walk away in the town centre. The 40 pitches here are flat and grassy, separated by laurel hedging and laid out amongst attractive and well maintained flower and shrub beds. There is some shade around the perimeter and all pitches have electricity.

Facilities

The single central sanitary block is clean and heated, providing open washbasins, children's wc's, good sized showers and a bathroom for disabled visitors. Dishwashing and laundry facilities under cover. Off site: No shop but a large supermarket is 300 m. Tennis courts and a park are adjacent. Water sports facilities or riding 2 km.

At a glance

Welcome & Ambience	✓✓✓✓	Location	✓✓✓✓
Quality of Pitches	✓✓✓✓	Range of Facilities	✓✓✓

Directions

Site is on northern edge of town, signed from main Lisieux-Argentan road next to large sports complex

Charges 2003

Per person	€ 2.65
child (under 10 yrs)	€ 1.55
pitch with electricity (6/10A)	€ 3.70 - € 4.10
car	€ 1.85

Reductions for 7th and subsequent days.

Reservations

Not normally necessary. Tel: 02 33 39 18 86. Email: mairie.vimoutiers@wanadoo.fr

Open

March - October.

FR76040 **Camping La Source**

Petit Appeville, 76550 Hautot-sur-Mer (Seine-Maritime)

This friendly, attractive, site is just four kilometres from Dieppe and is useful for those using the Newhaven - Dieppe ferry crossing. The 120 pitches are flat and shady, and the site is quietly located in a valley with the only disturbance the occasional passing train. A fast-flowing small river flows along one border (not protected for young children), with opportunities for eel fishing, rowing or canoeing. There are hardstandings for motorcaravans and electricity is available. The site is well lit and stays open for late night ferries (so there could be some noise late at night).

Facilities

A good, clean single toilet block (men to the left, ladies to the right) includes washbasins in cubicles and mainly British style WCs. Well equipped en-suite unit for disabled people but the unmade gravel roads may cause problems. Dishwashing under cover and laundry. Small bar and terrace (15/3-15/10). Small play field. TV room and room for young people with table tennis and amusement machines. Small gym with modern fitness machines, free for campers. Volleyball, basketball and badminton. Fishing. Off site: Riding 2 km, bicycle hire 1 km, golf 4 km.

At a glance

Welcome & Ambience	✓✓✓✓	Location	✓✓✓
Quality of Pitches	✓✓✓	Range of Facilities	✓✓✓

Directions

On leaving dock, follow one way system bearing left at Canadian War memorial, below the castle. Follow signs to Paris and Rouen and, after long hill, at large roundabout, take first exit to right on D925, Av. St Jaures. After 2 km. turn left at traffic lights on D153 (Pourville sur Mer to right). Just past railway station turn left under bridge (3.10 m.) into narrow road with stream on right. Site is a short distance on the left.

Charges 2003

Per person	€ 4.00
child (under 7 yrs)	€ 3.00
caravan	€ 7.00
tent	€ 5.00
motorcaravan	€ 8.00
electricity (6A)	€ 2.80

Reservations

Write to site. Tel: 02 35 84 27 04.

Open

15 March - 15 October.

FR76090M Camping Municipal d'Etennemare

Hameau d'Etennemare, 76460 St Valery-en-Caux (Seine-Maritime)

This comfortable, neat municipal site is 2 km. from the harbour and town, 30 km. west of Dieppe. Quietly located, it has 116 pitches of which 50% are available for touring units. The grassy pitches are all on a slight slope, all with electricity, water and drain, but there is very little shade. Reception is open daily from June - mid-Sept. but is closed on Wednesdays in low season and there is now a card operated security barrier. The site is close to the municipal sports complex with tennis and football field, and there are shops and restaurants in the town.

Facilities

Two modern, clean and well maintained sanitary buildings are side by side, one containing showers and the other, more recently refitted, has toilets, both open and cubicled washbasins and facilities for disabled people. Both blocks can be heated in winter. Dishwashing and laundry sinks. Washing machines. Small shop (July/Aug). Playground. Table tennis. Off site: Supermarket 1 km. Harbour 2 km.

At a glance

Welcome & Ambience	✓✓✓✓	Location	✓✓✓✓
Quality of Pitches	✓✓✓✓	Range of Facilities	✓✓✓

Directions

Site is southwest of town centre and is signed from the D925 (Fécamp) road, just west of the railway station. Follow signs to site or 'terrain de sports'.

Latest charges

Per unit incl. 2 adults and electricity (6A)	€ 12.50
extra person	€ 2.55
child (under 10 yrs)	€ 1.60

Reservations

Essential for July/Aug; contact site. Tel: 02 35 97 15 79.

Open

All year.

FR76100M Camping Municipal Cany-Barville

76450 Cany-Barville (Seine-Maritime)

This good quality site, first opened in 1997 next to the municipal sports stadium, has a floral entrance and tarmac roads. Of the 100 individual hedged pitches around 74 are available for tourists. There are around 40 concrete hardstandings and the remainder are on grass, all are fully serviced with water, drain and electric hook-ups. As yet, there is not very much shade from newly planted specimen trees. Cany-Barville is a bustling small town with a traditional Normandy market on Monday mornings. There is a Château and an Eco-museum (1/4-30/10), and the Durdent valley has numerous other châteaux, mills, churches and 'colombiers'.

Facilities

The modern, centrally located, sanitary unit can be heated and has some washbasins in cubicles. Dishwashing and laundry sinks. Separate suites for disabled people. Drive-over motorcaravan service point with chemical disposal facility. Table tennis, volleyball, boules. Off site: Sailing and windsurfing centre 2 km. Beach 10 km. Supermarket 1 km.

At a glance

Welcome & Ambience	✓✓✓✓	Location	✓✓✓✓
Quality of Pitches	✓✓✓✓	Range of Facilities	✓✓✓

Directions

From traffic lights on eastern side of town turn off D925 on to D268 towards Yvetot. Go under railway arch and continue straight on. Site is 600 m. from town centre adjacent to sports field.

Latest charges

Per person	€ 2.20
child (under 14 yrs)	€ 0.95
pitch with electricity (10A)	€ 4.80

Reservations

Advisable in July and August. Tel: 02 35 97 70 37.

Open

All year.

FR76110M Camping Municipal Les Boucaniers

76470 Le Tréport (Seine-Maritime)

This large, good quality, municipal site has an attractive entrance and some floral displays, tarmac roads and site lighting. The 320 pitches are on level grass, some with dividing hedges, and a variety of trees to provide a little shade. There are 16 good quality wooden chalets for rent, and some privately owned mobile homes, which leaves around 276 pitches for tourists, all with electric hook-ups. A small shop, bar and takeaway operates all season, the baker calls daily (not Mondays in low season). The town centre is within walking distance with a choice of many good seafood restaurants.

Facilities

Three well equipped sanitary blocks (one can be heated) provide mainly British style WCs, washbasins in cubicles, pre-set hot showers, with facilities for small children and disabled persons at block three (furthest from entrance). Shop, bar and takeaway (1/4-31/10). Multi-sport court. Minigolf. Boules. Off site: Tennis, football and gymnasium nearby. Fishing, golf or beach 2km. Markets at Le Tréport Monday and Saturday.

At a glance

Welcome & Ambience	✓✓✓✓	Location	✓✓✓✓✓
Quality of Pitches	✓✓✓✓	Range of Facilities	✓✓✓✓

Directions

From Eu on D1915, on entering the town of Le Tréport, at first set of traffic lights on a multi-way junction, turn right into Rue Pierre Mendès-France, and site entrance is on right (signed).

Latest charges

Per person	€ 2.50
child (2-10 yrs)	€ 1.40
pitch with electricity (5A)	€ 5.80

Reservations

Contact site. Tel: 02 35 86 35 47.

Open

1 April - 30 September.

FR76120M **Camping Municipal Veulettes-sur-Mer**

8 Rue de Greenock, 76450 Veulettes-sur-Mer (Seine-Maritime)

A good value, well kept municipal site in an attractive coastal town, just 500 m. from the beach and all town services. There are 116 marked pitches on open level grass, 40 of which are seasonal pitches, which leaves around 76 multi-service pitches for tourists, all with electric hook-ups, water and waste water drain. Reception keeps soft drinks and ices during July/August. Also on site is an attractive 'salle' (open all day in July/August) with a library and TV, a games area with electronic game, table tennis, babyfoot and further toilet facilities.

Facilities

Three good modern sanitary units in traditional style buildings are of varying ages (one can be heated). These provide pre-set hot showers, washbasins in cubicles, and facilities for disabled people in the smallest unit on the far side of the site. Laundry room with washing machine. Playground. Boules court. TV, library and table tennis. Off site: Public park with tennis courts and large playground, beach (pebble), watersports centre and all shops and services are within 500 m. level walk. Traffic free cycle path to the next village (4 km).

Directions

Veulettes-sur-Mer is on the coast approx. 45 km. WSW of Dieppe. Site is central in town, lying about 500 m. back from the main promenade (signed).

Latest charges

Per person	€ 2.50
child (4-10 yrs)	€ 1.25
pitch	€ 2.15
car	€ 1.00
electricity (10A)	€ 2.50
animal	€ 0.50

Reservations

Contact site. Tel: 02 35 97 53 44.

Open

1 April - 31 October.

At a glance

Welcome & Ambience	✓✓✓✓	Location	✓✓✓✓
Quality of Pitches	✓✓✓✓	Range of Facilities	✓✓✓✓

FR76130 **Camping de la Forêt**

Rue Mainberthe, 76480 Jumieges (Seine-Maritime)

This is a pretty family site with a friendly laid back atmosphere. It is located just 10 km. from the A13 Paris - Caen autoroute, and is best accessed by ferry across the River Seine. The great abbey at Jumieges was founded in 654 by St Philibert, rebuilt by the Normans and consecrated in the presence of William the Conqueror – well worth a visit! The site was formerly a municipal and has recently been taken on by the Joret family. The 90 grassy pitches are attractively located in woodland. Virtually all pitches are reasonably shaded and most have electrical connections. There is no site shop but a good range of shops, cafes, restaurants etc. are in Jumieges – just 600 m. away.

Facilities

Two toilet blocks, both of modern construction and maintained to a good standard with British toilets and pre-set showers. Washing and drying machines. Small heated pool. Playground. Chalets and mobile homes to let.

At a glance

Welcome & Ambience	✓✓✓✓	Location	✓✓✓
Quality of Pitches	✓✓✓✓	Range of Facilities	✓✓

Directions

Jumieges is around 10 km. north of the A13 Paris - Caen autoroute (Bourg-Achard exit). Take D313 towards Caudebec-en-Caux. Then, either take the ferry across the Seine (toll € 1.70 per car per single journey in 2003) from Heurtauville to Jumieges, or continue over the Pont de Brotonne and double back on D982 to Jumieges. Site clearly signed in the village.

Charges 2003

Pitch incl. 2 persons	€ 14.20 - € 15.00
extra person (over 4 yrs)	€ 3.40 - € 3.80
electricity	€ 2.50
tourist tax	€ 0.25 - € 0.50

Reduced charges in low season.
Camping Cheques accepted.

Reservations

Conatct site. Tel: 02 35 37 93 43.
Email: ci.junieges@free.fr

Open

5 April - 25 October.

Northern France

Map 3

Northern France, with its lush countryside and market towns, is much more than just a stop off en-route to or from the ports. The peaceful rural unspoilt charms of the region provide a real breath of fresh air.

Nord/Pas de Calais: 59 Nord, 62 Pas-de-Calais
Major City: Lille

Picardy: 02 Aisne, 60 Oise, 80 Somme
Major City: Amiens

This is a region where centuries of invaders have left their mark. At Vimy Ridge near Arras, World War One trenches have been preserved intact, a most poignant sight. Elsewhere almost every village between Arras and Amiens has its memorial. It is also the birthplace of Gothic architecture with six cathedrals, including Laon, Beauvais and Amiens, arguably the grandest in France.

The area however is predominately rural. Inland and south are long vistas of rolling farmland broken by little rivers and well scattered with pockets of forest woodland. The coastline is characterised by sandy beaches, shifting dunes and ports. It is a quiet and sparsely populated area with peaceful villages and churches that provide evidence of the glorious achievements of French Gothic architecture. Le Touquet combines the modernity of its sports facilities with an old world charm. Boulogne is home to Nausicaa, the world's largest sea-life centre and from Cap Griz-Nez you may be able to see the White Cliffs of Dover. There are also many huge hypermarkets where you may stock up on wine, beer and cheese.

Cuisine of the region

Carbonnade de Boeuf à la Flamande: braised beef with beer, onions and bacon

Caudière (Chaudière, Caudrée): versions of fish and potato soup

Ficelles Picardes: ham pancakes with mushroom sauce

Flamiche aux poireaux: puff pastry tart with cream and leeks

Hochepot: a thick Flemish soup with virtually everything in it but the kitchen sink

Soupe courquignoise: soup with white wine, fish, moules, leeks and Gruyère cheese

Tarte aux Maroilles: a hot creamy tart based on Maroilles cheese

Waterzooï: a cross between soup and stew, usually of fish or chicken

Places of interest

Amiens: Notre Dame cathedral, monument to 1918 Battle of the Somme

Chantilly: Château of Chantilly with a 17th century stable with a 'live' Horse museum.

Compiègne: Seven miles east of the town is Clairière de l'Armistice. The railway coach here is a replica of the one in which the 1918 Armistice was signed and in which Hitler received the French surrender in 1942

Laon: 12th century cathedral, WW1 trenches, Vauclair Abbey

Marquesterre: one of Europe's most important bird sanctuaries

Alan Rogers **tip**

A COLONY OF CALF SEALS LIVE IN THE SOMME BAY. THE TOWNS OF CROTOY AND ST VALÉRY ARE PARTICULARLY GOOD FOR OBSERVING THE SEALS.

FR02000 Camping Caravaning du Vivier aux Carpes

10 Rue Charles Voyeux, 02790 Seraucourt-le-Grand (Aisne)

Vivier aux Carpes is a small quiet site, close to the A26, two hours from Calais, so it is ideal for an overnight stop but is also worthy of a longer stay. A neat, purpose designed site is imaginatively set out taking full benefit of large ponds which are well stocked for fishing. There is also abundant wild life. The 60 well spaced pitches, are at least 100 sq.m. on flat grass with dividing hedges. The 45 for touring units all have electricity, some also with water points, and there are special pitches for motor-caravans. This peaceful site has a comfortable feel and is close to the village centre. The enthusiastic owners and the manager speak excellent English and are keen to welcome British visitors. Although there is no restaurant on site, good and reasonable hotels are close. The cathedral cities of St Quentin, Reims, Amiens and Laon are close, Disneyland just over an hour away, Compiegne and the WW1 battlefields are near and Paris easily reached by train (1 hr 15 mins from St Quentin). This site is good for couples or fishing enthusiasts.

Facilities

The spacious, clean toilet block has separate, heated facilities for disabled visitors, which are made available to other campers in the winter months. Laundry facilities. Motorcaravan service point (fresh water for large vans is charged). Above the toilet block is a large TV/games room with table tennis and snooker. Small play area. Bicycle hire. Petanque. Fishing (about € 5,50 p/day). Gates close 22.00 hrs, office open 09.00-21.30. Rallies welcome. Off site: Village has post office, doctor, chemist and small supermarket. Riding 500 m. Golf 12 km.

At a glance

| Welcome & Ambience | ✓✓✓✓ | Location | ✓✓✓✓ |
| Quality of Pitches | ✓✓✓✓ | Range of Facilities | ✓✓✓ |

Directions

Leave A26 (Calais - Reims) road at exit 11 and take D1 left towards Soissons for 4 km. Take D8 and on entering Essigny-la-Grand (4 km.) turn sharp right on D72 signed Seraucourt-le-Grand (5 km). Site is clearly signed - it is in the centre of the village.

Charges 2003

Per unit incl. 2 persons and electricity (6A)	€ 15.00
extra person	€ 2.80
child (under 10 yrs)	€ 2.00
pet	€ 0.60

Monthly, weekly or weekend rates available. Discounts for students with tents. No credit cards.

Reservations

Advised for peak season. Tel: 03 23 60 50 10. Email: camping.du.vivier@wanadoo.fr

Open

1 March - 30 October.

FR02060M Camping Municipal Guignicourt

14 Bis Rue Godins, 02190 Guignicourt (Aisne)

This very pleasant little municipal site has 100 pitches, 50 for long stay units and 50 for tourists. These two sections are separated by the main facilities on a higher terrace. Pitches are generally large and level, although you might need an extra long electric lead for some, but there are few dividing hedges. Pitches along the river bank have most shade, with a few specimen trees providing a little shade to some of the more open pitches. The town is quite attractive and is worthy of an evening stroll. At the junction of the N44 and D925, 7 km. west of the town, is the Chemin des Dames, Monument des Chars d'Assaut – a memorial to the WW1 tank campaign at Berry-au-Bac, with two remarkably well preserved tanks. Further to the west is the Caverne du Dragon, a former stone quarry which sheltered troops during the 1914-18 conflict, which is now a museum depicting everyday life on the front line.

Facilities

The modern sanitary unit has British and Turkish style toilets, washbasins (cold only except for the one in a cubicle), push-button hot showers, dishwashing and laundry sinks. Bar (1/4-30/9). Children's playground, tennis and boules courts, and fishing. Off site: The town has all services including a supermarket and bank. You may notice a low level hum from the nearby Generale Sucrière factory, a major industry of the town. Golf nearby.

At a glance

| Welcome & Ambience | ✓✓✓✓ | Location | ✓✓✓✓ |
| Quality of Pitches | ✓✓✓✓ | Range of Facilities | ✓✓✓ |

Directions

Guignicourt is about 20 km. north of Reims, just east of the A26, junction 14. The site is well signed from D925 in the village.

Charges 2003

Per adult	€ 2.00
child (2-10 yrs)	€ 1.20
pitch	€ 6.00 - € 11.00
animal	€ 1.00
electricity (6/10A)	€ 1.80 - € 4.60

Reservations

Contact site for details. Tel: 03 23 79 74 58. Email: mitche02@aol.com

Open

1 April - 30 September.

FR59010 Camping Caravaning La Chaumière

529 Langhemast Straete, 59285 Buysscheure (Nord)

This is a very friendly, pleasant site, tucked away in the département du Nord with a strong Flanders influence, well worth considering for those using the local Channel crossings. There is a real welcome here and the owners, Guy and Bernadette, are much liked by the regular British visitors. Set just behind the village of Buysscheure (with a shop and two cafés), the site has just 22 individual pitches separated by young trees and bushes. With 16 for touring units, mostly quite large and with some slope, they are on grass with a gravel hardstanding area for the car. Each pair of pitches shares a brick-built unit, decorated with flowers, incorporating a light, electricity connections, water points and rubbish container. A small, fenced fishing lake contains some large carp (seen!) and the ducks will help you eat your baguettes. A bonus is that Bernadette works for the local vet and can arrange all the documentation for British visitors' pets. English is spoken.

Facilities

Although modern, the unisex toilet facilities are simple with two WCs, one shower and one washbasin cabin. Facilities provided for disabled visitors may also be used (a toilet and separate washbasin/shower room). Dishwashing room. Laundry room. Motorcaravan services. Bar (daily) and restaurant (weekends only, all day, all season). Dog exercise area - with jumps etc. Heated swimming pool planned for 2004. Off site: Interesting local market (Monday) at Bergues. St Omer is an old town. This is a popular area for cycling. Shop and café/restaurants in the village.

At a glance

Welcome & Ambience	✓✓✓✓✓	Location	✓✓✓✓
Quality of Pitches	✓✓✓	Range of Facilities	✓✓✓✓

Directions

From Calais take N43 towards St Omer for 25 km. Just beyond Nordausques take D221 left to Watten. In Watten turn left for the centre, then right on D26 towards Cassel. Soon after Lederzeele the site is signed to the right (just before railway bridge). When you reach Buysscheure turn left and then right from where the site is signed again.

Charges 2003

Per unit incl. 2 persons and electricity (6A)	€ 14.00
extra person	€ 7.00
child (under 7 yrs)	€ 3.50
dog	€ 1.00

No credit cards.

Reservations

Contact site. Tel: 03 28 43 03 57.
E-mail: camping.LaChaumiere@wanadoo.fr

Open

1 April - 31 October.

FR02030 Caravaning La Croix du Vieux Pont

02290 Berny-Riviere (Aisne)

Attractively located on the banks of the River Aisne, La Croix du Vieux Pont is a very smart, modern site offering a high standard of facilities. Many pitches are occupied by mobile homes and tour operator tents, but there are many pleasant touring pitches, some on the banks of the Aisne. The site is maintained to a high standard with some excellent amenities, notably four heated swimming pools, one indoors with a waterslide. There are two tennis courts, an amusement arcade and volleyball court. At the heart of the site is a well-stocked fishing lake which is also used for pedaloes and canoes.

Facilities

The six toilet blocks are modern and kept very clean, with washbasins in cabins and free hot showers. Washing and drying machines. Facilities for disabled visitors. Large supermarket, Bar, takeaway and good value restaurant (most amenities open Easter - late Sept). Coach trips organised on a regular basis to Paris, Parc Asterix and Disneyland. Appartments to let. Dogs are not accepted.

At a glance

Welcome & Ambience	✓✓✓✓	Location	✓✓✓✓
Quality of Pitches	✓✓✓✓✓	Range of Facilities	✓✓✓✓✓

Directions

From Compiegne take N31 towards Soissons. At Vic-sur-Aisne turn right, towards Berny-Riviere and site is on right after 400 m.

Charges 2003

Per unit incl. 2 persons and electricity	€ 20.50
incl. 4 persons and electricity	€ 28.50

Camping Cheques accepted.

Reservations

Essential for high season and made with deposit (€ 40). Tel: 03 23 55 50 02.
Email: info@la-croix-du-vieux-pont.com

Open

Easter - 31 October.

FR59050M **Camping Municipal Mauberge**

Route de Mons, 59600 Maubeuge (Nord)

This is an attractive site convenient for a night-stop or for longer stays close to the RN2 road. It is a neat municipal site with 92 marked pitches of fair size. Mainly on level ground and separated by trim hedges, most have electrical connections and some have hardstanding. A variety of broadleaf trees provides shade when needed. When inspected, reception staff were friendly and helpful. Although there are few amenities on the site, the interesting town centre of Maubeuge itself is only about 1 km.

Facilities

Two circular sanitary blocks provide good modern facilities. Dishwashing sinks under cover and washing machines. The block used in winter can be heated. Motorcaravan service point. Small adventure-style playground. Fishing.
Off site: Riding and bicycle hire 2 km. Golf 2.5 km.

At a glance

Welcome & Ambience	✓✓✓✓	Location	✓✓✓✓
Quality of Pitches	✓✓✓✓	Range of Facilities	✓✓✓

Directions

Site is on the RN2 road (known as the N6 in Belgium) north of the town, on the right going towards Mons.

Charges 2003

Per person	€ 3.05
pitch	€ 3.05
electricity (3/10A)	€ 4.15 - € 5.03

Reservations

Not normally made or necessary, but if in doubt telephone site. Tel: 03 27 62 25 48.

Open

All year.

FR62050 **Camping Caravaning Saint Louis**

Rue Leulène, 62610 Autingues par Ardres (Pas-de-Calais)

Convenient for the ferry port at Calais, this is a peaceful little site with 84 pitches. Many are taken by privately owned holiday homes, but there are around 25 pitches for tourists. In a garden-like setting, they are individual and grassy with some shade. Electricity hook-ups are available for all. In high season the site is usually full by 17.00 hrs, so arrive early.

Facilities

Rather old but clean and tidy unisex toilet facilities which provide showers on payment € 1 token) and washbasins mostly in cubicles. Facilities for disabled people. Baby room. Dishwashing and laundry sinks, washing machine. Motorcaravan service point free to campers (€ 4 for non-residents). Snack bar and takeaway every evening in July/Aug. Playground, Games room.

At a glance

Welcome & Ambience	✓✓✓	Location	✓✓✓✓
Quality of Pitches	✓✓✓✓	Range of Facilities	✓✓✓

Directions

From Calais take N43 towards St Omer for 15 km, and east of Ardres, turn south on D224, where site signed.

Latest charges

Per adult	€ 2.50
pitch	€ 5.00
electricity (6A)	€ 2.50

Reservations

Advised for high season. Tel: 03 21 35 46 83.

Open

1 April - 31 October.

FR62030 **Camping Château du Gandspette**

62910 Eperlecques (Pas-de-Calais)

This friendly, comfortable, family run site is in the grounds of the Château du Gandspette. It is conveniently situated for the channel ports and tunnel, providing useful overnight accommodation and a range of facilities for a longer stay. The 17th century building adjacent to the château now houses an attractive bar/restaurant. A gravel road gives access to three different camping areas and a central open space. There are 170 pitches (100 or 150 sq.m), of which 55 are taken by semi-permanent French holiday caravans which intermix with some of the touring pitches giving a real French ambience. All pitches have electricity and are delineated by trees and some hedging. Mature trees form the perimeter of the site, through which there is access to woodland walks. Used by tour operators (8 pitches). A 'Sites et Paysages' member.

Facilities

A partially renovated sanitary block provides satisfactory facilities with a mixture of open and cubicled washbasins. The site reports a second new block. Covered dishwashing sinks. Washing machines and dryers. Good motorcaravan service point. Bar, grill restaurant and takeaway (all 15/5-15/9). Two swimming pools, one large and one smaller (15/5-30/9). New adventure style playground, and play field. Tennis, petanque and a children's room with table tennis and electronic games. Entertainment is organised in season. Off site: Fishing 3 km. Riding 5 km. Golf 10 km. Small supermarket in village 1 km. Market Watten (Friday) and St Omer (Saturday).

At a glance

Welcome & Ambience	✓✓✓✓	Location	✓✓✓✓
Quality of Pitches	✓✓✓✓	Range of Facilities	✓✓✓✓

Directions

From Calais follow N43 towards St Omer for 25 km. Southeast of Nordausques take D221 (east) and follow camp signs for 5-6 km. From St Omer follow N43 to roundabout with D600. Turn right on D600 towards Dunkirk, In 5 km. turn left on D221. Site is 1.5 km.

Charges 2003

Per unit incl. 2 persons	€ 15.00 - € 20.00
extra person (over 4 yrs)	€ 4.00 - € 5.00
electricity (6A)	€ 3.50
Camping Cheques accepted.	

Reservations

Write to site. Tel: 03 21 93 43 93.
Email: contact@chateau-gandspette.com

Open

1 April - 30 September.

FR62010 Camping Caravaning La Bien-Assise

D231, 62340 Guines (Pas-de-Calais)

A mature, well developed site, the history of La Bien-Assise goes back to the 1500s. Today the château, farm and mill are all in the hands of the Boutoille family who can provide you with a fascinating brief history. The farm buildings house the facilities and pool complex. The entrance to a more formal and excellent restaurant, 'La Ferme Gourmande' is in the mellow farmyard opposite the dovecote, with the Auberge du Colombier next door. There are 220 grass pitches mainly set among mature trees, apart from on the newer field. Connected by gravel roads and of a good size (up to 300 sq.m), shrubs and bushes divide most of the pitches. The site's position, 15 minutes from Calais, the Channel Tunnel exit 6 km. and 20 minutes from Boulogne, make it a popular venue en-route north or south, but it is well worth a longer stay. Reception opens for long hours to meet the needs of those crossing the Channel and the site can have heavy usage at times (when maintenance can be variable). Used by tour operators (50 pitches).

Facilities

Three well equipped toilet blocks provide many washbasins in cabins, mostly British style WCs and provision for babies, clothes and dishwashing. The main block is in four sections, two unisex. Motorcaravan service point. Shop. Restaurant (open all year, closed Mon. and Sat. lunchtime). Bar/grill and takeaway (evenings from 1/5). TV room. Pool complex (10/5-10/9) with a fun pool/toboggan, a covered paddling pool and a new outdoor swimming pool with sliding roof to suit all weather conditions. Play areas. Minigolf. Tennis court. Bicycle hire. Off site: Fishing 8 km, riding 10 km. Local market and walks from the site.

At a glance

Welcome & Ambience	✓✓✓✓	Location	✓✓✓✓
Quality of Pitches	✓✓✓✓	Range of Facilities	✓✓✓✓

Directions

From ferry follow A16 south (Boulogne) for junction 15, turning towards St Pierre de Calais to immediately pick up Guînes signs before going under autoroute following the D127. Continue beside canal to Guînes. Site is southwest of village on D231 road (Marquise). From Tunnel also follow A16 south (Boulogne) to pick up Guînes signs at exit 11 and following D215 past St Tricat to Guînes. From south on autoroute A26, use exit2 (Ardres, Guînes) onto N43 and D231 (15 km).

Charges 2003

Per adult	€ 4.50
child (under 8 yrs)	€ 3.50
pitch with electricity (6A)	€ 15.00
Less 10% in low seasons.	

Reservations

Advised for July/Aug. or if arriving late in the evening. Made for any length with deposit (€ 39) and fee (€ 7,62) for stays 5 days or more. Tel: 03 21 35 20 77. Email: castel@bien-assise.com

Open

25 April - 20 September.

FR62060 Caravaning L'Orée du Bois

Chemin Blanc, 62180 Rang-du-Fliers

This fairly peaceful but extensive campsite is in a natural woodland setting, and only 3 km. from a large sandy beach. From reception you pass through a corner of the mobile home (privately owned) section, then through an area of natural, preserved woodland which eparates the touring area. This has 80 individual, touring pitches, all with shade and electric hook-ups). On grass which can be slightly undulating, most are separated by hedges and bushes, but the emphasis is on 'nature'. Also on the touring site are 59 wooden camping lodges. A separate clearing in the woodland is reserved for tents, and useful for cyclists or backpackers is 'Camp Sherpa' comprising eight 2-berth wooden tents. A modern sanitary unit is central in the touring area, with a second smaller unit in the mobile homes area. Berck Plage is only 3 km. and has a magnificent sandy beach and promenade, with extensive free parking areas, with many bays for disabled motorists.

Facilities

Modern facilities with open and cubicle washbasins, controllable hot showers, a laundry with washing machines and dryer, and good facilities for disabled persons (with low level dishwashing and laundry sinks), small children and babies. Note: water for the toilets is obtained from a borehole, and has a slight brownish colour. Basic motorcaravan service point by reception, with a full service area located close to the nearby Intermarché. Bar/brasserie. Animation and dancing in July/Aug. Fishing lake. Tennis. Several playgrounds. The woodland area conceals a football field, volleyball, a fitness trail, and a course for quads and all terrain bikes. Off site: Small supermarket adjacent, large Intermarché complex 700 m. Sports centre at Berck-Plage. Also close by is Le Parc de Bagatelle, the largest amusement park in northern France.

At a glance

Welcome & Ambience	✓✓✓✓	Location	✓✓✓✓✓
Quality of Pitches	✓✓✓✓	Range of Facilities	✓✓✓✓

Directions

Rang du Fliers is just east of Berck Plage and 15 km. south of Le Touquet. From Berck Plage take D917 east to roundabout by supermarket, turn left (north) at next traffic lights (site signed), site entrance is 500 m. on left. From A16 exit 25, follow D917 towards Berck Plage. After four roundabouts, a railway crossing, and two more roundabouts, turn right at traffic lights (site signed), site entrance is 500 m. on left.

Charges 2003

Per unit incl. 2 persons and electricity (6A)	€ 15.00 - € 20.00
extra person	€ 3.00 - € 5.00
Discounts for stays of 14 days.	

Reservations

Essential for July/Aug, and advisable at other times. Made with deposit of 25% of total fees. Tel: 03 21 84 28 51. Email: oree.du.bois@wanadoo.fr

Open

30 March - 20 October.

FR80040 Camping Le Royon

1271 route de Quend, 80120 Fort-Mahon-Plage (Somme)

This busy family run site, some two kilometres from the sea, has 300 pitches of which 100 are used for touring units. Of either 95 or 120 sq.m, the marked and numbered pitches are divided by hedges and arranged either side of access roads. Electricity and water points are available to all. The site is well lit, fenced and guarded at night € 30 deposit for barrier card). Entertainment is organised for adults and children in July/Aug. The site is close to the Baie de L'Authie which is an area noted for migrating birds.

Facilities

Four toilet blocks provide mostly unisex facilities with British or Turkish style WCs and some washbasins in cubicles. Units for disabled people. Baby baths. Dishwashing and laundry sinks under cover. Small shop (July/Aug). Mobile takeaway calls each evening in July/Aug. Friendly clubroom and bar serves drinks and ices, sells bread and newspapers and has the usual games machines. Attractive, heated, covered swimming pool (16 x 8 m; 29/4-15/9) with open air children's pool and sun terrace. Playground. Table tennis, multi-court, tennis court and boules. Bicycle hire. Off site: Fishing, riding or golf within 1 km. Windsurfing, sailing, sand yachting, canoeing, swimming, climbing and shooting nearby. Cinema, disco and casino near.

Directions

Site is on outskirts of Fort Mahon Plage, on D32 towards Quend.

Charges 2003

Per pitch 95 sq.m. incl. water tap, caravan, car, electricity (6A) and 3 persons	€ 15.00 - € 24.00
pitch 120 sq.m, as above	€ 18.00 - € 27.00
extra person (over 1 yr)	€ 6.50
dog	€ 2.00

Reservations

Essential for July/Aug; made with deposit (€ 40 p/week) and fee (€ 10). Tel: 03 22 23 40 30. Email: barbara.dutot@wanadoo.fr

Open

1 March - 31 October.

At a glance

Welcome & Ambience	✓✓✓✓	Location	✓✓✓✓
Quality of Pitches	✓✓✓✓	Range of Facilities	✓✓✓✓

---

15 € ≈ PRIVILEGE CAMPING TICKET ≈ **15 €**

Present this Privilege Camping Ticket at reception and you will only pay 15 Euros per night for a pitch with electricity up to 3 people

Offer valid for year 2004, except in July and August

SUGGESTED BY AIROTEL CAMPING LE ROYON

Camping Qualité Picardie**** - 1271 Route de Quend - 80120 Fort-Mahon Plage
Tel: (33)3 22 23 40 30 - Fax (33)3 22 23 65 15 - www.campingleroyon.com

---

FR80090 Camping Caravaning Le Val d'Authie

20 route de Vercourt, 80120 Villers-sur-Authie (Somme)

In a village location, this well organised site is fairly close to several beaches, but also has its own excellent pool complex, small restaurant and bar. The owner has carefully controlled the size of the site, leaving space for a leisure area. There are 170 pitches in total, but with 104 holiday homes and 16 chalets, there are only 50 for touring units. These are on grass, some are divided by small hedges, with electric hook-ups, and 15 have full services. Ideas for excursions include the 15/16th century chapel and hospice and the Aviation Museum at Rue, a pottery at nearby Roussent, a flour mill at Maintenay, and the steam railway which runs from Le Crotoy to Cayeux-sur-Mer around the Baie de Somme.

Facilities

Good modern toilet facilities include some shower and washbasin units, washbasins in cubicles, and limited facilities for disabled people and babies. Facilities may be under pressure in high season and a reader reports poor cleaning at that time. Ice pack service. Shop for basics. Bar/restaurant serving good value meals (hours vary according to season). Swimming pool with small jacuzzi and paddling pool (April - mid-Sept, with lifeguards in July/Aug). Good playground for small children, club room with TV, and weekend entertainment in season (discos may be noisy until late). Multi-court, beach volleyball, football, boules and tennis court. Fitness trail and running track, mountain bike circuit, and plenty of good paths for evening strolls. Barbecues are not permitted.

Directions

Villers-sur-Authie is about 25 km. NNW of Abbeville. From A16 junction 24 take N1 to Vron, then left on D175 to Villers-sur-Authie. Alternatively use D85 from Rue, or D485 from Nampont St Martin. Site is at southern end of village at junction of minor road.

Charges 2003

Per person	€ 6.00
child (under 7 yrs)	€ 3.00
pitch with electricity (4-10A)	€ 7.50 - € 11.50
Camping Cheques accepted.	

Reservations

Advisable for high season, peak weekends and B.Hs. Tel: 03 22 29 92 47. Email: camping@valdauthie.fr

Open

30 March - 3 November.

At a glance

Welcome & Ambience	✓✓✓✓	Location	✓✓✓✓
Quality of Pitches	✓✓✓✓	Range of Facilities	✓✓✓✓✓

FR80010 Castel Camping Le Château de Drancourt

B.P. 22, 80230 St Valéry-sur-Somme (Somme)

A popular, busy and lively holiday site within easy distance of Channel ports, between Boulogne and Dieppe, Domaine de Drancourt is in four sections. The original section has 100 marked and numbered, grassy pitches of good size, with good shade. An extension taking some 90 units is in light woodland and two newer touring sections are on flat or gently sloping meadow, with little shade as yet. There are 356 pitches in total, of which 220 are occupied by several tour operators. The site also has 30 units for rent which leaves 80 pitches for touring units. Electricity is available in all areas. It can be dusty around the reception buildings and château in dry weather. The pools and toilet blocks can become stretched at times in peak season and maintenance and cleaning can be variable. English is spoken and the site is run personally by the energetic owner and his staff.

Facilities

Three modern, well equipped toilet blocks include washbasins in cubicles, family bathrooms and facilities for disabled visitors. Laundry and dishwashing sinks, washing machines and dryers. Drainage difficulties can still cause occasional problems. Shop (from 15/4). Pizzeria (from 20/4) open until late. Restaurant and takeaway (from 20/4, closed Tuesday in low season). Bar in château, new large first floor bar and pool-side bar with karaoke in season. Three TV rooms, one for children. Disco (free entry). Games room with table tennis. Three heated swimming pools (from 1/5), one indoor and two open air, one with water slide. Tennis court, golf practise range and minigolf. Bicycle hire. Pony riding in season (stables 15 km). Fishing (free). Off site: Stony beach at Cayeux 8 km, or sandy beach 25 km.

At a glance

Welcome & Ambience	✓✓✓✓	Location	✓✓✓✓
Quality of Pitches	✓✓✓✓	Range of Facilities	✓✓✓✓✓

Directions

Site is 2.5 km. south of St Valéry, near Estreboeuf, and is signed from the St Valéry road N40.

Charges 2003

Per person	€ 6.10
child (under 5 yrs)	€ 4.40
pitch for caravan or tent	€ 8.70
pitch for motorcaravan	€ 12.00
car	€ 2.80
dog	free
electricity (6A)	€ 3.10
local tax (over 10 yrs)	€ 0.30

Reservations

Advised for the main season and made for any length, with deposit for longer stays. Tel: 03 22 26 93 45. Email: chateau.drancourt@wanadoo.fr

Open

Easter - 15 September.

FR80070 Camping La Ferme des Aulnes

1 Rue du Marais, Fresne-sur-Authie, 80120 Nampont-St Martin (Somme)

This peaceful site has been developed on the grassy meadows of a small, 17th century farm on the edge of the village of Fresne. Restored outbuildings house reception and the site's facilities, arranged around a central, landscaped courtyard that boasts a fine heated swimming pool. Of the 85 pitches, 30 are available for touring units, with most of the remainder occupied by or for sale to private owners for holiday mobile homes. All tourist pitches have electricity and are fairly level. Many are individual and divided by shrubs and young trees, others are on an open, slightly sloping, grassy area.

Facilities

Sanitary fittings are smart, modern and well maintained, including washbasins in cubicles with a large cubicle for disabled people. Dishwashing and laundry sinks. Shop with local produce and necessities (all season). Piano bar and restaurant. TV room. Swimming pool (16 x 9 m; heated and open mid June - end Aug, with cover for cooler weather). Fitness room. Aquagym and Balneo therapy. Beach volleyball, football. Golf practice range. Playground for small children. Table tennis, boules and archery. Off site: Fishing is possible in the river 800 m. from the site. Gof 3 km. Riding 8 km.

At a glance

Welcome & Ambience	✓✓✓✓✓	Location	✓✓✓✓✓
Quality of Pitches	✓✓✓✓	Range of Facilities	✓✓✓✓

Directions

At Nampont St Martin turn off the N1 on to the D85E (site is signed), towards Fresne, site is on right after about 3 km.

Charges 2003

Per adult	€ 7.00
child (under 7 yrs)	€ 6.00
pitch	€ 6.00
dog	€ 4.00
electricity (6A)	€ 5.00

Camping Cheques accepted.

Reservations

Contact site for details. Tel: 03 22 29 22 69. Email: contact@fermedesaulnes.com

Open

29 March - 5 November.

FR80030 Camping du Port de Plaisance

Route de Paris, 80200 Péronne (Somme)

Run by a non-profit making association under the auspices of the Chamber of Commerce, this is a good quality site. Formerly a municipal site, it is informally laid out beside the Canal du Nord on the outskirts of the small town of Peronne, on the river Somme. The associations with the Great War (including a museum) are strong and the WW1 battlefields and cemeteries are numerous in this area. Only some two or three hours drive from the Channel ports and Tunnel, Peronne is convenient for overnight stops en-route to or from destinations further south or east. The site itself is attractive, being surrounded by trees, with 90 marked pitches (87 have electricity) of varying shapes and sizes on mainly level grass, some being seasonal. An attractive heated swimming pool is open when the weather is suitable.

Facilities

The modernised toilet block is kept spotlessly clean, well maintained and heated in winter. Excellent provision for people with disabilities. Laundry area with washing machine and dryer. Motorcaravan service point. New reception building includes a small shop, bar and TV room (bread orders are taken). Swimming pool. Play area. Fishing. Off site: Bicycle hire 2 km. Riding 10 km.

At a glance

Welcome & Ambience	✓✓✓✓	Location	✓✓✓✓
Quality of Pitches	✓✓✓✓	Range of Facilities	✓✓✓✓

Directions

From north and the ferries, on the A1 autoroute, take exit 14 and follow N17 south to Peronne. Take signs for town centre and continue through watching out for camp signs. Pass over river Somme and Canal du Nord and site is on right just past garage at Porte du Plaisance (2 km. from town centre). From south use exit 13 and follow RN29 to Villers Carbonnel to pick up the N17 going north. Look for signs on left

Charges 2003

Per unit incl. 1-3 persons	€ 12.50 - € 16.30
electricity (6/10A)	€ 3.80 - € 6.70
dog	€ 0.80 - € 1.00

Reservations

May be necessary in main season; contact site. Tel: 03 22 84 19 31.

Open

All year.

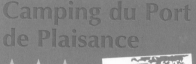

Route de Paris
80200 Péronne
Tel: 0033 322 84 19 31
Fax: 0033 322 73 36 37
Website: camping-plaisance.com
E-mail: contact@camping-plaisance.com

FR80080M Camping Municipal Le Bois des Pêcheurs

Route de Forges Les Eaux, 80290 Poix-de-Picardie (Somme)

In an area where good municipal sites are hard to find, the municipal site at Poix-de-Picardie is excellent for a one night stop, or even a few days to explore the region. The 135 pitches are on level, neatly mown grass, either individual or in hedged bays of four. Half the pitches at one end are often occupied by long stay or holiday groups, leaving the other half for tourists, with electricity available to most. The city of Amiens (28 km.) is worth visiting for its famous cathedral and quayside market (Thursday and Saturday) in the old, restored St Leu quarter.

Facilities

The well maintained, central toilet unit includes some washbasins in cubicles. Two separate rooms provide ample dishwashing and laundry sinks. Washing machine and dryer. Camping gaz stocked. Small playground. Volleyball, boules and table tennis. TV room. Caravan storage. Off site: Fishing 1 km. Supermarket 200 m, other shops, services and swimming pool in Poix de Picardie approx. 1.5 km.

At a glance

Welcome & Ambience	✓✓✓✓	Location	✓✓✓✓
Quality of Pitches	✓✓✓✓	Range of Facilities	✓✓✓

Directions

Site is southwest of the town on the D919 road, and is signed from the D901 Grandvilliers road.

Latest charges

Per unit incl. 1 or 2 adults	€ 10.00
electricity (10A)	€ 4.00
dog	€ 1.30

No credit cards.

Reservations

Write for details. Tel: 03 22 90 11 71. Email: mairie.poix.de.picardie@wanadoo.fr

Open

1 April - 30 September.

FR80060 Camping Le Val de Trie

Bouillancourt-sous-Miannay, 80870 Moyenneville (Somme)

Le Val de Trie is a natural countryside site in a woodland location, near a small village. It is maturing into a well managed site with modern facilities. The 100 numbered, grassy pitches are of a good size, divided by hedges and shrubs with mature trees providing good shade in most areas, and all have electricity and water. Access roads are gravel (the site is possibly not suitable for the largest motorcaravans). There are good walks around the area and a notice board keeps campers up to date with local market, shopping and activity news. The site has a friendly, relaxed atmosphere and English is spoken. Very much off the beaten track, it can be very quiet in April, June, September and October. If you visit at these times and there is no-one on site, just choose a pitch or call at the farm to book in. There are a few Dutch tour operator tents (5).

Facilities

The original sanitary building has been extended and a second unit was opened for 2000. They include washbasins in cubicles, units for disabled people, babies and children, plus laundry and dishwashing facilities. Washing machine and dryer. Basic motorcaravan services. Small shop (from 1/5) provides basic necessities, farm produce and wine, bread can be ordered each evening and butcher visits twice weekly in season. Bar, takeaway and terrace (1/5-15/9). Pleasant, heated small swimming pool (6 x 12 m. open 1/5-31/8), fenced with large paddling pool and jacuzzi. Table tennis, boules and volleyball. Fishing lake (free). Bicycle hire. Children's play areas and small animal enclosure. Off site: Riding 2 km, golf 5 km.

At a glance

Welcome & Ambience	✓✓✓✓	Location	✓✓✓✓✓
Quality of Pitches	✓✓✓✓	Range of Facilities	✓✓✓✓

Directions

From A28 take exit 3 for Moyenneville exit turning northwest on D173 to Moyenneville. In town (site signed) take road towards Miannay. After 2 km. turn left to Bouillancourt sous Miannay and site is signed in village

Charges 2004

Per unit incl. 2 persons	€ 12.00 - € 16.60
with electricity (6A)	€ 14.50 - € 19.80
extra person	€ 2.90 - € 4.20
child (under 7 yrs)	€ 1.90 - € 2.60
dog	€ 0.80 - € 1.30

No credit cards.

Reservations

Made with dates, plus deposit (€ 31; no fee for Alan Rogers readers). Tel: 03 22 31 48 88. Email: raphael@camping-levaldetrie.fr

Open

1 April - 1 November.

Camping le Val de Trie ***
Quiet and relaxing
Swimming pools
Fishing pond

Situated at only 1 hour from Calais (A16)
Ideal spot for first or last night or longer stay
12 km from the coast

Cottages to rent

Moyenneville
tel. 00 33 (0)3 22 31 48 88
raphael@camping-levaldetrie.fr
www.camping-levaldetrie.fr

Seven days stay, six days to pay (outside July/August).

Map 3

With its tree lined boulevards, museums, art galleries, the Arc de Triomphe and of course the famous Eiffel Tower, this cosmopolitan city has plenty to offer. Less than 30 miles from the heart of the capital, a fun-packed trip to Disneyland Paris is also within reach.

Départements: 75 Paris, 77 Seine-et-Marne, 78 Yvelines, 91 Essone, 92 Hauts-de-Seine, 93 Seine-St-Denis, 94 Val de Marne, 95 Val d'Oise

Major cities: Paris, Versailles, Ivry, Melun, Nanterre, Bobigny, Creteil and Pontoise.

One of the most chic and culturally rewarding cities in the world, Paris has something for everyone. The list of things to do is virtually endless and could easily fill many holidays - window shopping, the Eiffel Tower, Notre Dame, Montmartre, trips on the Seine, pavement cafés and the Moulin Rouge, the list goes on.

As a peaceful retreat, you can relax and enjoy the lush scenery of surrounding hills and secret woodlands of the Ile de France. Square bell towers in gentle valleys, white silos on endless plains of wheat; soft and harmonious landscapes painted and praised by La Fontaine, Corot and all the landscape painters. Paris is surrounded by forests, Fontainebleau, Compiègne, Saint-Germain-en-Laye and majestic châteaux such as Fontainbleau and Vaux-le-Vicomte.

Disneyland Resort Paris provides a great day out for all the family. It has two fantastic theme parks with over 70 attractions and shows to choose from. On the outskirts of Paris is Parc Asterix. The park has one of the most impressive roller-coasters in Europe offering breathtaking views.

Cuisine of the region

Although without a specific cuisine of its own, Paris and Ile de France offer a wide selection of dishes from all the regions of France. Paris also has a wide choice of foreign restaurants, such as Vietnamese and North African.

Places of interest

Fontainebleau: château and national museum, history of Napoléon from 1804-1815

Malmaison: château and national museum

Meaux: agricultural centre, Gothic cathedral, chapter house and palace

Paris: obviously! The list of places is too extensive to include here

St Germain-en-Laye: château, Gallo-roman and Merovingian archeological museum

Sèvres: ceramics museum

Thoiry: château and Parc Zoologique, 450-hectare park with gardens and African reserve containing 800 animals

Versailles: Royal Castle, Royal Apartments, Hall of Mirrors, Royal Opera and French History Museum

tip

USE THE RIVER BUS TO EXPLORE. WITH REGULAR DEPARTURES THROUGHOUT THE SUMMER A CRUISE ALONG THE SEINE IS A RELAXING WAY TO ENJOY THE SIGHTS.

FR75020 Camping du Bois de Boulogne

2 Allée du Bord de l'eau, 75016 Paris

A busy site and the nearest to the city, this site is set in a wooded area between the Seine and the Bois de Boulogne. One can reach the Champs Elysees in 10-15 minutes by car or, from April to October, a shuttle bus runs every half hour from the site to the Metro station. The site is quite extensive but nevertheless becomes very full with many international visitors of all ages. There are 510 pitches (including mobile homes and a few chalets) of which 280 are marked, with electricity (10A), water, drainage and TV aerial connections. At the entrance is a functional, modern reception building (open 24 hrs) with a card operated barrier system. The site has undergone a huge improvement and re-development programme including the refurbishment of all toilet blocks. Reservations are made for the pitches – if not booked, arrive early in season (in the morning). Note: you are in a major city environment – take care of valuables.

Facilities

All toilet blocks have British and Turkish style WCs, washbasins in cubicles and showers with divider and seat with hot water throughout. All these facilities suffer from heavy use in season. Washing machines and dryers. Motorcaravan service point. Mini-market. Bar and restaurant (1/4-15/10). Bar open 7 am. - midnight at most times and until 2 am. in peak season. Pizza bar and takeaway service. Playground. Information service. Off site: Organised excursions (July/Aug). Fishing 1 km, bicycle hire 2 km. Ticket sales for Disneyland, Asterix Parc, etc.

At a glance

Welcome & Ambience	✓✓✓	Location	✓✓✓✓
Quality of Pitches	✓✓✓✓	Range of Facilities	✓✓✓

Directions

Site is on east side of Seine between the river and the Bois de Boulogne, just north of the Pont de Suresnes. Easiest approach is from Port Maillot, watch for traffic lights at site entrance. Follow signs closely and use a good map

Charges 2003

Per unit incl. 2 persons	€ 18.00 - € 24.00
with services	€ 22.00 - € 31.00
tent incl. 2 persons	€ 11.00 - € 15.00
extra adult	€ 4.40 - € 6.10
child (under 7 yrs)	€ 2.20 - € 2.90
dog	€ 2.00 - € 2.40
local tax	€ 0.20

Reservations

Contact site. Tel: 01 45 24 30 00.
Email: camping-boulogne@steream.fr

Open

All year.

FR77040 Caravaning des 4 Vents

77610 Crévecoeur-en-Brie (Seine-et-Marne)

This peaceful, pleasant site has been owned and run by the same family for over 35 years and is within easy reach of Disneyland. There are around 200 pitches, with many permanent or seasonal units, however, there are 130 spacious grassy pitches for tourists, well separated by good hedges, all with 6A electricity and most with a water tap. The whole site is well landscaped with flowers and trees everywhere. This is a great family site with undercover and outdoor facilities and a superb swimming pool – located at the top end of the site so that campers are not disturbed. Crevecoeur-en-Brie celebrates the 'feast of small villages' on 21/22 June each year. Disneyland is an easy run up the D231 and then one intersection on the A4 (less than 16 km). Central Paris is just a 40 minute train ride from the nearest railway station (8 km) and there are also trains to Disneyland.

Facilities

Three modern sanitary units provide a good number of British style WCs but rather fewer washbasins. Facilities for disabled people. Washing machine and dryer. Good motorcaravan service point by the main gates. In high season (July/Aug) a mobile snack bar and pizzeria visit, and a baker calls in the mornings. Well fenced, circular swimming pool (16 m. diameter) open 09.00-21.00 hrs. June to Sept. Excellent playground, a large games room with table tennis and table football, volleyball court, a billiard hall and a boules court. Off site: La Houssaye (1 km) has a grocer, bakery and post office. Fontenay (5 km) has a supermarket and all other services.

At a glance

Welcome & Ambience	✓✓✓✓	Location	✓✓✓✓
Quality of Pitches	✓✓✓✓✓	Range of Facilities	✓✓✓✓

Directions

From A4 exit 13, take D231 towards Provins for about 12 km. After passing a large obelisk turn right at signs to Crevecoeur and follow signs to site. Site is on western side of village.

Charges 2004

Per unit incl. 2 persons and electricity	€ 21.00
extra person	€ 4.00
child (under 5 yrs)	free

Reservations

Essential for July/Aug. Tel: 01 64 07 41 11.
Email: f.george@free.fr

Open

1 March - 1 December.

FR77030M Camping International de Jablines

Base de Loisirs, 77450 Jablines (Seine-et-Marne)

Redesigned in 1997, Jablines replaces an older site in an upmarket, modern style which, with the accompanying leisure facilities of the adjacent 'Espace Loisirs', provides an interesting, if a little impersonal alternative to other sites in the region. The whole complex close to the Marne has been developed around old gravel workings. Man-made lakes provide marvellous water activities – dinghy sailing, windsurfing, canoeing, fishing and supervised swimming, plus a large equestrian centre. In season the activities at the leisure complex are supplemented by a bar/restaurant and a range of very French style group activities. The 'Great Lake' as it is called, is said to have the largest beach on the Ile-de-France! The site itself provides 132 pitches, most of a good size with gravel hardstanding and grass, accessed by tarmac roads and clearly marked by fencing panels and newly planted shrubs. All have 10A electrical connections, 60 with water and waste connections also.

Facilities

Two identical toilet blocks, heated in cool weather, are solidly built and well equipped. They include some washbasins in cubicles, indoor dishwashing and laundry facilities with washing machine and dryer. Motorcaravan service (charged). Shop (all season). Play area. Bar/restaurant adjacent at leisure centre/lake complex along with a range of watersports including 'water cable ski', riding activities, tennis and minigolf. Whilst staying on the campsite, admission to the leisure complex is free. Internet point. Ticket sales for Disneyland, Asterix and Sea Life.

At a glance

Welcome & Ambience	✓✓✓✓	Location	✓✓✓✓
Quality of Pitches	✓✓✓✓	Range of Facilities	✓✓✓✓

Directions

From A4 Paris - Rouen take A104 before Disneyland. Take exit 8 on D404 Meaux/Base de Loisirs Jablines. From A1 going south, follow signs for Disneyland immediately after airport using the A104. Take exit 6A Clay-Souilly on N3 towards Meaux. After 6 km. turn right on D404 and follow signs.

Charges 2003

Per unit incl. 2 persons, electricity	€ 18.00 - € 21.00
child (under 12 yrs)	€ 3.00 - € 4.00

Camping Cheques accepted.

Reservations

Essential for July/Aug and made with booking form from site and 30% deposit. Tel: 01 60 26 09 37. Email: welcome@camping-jablines.com

Open

28 March - 2 November.

Base Régionale de Plein-Air et de Loisirs de Jablines-Annet

Covering more than 450 hectares, a leisure and relaxation area unique in the Île de France.

L'espace loisirs
Jablines-Annet
www.camping-jablines.com

Camping ★★★

FR77080M Camping Municipal les Prés

77880 Grez sur Loing (Seine-et-Marne)

A typical municipal site, Les Prés has 136 grassy pitches and a fair number of long stay units. However, there are usually around 35 pitches available for tourists, all with electricity. The town of Grez sur Loing dates back to medieval times and is well worth investigating. The site makes an ideal base for fishing, cycling (the warden can provide a booklet with suggested routes), walking and rock climbing.

Facilities

A two storey building has separate male and female facilities on the upper level, and unisex facilities at ground level. British and Turkish style toilets, dishwashing and laundry facilities, Excellent suite for disabled people in separate new building. Small shop and limited takeaway (pizza and chips, 15/3-11/11). Off site: Golf 10 km. Riding 5 km. Bicycle hire 200 m.

At a glance

Welcome & Ambience	✓✓✓✓	Location	✓✓✓✓
Quality of Pitches	✓✓✓✓	Range of Facilities	✓✓✓

Directions

Grez sur Loing is northwest of Nemours and south of Fontainebleau. From N7 north of town, at roundabout take D40D towards Montcourt, cross bridge and turn right. This access is one-way. From south, continue on N7 to roundabout and follow as above. Do not follow campsite signs south of village as roads are narrow.

Charges 2003

Per adult	€ 2.45
pitch with electricity (5A)	€ 6.70 - € 7.90

Reservations

Advised for July/Aug; contact site. Tel: 01 64 45 72 75. Email: camping-grez@wanadoo.fr

Open

15 March - 11 November.

FR77070 Camping La Belle Etoile

Quai Joffre, La Rochette, 77000 Melun (Seine-et-Marne)

Ideally situated for visiting Fontainebleau and Paris, and alongside the River Seine, this site has an over-all mature and neat appearance, although the approach road along the banks of the river is some-what off putting with several industrial plants. Continue past this point and you discover that La Belle Etoile enjoys a pleasant position with pitches to the fore of the site within view of the barges which continually pass up and down the Seine. This is a friendly, family run site with English speaking owners who are pleasant and helpful. The 186 touring pitches, with electricity connections, are on grass and laid out between the many shrubs and trees. There are ten units for hire.

Facilities

The toilet blocks are not new but they are kept very clean and the water is very hot. Laundry room. Baby bath. Facilities for disabled visitors (shower, washbasin and WC). Motorcaravan service point. Small bar, snacks and shop with limited stock (all in high season). Swimming pool (high season). Play area. Tickets for Disney and Vaux le Vicomte are sold by the site. Off site: Fontainebleau is a short drive away and Paris easily accessible by train.

At a glance

Welcome & Ambience	✓✓✓✓	Location	✓✓✓
Quality of Pitches	✓✓✓	Range of Facilities	✓✓✓

Directions

Travelling north on N6 Fontainebleau - Melun road, on entering La Rochette, pass Total petrol station on left and turn immediately right into Ave de la Seine. Continue to end of road and turn left at river, site on left in approx. 500 m.

Charges 2003

Per person	€ 4.15 - € 4.65
baby (0-2 yrs)	€ 1.90 - € 2.10
child (3-11 yrs)	€ 2.70 - € 2.90
pitch	€ 4.20 - € 4.70
dog	€ 1.30
electricity (6A)	€ 2.90 - € 3.00
Camping Cheques accepted.	

Reservations

Made for a minimum of 3 nights. Tel: 01 64 39 48 12. Email: info@camp-la-belle-etoile.com

Open

1 April - 31 October.

FR78010 Camping Caravaning International

1 Rue Johnson, 78600 Maisons-Laffitte (Yvelines)

This busy, all year site on the banks of the Seine is convenient for Paris. Maisons-Laffitte is a pleasant suburb with a château, a racecourse and some large training stables. There is also a good train service to the centre of Paris, including an express service, to the Gare St Lazare. The site has multilingual and friendly reception staff and occupies a grassy, tree covered area bordering the river. There are 350 pitches, 57 occupied by mobile homes and 90 used by tour operators, plus two areas dedicated to tents. Most pitches are separated by hedges, are of a good size with some overlooking the Seine (unfenced access), and 200 have electricity hook-ups (6/10A). The roads leading to the site are a little narrow so large vehicles need to take care. Being so close to Paris this site is consistently busy. Train noise can be expected.

Facilities

There are three sanitary blocks, two insulated for winter use. The third, more open in style is only opened for July/August. The facilities are clean but with the volume of visitors, constant supervision is necessary. Provision for people with disabilities. Laundry and dishwashing areas. Motorcaravan service point - jeton available at reception. Self-service shop for summer months. Restaurant/bar with takeaway food and pizzeria. TV room, table tennis, billiards and football area. Internet point. Off site: Sports complex adjoins the site. The station for central Paris is 10 minutes walk with trains running every 10 minutes (journey time 15-30 minutes), returning until 12.30 am. Direct rail access to Disneyland (55 minutes). An SNC representative is on site every morning from 15 June until 15 August to offer travel advice.

At a glance

Welcome & Ambience	✓✓✓✓	Location	✓✓✓
Quality of Pitches	✓✓✓	Range of Facilities	✓✓✓

Directions

Site is best approached from A13 or A15 autoroute. From A13 take Poissy exit and follow signs to Maisons-Laffitte, then site signs before town centre. From A15 take N184 exit to St Germain, for approx. 300 m. After crossing large concrete bridge turn left at traffic lights to Maisons-Laffitte and follow camp signs. From A1 take the A86, then Bezons exit for Poissy, Houilles and Maisons-Laffitte.

Charges 2003

Per unit incl. 2 persons	€ 18.40 - € 22.60
with electricity	€ 21.90 - € 24.50
tent incl. 2 persons	€ 11.00 - € 12.00
extra adult	€ 4.90 - € 5.60
child (5-10 yrs)	€ 2.30 - € 2.70
animal	€ 2.50
local tax	€ 0.46

Reservations

Advisable for July/Aug. and made with deposit (€ 10). Tel: 01 39 12 21 91. Email: ci.mlaffitte@wanadoo.fr

Open

All year.

FR78040M Camping Municipal de L'Etang d'Or

Route du Château d'Eau, 78120 Rambouillet (Yvelines)

This is a pleasant site in a peaceful forest location, with good tarmac access roads, site lighting and 280 touring pitches. Some of the individual pitches are divided by hedges, others are more open and sunny. All have electricity (6/10A), 83 also have water and drainage, with a few hardstandings. Campers get a discount brochure for local sites or activities (e.g. the municipal swimming pool, animal park, bowling and billiards, bicycle hire), and a special permit for the fishing lake. There are many good cycle and footpaths in the area. It is possible to visit Paris by rail, the Mobilis 'transport package' ticket is available from the railway station.

Facilities

Two heated sanitary buildings include British and Turkish style WCs, washbasins (a few in cubicles), dishwashing and laundry sinks, plus facilities for baby changing and for disabled persons. Facilities could be a little stretched during the high season. Washing machine and dryer. One block is closed in winter. Motorcaravan service point (€ 1,29). Café/bar and small shop (1/4-30/9). Good playground. Off site: Large supermarket at southern end of the town.

At a glance

Welcome & Ambience	✓✓✓	Location	✓✓✓✓
Quality of Pitches	✓✓✓✓	Range of Facilities	✓✓✓✓

Directions

Rambouillet is 52 km. southwest of Paris, midway between Versailles and Chartres. Site is southeast of town, from N10 southbound take Rambouillet/Les Eveuses exit, northbound take Rambouillet centre exit, loop round and rejoin N10 southbound, taking next exit, where site is signed.

Charges 2003

Per person	€ 3.90 - € 4.30
child (2-10 yrs)	€ 2.70 - € 3.00
pitch	€ 4.30 - € 4.90
dog	€ 1.50
electricity (6-10A)	€ 3.00 - € 3.80

Reservations

Contact site for details. Tel: 01 30 41 07 34. Email: rambouillet.tourisme@wanadoo.fr

Open

All year.

FR95000 Parc de Séjours de L'Etang

10 Chemin des Bellevues, 95690 Nesles-la-Vallée (Val-d'Oise)

Parc de Sejour de L'Etang is small, informal site 33 km. northwest of Paris. It is situated on the southern outskirts of the village of Nesles-la-Vallée in a pretty, tree-lined river valley not far from L'Isle-Adam, which is a popular destination for Parisiens at weekends. Many of the 165 pitches are occupied by seasonal caravans but there are 65 pitches available for touring units. The site is informally arranged around a duck pond with many trees to provide shelter and shade and semi-tame rabbits competing with the ducks for food and attention. Pitches are large and flat with electricity available. Chantilly, Parc Asterix and Disneyland are easily reached by car. By far the best way to visit Paris is by train from Valmondois, 5 minutes away via the D15 road (trains every half hour, journey time about 50 minutes).

Facilities

The main, central toilet block (heated in cooler weather) is a plain substantial building including washbasins in rather small cubicles and, in separate rooms, rather older style British and Turkish WCs. Covered dishwashing and laundry sinks. Washing machine. Smaller, much older unit includes facilities for disabled people. Good playground, volleyball and basketball areas, and under cover play barn with table tennis. Off site: Village and restaurant within walking distance. Fishing permits for the river available in village. Riding 500 m, golf 7 km.

At a glance

Welcome & Ambience	✓✓✓	Location	✓✓✓
Quality of Pitches	✓✓✓	Range of Facilities	✓✓✓

Directions

From A15 exit 10 take D915 to Pontoise, then D27 to Beauais which joins the D927 and then D79 to Nesles-la-Vallée. From N1 or A16 (exit 11) take the N332 southwest towards L'Isle Adam, and then D64 northwest to Neslés la Vallée. Site is on the right as you enter the village.

Latest charges

Per person	€ 3.00 - € 4.00
child (1-6 yrs)	€ 2.00
pitch	€ 3.00 - € 4.00
with electricity (3/9A)	€ 6.50 - € 7.35
animal	€ 1.00
No credit cards.	

Reservations

Contact site. Tel: 01 34 70 62 89. Email: brehinier1@hotmail.com

Open

1 March - 15 November.

FR60010 Camping Campix

B.P. 37, 60340 St Leu-d'Esserent (Oise)

Opened in 1991, this informal site has been unusually developed in a former sandstone quarry on the outskirts of the small town. The quarry walls provide very different boundaries to most of the site, giving it a sheltered, peaceful environment. Trees have grown to soften the slopes. Not a neat, manicured site, the 160 pitches are arranged in small groups on the different levels with stone and gravel access roads (some fairly steep and possibly muddy in poor weather). Electricity is available to about 140 pitches. Torches are advised. There are very many secluded corners mostly for smaller units and tents and plenty of space for children to explore (parents must supervise – some areas, although fenced, could be dangerous). A footpath leads from the site to the town where there are shops, restaurants and an outdoor pool (in season). This site is best suited to those not needing sophisticated on-site facilities, or for visiting local places of interest and the friendly, English speaking owner will advise. These include Chantilly, the Asterix Park and the Mer de Sable, a Western theme amusements park, both 20 km. Disneyland is 70 km. It is also possible to visit Paris by train (information at reception).

Facilities

At the entrance to the site a large building houses reception and two clean, heated sanitary units - one for tourers, the other usually reserved for groups. Two suites for disabled people double as baby rooms. Laundry facilities with washing machine and dryer. At quieter times only one unit is opened but facilities may be congested at peak times. Motorcaravan service facilities. Bread and milk delivered daily. Basic snack bar operates from mobile unit (July/Aug). Off site: Fishing 1 or 5 km, riding or golf 5 km.

At a glance

Welcome & Ambience	✓✓✓	Location	✓✓✓
Quality of Pitches	✓✓✓	Range of Facilities	✓✓✓

Directions

St Leu-d'Esserent is 11 km. west of Senlis, 5 km. northwest of Chantilly. From the north on the A1 autoroute take the Senlis exit, from Paris the Chantilly exit. Site is north of the town off the D12 towards Cramoisy, and is signed in the village.

Charges 2003

Per unit	€ 3.00 - € 5.00
person	€ 3.00 - € 5.00
child (under 9 yrs)	€ 2.00 - € 3.00
small tent	€ 2.50 - € 4.00
electricity (6A)	€ 2.50 - € 3.50
dog	€ 1.00 - € 2.00

Reservations

Advisable for July/Aug. Tel: 03 44 56 08 48.
Email: campixfr@aol.com

Open

7 March - 30 November.

Map 2

Home to the Champagne region, the varied landscapes of Eastern France include dense forests, vineyards and winding rivers. The whole area is dotted with fascinating ancient churches and castles, towns and villages.

Eastern France is defined as:
Champagne-Ardenne: 08 Ardennes, 51 Marne, 10 Aube, 52 Haute-Marne.
Lorraine Vosges: 54 Meurthe-et-Moselle, 55 Meuse, 57 Moselle, 88 Vosges.
Alsace: 67 Bas-Rhin, 68 Haut-Rhin

Situated on the flatlands of Champagne are the most northerly vineyards in France where special processing turns the light, dry wine into 'le Champagne' and names such as Moet et Chandon and Veuve Clicquot spring to mind. Nowhere else in the world are you allowed to make sparkling wine and call it champagne. Travelling further east you come across the spa towns such as Vittel, Bains-les-Bains and Plombières and the birth place of St Joan of Arc at Domrémy.

Today you can descend from the mountains into the Alsace vineyards and fairy tale wine villages. The 'Route des Vins' follows the vineyards along the Rhine valley from Mulhouse to Colmar and north almost to Strasbourg. Alsace and Lorraine have been frequently fought over and today there are many poignant reminders of the turbulent past. You'll find noticeable German influence in architecture, cuisine and language. There are also numerous little wine towns, medieval villages and a host of ruined castles stretching along the north eastern margins of the Vosges.

Cuisine of the region

Quiche Lorraine: made only in the classical manner with cream, eggs and bacon.

Potage Lorraine: potato. leek and onion soup

Tart (aux mirabelles): golden plum tart. Also made with other fruits

Tarte a l'oignon Alsacienne: onion and cream tart

Places of interest

Épernay: home of champagne production

Le Linge: trenches including rusty barbed wire have been left as they were

Reims: 13th century Gothic cathedral

Riquewihr: traditional town, fortifications and medieval houses

Verdun: hill forts such as Fort de Vaux and Fort de Douaumont, large military cemetery at Douaumont

tip

TAKE ADVANTAGE OF THE FREE LOCAL ENTERTAINMENT IN REIMS THROUGHOUT JULY AND AUGUST. THE FLÂNERIES MUSICALES D'ÉTE HAS OVER 120 CONCERTS TO ENJOY.

95

FR08010M Camping Municipal du Mont Olympe

Rue des Paquis, 08000 Charleville-Mezieres (Ardennes)

Attractively situated alongside the Meuse River, within easy walking distance across a footbridge to the centre of the pleasant large town, this site was completely rebuilt in 2001/2, just a short distance from the old one. It now offers excellent facilities, with 128 grass pitches, all with electricity, water and waste water connections, 66 will be from 108 to 219 sq.m, 48 up to 106 sq.m. and 12 smaller pitches especially for motorcaravans.

Facilities

Three heated buildings provide first class showers, private cabins, baby rooms and facilities for the disabled, plus inside dishwashing (including one for the disabled) and a well-equipped laundry room. Motorcaravan service point. Children's play area and paddling pool. TV and games room. Off site: Municipal pool next door. Boat trips on the river. Attractive town centre close by.

At a glance

Welcome & Ambience	✓✓✓	Location	✓✓✓✓✓
Quality of Pitches	✓✓✓✓	Range of Facilities	✓✓✓

Directions

Site is north of Charleville on the island of Montcy St Pierre and is signed from the city centre 'Mont Olympe'. From the north D988/D1 follow the river, over the bridge, then immediately left. From the southeast (A203/N51/N43) take 'centre' exit, head for 'Gare' then follow Avenue Forest north and sharp left after the bridge. The site entrance is about 150 metres further on from where the old site was situated.

Charges 2003

Per person	€ 4.10
child (5-17yrs)	€ 2.80
pitch and vehicle	€ 4.50 - € 5.50
dog	€ 1.35
electricity (6/10A)	€ 2.50 - € 3.50
motorcaravan overnight	€ 10.00

Reservations

Contact site. Tel: 03 24 33 23 60.

Open

1 April - 15 October.

FR08040 Camping La Samaritaine

08240 Buzancy (Ardennes)

What a surprise and a pleasure it was to arrive at such a delightful new site in the heart of the Ardennes. It is peacefully situated just outside the village beside a stream, although there may be some high season noise from the nearby lake where you can swim or fish. Flowers decorate the entrance and bushes and saplings have been planted to separate the pitches, although there is not much shade at present. The 110 numbered touring pitches all have electricity and are on level grass off hard access roads. They vary in size up to 130 sq.m. 55 have water and waste water, and there are attractive small wooden containers for waste.

Facilities

A new building houses first class sanitary facilities, with private cabins, washing machine and dryer, inside dishwashing and facilities for the disabled. A large recreation room houses some games and there are tables to sit at. Table tennis is under cover. Bread is collected daily. A few essentials are kept in reception. A snack bar/takeaway operates from the middle of May to end September. High season accompanied walks and entertainment programme. Off site: Just along from the site towards the lake is the volleyball court and boules, whilst at the lake is some play equipment 'under adult supervision only'. Lake swimming is supervised at certain times (2 metres deep), with a 'paddling' area up to 1.2 metres depth. Restaurant in village.

At a glance

Welcome & Ambience	✓✓✓✓✓	Location	✓✓✓✓
Quality of Pitches	✓✓✓✓	Range of Facilities	✓✓✓✓

Directions

The village of Buzancy is about 22 km. east of Vouziers on the RD947 towards Stenay and Montmédy. The site is just over 1 km from the centre of the village down a small road, and is well signed.

Charges 2003

Per person	€ 3.00 - € 4.00
child (under 10 yrs)	€ 2.00 - € 3.00
pitch	€ 7.00
with water and waste water	€ 9.00
electricity (10A)	€ 3.50
animal	€ 2.00 - € 3.00
local tax	€ 0.50

Camping Cheques accepted.

Reservations

Contact site. Tel: 03 24 30 08 88.
Email: info@campinglasamaritaine.com

Open

21 March - 29 September.

FR51020M Camping Municipal en Champagne

Rue de Plaisance, 51000 Châlons-en Champagne (Marne)

The location of Châlons, south of Reims and near both the A4 and A26 autoroutes, about 200 miles from Calais and Boulogne, make this an ideal stopover. It is also ideally situated for exploring this famous region in the plain of the River Marne and its historical connections. This site on the southwest edge of town is an example of a good municipal site. The wide entrance with its well tended appearance of neatly mown grass and flower beds sets the tone for the rest of the site. About half of the 130 pitches, accessed from hard roads, are on a gravel base with the rest on grass. Most have electricity connections. The generously sized gravel pitches are separated by hedges and each group of four shares a water tap and drain. Trees abound although there is no shade in some parts.

Facilities

The two toilet blocks, one behind reception, the other at the far end of the site, have been refurbished. Sections of these facilities are of varying standards due to an ongoing programme of refurbishment. Some washbasins in cabins, facilities for disabled visitors, plus a washing machine and dryer. Numerous refuse bins enclosed by wooden palings which enhance the general appearance of the site. Bread to order. Snack bar. Gas supplies. Games and TV rooms. Playground. Tennis, table tennis, volleyball, boules and place for mini-football. Off site: Fishing (free for campers) nearby. Bus stop at site entrance.

At a glance

Welcome & Ambience	✓✓✓✓	Location	✓✓✓✓
Quality of Pitches	✓✓✓✓	Range of Facilities	✓✓✓✓

Directions

From the north on the A4, take La Veuve exit (27) onto the N44 which by-passes the town. Leave at last sign signed St Memmie and follow camping signs. From the south on A26, take exit 28 onto N77 and, head towards town. Site is well signed ' Camping'.

Charges 2003

Per person	€ 4.40
child (under 7 yrs)	€ 1.65
pitch	€ 4.10
vehicle	€ 2.95
electricity (10/15A)	€ 2.95

Reservations

Write to site. Tel: 03 26 68 38 00.

Open

30 March - 31 October.

FR52020 Castel Camping La Forge de Sainte Marie

52230 Thonnance-les-Moulins (Haute-Marne)

The département of Haute-Marne is situated between the better known areas of Champagne and the Vosges. It is a sleepy land of rolling hills, forests and farmland. In the heart of this lies Thonnance-les-Moulins, 12 km. east of Joinville and the north-south N67 main road between St Dizier and Chaumont. In 1994 the dilapidated old forge buildings and the surrounding 40,000 sq.m. were transformed into a most attractive campsite. As soon as one enters through the arched gateway, one is impressed by the setting. A picturesque bridge links the upper part of the site with a lower road going to the section near the river. Opposite reception, another old building has been skilfully converted into apartments for letting. Grass pitches, 115 for touring units, are of a generous size on terraces amongst the trees or in more open areas. Electricity (6A) and water are available and some pitches are fully serviced. There is much of interest in the area – Joan d'Arc and General de Gaulle lived near and it is not too far to the Champagne vineyards and cellars at Reims. Nigloland for the children is within range and Joinville is worth exploring. It is also possible to visit the largest man-made lake in Europe at Giffaumont-Champaubert. There is a high proportion of mobile homes and tour operators but the enthusiastic British and Dutch managers are determined to make a success of the site.

Facilities

There are two modern sanitary blocks. Maintenance may not be so good in early or late season. Shop and excellent restaurant (both 15/5-15/9). Splendid heated indoor pool with a smaller one for children. Four play areas imaginatively placed around the site. Level open grass area for football and volleyball. Bicycle hire. Free fishing. Games room. Organized games for children in high season. Varied programme for adults including a farm visit by tractor with a barbecue, music, dancing and excursions.

At a glance

Welcome & Ambience	✓✓✓✓✓	Location	✓✓✓✓
Quality of Pitches	✓✓✓✓	Range of Facilities	✓✓✓✓✓

Directions

Site is about 12 km. southeast of Joinville between Poissons and Germay on road D427. The site entrance may be a little tight for large units.

Charges 2004

Per pitch incl. 2 persons	€ 15.00 - € 25.00
extra person	€ 3.00 - € 6.00
child (2-7 yrs)	€ 1.50 - € 3.00
animal	free
local tax	€ 0.30

Less 20% outside July/Aug.
Camping Cheques accepted.

Reservations

Contact site for details. Tel: 03 25 94 42 00.
Email: la.forge.de.sainte.marie@wanadoo.fr

Open

24 April - 29 September.

FR52030 Camping Lac de la Liez

Peigney, 52200 Langres (Haute-Marne)

Managed by the enthusiastic Baude family, this newly renovated lakeside site is near the city of Langres. With its old ramparts and ancient city centre, Langres was elected one of the 50 most historic cities in France. Situated only 10 minutes from the A5, Camping Lac de la Liez provides an ideal spot for an overnight stop en-route to the south of France. There is also a lot on offer for a longer stay, including the lake and an impressive indoor pool complex, with a sauna. The site provides 135 fully serviced, terraced pitches with panoramic views of the 500 acre lake. There is easy access to the lake for swimming with a sandy beach and a harbour where boats and pedaloes may be hired.

Facilities

Two brand new toilet blocks have all facilities in cabins. Shop, bar and restaurant (with takeaway food). Indoor pool complex with spa and sauna. Extensive games area and tennis court (free in low season). Lake with beach and boat hire. Off site: Cycle tracks around the lake, horse riding, fishing.

At a glance

Welcome & Ambience	✓✓✓✓	Location	✓✓✓✓
Quality of Pitches	✓✓✓✓	Range of Facilities	✓✓✓✓

Directions

From Langres take the N19 towards Vesoul. After approximately 3 km. turn right, straight after the large river bridge, then follow site signs.

Charges 2003

Per person	€ 6.00
child (under 7 yrs)	€ 3.00 - € 3.00
pitch	€ 8.00
electricity	€ 4.00 - € 4.00
dog	€ 1.50

Reductions in low season.
Camping Cheques accepted.

Reservations

Contact site. Tel: 03 25 90 27 79.
Email: campingliez@free.fr

Open

1 April - 1 November

FR54000 Camping Le Brabois

Avenue Paul Muller, 54600 Villers les Nancy (Meurthe-et-Moselle)

This former municipal site, within the Nancy city boundary and 5 km. from the centre, was taken over by the Campeole group in 1998. Situated within a forest area, there is shade in most parts and, although the site is on a slight slope, the 190 good-sized, numbered and separated pitches are level. Of these, 160 pitches have electrical connections and 30 also have water and drainage. Being on one of the main routes from Luxembourg to the south of France, Le Brabois makes a good night stop. However, Nancy is a delightful city in the heart of Lorraine and well worth a longer stay, not only for the interesting 18th century Place Stanislas and 11th century city centre, but for the many other attractions of the area. The British manager has a wide range of tourist literature, publishes a monthly English newsletter and is pleased to help plan visits and day trips. Horse racing takes place every two weeks at the Nancy race track next to the campsite, and good wine is produced nearby.

Facilities

Six sanitary blocks spread around the site are old and due for refurbishment over the next few years. They have a mix of British and Turkish style WCs and some washbasins in cubicles. One block can be heated in cool weather. Two units for disabled visitors. Washing machine and dryer. Motorcaravan service point. Small shop (all season). Bread to order. Restaurant incorporating bar and small shop (15/6-31/8). Small library for book exchange. Playground for young children. Area for ball games and table tennis under cover. Off site: Restaurants and shops about 1 km. Excellent walks and cycle rides. Buses to Nancy every 15 minutes.

At a glance

Welcome & Ambience	✓✓✓✓	Location	✓✓✓✓
Quality of Pitches	✓✓✓✓	Range of Facilities	✓✓✓✓

Directions

Take exit 2b 'Brabois' from autoroute A33, continue for about 500 m. to 'Quick' restaurant on left. Turn left here, pass the racetrack to T-junction, turn right and after about 400 m. turn right on to site entrance road.

Charges 2003

Per unit incl. 2 persons	€ 9.40 - € 10.80
extra person	€ 3.50
child (2-7 yrs)	€ 2.00
electricity (5/15A)	€ 3.20
hiker	€ 6.50
dog	€ 1.80

Credit cards min, € 15. Barrier card deposit € 20.

Reservations

Advised for July but site say no-one is turned away.
Tel: 03 83 27 18 28.
Email: campeoles.brabois@wanadoo.fr

Open

1 April - 15 October.

Camping du Lac de la Liez

Open 01st April - 01st November ★★★★

Close to the Champagne and Ardennes regions of France, Lac de Liez is a top quality 4 star site, ideal for the whole family

 Comfort:
spacious toilet blocks and modern facilities

 Sport:
covered pool complex, tennis courts, lake

 Fun:
organised activities for both adults and children

 Relaxation:
sauna, spa

 Conviviality:
bar, restaurant, warm welcome

✔ Beautiful lakeside setting
✔ Beach for swimming
✔ Pedalos, water-bikes, boats...

Peigney, F-52200 Langres, tel 0033 (0)325 90 27 79, fax 0033 (0)325 90 66 79
campingliez@free.fr, http://www.camping-liez.com

FR55010 Camping Les Breuils

Allée des Breuils, 55100 Verdun (Meuse)

Thousands of soldiers of many nations are buried in the cemeteries around this famous town and the city is justly proud of its determined First World War resistance. Les Breuils is a pretty site beside a small fishing lake and close to the famous town and Citadel. It provides 184 flat pitches on two levels (144 for touring units), many with shade. Separated by trees or hedges, they are beside the lake and most offer the possibility of electricity connection. The overall appearance of the site is attractive.

Facilities

Sanitary facilities, in two blocks, are a mixture of old and new, the newer parts being of a good standard, including washbasins in cabins for ladies, washing machines and dryers. Conveniently sited among the pitches are sets of four dishwashing sinks under pitched roofs (cold water only; hot water at the blocks). Motorcaravan services. Small shop doubles as reception, selling essentials with various local guide books (1/5-31/8). Breakfast and evening snacks (July/Aug). Swimming pool (200 sq.m.) and children's pool (1/6-31/8). Large fenced play area on gravel. New multi-sports complex (football, volleyball, basektball). Off site: Bicycle hire 1 km, riding 5 km. Town centre 1 km.

At a glance

Welcome & Ambience	✓✓✓✓	Location	✓✓✓✓
Quality of Pitches	✓✓✓✓	Range of Facilities	✓✓✓✓

Directions

The RN3 forms a sort of ring road round the north of the town. Site is signed from this on the west side of the town (500 m. to site).

Charges 2003

Per adult	€ 4.00
caravan or motorcaravan	€ 4.00
double axle caravan	€ 15.00
electricity (5A)	€ 3.50

Discounts for low season and longer stays.

Reservations

Advised for high season. Tel: 03 29 86 15 31. Email: contact@camping-lesbreuils.com

Open

1 April - 30 September.

FR57050M Camping Municipal de Metz-Plage

Allée de Metz-Plage, 57000 Metz (Moselle)

As this site is just a short way from the autoroute exit and within easy walking distance for the city centre, it could make a useful night stop if travelling from Luxembourg to Nancy or for a longer stay if exploring the area. By the Moselle river, the 151 pitches are on level grass, most are under shade from tall trees and 73 have electricity and water. Tent pitches have a separate place on the river banks.

Facilities

The two sanitary blocks, one newer than the other, are acceptable if not luxurious. Baby room. Laundry and dishwashing sinks. Shop. Bar, restaurant and takeway. 3 pitches for over night stops for motorcaravans. Off site: Fishing nearby. Riding 5 km. Golf 8 km.

At a glance

Welcome & Ambience	✓✓✓✓	Location	✓✓✓✓✓
Quality of Pitches	✓✓✓✓	Range of Facilities	✓✓✓

Directions

From autoroute take Metz-Nord - Pontiffray exit (no. 33) and follow camp signs.

Charges 2003

Per adult	€ 2.45
pitch incl. electricity (10A)	€ 4.25

Reservations

Not possible. Tel: 03 87 68 26 48. Email: jmwingerter@mairie-metz.fr

Open

5 May - 26 September.

FR67010M Camping L'Oasis

Route de Zinswiller, 67110 Oberbronn (Bas Rhin)

This is an attractively situated, inexpensive site, set amidst the mountains and forests of northern Alsace, not far from the German border. There are good views over the valley to one side and the pretty village with trees sheltering the other. The circular internal road has pitches around the outside (120 for touring units, 30 for seasonals), as well as space in the centre where there is also a playground. The solar-heated swimming pool and paddling pool are of excellent quality. A 'Centre de Vacances' is being added for 2004, with a covered swimming pool, sauna and fitness room.

Facilities

The first well appointed toilet block, heated in cool weather, has some washbasins in cabins for ladies, washing machines and dryers, a baby room and facilities for disabled people. The second block is unisex and small. Small shop. General room with table football and air hockey. Swimming pool and children's pool (July/Aug). Indoor pool next to site. Playground. Tennis court. Off site: Supermarket in the village 1 km. Fitness circuit in the nearby forest. Riding 700 m. Fishing 3 km.

At a glance

Welcome & Ambience	✓✓✓✓	Location	✓✓✓✓
Quality of Pitches	✓✓✓✓	Range of Facilities	✓✓✓✓

Directions

Travel northwest from Haguenau on N62 for 20 km. South of Niederbronn turn left on D28 for Oberbronn-Zinswiller - site signed from here. From A4 take exit 42 to Sarreguemines, then N62 and D620 towards Haguenau and as above.

Charges 2003

Per adult	€ 3.30
pitch incl. electricity	€ 7.30

Less 5% outside 1/7-31/8. Less 10% for stays over 15 days. No credit cards.

Reservations

Advised for high season. Write with precise dates; no deposit required. Tel: 03 88 09 71 96.

Open

15 March - 14 November.

FR67030 Camping Caravaning du Ried

Route de Rhinau, 67860 Boofzheim (Bas Rhin)

The area between the main road from Strasbourg to Colmar and the river Rhine is usually bypassed by those who are exploring Alsace or passing through to Switzerland and Italy. However, if looking for a night stop or a different base in the region, Camping du Ried could well fit the bill. Situated on the edge of a small, picturesque village, it has 150 tourist pitches (with electricity) amongst the 120 static caravans. Most of these are under tall trees, on grass and separated by hedges. One might think that this is just another reasonable campsite until one sees the excellent pool complex just inside the site entrance which has an attractive outdoor pool for use in July and August and a heated indoor one open from May to September. We found this a pleasant site with very friendly management who would like to welcome more British visitors even though no English is spoken.

Facilities

The single toilet block is quite a large building and, although old, is well tiled and has all the usual facilities including facilities for disabled people. Washing machines and dryer. Bar/restaurant. Splendid indoor and outdoor pools. Playground. Boules. Minigolf. Canoeing. High season animation for children and daily programme including a variety of excursions, guided canoe trips and competitions. Library. Off site: Supermarket outside gates.

At a glance

Welcome & Ambience	✓✓✓✓	Location	✓✓✓
Quality of Pitches	✓✓✓✓	Range of Facilities	✓✓✓✓

Directions

Leave N83 Strasbourg - Colmar road at Benfeld and go east on D5 to Boofzheim. Site is 500 m. beyond village towards Rhinau.

Charges 2004

Per unit incl. 2 persons	€ 13.00 - € 17.50
child (under 7 yrs)	€ 6.00 - € 7.00
electricity (5A)	€ 6.00
animal	€ 2.50 - € 3.00

Reservations

Made with deposit and fee; contact site.
Tel: 03 88 74 68 27. Email: info@camping-ried.com

Open

1 April - 30 October.

BETWEEN STRASBOURG AND COLMAR
AT 2 km from the Rhine
2 HEATED SWIMMING POOL (which one is covered)
MObile HOMES WITH TERRACE FOR HIRE

CAMPING CARAVANING du RIED
1 RUE du CAMPING 67860 BOOFZHEIM
Tel : 0033 388 74 68 27 Fax : 0033 388 74 62 89
WWW.CAMPING-RIED.COM
FREE bROCHURES ON REQUEST

FR68030M Camping Municipal Masevaux

3 rue du Stade, 68290 Masevaux (Haut-Rhin)

Masevaux is a pleasant little town in the Haut-Rhin département of Alsace, just to the north of the A36 Belfort - Mulhouse motorway in the Des Ballons region. The municipal camping site is situated in a quiet edge of town next to the sporting complex which has a good indoor pool and other sporting opportunities. The pretty flower decked entrance promises a neat, excellent site and one is not disappointed. The neatly mown 120 pitches for tourists are on level grass, of reasonable size, marked by trees and hedges, and all have electricity. Most are well shaded by a variety of trees and have good views of the surrounding hills.The pleasant and helpful Gardien, who takes pride in the site, would like to welcome more British visitors. The attractive town is a short walk.

Facilities

A modern, well designed and well equipped sanitary block has most washbasins in private cabins. Baby room. Laundry and covered dishwashing area. Baker calls in high season. Ice-creams and soft drinks available at reception. Children`s play area. Tennis courts and minigolf (extra charge). Off site: Supermarket, restaurants and indoor pool near. Fishing.

At a glance

Welcome & Ambience	✓✓✓✓	Location	✓✓✓✓
Quality of Pitches	✓✓✓✓✓	Range of Facilities	✓✓✓✓

Directions

Site is well signed all around the town as `Camping Complexe Sportif`.

Charges 2003

Per person	€ 2.55
child (under 7 yrs)	€ 1.30
pitch with electricity (3/6A)	€ 5.10 - €7.35
No credit cards.	

Reservations

Made with € 31 deposit; contact site.
Tel: 03 89 82 42 29.

Open

Easter - 30 September.

FR68040M Camping Municipal Les Trois Châteaux

10 rue du Bassin, 68420 Eguisheim (Haut-Rhin)

The village of Eguisheim is on the Alsace `Rue du Vin` to the west of Colmar. The three châteaux from which the site gets its name are clearly visible on the distant hills. About 400 m. from the village, Les Trois Châteaux is busy and popular. Flowers, shrubs and a variety of trees, along with the well tended grass areas make this a very pleasant place. The 121 pitches, 115 with electricity, are either on a slight slope or a terrace, and are marked and numbered, most with good shade. The facilities of the fascinating village of Eguisheim are close and the site is well located for exploring this delightful part of Alsace.

Facilities

The single sanitary block in the centre of the site has hot showers but cold water elsewhere. Playground. Caravans over 7 m. and/or 1 ton in weight are not accepted. Off site: Fishing 3 km.

At a glance

| Welcome & Ambience | ✓✓✓✓ | Location | ✓✓✓✓ |
| Quality of Pitches | ✓✓✓✓ | Range of Facilities | ✓✓✓ |

Directions

Eguisheim is just off the N83 and the site is well signed in the village.

Charges 2003

Per person	€ 3.30
child (under 7 yrs)	€ 1.60
pitch	€ 3.50
electricity (6A)	€ 3.40
unit over 5.5 m. long plus	€ 1.50
dog	€ 1.10
local tax	€ 0.30

No credit cards.

Reservations

Contact site. Tel: 03 89 23 19 39.

Open

1 April - 30 September.

FR68060M Camping Intercommunal Riquewihr

Route des Vins, 68340 Riquewihr (Haut-Rhin)

Surrounded by vineyards and minutes from the delightful village of Riquewihr, this is a well run site which has earned its good reputation. Situated in the heart of the Alsace wine region the site covers three hectares with views across the open countryside. Immediately to the right of the security barrier stands a modern, part-timbered building housing reception and information area. Close by is a small summer house and both are heavily garlanded with flowers. The 161 spacious individual grass pitches, many with shade and divided by hedging, have electrical connections. Wine caves are just 200 m. walk from reception and you might just see a stork or two on site.

Facilities

There are three sanitary blocks, one of a more modern design. Facilities include private cabins with basins, good nursery room with baby bath, childs' wc and changing mat, and excellent facilities for disabled people. Dishwashing and laundry areas. Motorcaravan service point. Campers' room with tables and chairs. Shop for basic necessities, drinks and papers (from 1/5). Off site: Children's play area and sports field adjacent. Fishing 3 km, bicycle hire 5 km.

At a glance

| Welcome & Ambience | ✓✓✓✓ | Location | ✓✓✓✓ |
| Quality of Pitches | ✓✓✓✓ | Range of Facilities | ✓✓✓ |

Directions

From N83 north of Colmar take D4 westwards to Bennwihr. Turn north on D18 for 2 km. towards Ribeauvillé. Site is signed off roundabout at southern end of Riquewihr bypass. Do not enter village.

Charges 2003

Per person	€ 3.35 - € 3.70
child (under 7 yrs)	€ 1.50 - € 1.70
pitch	€ 3.60 - € 4.00
electricity (6A)	€ 4.10
use of motorcaravan services	€ 5.30
dog	€ 1.10 - € 1.20

Reservations

Not accepted. Tel: 03 89 47 90 08.
Email: camping.riquewihr@tiscah.fr

Open

Easter - 31 October.

FR68080 **Camping Clair Vacances**

Route de Herrlisheim, 68127 St Croix-en-Plaine (Haut-Rhin)

Alsace is a popular and picturesque area of lovely villages, large vineyards, mountains and forests, and is also on the route taken by many heading for Switzerland or Italy. Clair Vacances, opened in `97, and extended in `03 is a very neat, tidy and pretty site with 130 level pitches of generous size which are numbered and most are separated by trees and shrubs. All have electricity connections and 10 are fully serviced with water and drainage. The site has been imaginatively laid out with the pitches reached from hard access roads. This is a quiet family site. The friendly couple who own and run it will be pleased to advise on the attractions of the area. The site is 1 km. from the A35 exit, not far from Colmar.

Facilities

Two excellent, modern toilet blocks include washbasins in cabins, well equipped baby rooms and good facilities for disabled visitors. Laundry and dishwashing facilites. Shop with limited supplies. Swimming pool and children's pool with large sunbathing area. Playground. Table tennis. Volleyball. Community room. Archery in high season. Dogs are not accepted in July/Aug. Camping Gaz stocked. Off site: Colmar with restaurants and shops is not far away.

At a glance

Welcome & Ambience	✓✓✓✓	Location	✓✓✓✓
Quality of Pitches	✓✓✓✓	Range of Facilities	✓✓✓✓

Directions

Site is signed from exit 27 of the A35 south of Colmar on the Herrlisheim road (D1).

Charges 2003

Per unit incl. 2 adults	€ 11.00 - € 15.00
extra adult	€ 3.00 - € 5.00
child (under 7 yrs)	€ 1.50 - € 3.00
electricity (8/13A)	€ 3.00 - € 5.00

Reservations

Made with deposit of € 50 and € 14 fee per week. Tel: 03 89 49 27 28. Email: clairvacances@wanadoo.fr

Open

Week before Easter - 25 October.

FR68070 **Camping Les Sources**

Route des Crêtes, 68700 Wattwiller (Haut-Rhin)

Wattwiller is just off the N83 Alsace 'Rue du Vin', tucked away in the forest hills beyond the vineyards, but not far from them, in the popular region of the Vosges. Camping Les Sources occupies a very steep slope above the village under a covering of tall trees. Of the 350 pitches, 100 are occupied by mobile home pitches for rent and 20 by seasonal units, leaving 230 for touring units. All these pitches have electricity and most are on terraces of gravel hardstanding. The trees mean that the site is very shady, so it can be rather gloomy in overcast or wet weather. A narrow hard road meanders between pitches and is very steep in places making it difficult for large units, although staff will assist with a tractor if required. Les Sources would suit those who are fit (there is much up and down walking) and wish to enjoy the quiet, secluded location although there would appear to be plenty on offer during high season. The site issues a map for walking in the area and a sheet in English with places to visit, and staff will be pleased to give further information.

Facilities

Three old toilet blocks are spread around the site and are fully equipped, but cleaning and maintenance is variable. No provision for disabled visitors who would find the steep roads too difficult. Washing machines and dryers. Shop. Good restaurant. Two swimming pools, one outdoor (July/Aug. only) and another heated and covered (all season). Arena for horse riding activities. Tennis court, table tennis, minigolf and volleyball. Bicycle hire. Entertainment area. Play area. Games room. Internet point. Organised programme with walking, games and creative activities.

At a glance

Welcome & Ambience	✓✓✓	Location	✓✓✓
Quality of Pitches	✓✓✓	Range of Facilities	✓✓✓✓

Directions

From N66 Thann - Mulhouse road, go north to Cernay and continue through Uffholtz to Wattwiller. Turn left at roundabout on southern edge of village, left again and follow D5 for 2 km. uphill to site.

Charges 2003

Per unit incl. 2 persons	€ 17.00 - € 19.70
extra person	€ 5.00 - € 6.00
child (1-7 yrs)	€ 3.00 - € 3.50
electricity (5A)	€ 3.30
animal	€ 1.00 - € 1.70
local tax	€ 0.15

Less 15-20% in low seasons. Barrier card deposit € 10. Pool wristband deposit € 2. Camping Cheques accepted.

Reservations

Made with deposit (€ 80) and fee (€ 8). Tel: 03 89 75 44 94. Email: camping.les.sources@wanadoo.fr

Open

1 April - 15 October.

FR88070 Camping Caravaning Domaine des Messires

88600 Herpelmont (Vosges)

Domaine des Messires nestles under a cover of tall trees by a landscaped lake on the edge of the small village of Herpelmont. It is well situated for exploring the rural countryside of the Vosges, the lakes and mountains of the region and the interesting towns of St Dié, Colmar and Épinal. The 120 good sized pitches are on grass over stones, with some by the lakeside. Each has a water tap, drain and electricity (6A) and most have good shade cover, except for those at the end of the site which are in the open. The lake is available for non-powered boats and there are sections for both swimming and fishing. If you write to reserve a pitch, ask for their very comprehensive route from Calais to the site.

Facilities

The fully equipped modern toilet block includes all washbasins in cabins, provision for disabled visitors (key from reception) and a baby room. Small shop and restaurant overlooking the lake (both 1/7-1/9). Two small play areas. Games and TV room. Programme of activities for children and adults in high season. Off site: Weekly markets in nearby Bruyères, Corcieux and St Dié. Bicycle hire 5 km. Riding and golf 12 km.

At a glance

| Welcome & Ambience | ✓✓✓✓ | Location | ✓✓✓✓ |
| Quality of Pitches | ✓✓✓✓ | Range of Facilities | ✓✓✓✓ |

Directions

From Épinal, exit N57 on N420 for St Dié and follow signs until you pick up signs for Bruyères. Lac du Messires is signed as you leave Bruyères on D423, at Laveline go south to Herpelmont and site.

Charges 2003

Per person	€ 4.00 - € 5.50
child (0-6 yrs	€ 2.00 - € 2.50
pitch incl. 3 services	€ 10.00 - € 12.00
local tax	€ 0.33

Reservations

Made with 25% deposit and € 12, 00 fee.
Tel: 03 29 58 56 29.
Email: mail@domainedesmessires.com

Open

1 May - 15 September.

Camping-Caravaning
Domaine des Messires
Quiet 4 star campsite in the middle of nature
Private lake for fishing, boating & swimming
Ideal for discovering the Vosges & Alsace
English spoken
Campsite tel/fax: 0033 329 58 56 29
When closed tel/fax: 0031 321 33 14 56
88600 Herpelmont, Vosges France
www.domainedesmessires.com

FR88010 Camping Les Deux Ballons

17 rue du Stade, 88560 St Maurice sur Moselle (Vosges)

St Maurice-sur-Moselle is in a narrow valley 7 km. from the source of the River Moselle in the massif of Haute-Vosges, on the main N66 which leads to the Col de Bussang. This is a pleasant leafy area for winter skiing and summer outdoor activities. Les Deux Ballons lies in a small valley surrounded by mountains with a stream running through the site and a cover of trees giving shade in most parts. The 180 pitches are on stony ground under the firs or on two terraces, and all have electrical connections. English is spoken.

Facilities

Four good sanitary blocks, one new, the others recently renovated, include baby rooms. Washing machines and dryers. Motorcaravan service point. Gas supplies. Bar with terrace (30/6-25/8). Snack bar and takeaway incl. pizzas. Large swimming pool (30 x 20 m.) with water slide and smaller pool for children (15/6-31/8). Organised walks, fishing, bowls, riding, paragliding and summer sledging in high season. TV room. Internet point. Tennis court, table tennis, volleyball and basketball. Fishing. Off site: Bicycle hire 5 km, riding 3 km.

At a glance

| Welcome & Ambience | ✓✓✓✓✓ | Location | ✓✓✓✓ |
| Quality of Pitches | ✓✓✓✓ | Range of Facilities | ✓✓✓✓ |

Directions

Site is on main N66 Le Thillot - Bussang road on northern edge of St Maurice near Ners filling station (entrance partly obscured - keep a look out).

Charges 2003

Per caravan or tent	
incl. 1 or 2 persons	€ 17.95 - € 19.80
extra person	€ 4.20 - € 4.35
child (2-7 yrs)	€ 3.00 - € 3.20
electricity (4/15A)	€ 3.85 - € 5.00
dog	€ 2.10 - € 3.00
local tax	€ 0.15 - € 0.30

No credit cards.

Reservations

Write with deposit (25%) and booking fee (€ 12,50). Tel: 03 29 25 17 14. Email: vero@camping-deux-ballons.fr

Open

10 April - 15 September.

FR88040 Camping Club du Lac de Bouzey

19 rue du Lac, 88390 Sanchey (Vosges)

Camping-Club Lac de Bouzey is 8 km. west of Épinal, overlooking the lake, at the beginning of the Vosges Massif. It is well placed for exploring the hills, valleys, lakes and waterfalls of the south of Alsace Lorraine. The word 'Club' has been added to the name to indicate the number of activities organised in high season. The 160 individual 100sqm. back-to-back grass pitches are arranged on either side of tarmac roads with electricity. They are on a gentle slope, divided by trees or beech hedging, under a cover of tall, silver birch trees and some overlook the 130 ha. lake. Units can be close together when the site is busy. The lake has a number of sandy beaches. Many water sports may be enjoyed, from pedaloes to canoes, windsurfing and sailing. The large, imposing building at the entrance to the site houses a restaurant and bar with terraces overlooking the lake. Two bars by the lake would indicate that the lake-side is popular with the public in summer but the camping area is quiet, separated by a road and well back and above the main entrance. An 'all year' site, there is lots going on for teenagers. English is spoken. A 'Sites et Paysages' member.

Facilities

The central sanitary block, partly below ground level, includes a baby room and one for disabled people (although there is up and down hill walking on the site). In winter a small, heated section in the main building with toilet, washbasin and shower is used. Good laundry and dishwashing facilites. Motorcaravan service point. Well stocked shop. Bar, restaurant. Heated swimming pool (1/5-30/9) of an original shape and backed by two sunbathing terraces. Fishing, riding, volleyball, games room, archery and bicycle hire on site. Below ground, under the restaurant, is a sound-proof room for cinema shows and discos for those staying on site only. Staff escort young people back to their pitch at the end of the evening. High season programme of activities for all ages, including excursions, entertainment, sports and a mini-club. Off site: Golf 8 km

At a glance

| Welcome & Ambience | ✓✓✓✓ | Location | ✓✓✓✓ |
| Quality of Pitches | ✓✓✓ | Range of Facilities | ✓✓✓✓✓ |

Directions

Site is 8 km. west of Épinal on D460 and is signed from some parts of Épinal. Follow signs for Lac de Bouzey and Sanchey.

Charges 2003

Per unit incl. 2 adults	€ 15.00 - € 22.00
extra person	€ 5.00 - € 7.00
child (4-10 yrs)	free - € 4.50
electricity (6/10A)	€ 4.00 - € 5.00
dog	free - € 2.00
local tax (over 7 yrs)	€ 0.25

Camping Cheques accepted.

Reservations

Made with deposit (€ 12 per day booked) and fee (€ 25). Tel: 03 29 82 49 41. Email: camping.lac.de.bouzey@wanadoo.fr

Open

All year.

FR88080 Castel Camping Domaine des Bans

Rue James Wiese, 88430 Corcieux (Vosges)

Corcieux is in the heart of the Vosges mountains, near the lakeside resort of Gerardmer, the Alsace 'Route de Vin' and on the edge of the Ballons des Vosges National Park. Domaine des Bans is a large, busy campsite with around 600 pitches, in a country setting, where there are plenty of opportunities to be active. There is a very high percentage of static and tour operator units, but room for about 50 tourist units. Pitches (with electricity, water and drainage), numbered and separated by hedges, vary in size with some on low terraces. There is good shade. Some pitches are tucked away in quiet areas with others nearer to where activities take place. A new pool complex was under construction at the time of our visit. The older swimming pool is partly covered and is surrounded by a sun terrace with snack bar. Domaine des Bans is not really a site for short stays, but is a base for exploring the varied and interesting countryside, Haut Koenigsbourg Castle with Colmar, Épinal and Strasbourg within range for day trips.

Facilities

Three functional toilet blocks are spread around the site. Some washbasins are in cabins. Cleaning and mainrenance is variable. Shop (15/6-31/8). Bar, restaurant and takeaway (all 1/6-10/9). Swimming pool (1/6-10/9). Playground and open area for ball games. Tennis, table tennis, badminton, minigolf, volleyball and archery. Bicycle hire. Riding. Lakes for fishing and boating. High season entertainment programme including discos (sound-proof underground room), theatre performances and other live music. `Goats Castle` with about two dozen goats provides interest for children. Off site: Smaller restaurant just outside the site boundary with others a short distance away in the village.

Directions

From D8 St Dié - Gerardmer road, turn west on D60 just north of Gerbepal to Corcieux.

Charges 2003

Per person	€ 4.00 - € 7.00
child (under 6 yrs)	€ 2.00 - € 4.00
pitch incl. electricity	€ 12.00 - € 15.00
local tax	€ 0.34

Reservations

Advised in high season and made with 25% deposit and € 12 fee. Tel: 03 29 51 64 67. Email: les-bans@domaine-des-bans.com

Open

26 April - 25 October.

At a glance

Welcome & Ambience	✓✓	Location	✓✓✓✓
Quality of Pitches	✓✓✓	Range of Facilities	✓✓✓

FR88090 Base de Loisirs du Lac de la Moselotte

Les Amias - BP. 34, 88290 Saulxures-sur-Moselotte (Vosges)

This spacious lakeside site, part of a leisure village complex, has 75 generously sized individual hedged pitches. All have electrical hook-ups and 25 of these are multi-serviced with electricity, water and waste water drain. The site is fully fenced with a security barrier and a key for the pedestrian gates (to site and lakeside) issued by reception. The adjacent 'base de loisirs' has a wide variety of activities on offer, plus supervised swimming in the lake (July/Aug), and pedalo, canoe, kayak and bicycle rental. Also on site are a snack bar and bar (all year), a children's club in high season and fishing in the lake.

Facilities

The heated modern toilet block is light and airy with controllable hot showers, some washbasins in cubicles and good facilities for babies and disabled campers. Shop for basic supplies (July/Aug). Bar/snackbar. Bicycle hire. Fishing. Playground. 30 chalets for rent. Off site: The town is an easy level walk and has all services. Attractions in the region include the Route des Vins in summer, and skiing in winter.

Directions

Saulxures-sur-Moselotte is about 20 km. east of Remiremont. From Remiremont take D417 east to St Ame, then turn right (east) on D43 towards La Bresse for 10.5 km. Turn left into Saulxures (site is signed), and site entrance is on right after 0.5 km. by lake.

Charges 2003

Per person	€ 5.00
child (4-10 yrs)	€ 3.00
pitch	€ 5.00
electricity (10A)	€ 5.00 - € 6.00
animal	€ 1.00
local tax	€ 0.20

Reservations

Contact site. Tel: 03 29 24 56 56. Email: info@ville-saulxures-mtte.fr

Open

All year.

At a glance

Welcome & Ambience	✓✓✓✓	Location	✓✓✓✓
Quality of Pitches	✓✓✓✓	Range of Facilities	✓✓✓✓

Vendée

let yourself go...

It's not only the fine beaches that make this holiday region so appealing. Sleepy fishing harbours, historic ports and charming towns all create a great holiday atmosphere.

We have exercised a little license with this area taking one département from the official Western Loire region, 85 Vendée, and one from the Poitou-Charentes region, 17 Charente-Maritime

With a sunshine record to rival the south of France, the Vendée and Charente regions are among the most popular areas in France. Running alongside the coastal area stretching down from La Rochelle past Rochefort to Royan, it boasts gently shelving sandy beaches, warm shallow waters and fragrant pine forests. Explore the coasts for traditional fishing villages or head inland for fields of sunflowers and unspoilt rural villages.

The Vendée was the centre of the counter-revolutionary movement between 1793 and 1799 and a *'son et lumiere'* extravaganza held at the Chateau Puy-du-Fou tells the whole story. Les Sables d'Olonne is its main resort renowned for its excellent sandy beach. The area between the Vendée and Charente, the Marais Poitevin, is one of the most unusual in France – a vast tract of marshland with a thousand or more tree-lined canals and slow moving streams. The port of La Rochelle, with massive medieval towers, buzzes with life and the island of Ré is popular with those seeking beaches and small, quiet ports.

Cuisine of the region

Fish predominates, both fresh water (eel, trout, pike), sea water (shrimps, mussels, oysters). Drink includes light fruity wines from Haut-Poitou, Deux-Sèvres and Charente, and Cognac and Pineau des Charentes – an aperitif of grape juice and Cognac

Cagouilles: snails from Charentes

Chaudrée: ragout of fish cooked in white wine, shallots and butter

Mouclade: mussels cooked in wine, egg yolks and cream, served with Pineau des Charentes

Soupe de moules à la Rochelaise: soup of various fish, mussels, saffron, garlic, tomatoes, onions and red wine

Sourdons: cockles from the Charentes

Places of interest

Marais Poitevin: marshes known as the 'Green Venice'

Angoulême: Hill-top town surrouded by ramparts, cathedral, Renaissance château

La Rochelle: port, Porte de la Grosse Horloge (clock gate), Museum of the New World

Le Puy-du-Fou: 15th-16th century castle, sound and light show involving over 700 participants

Les Sables d'Olonne: fishing port and seaside resort

Noirmoutier: linked to the mainland by a 3 mile bridge

Saint Savin: 17th century abbey, mural painting

tip

FOR LESS CROWDED BEACHES AND GENERAL PEACE AND QUIET VISIT THE ISLANDS OF RÉ, A HAVEN FOR CYCLISTS, AND OLÉRON.

FR17020 **Airotel Le Puits de L'Auture**

151 avenue de La Grande-Côte, 17420 St Palais-sur-Mer (Charente-Maritime)

This popular region has a very sunny climate and Le Puits de l'Auture is well situated with the sea outside the gates, just across the road, and a long sandy beach starting 400 m. away. As soon as you enter the site there is a feeling that it is well cared for, with an abundance of flower beds at the entrance. The 400 numbered pitches are level and have electricity connections, a fair number are separated by bushes and some trees give shade (many were lost in recent storms). Water and drainage is provided on 120 pitches. There is a good number of mobile homes on site. Used by a tour operator (10%). Considering its close proximity to the beach and its popularity, there is a remarkably calm and relaxed atmosphere and it is well worth considering.

Facilities

Well maintained toilet blocks are more than adequate for the number of visitors. Most WCs are British type and all washbasins are in cabins, showers are adjustable and hot water is plentiful. Baby baths and showers, and full facilities for disabled people. Washing machines and ample sinks for dishwashing and laundry. Well stocked shop, takeaway food and bar (all 10/6-25/9). Three swimming pools with sunbathing areas which are most attractive with banana plants making a backdrop with a difference. Volleyball, table tennis and games room. Play area. Bicycle hire. Barbecues are only allowed in a special area. Dogs are not accepted. Off site: Riding and golf 800 m. Several restaurants nearby specialise in sea food.

Directions

Site is on the coast, 2 km. from St Palais and 8 km. from Royan. From Royan take D25 past St Palais following signs for La Palmyre. At two lane junction system turn back left signed Grande Côte and St Palais and site is 800 m.

Latest charges

Per unit incl. up to 3 persons	€ 17.60 - € 29.00
incl. 6A electricity	€ 23.00 - € 33.00
10A electricity	€ 26.00 - € 36.00
with water and drainage	€ 33.00 - € 41.00
extra person (over 3 yrs)	€ 4.60 - € 6.50

Plus local tax.

Reservations

Made for min. 5 days with deposit and fee. Tel: 05 46 23 20 31. Email: camping-lauture@wanadoo.fr

Open

1 May - 30 September.

At a glance

Welcome & Ambience	✓✓✓✓	Location	✓✓✓✓✓
Quality of Pitches	✓✓✓✓✓	Range of Facilities	✓✓✓✓✓

FR17040 **Camping International Bonne Anse Plage**

La Palmyre, 17570 Les Mathes (Charente-Maritime)

On the edge of the Forêt de la Coubre, just beyond the popular resort of La Palmyre, Bonne Anse has a lovely setting amongst pine trees, just a short stroll from an extensive tidal inlet. It is a spacious, gently undulating site, carefully designed to provide 865 level, marked pitches, of which 600 are for touring units (500 have electricity). Most are shaded by the pines, the ones nearer the sea less so (these are rather more sandy). The site's amenities are centred around the entrance and reception building and include a restaurant and bar with a spacious outdoor terrace and an impressive pool complex. This forms the social focus of the site and overlooks the boules area with the pool complex opposite. English is spoken and rallies welcomed with visit programmes organised. Used by tour operators (35 pitches). With plenty to do for the active, the site is perhaps a little impersonal.

Facilities

Seven sanitary blocks include some washbasins in cabins, British style toilets with a few Turkish, hot and cold showers. Facilities for disabled visitors and babies. Washing up and laundry sinks under cover. Launderette. Motorcaravan service point. Shopping centre (all season) includes a supermarket, excellent delicatessen and takeaway, crêperie, shops for bread and pastries, holiday goods and papers, plus visiting traders' stalls (wines, seafood, etc) in high season. Restaurant and bar (20/6-30/8). Takeaway (19/5-5/9). Splendid, lively swimming pool complex with heated pool (35 x 25 m), three water toboggans and a water slide. Children's playground, large video games room, TV (satellite), minigolf and table tennis. Enclosed area with an all-weather surface for football, volleyball or basketball. Direct access to cycle tracks (bicycle hire available) that avoid the main road. Entertainment in season. Only gas barbecues are permitted. Dogs are not accepted. Off site: Fishing or riding 1 km, golf 5 km. Watersports and tennis nearby. Supervised, safe beaches close by, also fitness track.

Directions

Leave A10 autoroute at Saintes and head for Royan (N150). In Royan take signs for La Palmyre (D25). At La Palmyre roundabout follow signs for Ronce-les-Bains and site is 1 km. on the left.

Charges 2003

Per unit incl. 1 or 2 persons	€ 26.00
incl. 3 persons	€ 30.00
extra person (over 1 yr)	€ 7.30
electricity (6A)	€ 5.20
local tax	€ 0.40

Reservations

Min. 5 days - phone, fax or write for details. Tel: 05 46 22 40 90. Email: Bonne.Anse@wanadoo.fr

Open

19 May - 5 September.

At a glance

Welcome & Ambience	✓✓✓	Location	✓✓✓
Quality of Pitches	✓✓✓✓	Range of Facilities	✓✓✓✓✓

Vendée & Charente

FR17010 Camping Bois Soleil

2 avenue de Suzac, 17110 St Georges-de-Didonne (Charente-Maritime)

Close to the sea and the resort of St Georges, Bois Soleil is a fairly large site in three separate parts, with 208 serviced pitches for touring caravans and several for tents. The main part, 'Les Pins', is mature and attractive with ornamental trees and shrubs providing shade. Opposite is 'La Mer' which has direct access to the beach and is used only in the main season. It has some areas with rather less shade and a raised central area for tents. The sandy beach here is a wide public one, sheltered from the Atlantic breakers although the sea goes out some way at low tide. The third and largest part of the site, 'La Forêt', is mainly for static holiday homes (many privately owned), although there are some touring pitches here for both tents and caravans. The areas are well tended with the named pitches (not numbered) cleared and raked between clients and with an all-in charge including electricity and water. This lively site offers something for everyone, whether they like a beach-side spot or a traditional pitch, plenty of activities or the quiet life – it is best to book for the area you prefer. It can be full mid-June - late August.

Facilities

Each area is served by one large sanitary block, supplemented by smaller blocks providing toilets only. Another heated block is near reception. Well designed and appointed buildings, cleaned twice daily, they include washbasins in cubicles, facilities for disabled people (WC, basin and shower) and for babies. Launderette. Nursery for babies. Supermarket, bakery (July/Aug) and beach shop. Upstairs restaurant and bar with terrace, excellent takeaway (from April). Swimming pool (15/6-15/9). Little pool for small children. 'Parc des Jeux' with tennis, table tennis, bicycle hire, boules and children's playground. TV room and library. Comprehensive tourist information and entertainment office. Internet terminal. Charcoal barbecues are not permitted but gas ones can be hired by the evening. Dogs or other animals are not accepted. Off site: Fishing and riding within 500 m, golf 2 km.

At a glance

Welcome & Ambience	✓✓✓✓	Location	✓✓✓✓✓
Quality of Pitches	✓✓✓✓	Range of Facilities	✓✓✓✓✓

Directions

From Royan centre take coast road (D25) along the sea-front of St Georges-de-Didonne towards Meschers. Site is signed at roundabout at end of the main beach.

Charges 2003

Per unit incl. 2 persons, and 6A electricity	€ 16.00 - € 27.50
3 persons	€ 19.00 - € 27.50
tent incl. 2 persons	€ 13.00 - € 24.50
extra person	€ 3.50 - € 5.00
child (3-7 yrs)	€ 1.50 - € 3.50
electricity 10A	€ 3.40 - € 5.00
local tax (1/7-31/8)	€ 0.25

Less 20% outside July/Aug.
Camping Cheques accepted.

Reservations

Made with 25% deposit and € 26 fee.
Tel: 05 46 05 05 94.
Email: camping.bois.soleil@wanadoo.fr.

Open

3 April - 6 November.

FR17110 Camping Caravaning Monplaisir

Route de la Palmyre, 17570 Les Mathes-La Palmyre (Charente-Maritime)

Monplaisir provides a small, quiet haven in an area with some very hectic campsites. It is ideal for couples or families with young children. The site is quite close to the town set back from the road, and the entrance leads through an avenue of trees, past the owners home to a well kept, garden-like site with many varieties of trees and shrubs. There are only 114 level, marked pitches and all but 9 have electrical connections. There is no shop, bar or restaurant but it is a happy, friendly site with visitors who return year after year.

Facilities

The toilet block has good facilities including some washbasins in cabins and excellent facilities for disabled people. Laundry and dishwashing sinks outside, but under cover. Washing machine and dryer. Ice pack service and gas supplies in reception. Bread delivered daily. Takeaway available from reception five days a week. TV, games room and library. Swimming pool and paddling pool (15/5-15/9). Small play area. Bicycle hire. Minigolf adjacent (owned by the site). Winter caravan storage. Off site: Fishing 500 m, riding 1 km, golf 5 km. Supermarket short walk.

At a glance

Welcome & Ambience	✓✓✓✓	Location	✓✓✓✓
Quality of Pitches	✓✓✓✓	Range of Facilities	✓✓✓✓

Directions

Follow the D25 to La Palmyre and, in the town, turn north to Les Mathes. At roundabout turn right to town centre and site is on left. From north on D14 La Tremblade road turn to Les Mathes at Arvert. Site is in western outskirts of the town on the D141 La Palmyre road.

Charges 2003

Per pitch incl. 2 persons	€ 15.00
incl. 3 persons	€ 17.00
extra person	€ 4.00
baby under 2 yrs	€ 2.00
electricity (6A)	€ 3.00
dog	€ 1.50
local tax	€ 0.40

Less 20% outside July/Aug.

Reservations

Made with deposit and fee, min. stay 4 nights.
Tel: 05 46 22 50 31.

Open

1 April - 1 October.

Bois Soleil

Camping ★ ★ ★ ★
Charente-Maritime

Surrounded by pine trees and a sandy beach on the Atlantic Coast, with one direct access to the beach, BoisSoleil proposes to you many attractions like tennis, tabletennis, children's playgrounds and entertainment. Shops, take-away and snack-bar with big TV screen.

Spring and Summer 2004

2, avenue de Suzac - 17110 ST GEORGES DE DIDONNE
Tel: 0033 546 05 05 94 - Fax: 0033 546 06 27 43
www.bois-soleil.com / e-mail: camping.bois.soleil@wanadoo.fr

FR17050 Camping L'Orée du Bois

225 route de la Bouverie, La Fouasse, 17570 Les Mathes (Charente-Maritime)

L'Orée du Bois has 388 pitches of about 100 sq.m. in a very spacious, pinewood setting. There are 150 for touring units, including 40 large pitches with hardstanding and individual sanitary facilities (built in small, neat blocks of four and containing your own shower, toilet, washbasin and washing up sink). The pitches are on flat, fairly sandy ground, separated by trees, shrubs and growing hedges and all have electrical connections (6A). The forest pines offer some shade. Sandy beaches (with lifeguards in season) are fairly near, plus opportunities for walking, riding or cycling in the 10,000 hectare Forêt de la Coubre. A very lively site in high season, suitable for all age groups, it can be noisy but is tranquil in low season with large, spacious pitches. Used by several tour operators.

Facilities

Four attractively designed, main toilet blocks have good fittings, including some washbasins in cabins. Three blocks have laundry rooms, dishwashing under cover and fully equipped units for disabled people. Well stocked shop. Excellent bar, restaurant, crêperie and takeaway service. Large swimming pools, including water toboggan, and paddling pool (proper swimming trunks, not shorts). Two children's play areas. Tennis court, boules, volleyball, table tennis, football and basketball areas. Games room and TV lounge (with satellite). Bicycle hire. Twice weekly discos and free, all day children's entertainment organised in July/Aug. Barbecues allowed in special areas. Off site: Fishing 4 km, riding 300 m, golf 20 km.

At a glance

Welcome & Ambience	✓✓✓✓	Location	✓✓✓
Quality of Pitches	✓✓✓	Range of Facilities	✓✓✓✓

Directions

From north follow D14 La Tremblade road. At Arvert turn on D141 to Les Mathes and turn east, signed La Palmyre, to second roundabout where site signed. From the south, at Royan take D25 towards La Palmyre, then towards Les Mathes to roundabout where site is signed. Note: there is now a new roundabout with a boat on it - follow sign for La Tremblade. Site is signed from this road, and this way is said to be quicker.

Charges 2004

Per unit incl. 2 persons	€ 15.00 - € 30.00
with private sanitary facility	€ 22.00 - € 38.00
extra person (over 3 yrs)	€ 6.00
animal	€ 3.50
local tax	€ 0.15 - € 0.30

Min. stay 7 days in high season.

Reservations

Made with 30% deposit plus fee (€ 21); min. 7 days in high season. Tel: 05 46 22 42 43. Email: info@camping-oree-du-bois.fr.

Open

24 April - 11 September.

L'Orée du Bois ★★★★

Hôtel de plein air - Camping Caravaning
225 route de la Bouverie
17570 LES MATHES - LA PALMYRE
Tel: 0033 546 224 243 - Fax: 0033 546 225 476
E-mail: info@camping-oree-du-bois.fr

FR17140 Yelloh! Village Sequoia Parc

La Josephtrie, 17320 St Just-Luzac (Charente-Maritime)

Approached by an impressive avenue of flowers, shrubs and trees, Séquoia Parc is a Castel site set in the grounds of La Josephtrie, a striking château with beautifully restored outbuildings and a spacious courtyard. The site itself is designed to a high specification with reception in a large, light and airy room retaining its original beams and leading to the courtyard area where you find the shop, bar and restaurant. The pitches are 140 sq.m. in size with electricity connections and separated by young shrubs. The pool complex with water slides, large children's pool and sunbathing area is impressive. The site has a good number of mobile homes and chalets. Used by tour operators (125 pitches). This is a popular site with entertainment and activities. Reservation is necessary in high season. A Yelloh Village member.

Facilities

Three luxurious toilet blocks, maintained to a high standard, include units with washbasin and shower, a laundry, dishwashing sinks, facilities for disabled visitors and baby baths. Motorcaravan service point. Gas supplies. Shop. Restaurant/bar and takeaway. Impressive swimming pool complex with paddling pool. Tennis, volleyball, football field. Games and TV rooms. Bicycle hire. Pony trekking. Organised entertainment in July/Aug.

At a glance

Welcome & Ambience	✓✓✓✓	Location	✓✓✓✓
Quality of Pitches	✓✓✓✓✓	Range of Facilities	✓✓✓✓✓

Directions

Site is 2.5 km. southeast of Marennes. From Rochefort take D733 south for 12 km. Turn west on D123 to Ile d'Oléron. Continue for 12 km. and turn southeast on D728 towards Saintes. Site clearly signed, in 1 km. on the left.

Charges 2003

Per unit incl. 2 persons	
and electricity (6A)	€ 15.00 - € 35.00
extra person	€ 6.00 - € 8.00
child (3-7 yrs)	€ 3.00 - € 5.00
dog	€ 3.00
local tax	€ 0.30

Camping Cheques accepted.

Reservations

Made with 25% deposit and € 30 booking fee.
Tel: 05 46 85 55 55. Email: sequoia.parc@wanadoo.fr

Open

15 May - 11 September, with all services.

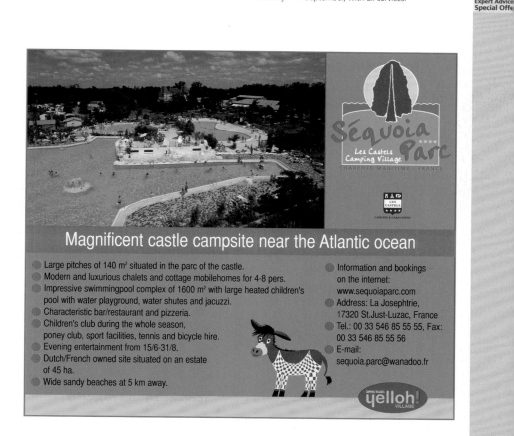

Magnificent castle campsite near the Atlantic ocean

- Large pitches of 140 m² situated in the parc of the castle.
- Modern and luxurious chalets and cottage mobilehomes for 4-8 pers.
- Impressive swimmingpool complex of 1600 m² with large heated children's pool with water playground, water shutes and jacuzzi.
- Characteristic bar/restaurant and pizzeria.
- Children's club during the whole season, poney club, sport facilities, tennis and bicycle hire.
- Evening entertainment from 15/6-31/8.
- Dutch/French owned site situated on an estate of 45 ha.
- Wide sandy beaches at 5 km away.

- Information and bookings on the internet: www.sequoiaparc.com
- Address: La Josephtrie, 17320 St.Just-Luzac, France
- Tel.: 00 33 546 85 55 55, Fax: 00 33 546 85 55 56
- E-mail: sequoia.parc@wanadoo.fr

Séquoia Parc
Les Castels Camping Village
CHARENTE MARITIME FRANCE

LES CASTELS
CAMPING & CARAVANING

yelloh! VILLAGE

FR17150M Camping Municipal du Château Benon

17170 Benon (Charente-Maritime)

Benon was once the capital of this area and had strong English connections, its castle being built in 1096, although now all that remains is a single round tower. However the mayor and villagers are still anxious to welcome English visitors. The municipal campsite is beautifully kept, with open and shady areas and is ideal for those wanting a peaceful stay, and to stroll or cycle through the fields and woods which surround Benon. There are 70 pitches on neat grass, 60 with electricity. High season entertainment includes dances and organised dinners. This is a pretty, quiet site where visitors are made welcome.

Facilities

The reasonably modern toilet block is fully equipped, with hot water always available and facilities for disabled visitors. Motorcaravan service point. Tennis court. Off site: Auberge, general shop and post office near and La Rochelle is within easy reach (25 minutes) for shopping, beaches, etc. Fishing or bicycle hire 7 km, riding 5 km, golf 13 km.

At a glance

Welcome & Ambience	✓✓✓✓	Location	✓✓✓✓
Quality of Pitches	✓✓✓✓	Range of Facilities	✓✓✓

Directions

Benon is 28 km. east of La Rochelle on the N11. Turn south at 'Relais de Benon', Benon 2 km. and site in centre of village.

Charges 2004

Per adult	€ 2.50
pitch with electricity (10A)	€ 3.60

No credit cards.

Reservations

Advised for 14 July - 15 Aug; contact the Mairie. Tel: 05 46 01 61 48. Email: mairie-benon@smic17.fr

Open

1 May - 30 September.

FR17160 Camping Le Clos Fleuri

8 impasse du Clos Fleuri, 17600 Médis (Charente-Maritime)

Camping Le Clos Fleuri really does live up to its name. The profusion of different trees and, in the more open area, the lawns and flower beds give this small site a very rural atmosphere. There is always a warm welcome from the Devais family who created the site in 1974. The 123 touring pitches are mostly of generous size (a little uneven in places), varying in the amount of shade they receive (from full sun to well shaded) and 100 have electrical connections. The bar/restaurant is a converted barn with chalk and stone walls and a high timbered ceiling – a cool haven on hot days and a very convivial venue for evening gatherings and entertainment. The surrounding countryside is very pleasant with crops of sunflowers, wheat and maize, while beaches of all sorts are within easy reach. All in all the Clos Fleuri combines a great deal of charm, beauty and friendliness with a location from which the attractions of the Charente Maritime may be discovered.

Facilities

Toilet facilities are in two blocks which are kept scrupulously clean. One block is segregated male and female, the other is unisex with each unit in its own cubicle. Baby baths, washing machines and dryers. Attractive small pool with separate paddling pool and sunbathing terrace. Sauna. Good shop with fresh meat and vegetables, restaurant (both 1/7-31/8) and bar (1/7-15/9) are housed in the old farm buildings, which form the nucleus of the site. In high season there are twice weekly 'soirees' and boules and archery competitions. Minigolf. Small football pitch. Security barrier closed at night. Off site: Shops in Médis 2 km.

At a glance

Welcome & Ambience	✓✓✓✓✓	Location	✓✓✓✓
Quality of Pitches	✓✓✓✓	Range of Facilities	✓✓✓✓

Directions

Médis is on the N150 from Saintes, halfway between Saujon and Royan. Site is signed to south at various points in Médis and is about 2 km. outside the village.

Charges 2003

Per pitch incl. 2 adults	€ 22.00
child (2-7 yrs)	€ 4.50
electricity (5/10A)	€ 4.00 - € 5.00

Less 20% in June and Sept.

Reservations

Essential for high season and made with deposit (€ 100) and fee (€ 20). Tel: 05 46 05 62 17. Email: clos-fleuri@wanadoo.fr

Open

1 June - 15 September.

FR17180 Haven Camping La Pignade

45 avenue de Monard, 17390 Ronce les Bains (Charente-Maritime)

If you are looking for a busy, active well appointed site offering a wide range of facilities and daily entertainment all season, then La Pignade, a Haven Europe park, may be just what you want. The 500 or so pitches, of which 150 are reserved for tourers, are located around well spaced pine trees which, while giving some shade, also give an open aspect. The ground is sandy but site roads are tarmac so dust is not a problem. The pitches are generous in size, most separated by low, evergreen hedges. The number of mobile homes is increasing each year. Entertainment and catering facilities are central, well constructed and maintained to a high standard with an impressive range of pools and water slides. The English speaking staff are welcoming and helpful. Good sandy beaches are nearby, while the fascinating oyster producing area of Marennes is only a few kilometres away. Also close by is the island of Oléron, reached by a magnificent road bridge, where there are more beaches and a number of historic buildings, pretty villages and excellent facilities for cycling and riding. All in all La Pignade offers a great holiday base in an area full of attractive and interesting places.

Facilities

Four refurbished, fully equipped toilet blocks are centrally placed in four separate areas. Open style dishwashing and laundry sinks. Baby packs for hire. Washing machines and dryers. Separate provision for disabled people. Large mini-market and gift shop. Waiter service restaurant or takeaway. Spacious well stocked and attractively staffed bar. Barbecue areas. Swimming pools (heated and supervised). Practice golf, crazy golf, archery and bicycle hire (charged). Clubs for children (free all season) and a daily programme of competitions, activities and entertainment. Dogs are not accepted. Off site: Nearby riding, tennis and watersports.

At a glance

Welcome & Ambience	✓✓✓✓	Location	✓✓✓✓
Quality of Pitches	✓✓✓✓	Range of Facilities	✓✓✓✓✓

Directions

Ronce-les-Bains is on the D25 north of La Tremblade and the D728 from Marennes. The site is clearly signed from all directions.

Charges 2004

Per unit incl. 2 persons, electricity	€ 13.00 - € 27.00
extra person	€ 3.00 - € 6.00

Reservations

Contact site or Haven Europe in the UK on Tel: 0870 242 7777 for information or reservation. Tel: 05 46 36 15 35.
Email: europe.website@bourne-leisure.co.uk

Open

30 April - 19 September.

FR17200 Camping Caravaning Au Fil de L'Eau

6 Rue de Courbiac, 17100 Saintes (Charente-Maritime)

Saintes is a 2,000 year old Gallo-Roman city, well worth a couple of days to visit the Cathedral, the Abbey, the Arch of Germanicus, the Amphitheatre and several museums, all of which are within walking distance of the campsite (reception can provide a city map). Do take a stroll through the well tended, very pretty public gardens by the riverside. There is a fresh produce market in the town centre every morning except Monday. This pleasant, well run site has 214 mostly shady and generally grassy level pitches, with 132 electric hook-ups, and a few mobile homes and caravans for rent.

Facilities

The main toilet block is a large and modern building, with two smaller older units opened at peak times. Washbasins in cubicles. Facilities for disabled people are in a unit by the laundry building. Motorcaravan service point. Bar, restaurant and takeaway (July/Aug). TV room. Boules pitch, table tennis, badminton, volleyball and minigolf. Small playground. Gates locked 22.00-07.00 hrs (22.30-7.00 July/Aug), and guardian lives on site. Off site: Open air adjacent pool complex is free for campers (23/6-10/9).

At a glance

Welcome & Ambience	✓✓✓✓	Location	✓✓✓
Quality of Pitches	✓✓✓✓	Range of Facilities	✓✓✓✓

Directions

From east and northeast follow signs for town centre, turning right after crossing river. To avoid centre and from all other directions, use bypass following signs for N137 La Rochelle to large roundabout at northern end. Turn right signed town centre and follow signs.

Charges 2003

Per adult	€ 4.10
pitch with electricity (5A)	€ 7.30

Reservations

Advisable for high season. Tel: 05 46 93 08 00.

Open

16 May - 15 September.

FR17170 Domaine Des Charmilles

St Laurent de la Prée, 17450 Fouras (Charente-Maritime)

Fouras is a relatively little known resort situated between La Rochelle and Rochefort which retains much of the charm missing from some of the larger, more heavily commercialised resorts in the area. Les Charmilles is located about a mile from the town centre. It is very easily accessed from the main La Rochelle - Rochefort road (N137). There are 270 large pitches, the majority taken up with the site's own mobile homes or chalets. The touring pitches all have electricity and many also have water and drainage. Roughly a third are well shaded, with the remainder having a sunnier, more open setting. The latter area also has the advantage of being well away from the busy road which runs past the front of the site. A variety of entertainment is provided which can mean that the site is noisy until at least midnight.

Facilities

Five modern toilet blocks provide most washbasins in cubicles and facilities for babies and disabled people. A reader reports that cleaning and the supply of hot water can be variable. Washing machines and dryers. Small shop (1/6-15/9). Bar and snack bar (15/5-15/9). Heated swimming pool and water slide, surrounded by a large sunbathing terrace (15/5-15/9). Sauna. Jacuzzi. Good playground. Minigolf, table tennis and concrete basketball court. Bicycle hire. Entertainment. Minibus service to the beach in July/Aug. Charcoal barbecues are not permitted.
Off site: Fishing 3 km. Golf 5 km. Riding 15 km.

Directions

Leave N137 at exit for Fouras and St Laurent de la Prée, joining D937 towards Fouras. Site is on left in about 800 m.

Charges 2004

Per pitch incl. 2 adults	€ 12.00 - € 25.00
with electricity (6A)	€ 15.50 - € 28.50
extra adult	€ 5.50
child (under 5 yrs)	€ 3.50
animal	€ 2.90

Reservations

Necessary for high season with deposit and fee. Contact site. Tel: 05 46 84 00 05.
Email: charmilles17@wanadoo.fr

Open

1 April - 25 September.

At a glance

Welcome & Ambience	✓✓✓✓	Location	✓✓✓
Quality of Pitches	✓✓✓✓	Range of Facilities	✓✓✓✓

FR17210 Camping Interlude

Plage de Gros Jonc, 17580 Le Bois-Plage-en-Ré (Charente-Maritime)

The island of Ré, which is no more than 30 km. long and 5 km. wide, lies off the coast at La Rochelle and is reached by a toll bridge. It is a paradise for cyclists, walkers and those who wish to commune with nature. Camping Interlude enjoys a pleasant location with access to an excellent beach. A popular site even in low season (it may become very crowded with overstretched facilities in high season), it is has 387 pitches, 136 of which are for touring units. Pitches are sand based, vary in size from 80-120 sq.m. and are mostly divided by hedged on part undulating, sandy terrain. Many are placed to the left of the site in a pine forest setting, others mingle with the tour operators and mobile homes. Choosing a shady pitch is not a problem for there are many trees. Interlude makes an ideal base for exploring the island of Re and for those planning an early holiday, the facilities on site are all operational from the beginning of April. It is a suitable site for all ages, with plenty of recreational pursuits to keep families happy, both on and off site.

Facilities

Two modern, clean and well equipped sanitary blocks provide washbasins in cabins and some shower units suitable for families with twin washbasins. Baby room, child size toilets, en suite facilities for disabled visitors, laundry sinks, washing machines and dryers, plus dishwashing areas. Motorcaravan service point. Restaurant/bar and shop (all season). Two swimming pools, one outdoor and one inside. Play area. Volleyball, boules. Organised events and entertainment for young and old. Games/TV room. Tennis courts. Bicycle hire. Communal barbecues.

Directions

After crossing toll bridge to Ile de Ré follow sign for Le Bois Plage. Turn left at first roundabout and continue straight on at next two, then left at fourth roundabout where site is signed.

Charges 2003

Per unit incl. 2 persons,	
100 sq.m. pitch	€ 12.00 - € 23.70
120 sq.m. pitch incl.	
water and electricity	€ 16.00 - € 23.90
140 sq.m. pitch incl. drainage also	€ 16.00 - € 33.50
extra person	€ 4.60 - € 9.15
pet	€ 2.22 - € 6.85
Camping Cheques accepted.	

Reservations

Advisable all season. Tel: 05 46 09 18 22.
Email: ifos@interlude.fr

Open

3 April - 19 September.

At a glance

Welcome & Ambience	✓✓✓✓	Location	✓✓✓✓✓
Quality of Pitches	✓✓✓	Range of Facilities	✓✓✓✓✓

FR17230 **Camping de L'Océan**

La Passe, La Couarde sur Mer, 17670 Ile de Ré (Charente-Maritime)

L'Océan lies close to the centre of the Ile de Ré, just 50m from a sandy beach. There are 330 pitches here although many are occupied by mobile homes and chalets. The camping area is well shaded and pitches are of a reasonable size, most with electrical connections. Pride of place goes to the large heated swimming pool which is surrounded by an attractive sunbathing terrace. Bike hire is popular here as the island offers over 100km of interesting cycle routes. There is a well-stocked shop, and a pleasant bar/restaurant with a terrace overlooking the pool. In peak season a range of entertainment is organised including disco evenings.

Facilities

The sanitary blocks are modern and well maintained. Special disabled facilities. Tennis court. Fishing pond adjacent. Basketball. Childrens' play area. Off site: South facing beach 50m. La Couarde (nearest restaurants, shops etc.) 2.5km.

At a glance

| Welcome & Ambience | ✓✓✓ | Location | ✓✓✓✓ |
| Quality of Pitches | ✓✓✓ | Range of Facilities | ✓✓✓✓ |

Directions

After crossing the toll bridge on to the island, join the D735 which runs along the north side of the island until you pass La Couarde. The site is approx. 2.5km beyond the village (in the direction of Ars en Re).

Charges 2004

Pitch and 3 persons	€ 23.50 - € 34.00
extra person	€ 5.50 - € 8.50
electricity (10A)	€ 5.00

Camping Cheques accepted.

Reservations

Contact site. Tel: 05 46 29 87 70.
Email: campingdelocean@wanadoo.fr

Open

1 April - 26 September.

17670 - La Couarde sur Mer
Tél. 05 46 29 87 70
Fax. 05 46 29 92 13
E.mail : campingdelocean@wanadoo.fr
site : campingocean.com

OUVERT DU 01/04 AU 26/09

CAMPING CARAVANING INTERNATIONAL

FR17220 Camping La Brande

Route des Huitres, 17480 Le Château-d'Oléron (Charente-Maritime)

A quality site, run and maintained to the highest standard, La Brande offers an ideal holiday environment on the delightful Ile d'Oleron, famed for its oysters. La Brande is situated on the oyster route and close to a sandy beach. The Barcat family ensure that their visitors not only enjoy quality facilities, but offer guided bicycle tours and canoe trips. This way you discover the nature and history of Oléron, which is joined to the mainland by a 3 km. bridge. Pitches here are generous and mostly separated by hedges and trees, the greater number for touring units. On level grass, all have electricity, some are fully serviced. A feature is the heated pool which can be covered under a sliding roof in cool weather. The many activities in high season, plus the natural surroundings, make it an ideal choice for families.

Facilities

Three heated, bright and clean sanitary blocks have spacious, well equipped showers and most washbasins in cabins. Baby bath/changing area. Excellent facilities for people with disabilities (separate large shower, washbasin and WC). Laundry room with hot water and sinks, plus washing machine and dryers. Motorcaravan service point. Restaurant/takeaway in July/Aug. Bar (late June - early Sept). Shop with basics in low season, but well stocked in main season. Play area on grass. Football field, tennis, minigolf, fishing and archery. Bicycle hire.

At a glance

Welcome & Ambience	✓✓✓✓	Location	✓✓✓✓
Quality of Pitches	✓✓✓✓	Range of Facilities	✓✓✓✓✓

Directions

After crossing bridge to L'Ile d'Oléron turn right towards Le Château d'Oléron. Go through village and follow sign for Route des Huitres. Site is 3 km.

Charges 2003

Per unit incl. 1 or 2 persons electricity (6-10A)	€ 15.00 - € 29.00 € 3.20 - € 3.80
Camping Cheques accepted.	

Reservations

Advised in high season and made with 25% deposit and € 16 fee. Tel: 05 46 47 62 37. Email: info@camping.labrande.com

Open

15 March - 15 November.

FR17190 Le Logis du Breuil

17570 St Augustin-sur-Mer (Charente-Maritime)

Space – no, not the final frontier, but the first impression on arrival at this impressive campsite. Between the site buildings and pool, and the camping area is a 200 m. expanse of farm pasture where (on different areas) cattle graze and children play. The camping areas themselves are set among rows of mature and shady trees which give a very restful, dappled effect to the tents, caravans and grassy pitches. The 320 pitches (with 3/6A electricity) are very large and have direct access to wide, unpaved alleys, which lead on to the few tarmac roads around the site. The campsite amenities are centred around the reception area and pool complex. The area around the site is very pleasant agricultural land and the beaches of the Atlantic coast are nearby, as are the oyster and the mussel beds of Marennes and La Tremblade. The Gagnard family take great pride in what it is a peaceful, friendly and very pleasant site from which to explore a delightful holiday area. A 'Sites et Paysages' member.

Facilities

Four very well maintained toilet blocks are well spaced around the camping area. Dishwashing and laundry facilities. Swimming pools. Shop, bar and snacks and takeaway (franchised) are well run. No evening entertainment. Play area. Indoor area providing archery, pool and table tennis. Bicycle hire. Tennis and basketball. Free archery. Excursions organised.

At a glance

Welcome & Ambience	✓✓✓✓✓	Location	✓✓✓✓
Quality of Pitches	✓✓✓✓✓	Range of Facilities	✓✓✓✓

Directions

Approaching Royan follow signs to St Palais sur Mer, bypassing Royan centre. Continue straight on past first traffic lights and roundabout. At second lights turn right. Site is 2 km, just before the village centre.

Charges 2003

Per unit incl. 2 persons with 3A electricity	€ 13.30 - € 15.40 € 16.60 - € 18.85

Reservations

Made with deposit (€ 46) and fee (€ 8). Tel: 05 46 23 23 45. Email: camping.Logis-du-Breuil@wanadoo.fr

Open

15 May - 15 September.

Quiet and space

Le Logis du Breuil

★★★

CAMPING   CARAVANING

17570 SAINT-AUGUSTIN-SUR-MER
Tel : (33) 05 46 23 23 45
Fax : (33) 05 46 23 43 33

CHALET AND MobilHOMES TO RENT

www.logis-du-breuil.com
camping.logis-du-breuil@wanadoo.fr

FR85510 Camping Le Bois Joli

2 rue de Châteauneuf, 85710 Bois de Céné (Vendée)

This site is a hidden gem in a small village away from the hustle and bustle of the seaside resorts. Suitable for people looking for a quiet holiday, it is still within driving distance of the Vendée coast (20 km). A warm welcome is given by the English speaking Urvoy family, who make every effort to make your stay enjoyable. On site is a small lake with free fishing (carp and eels), and a very large sports field (with a new portacabin style toilet block). The site also has a small swimming pool and paddling pool. A local farmer visits the site three times a week offering local produce. There are 130 pitches of which 90 are for touring units. All pitches have electricity, although not every pitch is serviced with water.

Facilities

Three toilet blocks - old, but with modern, bright tiles and very clean. All are unisex with some washbasins in cubicles, some controllable showers, two baby baths, two washing machines, dishwashing and laundry sinks. Bar with evening entertainment. Children's activities. Good play area with swings. Table tennis. Tennis court. Volleyball. Petanque. Bicycle hire. Off site: Supermarket in the village (two minutes walk). Walking, cycling and canoeing near. Riding 5 km.

At a glance

Welcome & Ambience	✓✓✓✓	Location	✓✓✓✓
Quality of Pitches	✓✓✓✓	Range of Facilities	✓✓✓✓

Directions

From Challans take D58 direct to Bois de Céné (10 km). Turn left at road junction in centre of village and site is immediately on right.

Latest charges

Per pitch incl. 2 persons	€ 8.40 - € 12.50
extra person	€ 2.40 - € 3.40
child (under 7 yrs)	€ 1.25 - € 1.80
electricity (6A)	€ 1.75 - € 2.50
animal	€ 1.35 - € 1.90

Reservations

Advised and made with deposit (€ 80 per week) and fee (€ 15). Tel: 02 51 68 20 05. Email: campingboisjoli@free.fr

Open

Easter - 15 September.

FR85200M Camping La Petite Boulogne

12 rue du Stade, 85670 St Etienne-du-Bois (Vendée)

Set in countryside 24 km. northwest of La Roche sur Yon, St Etienne-du-Bois is a quiet village, well away from the hustle and bustle of the big Vendée resorts. This site, owned by the local council, has 40 grassy pitches (most slightly sloping), all with electricity, water and drainage. Pitches are marked by low hedges giving the site an open and sunny aspect. Although the site is inland, it is only 20 km. to the coast with its large sandy beaches, but there are also many attractions and places to visit inland in the Vendée, and this good value municipal site provides a great base from which to explore the whole region.

Facilities

The modern, heated toilet block includes some washbasins in cabins. Laundry and dishwashing sinks. Room for disabled people with toilet and shower. Washing machine and dryer. Reception sells bread and a few other essentials. Small unheated pool (June - Aug). TV room. Table tennis. Small play area. Two free tennis courts. Bicycle hire. Daily events in area listed in reception and occasional animation organised in high season, introducing the region and its produce. Off site: Open-air, heated pool nearby. Bar and restaurant both few minutes walk away in village. Fishing possible in the nearby Petite Boulogne river. Volleyball and petanque at local sports centre (300 m). Supermarket 8 km at Legé.

At a glance

Welcome & Ambience	✓✓✓✓	Location	✓✓✓✓
Quality of Pitches	✓✓✓✓	Range of Facilities	✓✓✓

Directions

From Legé take D978 south towards Palluau for 7 km. then turn left on D94 towards St Etienne-du-Bois. Go straight through village and, as you come out the other side, cross a small bridge over the river. Site is 50 m. further on, on the right.

Charges 2003

Per unit incl. 2 persons	€ 10.00
extra person	€ 3.00
child (under 7 yrs)	€ 2.00
dog	€ 2.00
electricity (6A)	€ 2.50
No credit cards.	

Reservations

Made with deposit (€ 31). Tel: 02 51 34 54 51. Email: la.petite.boulogne@wanadoo.fr

Open

1 May - 31 October.

FR85630 Camping Maison Blanche au Perrier

85300 Le Perrier (Vendée)

A new venture in 2003 for an experienced campsite owner, Maison Blanche is undergoing a replanting program to eventually provide more shade and privacy to the 176 grassy touring pitches here. All are flat and of good size, most have electricity (6A) and water, but there are no dividing hedges. The pool is attractive and there are two tennis courts and a small playground. When we visited, the site was peaceful for high season, with no evening entertainment. A young English family described the site as a 'Little Paradise'! Only 500 m. from the small town of Le Perrier, bars and restaurants are an easy stroll, whilst Challans and St Jean de Monts (both about 6 km.) offer a wider range of facilities.

Facilities

Two toilet blocks provide washbasins (some open, some in cubicles), British and Turkish style toilets, showers, a baby room and toilet for disabled campers. Washing machine. No bar or restaurant, but a limited takeaway is provided. Heated swimming pool. TV/games room. Bicycle hire.Tennis. Football in a separate field. Some children's entertainment in high season. Off site: Small town 500 m. Beach 6 km.

At a glance

Welcome & Ambience	✓✓✓✓	Location	✓✓✓✓
Quality of Pitches	✓✓✓✓	Range of Facilities	✓✓✓✓

Directions

From D753 St Jean de Monts - Challans road, at traffic lights in the small town centre, turn north on D59. Turn left almost immediately and site is straight ahead.

Charges 2003

Per unit incl. 2 persons	€ 9.00 - € 10.10
electricity	€ 2.80

Reservations

Made with deposit and fee. Tel: 02 51 49 39 23. Email: camping.maisonblanche@wanadoo.fr

Open

1 May - 15 September.

FR85550 Camping Le Port de Moricq

Le Port de Moricq, 85750 Angles (Vendée)

Nestling amongst the marshes, this site was bought in 2002 by Mme Louche who is slowly but surely exerting her influence in carrying out improvements to the facilities. A comprehensive epicerie is planned for 2004. The 60 touring pitches are level and grassy and spread amongst the mobile homes. There are no tour operators on this site. There is little shade but hedges divide the pitches all of which have easy access to water and electricity. Outside high season the site is very quiet but in July and August there is a children's club twice a day and a varied evening entertainment programme.

Facilities

One traditional style, well maintained toilet block (a second is planned), has Turkish and British style toilets, washbasins in cubicles and open plan, a unit for disabled visitors. Dishwashing and laundry sinks under cover. Washing machine and dryer. Bar (15/3-15/10), Restaurant and takeaway (1/6-15/10). Heated outdoor pool (15/6-30/9). TV and games room with cable TV. Playground. Multi-sports pitch. Bicycle hire. Off site: Fishing in canals close by. Beaches, golf and riding all within 15 km.

At a glance

Welcome & Ambience	✓✓✓	Location	✓✓✓✓
Quality of Pitches	✓✓✓	Range of Facilities	✓✓✓

Directions

Site is signposted from roundabout on D747 (La Roche-sur-Yon - La Tranche), 7 km. south of the junction with D949 (Les Sables - Lucon) road.

Charges 2003

Per unit incl. 2 persons	€ 12.00 - € 17.00
with electricity (10/16A)	€ 14.00 - € 20.00

Reservations

Made with deposit (€ 80) and fee (€ 15). Tel: 02 51 28 95 21. Email: infos@camping-por-moricq.com

Open

15 March - 15 October.

FR85540 Domaine de L'Eden

La Railliere, 85600 Boissière de Montaigu (Vendée)

Hidden in the Haut Bocage area of the Vendée region, Le Domaine de l'Eden is a haven of tranquility in the traditional manner. This 35 acre site has 56 large, level touring pitches made up of grass and sand (long electricity cables may be needed) with mature trees providing varying amounts of shade. There are 44 mobile home pitches scattered throughout the site. The majority of visitors are French, many returning year after year, and there are no tour operators on the site. A limited programme of entertainment is provided in July and August and a good network of well marked footpaths and cycleways is easily accessible. Le Domaine de l'Eden offers the chance to taste the real France for oneself.

Facilities

Two well-maintained, heated toilet blocks include some washbasins in cabins; lighting is by time switch. Facilities for disabled visitors are opened on request. Washing machine and dryer. Dishwashing under cover. Small shop (11/4-31/10). Restaurant (1/6-30/9). Bar with TV open all year. Games room. Heated swimming pool with paddling area (15/6-15/9). Play areas. Tennis courts, multisports area, football pitch, minigolf and fitness course. Fishing in lake. Off site: Walking and cycling trails. Puy du Fou theme park.

At a glance

Welcome & Ambience	✓✓✓	Location	✓✓✓✓
Quality of Pitches	✓✓✓✓	Range of Facilities	✓✓✓✓

Directions

Site is signed from N137 Nantes - La Rochelle road, 7 km. south of Montaigu and 30 km. north of Chantonnay. At tourist office and Arrivé factory, take D62 northeast for 5 km. and follow signs.

Charges 2003

Per unit incl. 1 or 2 persons	€ 11.00 - € 17.00
extra person	€ 2.00 - € 4.00

Reservations

Contact site. Tel: 02 51 41 62 32. Email: domaine.eden@free.fr

Open

All year.

FR85370 Camping Les Mancellières

Route de Longeville-sur-Mer, 85440 Avrillé (Vendée)

This is a family run site on the edge of the small town of Avrillé, on the road between La Rochelle and Noirmoutiers, yet only a short drive from some of the delightful beaches of the southern Vendée. It is a simple, well-established site with 130 pitches (82 touring pitches), most with a mixture of sun and shade, but some very shaded. The fact that the snack bar is not licensed might appeal to those who prefer a simple life! Organised events include a weekly outdoor disco, accompanied by moules-frites and other activities including a France v. The Rest football match at the nearby stade (all July/Aug).

Facilities

The two sanitary blocks are kept clean, with mainly British style WCs, washbasins (some in cubicles), baby bath in the ladies' wash rooms, an en-suite unit for disabled visitors. Sinks for dishwashing and laundry. Washing machine. Small shop and adjacent snack bar open in July/Aug. Swimming pool and water slide (until 15 Sept). Play area and good sized sports area. Two games rooms. Off site: Tennis 800 m. Riding 7 km. Golf 10 km. Sea 5 km.

At a glance

Welcome & Ambience	✓✓✓✓	Location	✓✓✓✓
Quality of Pitches	✓✓✓	Range of Facilities	✓✓✓✓

Directions

Avrillé is on the D949 Les Sables d'Olonne - Luçon road, 23 km. from Les Sables. Site is about 1 km. south of the town, on D105 to Longeville-sur-Mer.

Latest charges

Per unit incl. 2 persons	€ 13.57
electricity (6A)	€ 2.74

Reservations

Advised for high season. Tel: 02 51 90 35 97.

Open

1 May - 30 September.

FR85320 Camping Caravaning Val de Vie

Rue du Stade, 85190 Maché (Vendée)

Opened in 1999, Val de Vie is a small, good quality site run with enthusiasm and dedication by its English owners on the outskirts of a rural village back from the coast. There are currently 52 pitches for touring units (42 with electricity) that vary in size from 80-137 sq.m. on mostly level grass with new hedging. The ground can become very hard so steel pegs are advised. The pitches are arranged in circular fashion around the toilet block which, with reception, is built in local style with attractive, red tiled roofs. The owners, the McClearns, want you to experience real French village life and culture and encourage you to enjoy the local amenities. If you are looking for a beach, the Vendée coast is 25 km.

Facilities

The toilet block provides excellent, modern facilities including some washbasins in cabins, baby bath, facilities for disabled people, dishwashing and laundry sinks, and washing machines. Reception also offers wine, beer, soft drinks and ice cream. Small play area for young children. Swimming pool (from mid May). Bicycle hire. Off site: Opposite site are a heated outdoor municipal pool and tennis courts. Shops, bar, tabac, etc. all within walking distance, with a good restaurant 2 km. away. Lake d'Apremont (300 m.) and Aprement itself with Renaissance château are 4 km. Vendée coast 20 km.

At a glance

Welcome & Ambience	✓✓✓✓	Location	✓✓✓✓
Quality of Pitches	✓✓✓✓	Range of Facilities	✓✓✓

Directions

From D948 at Aizenay take D107 northwest to Maché (6 km). Site signed in the village.

Charges 2003

Per unit incl. 2 persons	€ 17.00
child (under 10 yrs)	€ 3.00
electricity (4-10A)	€ 2.90 - € 3.50

Less 20% in low season (excl. electricity).
No credit cards.

Reservations

Contact site. Tel: 02 51 60 21 02.
Email: campingvaldevie@aol.com

Open

1 May - 30 September.

FR85580 Camping Les Blancs Chenes

Route de la Roche sur Yon, 85360 La Tranche-sur-Mer (Vendée)

Part of the Vagues Océanes group, this is a very well managed site with good facilities, excellent children's activities and a varied programme of high season entertainment for all the family. The manager and his staff take a real pride in their work. The 40 level touring pitches are on sandy grass, are separated by hedges and have access to electricity. They are scattered around the site and some have shade. The site is 1.8 km. from the town of La Tranche with its many shops, restaurants and its sandy beach. In high season a free bus service to the beach is provided.

Facilities

Three modern toilet blocks have washbasins in cabins, good baby units and facilities for disabled visitors. Shop (15/4-30/9). Bar with TV (15/4-30/9). Restaurant and takeaway (15/4-30/9). Large pool complex with vast sun terrace, indoor pool (15/4-30/9), outdoor pool (15/6- 15/9) with jacuzzi, paddling pool and slides. Good sports facilities include tennis (charged), minigolf, table tennis and a multi-sports terrain. Bicycle hire. Key-operated barrier.

At a glance

Welcome & Ambience	✓✓✓✓	Location	✓✓✓
Quality of Pitches	✓✓✓	Range of Facilities	✓✓✓✓

Directions

Site is well signed on the western side of the D747 (La Tranche - La Roche) road, 2 km. north of La Tranche.

Charges 2003

Per unit incl. 2 persons	€ 17.00 - € 21.00
electricity (5A)	€ 5.00

Reservations

Contact Vagues Océanes reservations office at Rte. de la Roche-sur-Yon, 85360 La Tranche-sur-Mer. Tel: 02 51 30 41 70. Email: vagues.oceanes@wanadoo.fr

Open

15 April - 30 September.

FR85020 Camping du Jard

123 Mal de Lattre de Tassigny, 85360 La Tranche-sur-Mer (Vendée)

Camping du Jard is a well maintained site between La Rochelle and Les Sables d'Olonne. First impressions on booking in are good, with a friendly welcome from M. Marton or his staff and each new arrival being personally shown to their pitch. The 350 pitches are level and grassy, hedged on two sides by bushes. The smallest are 100 sq.m. (the majority larger) and most are equipped with electricity, half with water and drainage. It is a comparatively new site, but the large variety of trees is beginning to provide a little shade. An impressive pool complex has a toboggan, paddling pool and an indoor pool with jacuzzi. The site is 700 m. from a sandy beach with many shops and restaurants near. Used by British tour operators (150 pitches).

Facilities

Three toilet blocks, well designed and maintained, are light and airy with excellent facilities for babies and disabled people and most washbasins are in cabins. Washing machines and dryer. Dishwashing and laundry sinks. Small shop for basics (1/6-10/9), restaurant and bar (both 25/5-10/9). Heated swimming pool with toboggan and paddling pool, plus good heated indoor pool with jacuzzi (no bermuda-style shorts in the pools). Sauna, solarium and fitness room with instructors. Tennis court, minigolf, table tennis. Bicycle hire. Play area, games room and TV room. Card operated barrier with outside parking. American motorhomes are not accepted. Dogs allowed with papers.

At a glance

Welcome & Ambience	✓✓✓✓	Location	✓✓✓✓
Quality of Pitches	✓✓✓✓	Range of Facilities	✓✓✓✓✓

Directions

Site is east of La Tranche-sur-Mer on the D46. From D747 (La Roche-sur-Yon to La Tranche) follow signs for La Faute-sur-mer along the new bypass. Take exit for La Grière and then turn east to site.

Charges 2003

Per standard pitch incl. 2 persons	€ 16.50 - € 21.50
with electricity (10A)	€ 19.60 - € 26.15
with electricity, water and drainage	€ 21.30 - € 28.40
extra person	€ 3.65 - € 4.85
child (under 5 yrs)	€ 2.55 - € 3.40

Plus local tax.

Reservations

Advisable for July/Aug. (min. 1 week, Sat.- Sat.) with deposit (€ 100). Tel: 02 51 27 43 79. Email: info@camping-du-jard.fr

Open

25 May - 15 September.

FR85440 Camping Les Brunelles

Le Bouil, 85560 Longeville sur Mer (Vendée)

This is a well managed site with good facilities and a varied programme of high season entertainment for all the family. The owner, M. Guinard is justifiably proud of his campsite. The leaflet given to all visitors on arrival (together with a bottle of wine) explains in detail the workings of the campsite and the standards of behaviour expected. In mid July the site was very busy but there was an atmosphere of well ordered calm. M. Guinard believes that if the children are happy and occupied then the parents are also happy. This approach certainly seems to work. This has to be one of the cleanest and neatest sites on the Vendée. The 60 touring pitches are all level on sandy grass and separated by hedges, away from most of the mobile homes on site. There is a mixture of sunny and shaded pitches and all have easy access to electricity. Water points are not so frequent. A good sandy beach is just 900 m.

Facilities

Four old but well maintained and modernised toilet blocks have British and Turkish style toilets, washbasins both open style and in cabins, plenty of sinks for dishwashing and laundry, five washing machines, two dryers and ironing. Shop (from 1/6). Takeaway (l5/6-7/9). Large modern, airy bar (15/6-15/9) with games area overlooks the impressive pool complex. Covered pool with jacuzzi (all season). Outdoor pool with slides and paddling pools (from 15/5), both pools are heated but unsupervised. Table tennis. Tennis. Bicycle hire.

At a glance

Welcome & Ambience	✓✓✓✓	Location	✓✓✓
Quality of Pitches	✓✓✓	Range of Facilities	✓✓✓✓✓

Directions

From the D21 Talmont - Longeville road, between St Vincent and Longueville, site is well signed south from the main road towards the coast. Turn left in village of Le Bouil (site signed) and site is 800 m. on left.

Latest charges

Per unit incl. 2 persons	€ 14.00 - € 18.00
with electricity (6A)	€ 17.00 - € 22.00

Camping Cheques accepted.

Reservations

Made with deposit and fee. Tel: 02 51 33 50 75. Email: camping@les-brunelles.com

Open

3 April - 8 September.

www.alanrogers.com for latest campsite news

FR85420 Camping 'Bel

Rue du Bottereau, 85360 La Tranche-sur-Mer (Vendée)

Camping 'Bel's owner, M. Guicau, who has a very dry sense of humour, takes an individual approach. The first priority is the contentment of the children, who receive various small gifts during their stay. His policy of 'word of mouth'; being the best form of publicity certainly seems to be effective. The site was almost full when we visited in July with a large proportion of returning French clients, despite the large presence of British tour operators (130 pitches). At this time other nearby sites did not have such high occupancy rates. The 70 touring pitches are on level, sandy grass which was well worn in July. They are separated by hedges with some mature trees giving shade. Only 20 of the pitches have electrical connections (10A). It is only 150 m. from a good sandy beach and 500 m. from the seaside town of La Tranche sur Mer. This is a good site for a family beach holiday.

Facilities

Two modern toilet blocks have washbasins in cabins, very good baby units and facilities for the disabled. Shop with basic provisions. Bar. Heated outdoor pool with jacuzzi. Entertainment for children aged 6-14 yrs July/Aug). Table tennis. Fitness area. Tennis. Pets are not accepted. Off site: Bicycle hire 100 m. Supermarket with fuel 200 m. Fishing 150 m. Watersports 150 m. Riding 5 km.

At a glance

| Welcome & Ambience | ✓✓✓✓ | Location | ✓✓✓✓ |
| Quality of Pitches | ✓✓✓✓ | Range of Facilities | ✓✓✓✓ |

Directions

Follow signs from the roundabout on the La Tranche bypass, near 'Super U' supermarket.

Charges 2004

Per unit with 2 persons and water	€ 19.50
with electricity (6A)	€ 22.80
child (under 5 yrs)	€ 3.30
local tax	€ 0.50

Reservations

Contact site. Tel: 02 51 30 47 39.

Open

25 May - 8 September with all services.

FR85240M Camping Caravaning Jarny–Ocean

Le Bouil, 85560 Longeville sur Mer (Vendée)

Jarny Ocean is the sort of the site the French love – wooded and with many pitches separated by thick hedges giving plenty of privacy. There are other areas, however, which are more open and with plenty of sun. There are 303 large, grassy pitches on level ground, of which 250 are for touring units, around 25% well shaded. All have electricity, about 15 also with water and drain. A beach is within easy walking distance (800 m) or a beach with lifeguards (and parking) is 4 km. English is spoken.

Facilities

Five toilet blocks of differing ages have a mix of British and Turkish style WCs. Small shop for basics in July/Aug, but bread, croissants, etc. can be ordered from reception all season. Takeaway in the Centre de Vacances that shares the site (from 1/5). Bar (weekends in low season, 11.00 - 01.00 hrs in July/Aug). Heated swimming pool (1/5 -15/9). Large central play area. Table tennis. Tennis. Bicycle hire. Volleyball and basketball.

At a glance

| Welcome & Ambience | ✓✓✓✓ | Location | ✓✓✓✓ |
| Quality of Pitches | ✓✓✓✓ | Range of Facilities | ✓✓✓✓ |

Directions

From D21 Talmont - Longeville road, soon after Jard, pass through St Vincent and very shortly the site is signed towards the coast (before Longeville).

Charges 2004

| Per unit incl. 2 adults | € 7.45 - € 18.20 |
| with 6A electricity | € 9.20 - € 21.00 |

Reservations

Made with deposit (€ 45.73) and fee (€ 15.24). Tel: 02 51 33 42 21. Email: jarny-ocean@wanadoo.fr

Open

1 May - 30 September.

FR85430 Camping Club La Bolée d'Air

Route de Longeville, 85520 St Vincent sur Jard (Vendée)

This is a well managed site with good facilities and a varied programme of high season entertainment. The 120 touring pitches are all level and well grassed on sandy soil. Many are situated around the perimeter of the site and are separated by trimmed hedges giving good privacy but little shade. Long electricity cables may be required on some pitches. The main road runs along one side of the site and may cause traffic noise at some times although when we visited in July there did not appear to be a problem. A refurbished complex at the entrance houses all the amenities. A good beach is just 900 m.

Facilities

Three modernised, unisex sanitary blocks provide washbasins in cabins, plenty of sinks for dishwashing and laundry, washing machines and dryers. Shop and takeaway (1/6-31/8). Bar (1/5-30/9). Heated indoor pool, outdoor pool (1/6-30/9) with slide, jacuzzi and paddling pool. Tennis. Minigolf. Bicycle hire. Table tennis. Good multi-sport all-weather terrain.

At a glance

| Welcome & Ambience | ✓✓✓✓ | Location | ✓✓✓ |
| Quality of Pitches | ✓✓✓ | Range of Facilities | ✓✓✓✓ |

Directions

Site is just off the D21 Les Sables La Franche road, just east of St Vincent-sur-Jard and is well signed.

Charges 2004

| Per unit with 2 persons and car | € 12.00 - € 22.00 |
| electricity | € 4.00 |

Reservations

Made with deposit, fee and cancellation insurance. Tel: 02 51 90 36 05. Email: info@chardotel.com

Open

1 April - 30 September.

FR85210 Camping Les Ecureuils

Route des Goffineaux, 85520 Jard-sur-Mer (Vendée)

Les Ecureuils is a wooded site in a quieter part of the southern Vendée. It is undoubtedly one of the prettiest sites on this stretch of coast, with an elegant reception area, attractive vegetation and large pitches separated by low hedges with plenty of shade. Of the 261 pitches, some 120 are for touring units, each with water and drainage, as well as easy access to electricity. Jard is rated among the most pleasant and least hectic of Vendée towns. The harbour is home to some fishing boats and rather more pleasure craft, and has a public slipway for those bringing their own boats. This site is very popular with tour operators (126 pitches). And in case you are curious, yes there are squirrels on site, including red ones! A new indoor pool and spa were added in 2002.

Facilities

Two toilet blocks, well equipped and kept very clean, include baby baths, and laundry rooms. Small shop. Takeaway service (pre-order). Snacks and ice-creams available from the friendly bar. Good sized L-shaped swimming pool and separate paddling pool. New indoor pool. Modern play area. Minigolf, table tennis and a pool table. Club for children (5-10 yrs) daily in July/Aug. Bicycle hire. Only gas barbecues are allowed. Dogs are not accepted. Off site: Nearest beach 400 m. Fishing 400 m. Many places to eat at nearby marina or in town which has good supermarket and weekly market.

At a glance

Welcome & Ambience	✓✓✓✓	Location	✓✓✓✓✓
Quality of Pitches	✓✓✓✓	Range of Facilities	✓✓✓✓

Directions

Jard-sur-Mer is on the D21 road between Talmont St Hilaire and Longeville sur Mer. Site is well signed from the main road - caravanners will need to follow these signs to avoid tight bends and narrow roads.

Charges 2003

Per person	€ 6.00
child (0-4 yrs)	€ 2.00
child (5-9 yrs)	€ 4.00
per pitch with water and drainage	€ 11.50
with electricity (10A)	€ 15.50

Less 10% outside 30/6-1/9.

Reservations

Advised for July/Aug. Tel: 02 51 33 42 74. Email: camping-ecureuils@wanadoo.fr

Open

15 May - 15 September.

FR85270 Chadotel Camping L'Oceano d'Or

58 rue Georges Clémenceau, BP 12, 85520 Jard-sur-Mer (Vendée)

This site should appeal to families with children of all ages. It is very lively in high season but appears to be well managed, with a full programme of activities in high season (it can therefore be noisy, sometimes late at night). The site is only 999 metres from the excellent beach. There are 431 flat, grass and sand pitches of which 40% are occupied by tour operators and mobile homes. The 200 for touring units, all with 10A electricity, are quite large (about 100 sq.m.). Some are separated by high hedges, others are more open with low bushes between them. A modern complex at the entrance houses all the facilities. There are shops, bars and restaurants, and a weekly market in the pleasant little town of Jard-sur-Mer.

Facilities

Four modern, unisex toilet blocks include washbasins all in cabins, plenty of dishwashing and laundry sinks and washing machines and dryers. Small shop (1/6-15/9). Bar and snack bar (both 15/6-15/9, but limited hours outside high season). Swimming pool (15/5-15/9) with 3 water slides, 2 waterfalls and children's pool. Walled (three sides) play area with lots of recently refurbished equipment. Tennis, table tennis, volleyball, pétanque and minigolf. Charcoal barbecues are not allowed. Off site: Golf, riding, karting and numerous other activities within 15 km. Excellent beach within walking distance.

At a glance

| Welcome & Ambience | ✓✓✓ | Location | ✓✓✓ |
| Quality of Pitches | ✓✓✓ | Range of Facilities | ✓✓✓✓ |

Directions

Site is on the D21 Talmont St Hilaire - Longeville sur Mer, just east of the turning to the town centre.

Charges 2003

Per pitch incl. 2 adults	€ 14.00 - € 22.00
with electricity	€ 18.00 - € 26.00
child (under 5 yrs)	€ 3.50

Reservations

Necessary for high season with deposit (€ 39) and fee (€ 22,87). Central reservations: Siege Social - Centrale de Reservation, BP 12, 85520 Jard-sur-Mer. Tel: 02 51 33 05 05. Email: chadotel@wanadoo.fr

Open

1 April - 25 September.

FR85570 Camping Caravaning Le Pomme de Pin

Rue Vincent Auriol, 85520 Jard-sur-Mer (Vendée)

This family run site, set amongst the pines is just 300 metres from a sandy beach and within easy reach of the town of Jard with its lively weekly market and fishing harbour. The site specialises in mobile homes (over 140) but there are six small touring pitches. The compact, attractively laid out swimming pool is overlooked by the bar and sun terrace. In the high season there is a good entertainment programme for all ages.

Facilities

Three unisex toilet blocks provide washbasins in cabins (warm water only) and preset showers. Simple facilities only for babies and disabled vsitors. Washing machines and dryer. Bar, restaurant, takeaway (1/6-30/9). Small well-stocked shop (15/6-30/9). Play area and outdoor table tennis table. No charcoal barbecues. Off site: Sailing school, water sports, minigolf, tennis and beaches all within 2 km.

At a glance

| Welcome & Ambience | ✓✓✓✓ | Location | ✓✓✓ |
| Quality of Pitches | ✓✓✓ | Range of Facilities | ✓✓✓ |

Directions

From the D21 (Talmont - Longeville) road, site is signed to the south.

Charges 2004

| Per pitch | € 14.00 - € 21.50 |
| with electricity | € 17.50 - € 25.20 |

Reservations

Contact site. Tel: 02 51 33 43 85. Email: info@pommedepin.net

Open

1 April - 30 September.

FR85560 Camping Caravaning Le Curtys

Rue de la Perpoise, 85520 Jard-sur-Mer (Vendée)

Situated on the very edge of the town of Jard-sur-Mer with its lively weekly market, shops and restaurants, this is a very well organised site with good facilities and plenty of entertainment for all ages in high season. There are varying amounts of shade from mature trees around the site and substantial hedges separate the pitches. A large swimming pool complex provides indoor and outdoor heated pools, a paddling pool and a slide. There are just 12 pitches for touring units here, with over 350 mobile homes.

Facilities

Three traditional style toilet blocks include washing machines and dryers. Shop (15/5-20/9). Bar, snack bar, and takeaway (19/4-20/9). Unsupervised indoor and outdoor swimming pools (19/4-20/9). Tennis court. Football pitch. Fitness centre. Multi-sports terrain. Three playgrounds. Volleyball. Table tennis. Games room. Bicycle hire. Off site: Beach 1.8 km. Town centre 0.5 km. Minigolf 100 m. Golf 12 km. Riding 3 km. Canoeing 7 km.

At a glance

| Welcome & Ambience | ✓✓✓✓ | Location | ✓✓✓ |
| Quality of Pitches | ✓✓✓ | Range of Facilities | ✓✓✓✓ |

Directions

Site is clearly signed from the D21 (Talmont St Hilaire - Longeville) at junction by the church on outskirts of Jard.

Charges 2003

Per pitch incl. 2 persons	€ 20.00
with 6A electricity	€ 25.00
child (under 5 yrs)	€ 4.00

Reservations

Tel: 02 51 33 06 55. Email: info@palmiers-ocean.fr

Open

19 April - 20 September.

(125)

FR85460 Camping La Dune des Sables

85100 Les Sables-d'Olonne (Vendée)

La Dune des Sables has a splendid coastal setting with views of the Vendée coastline. It has undulating terrain with no shade and limited protection from wind off the sea. Access to the sandy/rocky beach is by a locked gate (opened by your barrier key) at the bottom of the site. The 50 touring pitches, all with electricity and water (long cables may be required) are situated throughout the site and vary in size. There is little grass on the sandy pitches some of which are separated by hedges or fences. There are 90 mobile homes and 160 tour operator pitches. In high season there is a lively programme of animation. Some events take place outside the bar where there is a wide terrace and stage.

Facilities

Four well maintained toilet blocks provide washbasins in cabins, a unit for disabled people, a baby room, washing machines and dryers. Bar (1/6-7/9). Shop (15/6-7/9). Restaurant (1/7-31/8). Takeaway (15/6-9/9). Play area. Tennis. Minigolf. Table tennis. Basketball. Volleyball. Bicycle hire. Off site: golf, fishing, water sports, zoo, all near.

At a glance

Welcome & Ambience	✓✓✓✓	Location	✓✓✓✓
Quality of Pitches	✓✓✓	Range of Facilities	✓✓✓✓

Directions

From Les Sables or Brem-sur-Mer follow D87a and at autoroute follow signs west on minor road at small roundabout. Site is on right after 500 m.

Charges 2004

Per pitch incl. 2 persons	€ 14.00 - € 22.50
with electricity (6A)	€ 18.00 - € 26.50

Reservations

Contact site. Tel: 02 51 32 31 21. Email: chadotel@wanadoo.fr

Open

5 April - 25 September.

FR85470 Camping Les Pirons

Rue des Marchais, La Pironnière, 85180 Château-d'Olonne (Vendée)

This is a modern, well run site of which the new owner M. Chailloleau is very proud. The site is a short walk from the sandy beach and within easy reach of the attractive seaside town of Les Sables d'Olonne. The 114 grass touring pitches, either level or on a slight slope, are in one central area of the campsite away from the many mobile homes (over 300). The large new toilet block is impressive, as is the pool complex overlooked by the bar`s sun terrace. There are several small French tour operators on the site (56 pitches). At the start of the season the site is quiet and facilities are limited. In high season there is an excellent animation programme for all ages with evening entertainment nightly.

Facilities

Four toilet blocks, of which three are new, have washbasins in cubicles and units for disabled people, babies and dogs. Washing machines and dryers. Bar (29/6-31/8) with sun terrace overlooking the pool. Shop (29/6-31/8). Takeaway (29/6- 31/8). Covered, heated pool, outdoor pools with slide. Good play area. Table tennis, volleyball, football. Tennis. Pétanque. Indoor games area. Bicycle, scooter and motorbike hire. Activities for all ages (29/6-31/8). Off site: Beach, sea fishing, riding and sailing all within 5 km.

At a glance

Welcome & Ambience	✓✓✓✓	Location	✓✓✓✓
Quality of Pitches	✓✓✓	Range of Facilities	✓✓✓✓

Directions

From D949 Les Sables - La Rochelle road, site is well signed at traffic lights near Toyota garage on the western outskirts of Les Sables d'Olonne.

Charges 2003

Per unit incl. 3 persons	€ 15.00 - € 20.00
with electricity (6A)	€ 18.00 - € 24.00

Reservations

Made with 30% deposit and € 18.29 fee. Tel: 02 51 95 26 75. Email: camping.les.pirons@wanadoo.fr

Open

1 April - 31 October.

FR85450 Camping Les Roses

Rue des Roses, 85100 les Sables d'Olonne (Vendée)

Les Roses has an urban location, with the town centre and the beach just a short walk away. There is an informal air with the 210 pitches arranged interestingly on a knoll. Mature trees give good shade to parts of the site. There are 107 touring pitches of varying size, many being more suitable for tents than caravans. All pitches have access to electricity and water but long cables may be needed. In high season caravanners might find access to the site tricky at times due to town centre traffic. The site has 103 mobile homes and chalets, but no tour operators. An entertainment programme is arranged in high season for all ages. The town of Les Sables with its lively night life is readily accessible.

Facilities

There are three well maintained toilet blocks with washbasins in cubicles, unit for disabled visitors, baby room, washing machines and dryers. Bar (15/5-15/9). Simple shop. Small attractively laid out, heated, outdoor swimming pool with water slide and paddling pool (1/5-30/9). Play area. Volleyball, basketball, petanque and table tennis. Bicycle hire. Electric barbecues are not permitted. Off site: Golf, riding, water sports, sea and river fishing all near.

At a glance

Welcome & Ambience	✓✓✓	Location	✓✓✓✓✓
Quality of Pitches	✓✓✓	Range of Facilities	✓✓✓✓

Directions

Site is signed from the D949 Les Sables to La Rochelle road, north of the 'Géant Casino' roundabout. Turn south at minor junction.

Charges 2004

Per pitch incl. 2 persons	€ 14.00 - € 22.50
with electricity (10A)	€ 28.00 - € 26.50

Reservations

Contact site. Tel: 02 51 33 05 05. Email: info@chardotel.com

Open

1 April - 31 October.

FR85400 **Camping Bois Soleil**

Chemin des Barres, 85340 Olonne-sur-Mer (Vendée)

This site has a very French feel, the majority of the population when we visited seeming to be French. It is a traditionally laid out site with 199 marked pitches, separated by hedges, on flat or gently sloping ground. There are just two tour operators and a scattering of mobile homes and chalets, leaving some 87 pitches available for tourers and tents. All have electricity (French style sockets) and water points adjacent and many also have waste water pipes. The main buildings house a small reception and tourist information room as well as the bar and attached shop. There is an excellent new swimming pool complex with sunbathing areas, paddling pool and a separate pool for the two water slides and impressive flume. In July and August a range of daily activities is organised for adults and children.

Facilities

The two well equipped and maintained toilet blocks have copious hot water, mainly British style toilets, with washbasins in cubicles in the new block. This block is locked overnight, but basic toilet facilities are provided. Covered dishwashing and laundry sinks. Two washing machines. Shop (July/Aug. only) with 'eat in' or takeaway service; bread (and cooked chicken) must to be ordered the previous day. Swimming and paddling pools. Sandy play area (caged), trampoline and table tennis. Off site: Beaches are just 2 km. The thriving resort of Les Sables d'Olonne is 5 km. along the coast.

At a glance

Welcome & Ambience	✓✓✓✓	Location	✓✓✓
Quality of Pitches	✓✓✓	Range of Facilities	✓✓✓✓

Directions

Site is off the D80 coast road between Olonne-sur-Mer and is clearly signed on the inland side.

Charges 2003

Per unit incl. 2 persons	€ 14.00 - € 17.00
with electricity (6A)	€ 17.00 - € 20.00
extra person	€ 2.00 - € 2.50
child (under 7 yrs)	€ 2.00 - € 2.50
animal	€ 2.50

Reservations

Advised for July/Aug. and made with 25% deposit and booking fee in July/Aug of € 18. Tel: 02 51 33 11 97. Email: camping.boissoleil@wanadoo.fr

Open

5 April - 28 September.

FR85040 **Castel Camping Caravaning La Garangeoire**

St Julien-des-Landes, 85150 La Mothe-Achard (Vendée)

La Garangeoire is one of a relatively small number of seriously good sites in the Vendée, situated some 15 km. inland near the village of St Julien des Landes. One of its more memorable qualities is the view of the château through the gates as you drive in. Imaginative use has been made of the old Noirmoutiers 'main road' which passes through the centre of the site and now forms a delightful, quaint thoroughfare, nicknamed the Champs Elysée. Providing a village like atmosphere, it is busy at most times with the facilities opening directly off it. The site is set in the 200 ha. of parkland surrounding the small château of La Garangeoire. The peaceful fields and woods, where campers may walk, include three lakes, one of which is used for fishing and boating (life jackets supplied from reception). With a spacious, relaxed atmosphere, the main camping areas are arranged on either side of the old road, edged with mature trees. The 300 pitches, each with a name not a number and individually hedged, are especially large (most 150-200 sq.m.) and are well spaced. Most have electricity, some water and drainage also. The site is popular with tour operators (144 pitches).

Facilities

Ample sanitary facilities are of good standard, well situated for all areas. One excellent block has facilities for babies and disabled people. All have washbasins in cabins. Good laundry facilities. Motorcaravan service point. Good shop. Full restaurant, takeaway and a separate crêperie with bars and attractive courtyard terrace overlooking the swimming pool complex (from 1/5) with water slides, fountains and a children's pool. Large play field with play equipment for children's activities, whether organised or not. Games room. Two tennis courts. Bicycle hire. Table tennis, crazy golf, archery and volleyball. Riding in July/Aug. Fishing and boating. Off site: Beaches 15 km.

At a glance

Welcome & Ambience	✓✓✓✓✓	Location	✓✓✓✓
Quality of Pitches	✓✓✓✓	Range of Facilities	✓✓✓✓✓

Directions

Site is signed from St Julien; the entrance is to the east off the D21 road, 2.5 km north of St Julian-des-Landes.

Charges 2003

Per unit incl. 2 persons	€ 14.00 - € 24.00
with electricity (12A)	€ 17.00 - € 28.00
with services	€ 18.50 - € 30.00
extra person	€ 3.50 - € 5.50
child (under 10 yrs)	€ 2.00 - € 2.50
dog	€ 2.00 - € 3.00
local tax	free - € 0.51

Camping Cheques accepted.

Reservations

Made for min. 7 days with deposit (€ 61) and fee (€ 22,87). Tel: 02 51 46 65 39. Email: garangeoire@wanadoo.fr

Open

5 April - 24 September.

FR85260 Village de la Guyonnière

La Guyonnière, 85150 St Julien des Landes (Vendée)

La Guyonnière is a spacious, rural site, away from the hertic coast. It is popular for many reasons, the main ones being the free and easy atmosphere and its reasonable pricing. It is Dutch owned and the majority of its customers are Dutch, but English is spoken and British visitors are made very welcome. It is a farm type site with four different fields, each being reasonably level and each having a toilet block. The 182 pitches are sunny and very large (the few smaller ones are cheaper) and are separated by a tree and a few bushes. All have access to electricity connections although long leads may be required. Bar/restaurant facilities are housed in the original farm buildings attractively converted. Entertainment is provided in the bar on high season evenings. A perfect place for families, with large play areas on sand and grass,and paddling pond with shower. Being in the country it is a haven for cyclists and walkers, with many signed routes from the site. A pleasant 500 m. walk takes you to the Jaunay lake where fishing is possible (permits from the village), canoeing (lifejackets from reception) and pedaloes to hire. There are no tour operators and, needless to say, no road noise.

Facilities

Toilet blocks are modern, functional and central for each area. Most cubicles are quite small but they serve their purpose and were very clean when we visited; however, perhaps not adequate in high season. Washbasins are in cubicles. Provision for babies and disabled visitors. Dishwashing and laundry sinks at each block. Shop (1/5-15/9; order bread from reception outside these dates). Bar with TV and pool table and pleasant restaurant (1/5-15/9). Pizzeria with takeaway. Small swimming pool, new heated pool with jacuzzi and slide, very attractive and can be covered in cool weather. Paddling pool. Play areas, sand pit. Table tennis, volleyball and football fields. Bicycle hire. Off site: Riding 3 km, golf 8 km, beaches 10 km.

At a glance

Welcome & Ambience	✓✓✓✓	Location	✓✓✓✓
Quality of Pitches	✓✓✓	Range of Facilities	✓✓✓✓✓

Directions

Site is off the D12 road (La Mothe Achard - St Gilles Croix de Vie), approx. 4 km. west of St Julien-des-Landes. It is signed about 1 km. from the main road.

Charges 2004

Per unit incl. 2 persons and electricity	€ 27.45
extra person	€ 5.00
child (3-9 yrs)	€ 3.00
animal	€ 2.50
local tax	€ 0.51
Less 10-20% outside high season.	

Reservations

Made with 25% deposit. Tel: 02 51 46 62 59. Email: info@laguyonniere.com

Open

1 May - 20 September.

FR85130 Camping Pong

Rue du Stade, 85220 Landevieille (Vendée)

A comfortable family run site, Camping Pong is in a rural situation on the edge of a neat village, 12 km. southeast of St Gilles-Croix-de-Vie, and 5 km. from the coast at Brétignolles. It has 230 pitches, all with electricity and of a good size with some larger ones costing a little more. The redeveloped entrance and reception area provides an efficient welcome and the bar, restaurant, function room, games room, gym and shop have all recently been rebuilt. The original part of the site around the small, lightly fenced fishing lake (there are warning signs) has a mixture of mature trees, whereas, in the newer areas the vegetation is less developed. An attractive pool area includes a delightful paddling pool with many fascinating features for children and a pretty patio area overlooked by the bar. There are no tour operator pitches.

Facilities

Four modern, unisex sanitary blocks provide toilets of mixed styles and some washbasins in cabins. Facilities for disabled people, separate baby room, dishwashing under cover and laundry room. Maintenance can be variable. New shop, takeaway, bar and restaurant (15/6-15/9). Swimming pools including heated pool with jacuzzi, toboggan and paddling pool (from 15/5). Small gym, TV lounge and games room. Bicycle hire. Exciting new fenced play area and regular children's club. Off site: Tennis 200 m. Golf or riding 5 km. Large Lac du Jaunay 2.5 km. (canoeing and pedaloes), Lac d'Apremont and its XV1 century château 14 km. Nearest beach 6 km.

At a glance

Welcome & Ambience	✓✓✓✓	Location	✓✓✓✓
Quality of Pitches	✓✓✓✓	Range of Facilities	✓✓✓✓

Directions

Site is on the edge of Landevieille and is signed from both the D32 (Challons-Les Sables d'Olonne) and D12 (La Mothe Achard-St Gilles Croix de Vie) roads.

Charges 2003

Per unit incl. 2 persons	€ 11.50 - € 23.00
extra person	€ 4.00
child (under 5 yrs)	€ 3.00
electricity (4-6A)	€ 3.00 - € 4.00
water and drainage	€ 1.00
dog	€ 3.00

Reservations

Made with dates of arrival and departure, plus deposit and fee. Tel: 02 51 22 92 63. Email: lepong@free.fr

Open

Easter - 30 September.

FR85310 Chadotel Camping La Trévillière

Rue de Bellevue, 85470 Bretignolles-sur-Mer (Vendée)

A member of the Chadotel group, La Trévillière has a pleasant semi-rural setting on the edge of the little resort town of Bretignolles. Although just 2 km. from the nearest beach and less than 5 km, from the Plage des Dunes (one of southern Vendée's best beaches), La Trévillière has a more 'laid-back' feel than many other sites in the area, particularly in low season. After a new extension, there are now 203 pitches, all with easy access to electricity and water. The original area provides either level or slightly sloping pitches separated by hedges or low bushes and there is a mix of shady or more open positions. The new area has no shade as yet from newly planted trees and bushes. The site has around 50 mobile homes and chalets on site and it is used by three small tour operators, but it remains very much a camping and caravanning site. In early season the site is very quiet; in July/Aug. it becomes much livelier with a good range of morning activities for children, afternoon events for families and evening entertainment for all.

Facilities

Three modern, clean toilet blocks include washbasins in cubicles, a unit for disabled people and baby room with bath, shower and toilet. Washing machines and dryers. Bar (limited opening in low season). Small independently operated shop and snack bar with takeaway (20/6-8/9). New restaurant. Play area. Mingolf, table tennis. Charcoal barbecues are not allowed. Off site: Golf, riding, karting, water sports and water parks are all within easy reach.

At a glance

Welcome & Ambience	✓✓✓✓	Location	✓✓✓✓
Quality of Pitches	✓✓✓✓	Range of Facilities	✓✓✓✓

Directions

Bretignolles is on the D38 coast road (Noirmoutier - Les Sables d'Olonne). From north, after St Gilles go through Bretignolles-La Sauzaie (take left fork) and before reaching Bretignolles itself turn left (sign for site) on sharp right hand bend, heading for water tower. Site is on right in 800 m. From south, after centre of Bretignolles, turn right (sign 'Ecoles') and then left (signs for sports centre and site). Site is signed to left after stadium.

Charges 2004

Per pitch incl. 2 adults	€ 12.00 - € 22.00
with electricity (6A)	€ 16.00 - € 26.00
child (under 5 yrs)	€ 3.50
Plus local tax.	

Reservations

Necessary for high season with deposit and fee. Central reservations: Siege Social - Centrale de Reservation, BP 12, 85520 Jard sur Mer. Tel: 02 51 33 05 05. Fax: 02 51.33 94 04. Email: chadotel@wanadoo.fr. Tel: 02 51 33 05 05.

Open

1 April - 25 September.

FR85500 Camping Le Bahamas Beach

168 Routes des Sable, 85800 St. Gilles (Vendée)

A member of the Chadotel group, Le Bahamas Beach is separated from the sandy beach by 600 m. of sand dunes and the River Jaunay. The site attracts a greater proportion of French holidaymakers than many others in the area. The 80 touring pitches are scattered amongst the total of 225, of which 90 are mobile homes. There are two tour operators, one French, one British (84 pitches). The pitches are grassy and level on sandy soil, separated by hedges or low bushes and all have easy access to electricity and water. There are few trees and little shelter from the wind off the sea. There is a good range of daytime and evening entertainment for all ages in July and August.

Facilities

Three well maintained toilet blocks include washbasins in cubicles, a unit for disabled people and baby rooms with bath, shower and toilet. Washing machines and dryers. Bar, restaurant and takeaway (25/5- 15/9) with limited opening hours in low season. Shop (25/5-15/9). Heated outdoor pool with cover for cooler weather, slide, paddling pool and large sun terrace (15/4-25/9). Play area. Minigolf. Table tennis. Football, basketball and volleyball. Bicycle hire. Off site: Golf, riding, karting, watersports and water parks are all within easy reach.

At a glance

Welcome & Ambience	✓✓✓	Location	✓✓✓
Quality of Pitches	✓✓✓	Range of Facilities	✓✓✓✓

Directions

From roundabout at southern end of D38 St Gilles bypass, take exit signed St Gilles Grande Plage. Campsite is 500 m. on left.

Charges 2004

Per unit incl. 2 persons	€ 14.00 - € 22.50
with electricity	€ 18.00 - € 26.50
extra person	€ 5.50
child (under 5 yrs)	€ 3.50 - € 4.00

Reservations

Made with deposit (€ 40 per week), fee (€ 25) and cancelleation insurance. Tel: 02 51 33 05 05. Email: chadotel@wanadoo.fr

Open

1 April - 30 September.

FR85490 Domaine de Beaulieu

Givrand, 85800 St Gilles-Croix-de-Vie (Vendée)

Domaine de Beaulieu has an open airy feel in a pleasant semi-rural setting on the edge of the village of Givrand, just one km. from a good sandy beach. The shops and restaurants of the fishing port and resort of St Gilles-Croix-de-Vie are 3 km. The 180 touring pitches all have easy access to electricity and water; those in the older part have shade from mature trees and are divided by hedges whilst those in the newer part are more open. Some pitches may be subject to traffic noise in high season. The site has 130 mobile homes and tour operators occupy 100 pitches. Early and late in the season the site is quiet, whereas in July/August there is a lively and wide-ranging entertainment programme for all ages.

Facilities

Three well maintained toilet blocks include washbasins in cubicles, baby room, unit for disabled people, washing machines and dryers. Shop (15/6-10/9). Bar (1/5-10/9). Takeaway and restaurant (1/7-31/8). Heated outdoor swimming pool with toboggan and paddling pool. Play area. Multi-sport terrain. Minigolf. Tennis. Table tennis. Bicycle hire. Off site: Golf, riding, karting, quad bikes, water sports and water parks all within easy reach.

At a glance

Welcome & Ambience	✓✓✓✓	Location	✓✓✓
Quality of Pitches	✓✓✓	Range of Facilities	✓✓✓✓

Directions

Site is signed from roundabout on D38 at Givrand, 3 km. south of St Gilles-Croix-de-vie.

Charges 2004

Per unit incl. 2 persons	€ 12.00 - € 22.00
electricity (10A)	€ 4.00

Reservations

Contact site. Tel: 02 51 33 05 05. Email: chadotel@wanadoo.fr

Open

1 April - 25 September.

FR85520 Camping Domaine des Renardieres

13 Chemin du Chêne Vert, 85270 Notre Dame de Riez (Vendée)

Just 7 kilometres from the busy coastal strip with its many large, multi-activity campsites, Domaine des Renardières is an oasis of calm in the traditional French manner. Converted from the family farm in 1970, the site consists of three fields with varying amounts of shade. The visitors are 65% French, many of whom, together with British visitors, return year after year. The 100 touring pitches are well grassed and level; torches and long cables are advisable. There is an abundance of flowers and plants, the facilities are scrupulously maintained and visitors receive a set of campsite rules which are also explained at the regular Sunday aperitif welcome meeting. The site is very well organised with a soft touch.

Facilities

The toilet block is old but well maintained and meticulously cleaned. A mixture of toilet types, some open washbasins, some in cubicles. Showers are closed at night except for one cold shower. Dishwashing under cover. Washing machine and dryer. Small shop and takeaway (1/7-30/8). Bar with TV, video games and pool (1/7-30/8). Small pool (15/4-15/9). Play area. Only gas barbecues are permitted. Off site: St Hilaire de Riez 7 km. Bicycle hire 6 km.

At a glance

Welcome & Ambience	✓✓✓✓	Location	✓✓✓✓
Quality of Pitches	✓✓✓	Range of Facilities	✓✓✓✓

Directions

Site is well signed from the centre of the village.

Charges 2004

Per unit incl. 2 persons	€ 12.00
with electricity (6A)	€ 14.95
Less 10-20% outside 15/7-21/8. No credit cards.	

Reservations

Made with deposit and € 10 fee. Tel: 02 51 55 14 17. Email: caroline.raffin@free.fr

Open

Easter - 15 September.

FR85640 Camping Les Chouans

108 ave. de la Faye, 85270 St Hilire de Riez (Vendée)

This family run campsite is within a short drive of the wonderful Vendée beaches. A friendly greeting from Josée and Stephane is a welcome arrival before entering this well organized, smart site. Cleanliness is important here! In high season it is bustling and lively, with many activities available daytime and evening. The restaurant and bar area is attractive, and the pool with its slides is popular. The site mainly caters for privately owned mobile homes and touring pitches are minimal (early booking advised). Some pitches are shaded, and smaller than average but each has electricity (10A). Water points are close by. Late night discos may be noisy in July/Aug. Tour operators occupy 52 pitches.

Facilities

Two sanitary blocks (one unisex) both have open, vanity style washbasins. Shower room and separate toilet for disabled campers. Baby room. Washing machines and dryer. Small well stocked shop. Bicycle hire. Swimming pools and slides. Good sports area with tennis court, basketball, boules and table tennis. Small fitness gym (charged). Good entertainment programme for all ages. Weekly excursions. Off site: Beach 1.6 km. Small town of St Hillaire de Riez approx 3 km. Riding, golf and fishing within 6 km.

At a glance

Welcome & Ambience	✓✓✓✓	Location	✓✓✓✓
Quality of Pitches	✓✓✓✓	Range of Facilities	✓✓✓✓✓

Directions

Travel south on D38 from St Jean de Monts and turn right at Oruet towards Les Mouettes. At the coast join D23 southwards and follow road to first roundabout (2.5 km). Site is signed here and is 2 km. on left.

Charges 2003

Per unit incl. 3 persons	€ 28.00

Reservations

Made with deposit (€ 80). Tel: 02 51 54 34 90. Email: info@sunmarina.com

Open

15 May - 15 September.

FR85530 Camping La Parée Préneau

23 Avenue de la Parée Préneau, 85270 St Hilire de Riez (Vendée)

This site was founded in 1968 by the grandfather of the present owner. It has been gradually and thoughtfully expanded to its present size (206 pitches). Of these, 150 are touring pitches of varying shapes and sizes, interestingly arranged. Mature trees proliferate to give varying amounts of shade to the undulating site, although the pitches are level. Of sandy grass or pine needles, all have electricity and many also have water and drainage. The calm atmosphere is enhanced by the absence of tour operators. All amenities are very clean and well maintained. The cosy welcoming bar overlooks the pool area. The friendly welcome is indicative of the caring attitude of those running the site.

Facilities

The two sanitary blocks are modern and include washbasins (some in cubicles), facilities for babies and disabled visitors. WCs are a mixture of British, seatless and Turkish, all thoroughly cleaned twice a day. Laundry and dishwashing sinks, washing machine and dryer. No restaurant or shop but bread, milk and other essentials are available. Mobile takeaway vendors call in high season. Heated indoor and outdoor swimming pools with jacuzzi and paddling pool surrounded by wide sun terrace. Large play area with football, volleyball/basketball pitch. Table tennis (indoor). Bicycle hire. Off site: Fishing 7 km. Golf 7 km. Riding 3 km. Sailing 7 km. Beach 1 km. Shops, bars, restaurants 5 km.

At a glance

Welcome & Ambience	✓✓✓✓	Location	✓✓✓✓	
Quality of Pitches	✓✓✓✓	Range of Facilities	✓✓✓✓	

Directions

From large roundabout on D38 just north of St Hilaire-de-Riez, turn south signed St Hilaire for 400 m. Take first exit at next roundabout signed Les Plages and after another 400 m. continue straight on at junction. Site is on left after 3 km.

Charges 2004

Per unit incl. 2 persons	€ 13.40 - € 17.80
with electricity (6A)	€ 15.50 - € 20.00
extra person	€ 3.30 - € 4.20
child (under 5 yrs)	€ 2.10 - € 2.50

Reservations

Made with deposit (€ 35) and fee (€ 15).
Tel: 02 51 54 33 84.
Email: camplaparepreneau@free.fr

Open

1 May - 15 September.

FR85350 Camping Caravaning La Ningle

Chemin des Roselières, 85270 St Hilaire de Riez (Vendée)

Camping La Ningle is well situated to explore the beautiful port of St Gilles Croix de Vie, with its abundance of restaurants (where seafood is served direct from the morning's catch) and pedestrianised shopping area with a variety of individual boutiques. You are guaranteed to receive a warm welcome at this site from M. & Mme. Guibert, who have established a very pleasant campsite with a friendly, family atmosphere. There are 155 pitches, 90 for touring units. All have electricity and a limited number are fully serviced (electricity, water and drainage). Pitches are spacious with dividing hedges and all have some shade. The nearest beach is a 500 m. walk through a pine forest, but there are also three small swimming pools on site.

Facilities

Two regularly cleaned toilet blocks include some washbasins in cubicles. Well equipped toilet/shower room for disabled people and large family shower room in the main block. Laundry and dishwashing facilities. Washing machines and dryer. Bread available July/Aug. Takeaway three evenings per week. Bar (July/Aug) with entertainment twice a week in high season. Main swimming pool, larger children's pool, paddling pool and water slide. Small fitness suite with range of equipment (no instructor, but free). Tennis court. Games field with volleyball and table tennis. Games room with pinball and arcade machines. Small lake for fishing (free). Children's activities (July/Aug), and regular petanque and tennis competitions. Off site: Small supermarket and takeaway 200 m.

At a glance

Welcome & Ambience	✓✓✓✓	Location	✓✓✓✓	
Quality of Pitches	✓✓✓✓	Range of Facilities	✓✓✓✓	

Directions

Driving south on D38 St Jean de Monts - St Gilles road, turn right at L'Oasis hotel/restaurant in Orouet (6 km. outside St Jean de Monts), signed Les Mouettes. After 1.5 km. you come to a roundabout. Turn left here signed St Hilaire de Riez. After passing two campsites (Les Ecureuils and Bois Tordu) take next left turn, signed La Ningle. Site is approx. 150 m. on the left.

Charges 2003

Per pitch incl. 2 persons	€ 12.00 - € 17.50
with 6A electricity	€ 14.70 - € 20.20
with 10A electricity	€ 16.50 - € 22.00
extra person	€ 3.00 - € 4.00
child (under 7 yrs)	€ 1.60 - € 2.40
No credit cards.	

Reservations

Made with deposit (€ 77.50) and fee (€ 15,25).
Tel: 02 51 54 07 11.
Email: campingdelaningle@wanadoo.fr

Open

15 May - 15 September.

FR85190 Camping Le Marais Braud

298 route du Perrier, 85270 St Hilaire-de-Riez (Vendée)

Le Marais Braud is a small, unsophisticated site occupying a peaceful wooded setting, slightly inland from the busy coastal areas of the Vendée, but only 7 km. from sandy beaches. There are 150 spacious pitches, of which 109 are available for touring units. The level, shaded pitches are sandy with some grass, and some are divided by low hedges. Electricity is available within 30 m. of every pitch (although this may sometimes require that cables cross the road). At the far end of the site is a small lake for fishing, which is also home to white and black swans, and geese. There are no tour operators. Although the site is only open for a short season, the owners, M. & Mme Besseau, ensure that it provides a welcoming, family atmosphere, suitable for families or couples looking for a budget holiday.

Facilities

Two toilet blocks (one smaller and newer than the other), both provide mostly British style toilets, some washbasins in cabins, dishwashing and laundry sinks and a washing machine. Facilities for disabled visitors. Little shop for basics. Friendly bar incorporating a games area with a skittle alley and crêperie with takeaway (all 1/7-31/8). Small heated swimming pool with water slide and children's pool (from 1/6; no bermuda style shorts). Tennis court, boules area and play areas. Caravan storage. Off site: Bicycle hire 6 km, riding 7 km.

At a glance

Welcome & Ambience	✓✓✓✓	Location	✓✓✓✓
Quality of Pitches	✓✓✓	Range of Facilities	✓✓✓

Directions

From Le Pissot roundabout (north of St Hilaire de Riez), take D59 signed Le Perrier. Site is well signed about 3 km. along this road on the right.

Charges 2003

Per unit incl. 2 persons	€ 13.72
with electricity (6A)	€ 16.16
with water also	€ 18.60
extra person	€ 3.35
child (under 7 yrs)	€ 2.13
dog	€ 1.52
local tax	€ 0.30

Reservations

Advised in high season and made with deposit (€ 69) and fee (€ 15,24). Tel: 02 51 68 33 71.

Open

1 June - 15 September.

FR85080 Hotellerie de Plein Air La Puerta del Sol

Les Borderies, chemin de Hommeaux, 85270 St Hilaire-de-Riez (Vendée)

La Puerta del Sol is a good quality campsite a short distance away from the busy coast. It is suitable not only for families with teenage children to entertain, but also for those seeking a more peaceful and relaxing holiday. There are 216 pitches, of which 158 are used for touring units. Pitches are level with dividing hedges and many receive shade from the mature trees on the site. Each pitch is fully serviced with water, waste water point and electricity. In July/Aug. a range of activities is provided for adults and children, including a children's club, aqua aerobics, swimming lessons, tournaments and games, with evening entertainment in the bar. There is one small French tour operator on site (20 pitches).

Facilities

Three well maintained toilet blocks of identical design have a mix of Turkish and British style WCs, washbasins in cabins and baby baths. Dishwashing and laundry sinks. Laundry with washing machines and irons. Fully equipped rooms for disabled visitors. Small shop (1/7-31/8). Bar (15/5-15/9). Self-service restaurant and takeaway (1/7-31/8) with reasonably priced food and overlooking the swimming and paddling pools (15/5-15/9; no bermuda style shorts). Play area. Tennis court. Bicycle hire. Volleyball, table tennis and video games. American motorhomes are accepted in limited numbers with reservation. Off site: Riding, fishing and golf within 5 km. Nearest sandy beach 5 km. St Jean de Monts 7 km.

At a glance

Welcome & Ambience	✓✓✓✓	Location	✓✓✓✓
Quality of Pitches	✓✓✓✓	Range of Facilities	✓✓✓✓

Directions

From Le Pissot (which is 7 km. north of St Gilles Croix-de-Vie on D38) take the D59 towards Le Perrier. The site is 2 km. along this road on the right side down a short side road. There is a large sign for the site 200 m. before the turning and another sign on the left directly opposite the turning.

Charges 2003

Per unit incl. up to	
3 persons and services	€ 17.00 - € 31.50
extra person	€ 4.50 - € 6.00
child (under 7 yrs)	€ 2.25 - € 3.00
animal	€ 1.60

Reservations

Advised for high season and made for any period with deposit (€ 138) and fee (€ 30,49).
Tel: 02 51 49 10 10.
Email: puerta-del-sol@wanadoo.fr

Open

1 May - 15 September.

FR85070 Camping Les Biches

Route de Notre-Dame-de-Riez, 85270 St Hilaire-de-Riez (Vendée)

Les Biches is a popular, quality site 4 km. from the sea. It is set in a pinewood so nearly everywhere has shade. There are almost 400 pitches with around 90 available for touring units. The large, spacious pitches are mostly hedged and on fairly sandy ground, all with electricity, water and drainage. The majority for tents and caravans are in the far part of the campsite behind the tennis courts, although a few others are scattered through the rest of the site. A very attractive pool complex is near the site entrance, overlooked by the bar and terraces. Various activities such as boules tournaments and sporting events are organised during high season. It is a useful site for families with children and, as it is popular with British tour operators (65%), it tends to be busy and active all season.

Facilities

The four sanitary blocks are clean and well maintained, with extremely spacious cubicles for pre-set showers. Some washbasins are in cabins with a bidet alongside. All blocks have laundry and dishwashing facilities. Washing machines and dryers. Facilities for disabled visitors. Shop (all season) with ice service. Large bar (all season). Restaurant and crèperie (1/6-9/9).Takeaway (20/5-16/9). Two heated swimming pools (unsupervised), children's pool, water slide with splash pool, jacuzzi and indoor pool. Tennis courts. Volleyball, table tennis and minigolf. Games room. Large adventure type playground. Bicycle hire. Disco. TV room with satellite TV. Internet terminal. Off site: Private fishing lake 1.5 km., riding 4.5 km. and golf 6 km. Beach 4 km.

At a glance

Welcome & Ambience	✓✓✓	Location	✓✓✓
Quality of Pitches	✓✓✓✓	Range of Facilities	✓✓✓✓✓

Directions

Site is about 2 km. north of St Hilaire, close to and well signed from the main D38 road.

Charges 2003

Per unit incl. 3 persons	€ 37.00
with electricity	€ 41.00
child (under 7 yrs)	€ 5.00
dog	€ 2.00
local tax	€ 0.45

Less 30% May, June and Sept. No credit cards

Reservations

Required for high season and made with deposit (€ 61) and fee (€ 15,24). Tel: 02 51 54 38 82. Email: campingdesbiches@wanadoo.fr

Open

15 May - 15 September.

Camping Les Biches, 85270 St. Hilaire-de-Riez
Tel: 0033 251 54 38 82 Fax: 0033 251 54 30 74

LARGE SHADY PITCHES - NEW INDOOR POOL - SWIMMING POOL with SPA and 'TOBOGGAN AQUATIQUE'
TENNIS - COMFORTABLE TOILET BLOCKS WITH PLENTIFUL HOT WATER
RESERVATIONS ARE RECOMMENDED FOR MAIN SEASON

FR85390 Camping des Batardières

85440 St Hilaire-la-Foret (Vendée)

Camping des Batardières is a haven of tranquillity on the edge of an unspoilt village, yet just 5 km. from the sea. It is an attractive, unsophisticated little site, lovingly maintained by its owners for the past 23 years. Many clients (including British) return year after year, and it was one of these who described it as a 'haven of tranquillity'. There are 75 good-sized pitches (a few up to 130 sq.m.) and all are available for touring units (there are no mobile homes and no tour operators!) All have easy access to water and electricity (6A, or 2A for tents). Otherwise there are few facilities on site.

Facilities

The centrally positioned sanitary block is kept very clean and visitors are encouraged to keep it that way (no shoes in the shower cubicles, for instance) - it seems to work. Some washbasins in cubicles for ladies. Dishwashing and laundry facilities, including a washing machine and a dryer. TV room, table tennis and a tennis court. Play area and a huge field for games, kite-flying etc. Off site: Village shop and bar only a short walk (200 m.) from the entrance. Nearby Jard-sur-Mer (5 km.) has good supermarkets, shops, bars, restaurants, a weekly market and the sea.

At a glance

Welcome & Ambience	✓✓✓✓✓	Location	✓✓✓✓
Quality of Pitches	✓✓✓✓	Range of Facilities	✓✓✓

Directions

Site is on edge of St Hilaire-la-Forêt. From Les Sables d'Olonne take D949 (la Rochelle) road towards Talmont St Hilaire and Luçon. 7 km. after Talmont turn right on D70 to St Hilaire-la-Forêt and site is signed to the right as you approach the village.

Charges 2003

Per unit incl. 2 persons	€ 14.00
with electricity	€ 17.00
child (under 7 yrs)	€ 2.00

Reservations

Contact site. Tel: 02 51 33 33 85.

Open

27 June - 5 September.

FR8533N Camping Naturiste Cap Natur'

151 ave de la Faye, 85270 St Hilaire-de-Riez (Vendée)

Situated on the northern outskirts of the busy resort of St Hilaire-de-Riez, and only about 1 kilometre from the nearest beach (6 km. from the nearest official naturist beach beside Plage des 60 Bornes) this family campsite for naturists is in an area of undulating sand dunes and pine trees. The 140 touring pitches nestle among the dunes and trees and offer a wide choice to suit most tastes, including the possibility of electrical connections, although in some cases long leads are needed. Despite the undulating terrain, some pitches are quite level and thus suitable for motorcaravans. The modern facilities are excellent and include both open air and indoor pools, and a jacuzzi. Around the pool is an ample paved sunbathing area, including a stepped 'solarium'. The whole of the indoor complex is a designated non-smoking area. In season a regular Saturday evening 'soirée' is held with a set Vendéen meal, wine and entertainment. There is an air of peace and quiet about this site which contrasts with the somewhat frenzied activity which pervades many of the resorts in this popular tourist area, with a friendly, warm welcome from the family that own it. A number of apartments, tents and mobile homes are on site.

Facilities

Sanitary facilities are basic, but clean, consisting of one indoor (heated) and one outdoor (but roofed) block. Both blocks have open plan hot showers, British style WCs, washbasins, baby baths and children's toilets. Small shop (with takeaway pizzas) and restaurant (menu includes some local specialities), good sized bar, with TV, pool tables and various indoor table games. Indoor and outdoor swimming pools. Fitness classe's in high season. Massage room. Play area on soft sand. Volleyball and archery. Torches useful. Bicycle hire. Off site: Beach 2 km. Naturist beach 6 km. Fishing 5 km. Golf, riding and boat launching 10 km.

At a glance

Welcome & Ambience	✓✓✓✓	Location	✓✓✓✓	
Quality of Pitches	✓✓✓✓	Range of Facilities	✓✓✓✓	

Directions

Site is on the north side of St Hilaire-de-Riez. From Le Pissot roundabout go south on the D38, follow signs for St Hilaire at first roundabout you come to (first exit off roundabout), then at second roundabout (garage) turn right signed 'Terre Fort'. At third Y-shaped junction turn right again signed 'Parée Prèneau' (also site sign here). The site is 2 km on the left.

Charges 2003

Per unit incl. 2 adults	€ 14.50 - € 26.50
extra person	€ 2.50 - € 5.70
child (under 10 yrs)	€ 1.60 - € 4.10
electricity (10A)	€ 4.20

Reservations

Advised in high season and for French holidays. Made with 25% deposit and booking fee (€ 27,44). Single male visitors are not accepted. Tel: 02 51 60 11 66. Email: info@cap-natur.com

Open

3 April - 2 November.

FR85610 Camping Les Aventuriers de la Calypso

Route de Notre Dame de Monts, Les Tonnelles, 85160 St Jean-de-Monts (Vendée)

This site is ideally situated within 700 metres of the beautiful, sandy Vendée beaches and close to St Jean de Monts (4 km.) with its wide variety of shops and restaurants. Although there are 253 pitches, only a limited number are for touring units, and these are situated amongst the site's own mobile homes (there are no tour operators here). The pitches are level, grassy and of good size, and are either in the open or shade, with hedges providing privacy. All have electricity and some have water and drainage. The site is neatly maintained with an attractive pool complex and amenities. There is a good variety of entertainment for all ages during the high season. A useful complex with facilities is 150 m. from the site which includes a pizzeria, supermarket and a popular seafood shop.

Facilities

The modern sanitary block is fully equipped including facilities for babies and disabled campers. A 'portacabin' style block has WCs, showers and washbasins. Both are very clean and well maintained. Laundry. Bar with restaurant area (high season). Very small shop with basic supplies. Games area. Tennis court. Bicycle hire. Entertainment in July and August. Off site: Nearest beach 700 m. Numerous cycle routes. Notre Dame de Monts 3 km. St Jean de Monts 4 km. Commercial centre 150 m.

At a glance

Welcome & Ambience	✓✓✓✓	Location	✓✓✓✓	
Quality of Pitches	✓✓✓✓	Range of Facilities	✓✓✓✓	

Directions

Site is on the D38 St Jean de Monts - Notre Dame de Monts road, at the Les Tonnelles roundabout.

Charges 2004

Per unit incl. 2 persons	€ 21.00
serviced pitch	€ 24.00
extra person	€ 5.00
child (under 5 yrs)	€ 2.50
electricity (3-10A)	€ 2.50 - € 4.00

Reservations

Made with deposit (€ 100) and fee (€ 15). Tel: 02 51 97 55 50.

Open

1 April - 30 September.

FR85300 Camping La Grand' Métairie

8 rue de la Vineuse en Plaine, 85440 St Hilaire la Forêt (Vendée)

Just five kilometres from the super sandy beach at Jard sur Mer, La Grand' Métairie offers many of the amenities of its seaside counterparts, but with the important advantage of being on the edge of a delightful, sleepy village, otherwise untouched by tourism. It is a busy well run site with a lively entertainment programme in high season and a new covered pool planned. The site has 172 pitches (72 touring pitches), all with electricity, water and drainage. The pitches as yet have little shade but are all separated by small trees and bushes and are generous in size.

Facilities

Two modern toilet blocks are kept very clean and include washbasins mainly in cabins. Units for disabled people. Washing machines and dryers. Fridge hire. Basic provisions available on site, with useful village store just 100 m. from the gate. Smart bar/restaurant (all 1/5-10/9). Attractive, kidney-shaped heated pool with jacuzzi and paddling pool. Tennis, minigolf (both free in low season). Visiting hairdressing salon. Off site: Riding and fishing within 5 km.

At a glance

Welcome & Ambience	✓✓✓✓	Location	✓✓✓✓
Quality of Pitches	✓✓✓	Range of Facilities	✓✓✓✓✓

Directions

Site is in centre of St Hilaire la Forêt. From Les Sables d'Olonne take D949 towards Talmont St Hilaire and Luçon. 7 km. after Talmont turn right on D70 to St Hilaire la Forêt. Site is on the left before village centre.

Charges 2004

Per unit incl. 2 persons and electricity (6A)	€ 16.00 - € 24.00
extra person	€ 6.00 - € 7.00
child (2-5 yrs)	€ 4.00
dog	€ 3.00

Reservations

Advised for high season with 25% deposit and fee (€ 25). Tel: 02 51 33 32 38. Email: grand-metairie@wanadoo.fr

Open

1 April - 30 September.

La Grand' Métairie Camping Club ★★★★
The appeal of country 5 minutes away the ocean.
Indoor swimming pool - Torrential river
Fitness and sauna area / Kids Club
Bare pitches, mobile home and chalets renting.
8, rue de la Vineuse en Plaine - 85440 ST HILAIRE LA FORET
FREE DOCUMENTATION
Tél : 02 51 33 32 38 - Fax : 02 51 33 25 69 - http://www.la-grand-metairie.com - E-mail : grand-

FR85590 Camping Plein Sud

246 route de Notre Dame de Monts, 85160 St Jean de Monts (Vendée)

Plein Sud is a small welcoming site with 110 grassy pitches, many with adequate shade and separated by hedges. All are of about 100 sq.m. and have electricity, water and drainage. There is one main drive through the site and site owned and private mobile homes are mostly positioned nearer the entrance. Touring pitches are situated further from the main road and bar area and are more pleasantly peaceful. The pool is inviting with a small children's pool and fountain alongside. Only 800 m. away is the beautiful long stretch of safe sandy beach, which is accessed via a pleasant walk through pines and sand dunes. In high season there is a security guard and gate. There are no tour operators.

Facilities

Two modern, clean sanitary blocks provide washbasins in cabins. One block has a baby room. Dishwashing facilities. Washing machines and dryers. Small bar with TV and terrace. Heated pool (no Bermuda style shorts). Play area with volleyball and table tennis. Bread and milk can be ordered daily at reception. Bicycle hire. Daily pony and trap rides for young children (free). Children's entertainment in high season. Off site: Golf, fishing and riding within 5 km.

At a glance

Welcome & Ambience	✓✓✓✓	Location	✓✓✓✓
Quality of Pitches	✓✓✓✓	Range of Facilities	✓✓✓✓

Directions

Site is 1 km. north of St Jean de Monts on the D38, Route de Notre Dame de Monts, on the right.

Charges 2003

Per unit incl. 3 persons	€ 12.00 - € 22.00
incl. 4A electricity	€ 14.00 - € 24.00
extra person	€ 2.50 - € 4.50

Reservations

Made with deposit and fee. Tel: 02 51 59 10 40. Email: camping-pleinsud@club-internet.fr

Open

1 May - 15 September.

FR85120 Haven Camping Le Bois Masson

168 rue des Sables, 85167 St Jean-de-Monts (Vendée)

Le Bois Masson is a large, lively site with modern buildings and facilities in the seaside resort of St Jean-de-Monts. As with other sites here, the long, sandy beach is a few minutes away by car, reached through a pine wood. This site, popular with tour operators, offers 480 good sized pitches, all with electricity. Many are occupied by mobile homes. Pitches are of sandy grass, mostly separated by hedges, with medium sized trees providing some shade. There are some pitches with water and drainage and an area kept for those who prefer a quieter pitch around a pond used for fishing. There is plenty of on-site entertainment over a long season. The swimming pool complex is impressive and includes a large outdoor pool, a paddling pool, a separate slide and landing pool and, for cooler weather, an indoor pool, with sliding doors to the outside. A jacuzzi, sauna and fitness room are also provided together with many other sports. Very busy in high season, this is not a site for those seeking somewhere quiet, but there is plenty to do for those perhaps with older children.

Facilities

Four sanitary blocks of excellent design provide modern showers with mixer taps, washbasins in cabins and British style WCs. Facilities for disabled visitors and babies. Dishwashing room (with dishwashers). Laundry. Comprehensive amenities housed in modern buildings fronting on to the road include a good supermarket, a large, lively bar with entertainment room above, overlooking the pools, a restaurant and a creperie. Many activities including tennis, volleyball, table tennis and bicycle hire. Fishing. Barbecues are not permitted. Mobile homes and rooms to rent. Off site: Riding, golf, squash, watersports near.

Directions

From the roundabout at the southeast end of the St Jean de Monts bypass road, turn into town following signs to 'Centre Ville' and site, which is on the right after 400 m.

Charges 2003

Per child. up to 6 persons and electricity	€ 12.00 - € 47.00

Reservations

Contact site. Tel: 02 51 58 62 62.
Email: boismasson@haven.fr.

Open

3 April -2 October.

At a glance

Welcome & Ambience	✓✓✓	Location	✓✓✓
Quality of Pitches	✓✓✓✓	Range of Facilities	✓✓✓✓✓

Le Bois Masson

One of two great parcs with swimming pools, sports & family activities. Enjoy the lively life at Le Bois Masson, or relax at the more peaceful sister - Le Bois Dormant.

Haven
Europe

- 80m² standard pitch size
- Superb spring & autumn prices
- Ferry inclusive package
- High standard facilities open all season
- Free use of superb indoor & outdoor pools
- Free use of 3 childrens clubs for all ages
- Bilingual friendly staff
- Site open from: 3 April - 2 October

Le Bois Masson, 168 Rue des Sables, 85167 St Jean des Monts, France Tel: 00 33 251 58 62 62 Fax: 00 33 251 58 29 97
To book please call the number above, quoting code TOAR01 or request a brochure by calling 0870 242 6666

ABTA
V2819

FR85220 Camping Acapulco

Avenue des Epines, 85160 St Jean-de-Monts (Vendée)

Ideal for family holidays, this friendly site is situated mid-way between St Jean de Monts and St Hilaire de Riez, and 600 m. from the beach. The young, friendly site owner provides lively entertainment and sporting activities for all ages in high season. The site has 410 pitches (30 for touring units). All pitches have water and electricity, but few have any shade. Popular with tour operators (150 pitches).

Facilities

Three main sanitary blocks boast clean, modern facilities including washbasins in cabins, baby baths and facilities for disabled visitors. Sinks for laundry and dishwashing. Washing machines in each block. Motorcaravan service point. Well stocked shop (all season). Large bar and snack bar. Games room. Interestingly shaped, heated swimming pool with five water slides and paddling pool. Off site: Shops, bars and restaurants all within 1 km. Golf 10 km, bicycle hire 200 m, riding 2 km.

Directions

Driving south on the D38 St Jean de Monts - St Gilles road, turn right at L'Oasis bar/restaurant in Orouet, signed Les Mouettes. Site is on left after 1 km.

Charges 2004

Per unit incl. 3 persons and electricity	€ 28.00
extra person	€ 6.00
child (under 5 yrs)	€ 3.00

Reservations

Necessary in July/Aug. Tel: 02 51 59 20 64.
Email: info@sunmarina.com

Open

8 May - 15 September.

At a glance

Welcome & Ambience	✓✓✓✓	Location	✓✓✓✓
Quality of Pitches	✓✓✓	Range of Facilities	✓✓✓✓

136

FR85150 Camping La Yole

Chemin des Bosses, Orouet, 85160 St Jean-de-Monts (Vendée)

La Yole is an attractive, popular and well run site, 1 km. from a sandy beach. It offers 278 pitches, (130 touring pitches) the majority under trees with ample shade and separated by bushes and the trees. All have electricity (10A), water and drainage and are of 100 sq.m. or more. The pool complex is surrounded by a paved sunbathing area and overlooked by a new bar and restaurant which have a large terrace. A pleasant walk through pine woods then by road leads to two sandy beaches. The security barrier is closed at night. A 'Sites et Paysages' member. Used by tour operators (50%). This a friendly, popular site with welcoming owners.

Facilities

Two toilet blocks of older design, one refurbished, include washbasins in cabins, units for disabled people and baby baths, all kept very clean. The third block in the newer part of site is very modern with baby room. Laundry with washing machine, dryer and iron. Well stocked shop. Takeaway. Bar (all season) and restaurant (18/5-31/8). Swimming pool with water slide, paddling pool and an indoor heated pool with jacuzzi. Play area on sand, large field for ball games and a club room. Tennis. Table tennis, pool and video games. Organised entertainment in high season. Dogs are not accepted. Only gas barbecues are permitted. Off site: Fishing, golf and watersports 6 km. at St Jean.

At a glance

Welcome & Ambience	✓✓✓✓✓	Location	✓✓✓✓
Quality of Pitches	✓✓✓✓	Range of Facilities	✓✓✓✓✓

Directions

Signed off the D38, 6 km. south of St Jean de Monts in the village of Orouet.

Charges 2003

Per unit incl. 2 persons, electricity, water and drainage	€ 16.70 - € 27.50
tent incl. 2 persons, electricity and water	€ 14.50 - € 22.30
extra person	€ 3.60 - € 5.80
baby (0-2 yrs)	free - € 3.20
child (2-9 yrs)	€ 2.00 - € 4.20
local tax	€ 0.44

Camping Cheques accepted.

Reservations

Advised, particularly for July/Aug. Tel: 02 51 58 67 17. Email: contact@la-yole.com

Open

8 May - 15 September.

Camping La Yole ★★★★

Wake up to the sound of birdsong in a wooded park of 17 acres with four star comfort. Space, security, informal atmosphere: LA YOLE, tucked away between fields and pine trees, only 1 km from the beach.

– Chemin des Bosses - Orouet - F 85160 Saint Jean de Monts –
– Tel: 0033 251 58 67 17 - Fax: 0033 251 59 05 35 –
– contact@la-yole.com / www.la-yole.com –

FR85280 Camping Les Places Dorées

Route de Notre Dame de Monts, 85160 St Jean-de-Monts (Vendée)

Les Places Dorées is owned by the same family as L'Abri des Pins (85090) which is just across the road. It is a much newer site, but maturing trees are gradually beginning to offer some shade. The site has a range of facilities, including a pool complex, but one of the main reasons for visiting the Vendée is for its beaches and the closest beach to Les Places Dorées is a pleasant 15 minute walk (through L'Abri des Pins and then alongside the forest and sand dunes). The site has 245 grassy pitches, the quietest being towards the back of the site. Each one is separated, all have electrical connections and some are also equipped with water and drainage. One small British tour operator is on site (18 pitches). In low season the site is quiet but it can be noisy in high season with the bar and disco closing late.

Facilities

Three modern toilet blocks include washbasins in cubicles. Facilities for disabled visitors. Laundry and dishwashing sinks. Washing machines and dryers. Swimming pool complex with water slides, jacuzzi area and waterfall (no bermuda style shorts). In high season the site becomes quite lively with plenty of organised entertainment, most based around the bar/restaurant area. High season children's club at L'Abri des Pins, also organised activities for adults (petanque tournaments, aqua aerobics, etc). The facilities at L'Abri des Pins may be used - well stocked shop (July/Aug), tennis court, fitness room, swimming pools and games room.

At a glance

| Welcome & Ambience | ✓✓✓ | Location | ✓✓✓✓ |
| Quality of Pitches | ✓✓✓✓ | Range of Facilities | ✓✓✓✓ |

Directions

Site is 4 km. north of St Jean de Monts on the D38 St Jean de Monts - Notre Dames de Monts road on the right hand side, almost opposite L'Abri des Pins.

Latest charges

Per pitch incl. 3 persons and electricity (6A)	€ 18.20 - € 26.70
extra person	€ 2.80 - € 4.40
child	€ 1.70 - € 2.80
dog	free - € 2.50
local tax	€ 0.34

Reservations

Advised for high season; min. stay 12 nights between 14/7-15/8. Tel: 02 51 59 02 93.

Open

16 June - 1 September.

FR85090 Camping L'Abri des Pins

Route de Notre Dame de Monts, 85160 St Jean-de-Monts (Vendée)

L'Abri des Pins is situated on the outskirts of the pleasant, modern resort of St Jean-de-Monts and is separated from the sea and long sandy beach by a strip of pinewood. From the back entrance of the site it is a pleasant 15 minute walk to the beach. Bathing is said to be safer here than on most of the beaches on this coast, but is nevertheless supervised in July/August. The site has 218 pitches, 78 of which are for touring units with 30 larger than average, with electricity, water and drainage. Electricity is also available to the other pitches which are around 100 sq.m, fully marked out with dividing hedges and quite shady. Many pitches are occupied by privately owned mobile homes, but there are no tour operators on the site. Throughout the season visitors may use the facilities at Les Places Dorées (under the same family ownership) across the road.

Facilities

The two sanitary blocks have been modernised and include washbasins in cabins, laundry and dishwashing sinks. Good small shop and bar/restaurant on the far side of the site provides good quality, value for money meals, both to eat in and take away (all 1/7-31/8). Outdoor, heated swimming pool and water slide, plus small pool for children, with decked sunbathing area (1/6-15/9; no bermuda style shorts). Daily children's club, football, petanque, aqua aerobics. Off site: Supermarket 10 minutes walk. Many restaurants close. Walking, cycling, fishing and riding within 1 km.

At a glance

| Welcome & Ambience | ✓✓✓✓ | Location | ✓✓✓✓ |
| Quality of Pitches | ✓✓✓ | Range of Facilities | ✓✓✓✓ |

Directions

Site is 4 km. from the town centre on St Jean-de-Monts - Notre Dame-de Monts/Noirmoutiers road (D38), on left heading north, just after Camping les Amiaux.

Charges 2003

Per unit incl. 3 persons and electricity	€ 18.20 - € 28.00
with water	€ 19.00 - € 29.00
extra person	€ 2.80 - € 4.70
child (under 5 yrs)	€ 1.70 - € 3.00
pet	free - € 2.80
local tax	€ 0.44

Deposit required for armband for access to pool and site (high season only).

Reservations

Advised for high season; min. stay 12 nights between 14/7-15/8. Made with deposit (€ 92) and fee (€ 23). Tel: 02 51 58 83 86. Email: abridespins@aol.com

Open

1 June - 15 September.

FR85360 Camping La Forêt

190 chemin de la Rive, 85160 St Jean-de-Monts (Vendée)

Camping La Forêt has been owned by M. and Mme. Jolivet for the past few years and they work hard to provide a small, quality site. Well run and attractive, with a friendly, family atmosphere, it provides just 60 pitches with 51 for touring units. Of 100 sq.m. in size, the pitches are surrounded by mature hedges and have water and electricity. Over 50 species of trees are planted on the site, providing shade to every pitch, and the Jolivets provide an information panel by reception to help you identify the various types. There is one tour operator on the site (15 pitches), but their presence is in no way intrusive and the site has a quiet and relaxed atmosphere, ideal for couples or families with young children.

Facilities

The central toilet block is kept very clean and includes washbasins in cubicles. Laundry and dishwashing sinks. Baby bath. Facilities for disabled people. Washing machine and although clothes lines are prohibited, free-standing clothes airers are loaned for drying. Motorcaravan waste tanks can be emptied on request. Basic provisions sold in reception, including fresh bread. Takeaway at excellent prices all season. Small, but inviting swimming pool (end May - Sept). Play area. Table tennis. Bicycle hire. Only gas and electric barbecues allowed, communal barbecue in centre of site. Off site: Local beach 400 m. along forest path. Network of cycle paths runs through the forest and local marshland.

At a glance

Welcome & Ambience	✓✓✓✓	Location	✓✓✓✓
Quality of Pitches	✓✓✓✓	Range of Facilities	✓✓✓✓

Directions

Site is 5.5 km. from town centre, just off the D38. Follow D38 out of St Jean de Monts, towards Notre Dame. After 4.5 km. at roundabout with a pizzeria, go straight over roundabout. In 1 km. turn left at sign for site and 'Plage de Pont d'Yeu'. Follow road as it almost doubles back on itself and site is on left in 100 m.

Charges 2003

Per pitch incl. 2 persons	€ 16.00 - € 23.50
extra person	€ 3.00 - € 4.50
electricity (6A)	€ 3.80
No credit cards.	

Reservations

Advised and made with € 34 deposit; min. 15 nights 2/7-19/8. Tel: 02 51 58 84 63.

Open

15 April - 30 September.

FR85620 Camping Le Caravan'ile

B.P. No. 4, La Guérinière, 85680 Ile de Noirmoutier (Vendée)

This well appointed, 8.5 hectare, family run site is reached by crossing the bridge on the D38 to the pretty island of Noirmoutier. It is also accessible via the causeway (Le Gois) at low tide. Not far from the town centre, with an adjoining sandy beach, the site offers indoor and outdoor swimming pools, a popular sauna, jacuzzi and mini gym and a variety of entertainment in high season to suit all ages. The level touring pitches are mainly situated near the beach (shielded by the sand dune) and all have electricity. Some also have a water point, but no dividing hedges or shade. A few are situated on a ridge with sea views to the front and rear. Camping Le Caravan'ile has a very French ambience, with no tour operators.

Facilities

Three immaculately clean sanitary blocks, each with showers, British toilets, some enclosed wash cabins and facilities for disabled people. Hot showers only available 0800-1200 and 1700-2100 hrs. Laundry. Dishwashing. Heated indoor and outdoor swimming pools, paddling pools and flume. Fitness room, sauna and jacuzzi. Bar/takeaway (July/August). Games and sports area. Electronic games room. Organised entertainment in July/August. Off site: Bar, restaurant, ATM, small supermarket and minigolf, all 500 m. Riding, cycling, windsurfing, aquarium, water theme park and salt marshes within close proximity.

At a glance

Welcome & Ambience	✓✓✓✓	Location	✓✓✓✓✓
Quality of Pitches	✓✓✓	Range of Facilities	✓✓✓✓

Directions

Take the D38 road from the mainland, crossing the bridge to Ile De Noirmoutier. The campsite can be found at the roundabout at La Guérinière, on the left.

Charges 2003

Per unit incl. 2 persons	€ 8.90 - € 16.90
incl. 5A electricity	€ 10.90 - € 19.90
extra person	€ 2.60 - € 4.10
child (2-7 yrs)	€ 1.60 - € 2.60
animal	€ 1.50 - € 2.50

Reservations

Contact site. Tel: 02 51 39 50 29. Email: contact@camping-caravan-ile.com

Open

1 March - 15 November.

Loire Valley

With over one hundred of France's finest châteaux, this is a region to inspire the imagination. The Loire valley is a charming region of lush countryside, fields of sunflowers, rolling vineyards and of course the great river itself.

Our tourist regions includes all the Loire Valley: 18 Cher, 28 Eure-et-Loir, 36 Indre, 37 Indre-et-Loire, 41 Loir-et-Cher, 45 Loiret. From Western Loire: 49 Maine-et-Loire, 53 Mayenne, 72 Sarthe. And from Poitou-Charentes: 79 Deux Sèvres, 86 Vienne

For centuries the Loire valley was frequented by French royalty and the great river winds its way past some of France's most magnificent châteaux: Amboise, Azey-le-Rideau, Chenonceau, with its famous arches that span the river and appear to 'float' on the water, and the fairytale Usse with a myriad of magical turrets are just some of the highlights. 'Son et Lumière' shows are also a wonderful experience.

Known as the Garden of France, the Loire's mild climate and fertile landscape of soft green valleys, lush vineyards and fields of flowers makes it a favourite with the visitors. Renowned for its wines, with hundreds to choose from, all are produced from vineyards stretching along the main course of the River Loire. Imposing abbeys, troglodyte caves, tiny Romanesque churches, woodland areas such as the Sologne and sleepy, picturesque villages reward exploration. Cities like Blois and Tours are elegant with fine architecture and museums and Paris is only one hour by TGV. One of the oldest towns of Loire valley is Saumur. Its old quarter, grouped around the riverbank beneath the imposing château, is particularly pleasant to wander around.

Cuisine of the region

Wild duck, pheasant, hare, deer, and quail are classics and fresh water fish such as salmon, perch and trout are favourite. Specialties include rillettes, andouillettes, tripes, mushrooms and the regional cheeses of Trappiste d'Entrammes and Cremet d' Angers, Petit Sable and Ardoises d'Angers cookies

Bourdaines: apples stuffed with jam and baked

Tarte a la citrouille: pumpkin tart

Tarte Tatin: upside down tart of caramelised apples and pastry

Places of interest

Amboise: château, Leonardo da Vinci museum

Beauregard: château with Delft tiled floors

Blois: château with architecture from Middle Ages to Neo-Classical periods

Chambord: Renaissance château

Chartres: cathedral with stained glass windows

Chinon: old town, Joan of Arc museum

Loches: old town, château and its fortifications

Orléans: Holy Cross cathedral, house of Joan of Arc

Tours: Renaissance and Neo-Classical mansions, cathedral of St Gatien,

Vendôme: Tour St Martin, La Trinité

Villandry: famous renaissance gardens

Alan Rogers **tip**

PUBLIC TRANSPORT IS LIMITED IN THIS REGION SO RENT A CAR OR BIKE - THIS IS EASY CYCLING COUNTRY, AND A BIKE RIDE ALONG THE RIVER BANKS WILL PROVE ENJOYABLE.

FR28120 Camping Municipal du Pré de l'Eglise

Avenue du Pré de l'Eglise, 28380 St. Remy-sur-Avre (Eure et Loir)

This neatly kept, useful little site has only 45 pitches, but is quite popular as a short stay or transit site as it lies just off the main N12 cross country route. The pitches are on level grass and divided by hedges, with electricity hook-ups, and are arranged around a circular access road, with some shade from specimen trees. The guardian lives next to the site entrance. No double axle caravans are accepted.

Facilities

The sanitary unit, in the older style, is adequate and includes facilities for disabled people. Dishwashing and laundry sinks and under cover washing lines. Salle with TV. Off site: Supermarket 2 km. in the direction of Nonancourt.

At a glance

| Welcome & Ambience | ✓✓✓✓ | Location | ✓✓✓✓ |
| Quality of Pitches | ✓✓✓✓ | Range of Facilities | ✓✓✓✓ |

Directions

St Remy-sur-Avre is 9 km. west of Dreux on N12. Turn towards town centre and almost immediately turn right. Following signs turn left, and then left again. Site is on right with parking space outside the barrier.

Charges 2003

Per person	€ 2.46
pitch	€ 3.27
electricity (10A)	€ 2.46 - € 6.00

Reservations

Contact site. Tel: 02 37 48 93 87.

Open

1 April - 30 September.

FR28110M Camping Municipal de Bonneval

Bois de Chievre, 28800 Bonneval (Eure et Loir)

On the outskirts of Bonneval and within walking distance of the centre, this municipal site offers good facilities in peaceful surroundings. The site has thick cover from trees in most parts with some pitches entirely hidden for those who like lots of privacy. Nearly all the pitches are marked out on grass in clearings, some on a slope, but the majority fairly flat. Of the 130 pitches, 120 have electricity, some hardstanding. The site has no bar, restaurant or shop, but all are available in Bonneval itself or, when open, in the municipal swimming pool and tennis complex adjacent (reduced rates for campers). Caravans with double axles or more than 5.6 m. are not accepted.

Facilities

Sanitary facilities consist of one large block, plus three smaller units without showers. The large block has mostly chain operated hot showers, some washbasins in cubicles and facilities for disabled people. Laundry room with washing machine and ironing facilities. Laundry and dishwashing sinks. Motorcaravan services. Large TV/games room. Playground. Bicycle hire. Fishing. Boules court. Off site: Swimming pool and tennis next to site.

At a glance

| Welcome & Ambience | ✓✓✓✓ | Location | ✓✓✓✓ |
| Quality of Pitches | ✓✓✓✓ | Range of Facilities | ✓✓✓✓ |

Directions

Site signed from Bonneval town centre on N10 from Châteaudun to Chartres (on Rte de Vouvray).

Charges 2003

Per pitch incl. 1 person	€ 5.50
incl. 2 persons	€ 8.50 - € 10.50
with electricity (6A)	€ 7.50

No credit cards. Barrier card deposit € 15.

Reservations

Contact site. Tel: 02 37 47 54 01.
Email: camping.bonneval@wanadoo.fr

Open

March - 30 November.

FR36050M Camping Municipal Les Vieux Chênes

36310 Chaillac (Indre)

A delightful site on the outskirts of an attractive village, this is another little gem – a small site within walking distance of the centre, where there are shops, bars, cafés and restaurants. The 34 grass pitches, all with electricity, are very generous in size, slightly sloping, with hedging and some mature trees. It has a well manicured appearance and relaxed atmosphere. The adjacent lake is for fishing only, although there is access to a larger lake just one km. away where a variety of watersports can be enjoyed. In high season it is possible some noise may carry from this area to the site.

Facilities

Heated sanitary facilities are insulated for winter use and include washbasins in private cabins. Bicycle hire. Winter caravan storage. Off site: Shops 200 m. Fishing 25m. Watersports 1 km.

At a glance

| Welcome & Ambience | ✓✓✓✓ | Location | ✓✓✓✓ |
| Quality of Pitches | ✓✓✓✓ | Range of Facilities | ✓✓✓ |

Directions

From the north leave A20, south of Argenton sur Creuse, take D1 to St Benoit (16 km.) and then west to Chaillac on D36 (8.5 km.). From the south leave A20 at exit 21, take D10 to St Benoit, then D36 as before. Go through the village and turn left by the Mairie.

Charges 2004

Per person	€ 1.55
pitch	€ 2.05 - € 2.55
electricity (15A)	€ 1.55

Reservations

Contact site. Tel: 02 54 25 61 39.

Open

All year.

FR37070M Camping de L'Ile Auger

Quai Danton, 37500 Chinon (Indre-et-Loire)

This is a well-placed site for exploring the old medieval town of Chinon and its impressive castle that was a home of England's Henry II and includes a museum to Joan of Arc. Alongside the River Vienne, it is a five minute walk over the main bridge to the town centre. The 277 pitches are numbered but not separated, with electricity. A few are shaded by tall shrubs.

Facilities

Six toilet blocks around the site have British style WCs. A very good new block is next to the office building. Washing up sinks. Barrier locked 22.00 - 07.00 hrs. Off site: Tennis. Indoor and outdoor swimming pools nearby. Bicycle hire 1 km. Shop 1 km. Fishing 3 km. Riding 10 km.

At a glance

Welcome & Ambience	✓✓✓✓	Location	✓✓✓✓✓
Quality of Pitches	✓✓✓✓	Range of Facilities	✓✓✓

Directions

From Chinon town cross the river and turn right at the end of the bridge, the campsite entrance is about 100 m. on the right.

Latest charges

Per person	€ 1.70
child (under 7 yrs)	€ 1.20
pitch	€ 3.30 - € 3.90
electricity (4/8A)	€ 1.70 - € 2.30

Reservations

Contact site. Tel: 02 47 93 08 35. Or the Mairie. Tel: 02 47 93 53 00.

Open

15 March - 15 October.

FR37010 Camping de la Mignardière

22 avenue des Aubépines, 37510 Ballan-Miré (Indre-et-Loire)

The situation of this site may appeal, it being just southwest of the city of Tours, yet within easy reach of several of the Loire châteaux, notably Azay-le-Rideau, and with various sports amenities on or very close to it. There are 177 numbered pitches of which 157 are for touring units, all with electricity and 37 also with drainage and water. The pitches are on rather uneven grass but are of good size. Onsite facilities are limited because just across the road is a small 'parc de loisirs' with refreshments and bar, pony rides, minigolf, small cars, playground and other amusements. The barrier gates with card (with deposit) are closed 22.30 - 07.30 hrs. Reservation is essential for most of July/August.

Facilities

Four rather ordinary sanitary blocks include washbasins in private cabins, a unit for disabled people, baby bath in heated block near reception, and laundry facilities. Motorcaravan service point. Shop (15/5-15/9). Takeaway (1/7-31/8). Two heated, large swimming pools (15/5-15/9). Good tennis court. Table tennis. Bicycle hire. Off site: Fishing 500 m, riding 1 km, golf 2 km. Attractive lake catering particularly for windsurfing 300 m. (boards can be hired or use your own) and family fitness run. Tours centre 8 km.

At a glance

Welcome & Ambience	✓✓✓✓	Location	✓✓✓✓
Quality of Pitches	✓✓✓✓	Range of Facilities	✓✓✓✓

Directions

From A10 autoroute take exit 24 and D751 towards Chinon. Turn right after 5 km. at Campanile Hotel following signs to site. From Tours take D751 towards Chinon.

Latest charges

Per unit incl. 2 persons	€ 13.50 - € 17.50
with electricity (6A), water and drainage	€ 19.00 - € 23.60
extra person	€ 3.80 - € 4.80
child (2-10 yrs)	€ 2.44 - € 2.85

Reservations

Made for any length with 30% deposit (minimum amount € 40). Tel: 02 47 73 31 00. Email: info@mignardiere.com

Open

10 April - 30 September.

FR37060 Camping L'Arada Parc

Rue de la Baratière, 37360 Sonzay (Indre-et-Loire)

Although Camping L'Arada Parc is a relatively new site (only in its third full year) it has already become popular as an overnight stop, or as a quiet location from which to visit the numerous châteaux in this beautiful part of France. The 87 grass pitches all have a 10A hook-up, and 28 of them have fresh water and waste disposal points. Pitches are clearly marked and separated by maturing trees, shrubs and flowers that will, in time, provide some shade. Snacks and meals in the restaurant are cooked to order with barbecue chicken available at weekends. Campers can enjoy a snack or drink on the terrace overlooking the attractive (unheated) swimming pool.

Facilities

Two modern toilet blocks provide unisex toilets, showers and washbasins in cubicles. Excellent baby/toddler room and en suite facilities for disabled visitors (wheelchair users may find it a little difficult to manoeuvre over the gravel in front of the lower block). Dishwashing and laundry sinks under cover at each block. Laundry with washing machine, dryer and ironing board. Shop, bar, restaurant and takeaway (27/3-31/10). Swimming pools (1/6-15/9). Play area, covered games area. Boules, volleyball, badminton and table tennis. TV room. Bicycle hire. Entertainment, themed evenings and activities for children organised in July/Aug. Off site: Tennis 200 m. Fishing 9 km. Golf 12 km. Riding 7 km.

At a glance

Welcome & Ambience	✓✓✓✓✓	Location	✓✓✓✓
Quality of Pitches	✓✓✓✓	Range of Facilities	✓✓✓✓

Directions

Sonzay is northwest of Tours. Take D959 Tours - Château-la-Vallière road, then D6 to Sonzay and follow camping signs. Site is signed from the D959.

Charges 2004

Per unit incl. 2 persons	€ 14.50
extra person	€ 4.50
child (2-7 yrs)	€ 3.00
animal	€ 1.25

Less 20% 1/4-5/7 and 24/8-3/11.
Camping Cheques included.

Reservations

Made with deposit (€ 45); contact site.
Tel: 02 47 24 72 69. Email: laradaparc@free.fr

Open

27 March - 31 October.

Open from 1st April to 1st November

Camping - Caravaning
★★★

L'Arada Parc

At the heart of the Loire's chateau country and the vineyards of Touraine.

Bar, Restaurant, Swimming pool, Activities
CHALETS AND MOBILE HOMES RENTING
Mini-golf, Tennis, Bike renting.
Accessible via the D 766, the D 959 or the N 138

"Golf at 10mn"

L'ARADA PARC • 37 360 SONZAY
Tél/Fax. +33 (0)2 47 24 72 69
Web : www.laradaparc.com • E-mail : laradaparc@free.fr

FR37110M Camping Municipal Au Bord du Cher

RN 76, 37270 Veretz (Indre-et-Loire)

This is an inexpensive, well laid out site on the banks of the River Cher with views through tall elm trees to the Château de Veretz. Monsieur Menard and his wife live in a caravan on site during the season and are always pleased to welcome British tourists. With 64 pitches, most divided by small hedges and all with electricity, the site is just outside the town of Veretz where shops, restaurants, bars, etc. can be found. A wooden chalet houses reception and plenty of tourist information, with notice boards giving weather forecasts, etc. In addition, the manager is always willing to offer information and advice about where to go and what to see in the area. English is spoken.

Facilities

Large, modern sanitary block includes British and Turkish style WCs, dishwashing under cover, laundry and washing machine. Motorcaravan service point. Takeaway with covered area to sit and eat (from mid-June). Communal barbecue. Playground. Table tennis. Off site: Fishing nearby. Outdoor swimming pool (July/Aug) 4 km. Bicycle hire 12 km. Riding 3 km. Tennis 1 km. Baker 700 m. Bus service from Tours station to Bleré passes site entrance.

At a glance

Welcome & Ambience	✓✓✓✓✓	Location	✓✓✓✓
Quality of Pitches	✓✓✓✓	Range of Facilities	✓✓✓

Directions

Site is at Veretz, via the N76 road, 10 km. southeast of Tours (much better than the municipal at St Avertin en-route).

Latest charges

Per adult	€ 1.83
child (under 7 yrs)	€ 0.76
pitch	€ 1.83
vehicle	€ 1.83
electricity (6A)	€ 2.29

No credit cards.

Reservations

Contact site. Tel: 02 47 50 50 48.

Open

22 May - 26 September.

(143)

FR37030 Camping Le Moulin Fort

37150 Francueil-Chenonceaux (Indre-et-Loire)

Camping Le Moulin Fort is a tranquil, riverside site that has been redeveloped by British owners, John and Sarah Scarratt. The 137 pitches are enhanced by a variety of trees and shrubs offering some shade and 80 pitches have electricity. The attractive (unheated) swimming pool is accessed by a timber walk-way over the mill race from the snack bar terrace next to the restored mill building. The picturesque Chateau of Chenonceaux is little more than one km. along the Rive Cher and many of the Loire châteaux are within easy reach, particularly Amboise and its famous Leonardo de Vinci museum. Although not intrusive there is some noise from the railway line across the river and a few trains run at night. The site is more suitable for couples and families with young children.

Facilities

Two toilet blocks with all the usual amenities of a good standard, including washbasins in cubicles and baby baths. Bar. Swimming pool. Minigolf. Games room and TV. Regular family entertainment including wine tasting, quiz evenings, activities for children and light-hearted games tournaments. Fishing. Bicycle hire.

At a glance

Welcome & Ambience	✓✓✓✓✓	Location	✓✓✓✓✓
Quality of Pitches	✓✓✓✓✓	Range of Facilities	✓✓✓✓

Directions

Take D40 Tours - Chenonceaux road, go through the village and after 2 km. turn right on D80 to cross the river at Chisseaux. Site is on left just after the bridge.

Charges 2004

Per unit incl. 2 persons	€ 8.00 - € 18.00
extra adult	€ 4.00 - € 5.00
child (4-112 yrs)	€ 2.00 - € 4.00
electricity (6A)	€ 4.00
dog	€ 3.00

Reservations

Recommended for high season, contact site.
Tel: 02 47 23 86 22. Email: lemoulinfort@wanadoo.fr

Open

1 April - 30 September.

FR37050 Camping Caravaning La Citadelle

Avenue Aristide Briand, 37600 Loches en Touraine (Indre-et-Loire)

A pleasant, well maintained site, La Citadelle is within walking distance of Loches, noted for its perfect architecture and its glorious history, at the same time offering a rural atmosphere in the site itself. Most of the 97 level, good-sized pitches (all with electricity) offer some shade from trees, although sun lovers can opt for a more open spot. Campers are given free entry to the adjacent municipal swimming pool and tennis courts and there are many organised activities during July and August. Loches, its château and dungeons, is 500 m. A free bus/little train runs from the campsite to the centre of Loches during the summer. A `Sites et Paysage` member.

Facilities

Three sanitary blocks provide British and Turkish style WCs, washbasins (mostly in cabins) and showers. Dishwashing and laundry sinks. Laundry facilities and a motorcaravan service area at the block nearest reception. Two excellent baby units and provision for disabled people. Play equipment for children. Boules, volleyball and games room. Small snack bar offering a variety of food and drink in a lively environment (July/August). Off site: Riding 3 km. Golf 7 km. Supermarket 3 km; market on Wednesday and Saturday mornings.

At a glance

Welcome & Ambience	✓✓✓✓	Location	✓✓✓✓✓
Quality of Pitches	✓✓✓✓✓	Range of Facilities	✓✓✓✓

Directions

Site is south of Loches. From RN143 Châteauroux - Tours, follow signs to Loches centre at roundabout (look for Leclerc supermarket). The campsite is about 3 km. on right (well signed from ring road).

Charges 2004

Per pitch incl. 2 adults	€ 12.40 - € 17.30
with water and drainage	€ 16.50 - € 21.50
extra person	€ 3.20 - € 4.20
child (2-10 yrs)	€ 2.00 - € 3.00
electricity (10A)	€ 3.10
dog	€ 1.00 - € 1.50

Camping Cheques accepted.

Reservations

Advised in July/Aug. Tel: 02 47 59 05 91.
Email: camping@lacitadelle.com

Open

19 March - 19 October.

Le Moulin Fort

CAMPING ★★★
37150 FRANCUEIL-CHENONCEAUX
Téléphone : +33 (0) 2 47 23 86 22 - Fax : +33 (0) 2 47 23 80 93 - E-mail : lemoulinfort@wanadoo.fr

Camping
LE MOULIN FORT
offers you :

➤ An unbeatable location within walking distance of Chenonceau castle

➤ An ideal base for exploring the Loire region of France

➤ A warm welcome from the English owners

➤ A perfect place for relaxing by the river or enjoying the wide range of facilities and animation available on site

➤ A good stopover point within easy reach of the UK ports, well-signposted and easy to find

On-site facilities :
*Shop *Bar *Take-away *Swimming pool
*TV room *Animation *Play-area
*Themed evenings *Bicycle hire
*Canoe hire *Barbecues permitted

*Motorcaravan service area
**Covered caravan storage available
***Reservation recommended for high season

FR37090 Camping du Château de La Rolandière

37220 Trogues (Indre-et-Loire)

This is charming little site set in the grounds of a small château which has the appearance of a Queen Anne style dolls house. There are 30 medium sized, flat pitches, some gently sloping front to rear, and all separated by neat hedges. All but four have electricity and water taps nearby and the parkland trees give shade. The château and adjoining buildings contain chambre d'hotes and a small swimming pool serves them and the campsite. An eighteen hole minigolf meanders through the parkland and there is an area set aside for ball games, swings and slides for younger children. Sabine Toulemonde and her husband, who bought the château in 2002, offer a very warm welcome. Situated on the D760 between Ille Bouchard and St Maure-de-Touraine, the site is 5 km. west of the A10, convenient for an overnight break or for longer stays to explore the châteaux at Chinon, Loches or Azay-le-Rideau and the villages of Richelieu and Crissay-s-Manse.

Facilities

The refurbished French style toilet block provides showers, washbasins, dishwashing and laundry areas around central British style WC's with a separate provision for disabled visitors. There is a single washbasin cabin in both the male and female units. Washing machine and dryer available via reception. Swimming pool. Minigolf. Children's play area. Bar with terrace and snacks. Small shop in reception for basic provisions. Bicycle hire. Off site: Fishing 1 km. to River Vienne. Restaurant 5km. adjacent to A10 junction. Full range of shops and commercial facilities in St Maure 8 km.

At a glance

Welcome & Ambience	✓✓✓✓✓	Location	✓✓✓✓
Quality of Pitches	✓✓✓✓	Range of Facilities	✓✓✓✓

Directions

The site is 5 km. west from junction 25 on A10 at St Maure-de-Touraine on the D760 towards Chinon. The entrance is clearly signed and marked by a model of the château.

Charges 2003

Per adult	€ 5.00 - € 6.00
child	€ 2.50 - € 3.00
pitch	€ 7.00 - € 8.50
animal	€ 1.50 - € 2.00
electricity (10A)	€ 3.50
local tax	€ 0.25

Credit cards not accepted.

Reservations

Contact site. Tel: 02 47 58 53 71.
Email: contact@larolandiere.com

Open

15 April - 30 September.

FR41030 Yelloh! Village Le Parc des Alicourts

Domaine des Alicourts, 41300 Pierrefitte-sur-Sauldre (Loir-et-Cher)

A secluded holiday village set in the heart of the forest and with many sporting facilities, Parc des Alicourts is midway between Orléans and Bourges. There are 420 pitches (just under half used by tour operators and with a number of mobile homes and chalets). All pitches have electricity connections (6A) and good provision for water, and most are 150 sq.m. (min. 100 sq.m.). Locations vary from wooded to more open areas, thus giving a choice of amount of shade. All facilities are open all season and the leisure amenities are exceptional. Competitions are organised for adults as well as children and, in high season organised activities include a club for children with an entertainer twice a day, a disco once a week and a dance for adults. An inviting water complex (all season) includes two swimming pools, a pool with wave machine and beach area, and a spa, not forgetting three water slides.

Facilities

Three modern sanitary blocks include some washbasins in cabins and baby bathrooms. Washing machines and dryers. Excellent facilities for disabled visitors in one block (but with shallow step to reach them). Motorcaravan services. Shop with good range of produce (the nearest good-sized town is some distance). Restaurant with reasonable prices, plus takeaway in a pleasant bar with terrace. Water complex. 7 hectare lake with fishing, bathing, canoes, pedaloes and play area. Nine hole golf course (very popular). Well equipped play area. Football pitch, volleyball, tennis, minigolf, table tennis, boules. Roller skating/skateboard area (bring your own equipment). Bicycle hire with cyclo-cross and mountain bikes and a way-marked path for walking and cycling.

At a glance

Welcome & Ambience	✓✓✓✓	Location	✓✓✓✓✓
Quality of Pitches	✓✓✓✓	Range of Facilities	✓✓✓✓✓

Directions

From A71, take the Lamotte Beuvron exit (no 3) or from N20 Orléons to Vierzon (which runs parallel with the A71) turn left on to D923 towards Aubigny. After 14 km, turn right at camping sign on to D24E. Site is clearly marked from there in about 4 km.

Charges 2003

Per unit incl. 2 persons	€ 13.00 - € 31.00
with electricity	€ 15.00 - € 36.00
with water and drainage	€ 25.00 - € 41.00
extra person	€ 6.00 - € 8.50
child 1-6 yrs	free - € 5.50
child 7-17 yrs	€ 4.00 - € 6.50
dog	€ 7.00
local tax	€ 0.15 - € 0.30

Reductions for low season longer stays.

Reservations

Made for min. 7 days for July/Aug. only, with 25% deposit and fee (€ 15,24). Tel: 02 54 88 63 34. Email: parcdesalicourts@wanadoo.fr

Open

17 May - 7 September.

FR41010 Le Parc du Val de Loire

Route de Fleuray, 41150 Mesland (Loir-et-Cher)

Between Blois and Tours, quietly situated among vineyards away from the main roads and towns, this family owned site is nevertheless centrally placed for visits to the châteaux; Chaumont, Amboise and Blois (21 km.) are the nearest in that order. There are 232 touring pitches of reasonable size, either in light woodland marked by trees or on open meadow with separators. All of the pitches have electricity, and 100 of them also have water and drainage. Sports and competitions are organised in July/Aug. with weekly disco and dance for adults. Wine tasting opportunities each Friday and a coach to Paris one day each week. There are local walks on marked footpaths (maps € 0,30). Used by tour operators (100 pitches).

Facilities

Two original toilet blocks of varying standards include washbasins in cabins. Units for disabled visitors, baby bathrooms and laundry facilities. Motorcaravan service point. Large shop with bakery. Bar next to the pools, with restaurant, snack service, pizzeria and takeaway, TV room and large recreation room. Three swimming pools, the newest (200 sq.m.) heated all season, plus smaller pool with popular water slide, and small children`s pool. Tennis court with floodlighting, good playgrounds with skate board facilities, bicycle hire, table tennis, minigolf, BMX track, tennis training wall, football pitch, volleyball, badminton and basketball. Pony rides. Barbecue area - some organised or DIY (free wood). Off site: Fishing 2 km. Riding 10 km. Golf 2 km.

At a glance

Welcome & Ambience	✓✓✓✓	Location	✓✓✓✓
Quality of Pitches	✓✓✓	Range of Facilities	✓✓✓

Directions

The village of Mesland is 5 km. northwest of Onzain, accessible from the Château-Renault/Amboise exit of A10 autoroute via D31 to Autrèche, continue 5 km. then left at La Hargardière at camp sign and 8 km. to site.

Charges 2003

Standard pitch (100 sq.m.) incl. 2 persons	€ 10.00 - € 21.70
large pitch (150 sq.m.) incl water and drainage	€ 14.80 - € 27.10
extra person	€ 2.00 - € 5.50
child (2-7 yrs)	€ 1.50 - € 3.10
electricity 6-10A	€ 2.50 - € 3.60
animal	€ 2.00

Reservations

Made for min. 4 days with deposit (€ 77) and fee (€ 20). Tel: 02 54 70 27 18. Email: parc.du.val.de.loire@wanadoo.fr

Open

1 April - 11 November.

FR41020 Castel Camping Château de la Grenouillière

41500 Suévres (Loir-et-Cher)

Château de la Grenouillère is a comfortable site with good amenities on the N152 midway between Orléans and Tours. It is well situated for visiting many of the Loire châteaux and there are enough attractions on site and locally to make it suitable for a longer stay holiday. It is set in a 28-acre park and the 250 pitches (including 88 for tour operators and mobile homes) are in three distinct areas. The majority are in a well wooded area, with about 60 in the old orchard and the remainder in open meadow, although all pitches are separated by hedges. There is one water point for every four pitches and only ten lack an electric hook-up. There are 14 `grand confort` pitches with a separate luxury sanitary block in the outbuildings of the château itself. A weekly trip to Paris, a canoe-kayak trip, wine cellar and cheese tasting visits, musical evenings and children's entertainment are organised in high season.

Facilities

Three sanitary blocks, one for each area, are modern and well appointed, including some washbasins in cabins. Washing machines and dryers in a small laundry. Shop. Bar. Pizza takeaway. Restaurant. New bar. Swimming complex of four pools (one covered) and a water slide. Tennis, squash, table tennis, pool, baby foot and video games. Internet point. Bicycle and canoe hire (July/Aug). Guided tours organised once a week. Off site: Fishing 5 km. Golf 10 km. Rding 5 km. Aqua sports 5 km.

At a glance

| Welcome & Ambience | ✓✓✓✓ | Location | ✓✓✓✓ |
| Quality of Pitches | ✓✓✓✓ | Range of Facilities | ✓✓✓✓✓ |

Directions

Site is between Suevres and Mer on north side of N152 and is well signed.

Latest charges

Per unit incl. 2 persons	€ 27.50
with 5A electricity	€ 31.00
with full services	€ 40.00
extra person	€ 6.00
child (under 7 yrs)	€ 4.00

Less 10% during middle season, and 35% during low season.

Reservations

Made for min. 5 days with € 77 deposit.
Tel: 02 54 87 80 37. Email: la.grenouillere@wanadoo.fr

Open

15 May - 10 September.

FR41040 Camping Château des Marais

27 rue de Chambord, 41500 Muides-sur-Loire (Loir-et-Cher)

The Château des Marais campsite is well situated to visit the chateau at Chambord (its park is impressive) and the other châteaux in the 'Vallée des Rois'. The site, providing 133 large touring pitches, all with electricity, water and drainage and with ample shade, is situated in the oak and hornbeam woods of its own small château (in which there are rooms to let). An excellent swimming complex offers pools and two flumes. English is spoken and the reception from the enthusiastic owners and the staff is very welcoming. In high season, canoe trips on the Loire are popular – campers are taken by coach to Muides-sur-Loire and are collected three hours later at Boire. The site is used by tour operators (90 pitches). A `Sites et Paysages` member.

Facilities

Four modern, purpose built sanitary blocks have good facilities including some large showers and washbasins en-suite. Washing machine. Motorcaravan service point. Shop and takeaway. Bar/restaurant with large terrace. Swimming complex with heated and unheated pools, water slide and cover for cooler weather. TV room. Bicycle hire. Fishing lake. Excursions by coach to Paris, an entertainment programme and canoe trips organised in high season. Off site: Riding 5 km, golf 12 km. Village of Muides sur Loire, with a variety of small shops, etc. five minutes walk.

At a glance

| Welcome & Ambience | ✓✓✓✓ | Location | ✓✓✓✓ |
| Quality of Pitches | ✓✓✓✓ | Range of Facilities | ✓✓✓✓✓ |

Directions

From A10 autoroute take exit 16 to Mer, then cross the Loire to join the D951 and follow signs. Site is signed off D103 to southwest of village. 600 m. from junction with the D112.

Charges 2004

Per pitch incl. 2 persons	€ 22.00 - € 28.00
extra person	€ 6.00
child (under 5 yrs)	€ 4.00
electricity (6/10A)	€ 4.00 - € 6.00
dog	€ 4.00
local tax (over 16 yrs)	€ 0.35

Credit cards accepted for amounts over € 80.

Reservations

Advised July/Aug. Tel: 02 54 87 05 42.
Email: chateau.des.marais@wanadoo.fr

Open

15 May - 15 September.

FR41070 Camping Caravaning La Grande Tortue

3 Route de Pontlevoy, 41120 Candé-sur-Beuvron (Loir-et-Cher)

This is a pleasant, rustic site that has been tastefully developed in an old forest. It provides 106 touring pitches set amongst trees which provide shade as well as some sunshine. The grass is kept a little longer than normal, especially during the early season, to maintain the forest environment. The majority of the pitches are more than 100 sq.m. and all have electricity. During July and August, the family owners organise a programme of trips including wine and cheese tastings, canoeing, and an all-day visit to the Loire Valley. There are markets at Amboise (Sunday), Montrichard (Monday) and Blois (Monday). Used by tour operators.

Facilities

Three sanitary blocks offer British and Turkish style WCs, washbasins in cabins, showers (chain operated in two blocks and press button in the third), plus a very basic chemical emptying point. Laundry with deep sinks, washing machine, dryer and ironing board. Shop selling provisions, and small gifts. Terraced bar and restaurant with reasonably priced food and drink (15/5-15/9). Swimming pool and two shallower pools for children (15/5-30/9). Trampolines, a ball crawl with slide and climbing wall, bouncy castle, table tennis. Bicycle hire (July/August). Off site: Walking and cycling. Fishing 500 m. Golf 7 km. Riding 8 km.

At a glance

Welcome & Ambience	✓✓✓✓✓	Location	✓✓✓✓
Quality of Pitches	✓✓✓	Range of Facilities	✓✓✓✓

Directions

Site is just outside Candé-sur-Beuvron on the D651, midway between Amboise and Blois. From Amboise, turn right just before entering Candé, then immediately left into the campsite - well signed from the road.

Charges 2003

Per unit incl. 2 persons	€ 12.50 - € 19.00
incl. electricity (6/10A)	€ 16.00 - € 22.50
extra adult	€ 4.20 - € 5.70
child (under 7 yrs)	€ 3.20 - € 4.00
animal	€ 2.50
local tax	€ 0.15 - € 0.30

Camping Cheques accepted.

Reservations

Necessary in July and August. Tel: 02 54 44 15 20. Email: grandetortue@libertysurf.fr

Open

5 April - 30 September.

Camping Caravaning International ★★★★

La Grande Tortue

3, route de Pontlevoy
41120 CANDÉ-sur-BEUVRON
Tel: 0033 254 44 15 20 - Fax: 0033 254 44 19 45
Website: www.la-grande-tortue.com

FR41060 Camping de Dugny

CD 45 (la Cabinette), 41150 Onzain (Loir-et-Cher)

This well organised campsite started life as an 'á la ferme' back in 1976. Since then it has grown into a eight hectare camping site surrounded by many acres of wonderfully quiet farmland. Still under the same ownership, it now opens all year round. There are 226 pitches, with mobile homes (privately owned and to rent) leaving 160 tourist pitches. Generously sized, they are partially separated, some with shade and others open. All have electricity, water and drainage. This is a campsite for active people, both young and older. Play areas and sports fields includes equipment for youngsters, a trampoline, minigolf, football and basket ball. A marquee provides entertainment for up to 12 year-olds and a large barn offers undercover table tennis. Adult and children's quad bikes can be hired or you can take a flight in a microlight from the site landing strip. Most activities take place away from the camping area to guard a quiet atmosphere. Coach trips to chateaux, wine cellars and other places of interest are arranged in July and August or when numbers are adequate.

Facilities

Three sanitary units include some washbasins in cubicles and provision for disabled people. Dishwashing and laundry sinks. Bread, ices, soft drinks and gas are stocked. Small restaurant and takeaway, with barbecue evenings organised on the terrace. Heated outdoor swimming pool (15 x 7 m) and paddling pool. Large play areas for 4-12 year olds. Minigolf, table tennis, volleyball, basketball and a pétanque court. Internet point. Pony and horse riding around the farmland. Microlight flights. Pedaloes and row boats for hire. Varied activity programme including children's disco, boules and table tennis tournaments and camp-fire evenings. A new swimming complex is planned for 2004. Off site: Local markets at Onzain, Montrichard, Blois and Amboise. A little train takes guests to a nearby wine cave, and a local farm that produces goats cheese.

At a glance

Welcome & Ambience	✓✓✓✓✓	Location	✓✓✓✓
Quality of Pitches	✓✓✓✓	Range of Facilities	✓✓✓✓

Directions

Onzain is southwest of Blois (15km) and on the opposite side of the river from Chaumont-sur-Loire. Take N152 Blois to Tours road, turn right onto D1 signed Onsain. Site is signed after the railway bridge. Turn right onto D58, then left onto D45. Keep following signs.

Charges 2004

Per adult	€ 5.80 - € 8.90
child (5-14 yrs)	€ 4.00 - € 5.00
pitch	€ 3.10 - € 3.60
animal	€ 4.00
electricity (10A)	€ 3.60 - € 5.10

Camping Cheques accepted.

Reservations

Not normally required, but made with 25% deposit. Tel: 02 54 20 70 66. Email: info@camping-de-dugny.fr

Open

All year.

FR41090 Camping Municipal de la Varenne

41210 Neung-sur-Beuvron (Loir-et-Cher)

This is a particularly well organised site in a peaceful location, yet within easy walking distance of the town centre. It is a good economic base for visiting Orleans, Blois or the Chateaux of the Loire. The site has a slight slope but most of the 69 grass touring pitches are fairly level, all with electricity hook-ups. Some pitches are individual, others in bays of four, and some for tents amongst the trees. There is good shade in most areas. At the rear of the site is a large open field which slopes down to the small river – a popular place with the children on hot days. Each evening the warden visits every pitch to take the bread order, which is available from reception at 8 am the next morning. Four mobile homes are for rent.

Facilities

An excellent, clean and well equipped modern building includes spacious showers, baby changing facilities, a suite for disabled people, and a washing machine. A second older unit at the rear of the reception building has additional good facilities. Freezer for Ice blocks. Motorcaravan service point. Playground. Volleyball. Two tennis courts. Table tennis. Bicycle hire. River fishing next to site. Off site: The town has all services including restaurants, bars, small supermarket.

At a glance

Welcome & Ambience	✓✓✓✓	Location	✓✓✓✓
Quality of Pitches	✓✓✓✓	Range of Facilities	✓✓✓✓

Directions

Neung-sur-Beuvron is about 40 km. east of Blois, and is 2 km. west of the 0922 about 22 km. north of Romarantin-Lanthenay. Site is 1 km. northeast of town centre (well signed).

Charges 2003

Per adult	€ 1.80
child (5-16 yrs)	€ 0.95
pitch	€ 2.45
electricity (10A)	€ 2.30

Reservations

Contact site. Tel: 02 54 83 68 52.

Open

Easter - 30 September.

FR45010 Sunêlia Les Bois du Bardelet

Route de Bourges, Poilly, 45500 Gien (Loiret)

This attractive, lively family site, in a rural setting, is well situated for exploring the less well known eastern part of the Loire Valley. A lake and swimming pool complex have been attractively landscaped in 12 hectares of former farmland, blending old and new with natural wooded areas and more open field areas with rural views. Bois du Bardelet provides 260 pitches with around 140 for touring units. All are larger than 100 sq.m. and have electrical connections, with some fully serviced. The communal areas are based on attractively converted former farm buildings with a wide range of leisure facilities. A family club card can be purchased to make use of the many activities on a daily basis (some high season only). Various activities and excursions are organised, the most popular being a trip to Paris on Wednesdays, which can be pre-booked.

Facilities

Three sanitary blocks (only one open outside 15/6-31/8) include washbasins in cabins and facilities for people with disabilities and babies. Washing machines. Shop (1/4-15/9). Pleasant terraced bar. Snack bar, takeaway and restaurant (1/4-15/9) and pizzeria. Three swimming pools, one for serious swimmers, one with a child's pool, both free, and the other indoor, heated and charged for. Aqua gym, fitness and jacuzzi room. Archery. Lake for canoeing and fishing. Tennis, minigolf, boules and table tennis. Bicycle hire. Playground for the under-8s. Off site: Supermarket 5 km. Walking and cycling routes of different lengths are available at reception.

At a glance

Welcome & Ambience ✓✓✓✓✓ Location ✓✓✓✓
Quality of Pitches ✓✓✓✓ Range of Facilities ✓✓✓✓✓

Directions

From Gien take D940 towards Bourges. After 5 km. turn right (signed) and right again and follow signs to site. From Argens sur Sauldre take D940 towards Gien; site is signed to right after 15 km. (narrow road).

Charges 2003

Per unit incl. 2 persons	€ 21.40
with 10A electricity and water	€ 26.00
family leisure card (per week)	€ 35.00 - € 45.00

Less 15-25% in low seasons (40% for over 60s). Camping Cheques accepted.

Reservations

Made with deposit (€ 54) and fee (€ 16). Tel: 02 38 67 47 39. Email: contact@bardelet.com

Open

1 April - 30 September.

Les Bois du Bardelet ★★★★ LOIRE VALLEY
With the family card: Canoeing, Archery Tennis, Heated Indoor Swimming Pool, Mini-golf, Fishing. Visit Paris Wednesday in high season. Evenings with entertainment.
www.bardelet.com
Club Vacances
Sunêlia open style

FR49000 Camping du Lac de Maine

Avenue du Lac de Maine, 49000 Angers (Maine-et-Loire)

The Parc de Loisirs du Lac de Maine is a leisure area with all sorts of activities, and the campsite is at the southern end of the Parc towards Bouchmaine. Most of the level 141 individual pitches for tourists are part grass and part gravel hardstanding, with the remainder being all gravel. All have water, drain and electricity hook-up. The park entrance has a height restriction of 3.2 m, however there is an alternative gate for larger vehicles. With a sandy beach, the adjacent 100 acre lake is good for swimming, windsurfing and sailing, while the parkland has tennis courts and a nature reserve. This is a useful site, only five minutes from the city. With wide access roads, it's also suitable for American RVs.

Facilities

Two sanitary blocks, one which can be heated and includes some washbasins in cubicles. Facilities for babies and visitors with disabilities. Dishwashing and laundry sinks. Washing machines. Excellent motorcaravan service point. Reception stocks gas. Restaurant/bar (both early June - mid Sept). Heated swimming pool. Volleyball. Pétanque. Bicycle hire. Playground. Internet point. Barrier card deposit € 15,24.

At a glance

Welcome & Ambience ✓✓✓✓ Location ✓✓✓✓✓
Quality of Pitches ✓✓✓✓✓ Range of Facilities ✓✓✓✓

Directions

Leave N23 at signs for Quartier de Maine and Lac de Maine. Follow signs for Pruniers and Bouchemaine. Site is on the D111 and is well signed.

Charges 2003

Per unit incl. 2 persons	€ 9.90 - € 13.40
child (under 7 yrs)	€ 1.25
electricity (10A)	€ 3.00

Reservations

Advised for July/Aug. and made with € 6 fee and deposit of € 8 per night of stay. Tel: 02 41 73 05 03. Email: camping@lacdemaine.fr

Open

25 March - 10 October.

FR49020 Camping de Chantepie

St Hilaire-St. Florent, 49400 Saumur (Maine-et-Loire)

The drive along the winding road bordered by apple orchards and vineyards is well rewarded on arriving at the floral entrance to Camping de Chantepie. Reception at this friendly site is housed in a tastefully restored ancient farmhouse. Linked by gravel roads (can be dusty), the 150 grass pitches are all level and spacious. They are separated by low hedges of flowers and trees which offer some shade and most have electrical connections. The panoramic views over the Loire from the pitches on the terraced perimeter of the meadow are stunning. There is, from here, a footpath leading to the river valley. Leisure activities for all ages are catered for in July/August by the Chantepie Club, including wine tastings, excursions and canoeing. This is a good site for families.

Facilities

The toilet block is very clean and the provision of facilities is adequate with washbasins in cubicles and facilities for disabled visitors. Well stocked shop. Bar, terraced café and separate takeaway (from 19/5). A paddling pool and two heated swimming pools are protected from the wind by a stone wall. Play area with wide variety of apparatus. Terraced minigolf. Volleyball, TV, video games and table tennis. Pony rides. Bicycle and mountain bike hire (maps from reception). Off site: Fishing 200 m. Riding 6 km. Golf 2 km.

At a glance

Welcome & Ambience	✓✓✓✓✓	Location	✓✓✓✓
Quality of Pitches	✓✓✓✓	Range of Facilities	✓✓✓✓

Directions

From Saumur take D751 signed Gennes. Turn right at roundabout in St Hilaire-St Florent and continue until you reach Le Poitrinea and campsite sign, then turn left. Continue for about 3 km. and then turn right into road leading to site.

Charges 2004

Per unit incl. 2 persons	€ 17.00 - € 22.00
extra person	€ 4.50 - € 6.00
child (2-10 yrs)	€ 3.00 - € 3.50
electricity (5A)	€ 3.00 - € 3.00
local tax	€ 0.15 - € 0.30
dog	€ 2.00

Reservations

Made with € 11 fee; contact site for details.
Tel: 02 41 67 95 34.
Email: info@campingchantepie.com

Open

29 April - 14 September.

FR49040 Camping de L'Etang

Route de St. Mathurin, 49320 Brissac (Maine-et-Loire)

Originally the farm of the ancient Château de Brissac (yet only 24 km. from the lovely town of Angers), the tasteful conversion has retained the tranquillity and ambience of bye-gone days and added the necessary comforts expected by today's campers. A rural campsite with pleasant views across the countryside, there are now 150 generously sized, level touring pitches. Separated and numbered, some have shade and all have electricity with water and drainage nearby. A small bridge crosses the river Aubance which runs through the site and there are two lakes where fisherman can enjoy free fishing. The site has its own vineyard and the wine produced is highly recommended and can be purchased on the campsite.

Facilities

Three well maintained sanitary blocks are of a high standard, with all the usual facilities. Laundry room with washing machines, dryer and sinks for hand washing, together with baby and toddler facilities. Disabled visitors are well catered for. Motorcaravan service point. The adapted farmhouse houses reception, small shop, bar and takeaway (from 15/6). Restaurant. Two swimming pools (one heated) and paddling pool. Wide variety of evening entertainment in high season. Off site: The adjacent Parc de Loisirs is a paradise for young children with many activities including boating, pedaloes, pony rides, miniature train, water slide, bouncy castle and swings (free entry for campers). Golf 10 km.

At a glance

Welcome & Ambience	✓✓✓✓✓	Location	✓✓✓✓
Quality of Pitches	✓✓✓✓	Range of Facilities	✓✓✓✓

Directions

Take D748 south from Angers. Follow signs to Brissac-Quincé but do not enter the town, proceed to site along D55 (well signed) in direction of St Mathurin.

Charges 2004

Per unit incl. 2 persons	€ 17.00 - € 22.00
extra person	€ 4.50 - € 6.00
child (2-10 yrs)	€ 3.00 - € 3.50
electricity (10A)	€ 3.00 - € 3.00
local tax	€ 0.15 - € 0.31

Reservations

Contact site. Tel: 02 41 91 70 61.
Email: info@campingetang.com

Open

19 May - 13 September.

FR49010 Castel Camping L'Etang de la Brèche

Route Nationale 152, 5 Impasse de la Breche, 49730 Varennes-sur-Loire (Maine-et-Loire)

The Saint Cast family have developed L'Etang de la Brèche with loving care and attention on a 15 ha. estate 4 km. southeast of Saumur on the edge of the Loire behind the dykes. It is a peaceful base from which to explore the famous châteaux, abbeys, wine cellars, mushroom caves and Troglodyte villages in this region. The site provides 201 large, level pitches with shade from mixed tall trees and bushes, facing central, less shaded grass areas used for recreation. There are electrical connections to all pitches (in some cases a long cable may be required due to the size of the pitches), with water and drainaway on some of them. The restaurant, also open to the public, blends well with the existing architecture and, together with the bar area and terrace, provides a social base and is probably one of the reasons why the site is popular with British visitors. The swimming complex includes three pools: one with a removable cover, one outdoor, and a lovely pool for toddlers. The site includes a small lake (used for fishing) and a wooded area ensuring a quiet, relaxed and rural atmosphere, making L'Étang de la Brèche a comfortable holiday base for couples and families. A Les Castels site used by tour operators (85 pitches).

Facilities

Three toilet blocks, modernised to good standards, include facilities for babies with two units for people with disabilities. Washing up sinks and laundry. Shop and epicerie. Restaurant, pizzeria and takeaway. Three heated pools. Tennis, basketball, minigolf and a field for football. Bicycle hire. General room, games and TV rooms. Internet point. Well organised, varied sporting and entertainment programme (10/7-25/8). Child minding is arranged in afternoons. Low season excursions 'Getting to know the Area' and wine tastings are organised. Torch useful. Off site: Riding 2 km. Golf 8 km.

At a glance

Welcome & Ambience	✓✓✓✓	Location	✓✓✓✓
Quality of Pitches	✓✓✓✓✓	Range of Facilities	✓✓✓✓✓

Directions

Site is 100 m. north off the main N152, about 4 km. southeast of Saumur on the north bank of the Loire.

Charges 2004

Per unit incl. 2 persons	€ 16.50 - € 27.00
incl. 3 persons	€ 20.50 - € 33.00
extra person	€ 4.00 - € 6.00
child (under 10 yrs)	€ 2.50 - € 3.00
electricity (10A)	free - € 3.00
water and drainage	€ 2.50
local tax (over 18 yrs)	€ 0.20
7th night free in low season.	

Reservations

Made for min. 7 nights in high season (3 days in low season) with deposit and fee. Tel: 02 41 51 22 92. Email: mail@etang-breche.com

Open

15 May - 15 September.

Castel Camping

LES CASTELS

L'Etang de la Brèche

49730 Varennes sur Loire
Tel : 0033 241 51 22 92
Fax : 0033 241 51 27 24

mail@etang-breche.com
www.etang-breche.com

Camping Qualité

AT 5 KM OF SAUMUR

FR49070 Camping Caravaning La Vallée des Vignes

La Croix Patron, 49700 Concourson-sur-Layon (Maine-et-Loire)

Seldom does one experience such genuine effort and the interest shown in the guests who are made to feel like personal friends. The English owners at La Vallée des Vignes are truly proud of their quality campsite and this is reflected in their care and attention to detail. Flowers, vines and an old wine press at the entrance welcome visitors to the purpose-built reception. Many young trees and shrubs have been planted to add to the existing mature trees that surround the site. Bordering the river Layon, the 54 good sized touring pitches are reasonably level and fully serviced (electricity, water tap and waste). Five pitches have a hardstanding for cars. Attractions include a generously sized sun terrace surrounding the pool and in high season activities are organised for children and adults. These include a hog roast (or similar) followed by boules and palet competitions (palet is a game unique to the region). The site is also an ideal base for visiting the zoo and rose gardens at Doué-la-Fontaine, châteaux of the Loire, the Grand Parc Puy du Fou and the many caves and vineyards in the area.

Facilities

The comfortable and well appointed toilet block includes washbasins in cabins, with dishwashing and laundry facilities at either end, under cover. Bar from 15/5, serving meals, snacks and takeaway 1/6-15/9. Swimming and paddling pools (from 15/5). Playground, games area and small football pitch. Minigolf, volleyball, basketball, table tennis. Fishing on site's own stretch of river. Caravan storage.

At a glance

| Welcome & Ambience | ✓✓✓✓✓ | Location | ✓✓✓✓ |
| Quality of Pitches | ✓✓✓✓✓ | Range of Facilities | ✓✓✓✓ |

Directions

Site signed off D960 Doué - Vihiers road, just west of Concourson-sur-Layon.

Charges 2004

Per unit incl. 2 persons	€ 15.00 - € 20.00
extra person	€ 3.50 - € 4.50
child (2-12 yrs)	€ 2.00 - € 2.50
electricity (10A)	€ 3.00
dog	€ 2.50

Plus local tax. Special offers available.

Reservations

Contact site. Tel: 02 41 59 86 35.
Email: Campingvdv@wanadoo.fr

Open

Easter - 31 October.

FR49080 Camping Ile d'Offard

Rue de Verden, Ile d'Offard, 49400 Saumur (Maine-et-Loire)

Situated on an island between the banks of the Loire and within walking distance of the centre of Saumur, this site is useful as an overnight stop en-route south or as a short-term base from which to visit the numerous châteaux in the region. The 190 touring pitches are on grass at the far end or hardstanding nearer the entrance. Some 67 pitches are occupied by tour operators and caravan holiday homes and these can be intrusive in some areas. As the site only closes from mid December until mid January, it is ideal for winter travellers. Some pitches have access to an electric hook-up. The adjacent municipal swimming pools and minigolf (open in July/Aug) are free for campers.

Facilities

Three sanitary blocks, one heated in winter, include provision for disabled visitors. Toilet facilities in all blocks are unisex. Block 1 has a well equipped laundry. The other blocks are only open in high season. Basic restaurant and bar (early May - late Sept) with takeaway. Table tennis, volleyball. Play area. Some activities with a children's club, wine tastings, etc. in high season. Off site: Riding 5 km. Fishing in the Loire (permits from Saumur). Thursday market 500 m, Saturday morning market 2 km.

At a glance

| Welcome & Ambience | ✓✓✓✓ | Location | ✓✓✓✓✓ |
| Quality of Pitches | ✓✓✓✓ | Range of Facilities | ✓✓✓✓ |

Directions

From N147 take exit for 'Saumur Centre'. At roundabout follow signs for Châtellerault and Chinon (keeping McDonalds on left) and continue alongside river towards town centre. At next roundabout (Office du Tourisme in front) turn left over bridge (Pont Cessart) onto island. Drive through shops and just before next bridge turn right past Hotel Adagio. Site is ahead beside municipal pool and sports stadium.

Charges 2004

Per unit incl. 2 adults	€ 14.50 - € 18.50
extra person	€ 4.00
child (2-10 yrs)	€ 2.00
electricity (5-16A)	€ 3.00
local tax	€ 0.20

Motorcaravan service point € 4,50 - € 7,50 (free to campers). Camping Cheques accepted.

Reservations

Advised for July/Aug. with 25% deposit plus charge for registration. Tel: 02 41 40 30 00.
Email: iledoffard@wanadoo.fr

Open

1 March - 31 October.

FR49060 Camping L'Européen de Montsabert

Montsabert, 49320 Coutures (Maine-et-Loire)

This extensive campsite, now under new ownership, has a rural atmosphere in the shadow of the Montsabert château, from where visiting peacocks happily roam in the spacious surroundings. Mature trees provide shade to the mostly large (some are enormous) pitches that are divided by hedges and are well marked. A few of the 107 pitches for touring units have a hardstanding, all have water tap, waste water point and electricity close by. Fringed by impressive redwood trees, this partially wooded site offers the peace of the countryside and yet easy access to Saumur and Angers. It is an ideal base for exploring, whether by foot, bicycle or car. Used by tour operators (19 pitches).

Facilities

The main central toilet block can be heated and has washbasins and bidets in cabins and a baby room. Outside dishwashing and laundry facilities. Washing machine and dryer. A second block serves the pool and another unit provides more WCs. Restaurant and takeaway (both 15/6-15/9). Bar (1/6-15/9). Shop (15/6-30/8). Large 25 m. heated swimming pool (20/5-12/9; no bermuda style shorts) and separate children's pool. Sports hall, minigolf, volley and basketball, table tennis and tennis. Bicycle hire. Picnic tables are provided in the shade near the entrance with a communal barbecue area. An entertainment programme is organised in high season. Off site: Windsurfing, canoeing and sailing near. Fishing 5 km. Golf 5km. Riding 8 km.

At a glance

| Welcome & Ambience | ✓✓✓✓✓ | Location | ✓✓✓✓ |
| Quality of Pitches | ✓✓✓✓✓ | Range of Facilities | ✓✓✓✓ |

Directions

From Le Mans, direction Angers, take exit 12 direction Seiches s Loire. Turn left to the D74 signed Bauné, Château Montgeoffroy, Mazé. In Mazé take the D55 towards St Maturin s Loire, pass the bridge and follow the signs L'Européen and Coutures.

Charges 2003

Per pitch incl. 2 persons	€ 13.00 - € 18.30
extra person	€ 3.30 - € 4.25
electricity (5/10A)	€ 2.75
cyclists (1 or 2 persons)	€ 10.70

Reservations

Made with 30% deposit and fee (€ 7,62).
Tel: 02 41 57 91 63. Email: anjoucamp@wanadoo.fr

Open

24 April - 19 September.

L'EUROPÉEN de MONTSABERT

Spacious Pitches Heated Swimmingpool, Childrens pool, Sportshall, Tennis, Tabletennis, Volley, Soccer, Midget Golf, etc. Bicycle rent, Walking- and Cyclingroutes Restaurant, Entertainment English spoken Holiday homes to let

www.camping-europeen.com   Tel: (0033) 241 57 91 63

FR49090 Camping L'Isle Verte

Avenue de la Loire, 49730 Montsoreau (Maine-et-Loire)

This friendly, natural site, with pitches overlooking the Loire, is just 100 metres from the centre of Montsoreau, an ideal starting point to visit the western Loire area. Most of the 83 shaded, level and good-sized pitches are separated by low hedges. Fishermen are particularly well catered for here, there being an area to store their equipment and live bait (permits are available in Saumur). Attractions within walking distance of the campsite include the château (500 m), Troglodyte (mushroom caves and restaurant) 500 m, wine tasting in the cellars opposite the site, and a Sunday market in the town. Excellent English is spoken in the reception and bar.

Facilities

A single building provides separate male and female toilets. Washbasins, some in cabins, and showers are unisex. Separate facilities for disabled campers. Baby room. Laundry room with deep sinks, washing machine and dryer. Dishwashing area under cover at the front of the building. Bar and snack bar (1/5-30/9). Swimming and paddling pools (15/5-30/9). Small play area. Table tennis, volleyball. Bicycle hire (June - August or by special request). Fishing. Off site: Golf 6 km. Riding 15 km.

At a glance

| Welcome & Ambience | ✓✓✓✓ | Location | ✓✓✓✓ |
| Quality of Pitches | ✓✓✓ | Range of Facilities | ✓✓✓ |

Directions

Take D947 from Saumur to Montsoreau and site is clearly signed on left along the road into town.

Charges 2004

Per unit incl. 2 adults	€ 12.50 - € 16.00
extra person	€ 3.00
child (2-10 yrs)	€ 1.50
electricity (16A)	€ 3.00
local tax	€ 0.20

Camping Cheques accepted.

Reservations

Advised for July/Aug. with 25% fee and booking fee.
Tel: 02 41 51 76 60. Email: isleverte@wanadoo.fr

Open

1 April - 30 September.

FR72030 Castel Camping Le Château de Chanteloup

72460 Sillé-le-Philippe (Sarthe)

A peaceful, pleasant site with a certain rural charm, 15 km. from Le Mans, Chanteloup is situated in the park of a 19th century château in the heart of the Sarthe countryside. There are 148 pitches, some along the edge of the woods, many on the lawn and completely open, and a few overlooking the lake, so the degree of shade varies. The pitches are open and all have electricity, although long leads will be required in some instances. This lack of regimentation enhances the atmosphere and feeling of spaciousness. Tours of the grounds and the village by pony and cart can be arranged.

Facilities

Sanitary facilities in the château outbuildings are a long way from some pitches and maintenance can be variable. Washbasins are in cabins. Dishwashing and laundry sinks, and washing machine under cover. Small shop. Pleasant bar (31/5-6/9) with terrace in the château with breakfast, lunch and dinner served (all 10/6-22/8). Swimming pool (fenced). Play area (parental supervision essential). Games room, tennis, volleyball, table tennis. Mountain bike hire. Organised activities in high season. Off site: Golf 14 km, riding 7 km. Free use of tennis club in Le Mans (tennis, squash and badminton).

At a glance

Welcome & Ambience	✓✓✓✓	Location	✓✓✓✓
Quality of Pitches	✓✓✓	Range of Facilities	✓✓✓✓

Directions

From autoroute take exit 23 and follow signs for Le Mans and Tours, then Le Mans and Savigne l'Evèque. Site is between Bonnétable and Savigne l'Evèque (road is narrow) on edge of Sille-le-Phillipe village.

Charges 2003

Per person	€ 4.50 - € 6.00
pitch	€ 8.00 - € 10.00
electricity (6A)	€ 3.00

Less 10% outside 24/6-20/8. Charges are higher during the 24 hr raceweek at Le Mans.

Reservations

No minimum length. Tel: 02 43 27 51 07. Email: chanteloup.souffront@wanadoo.fr

Open

1 June - 8 September.

FR72020M Camping Municipal du Lac

Rue du Lac, 72120 St. Calais (Sarthe)

Camping du Lac has 59 marked pitches, most separated by hedges and all with electricity, water and drain. A separate area is for tents. In high season there are theme evenings (crêpes or pizzas with guitar music), walks, competitions, children's activities, and communal meals (campers take own food and dance to music). Reception is welcoming and the value is excellent. There is some road noise.

Facilities

Two sanitary blocks provide some washbasins in private cabins. Washing machine in larger block. Bread and croissants (to order), post cards and T-shirts available at reception. Two small play areas. Off site: Swimming pool next to site. Local supermarket just a short walk.

At a glance

Welcome & Ambience	✓✓✓✓	Location	✓✓✓✓
Quality of Pitches	✓✓✓✓	Range of Facilities	✓✓✓

Directions

Well signed from N157, site is beside lake, near the station. Follow signs for `Camping Plan d'eau`.

Charges 2003

Per person	€ 2.30
child (under 10 yrs)	€ 1.10
pitch	€ 2.05
electricity (3/6A)	€ 1.50 - € 2.45

Reservations

Made with deposit (€ 15,24). Tel: 02 43 35 04 81.

Open

1 April - 15 October.

FR72060M Camping Municipal du Val de Sarthe

72170 Beaumont sur Sarthe (Sarthe)

This delightful, inexpensive riverside site is conveniently located just a short walk from the pretty little town. The 73 level, grassy individual pitches are large, divided by growing hedges and all have electricity. Some of the pitches including those along the river's edge may require a longer cable. An excellent activity area provides swings and other play equipment, boules pitches, tennis, netball, and a trim trail. Those intending to stay longer than one night require a barrier card (refundable deposit € 30). No double axle caravans are accepted.

Facilities

The central sanitary unit is accessed by a flight of steps although there is a long and fairly steep ramp for disabled people. Modern and well looked after facilities include some washbasins in cubicles and spacious showers. Dishwashing and laundry sinks, washing machine. Motorcaravan service point. Bread and croissants to order, and soft drinks available from reception. Activity area. River fishing. Room for campers' use (July/Aug).

At a glance

Welcome & Ambience	✓✓✓✓	Location	✓✓✓✓
Quality of Pitches	✓✓✓✓	Range of Facilities	✓✓✓

Directions

Site is well signed from approach roads and from the town centre.

Charges 2003

Per person	€ 1.52
pitch	€ 1.19 - € 2.06
electricity (5A)	€ 2.00

Reservations

Not normally necessary. Tel: 02 43 97 01 93. Email: beaumont.sur.sarthe@wanadoo.fr

Open

1 May - 30 September.

FR79020 Camping de Courte Vallée

79600 Airvault (Deux-Sèvres)

A warm welcome is given to all visitors here with a glass of wine and a friendly chat from the owners, Irene and Bruce Gibson. This very attractive site has 65 pitches on level grass amongst trees and shrubs, all with electricity. The owners are spending lots of time and work improving what is already a well laid out site, and have recently added several hardstanding pitches and four 'super' pitches. This is an ideal location for a short stay or as a base for touring the Poitou-Charentes region and the Loire valley. Nearby are Futuroscope and the Puy-Du-Fou medieval theme park.

Facilities

A modern unisex block has spacious cubicles for showers and washbasins, and shower and WC cubicles for disabled visitors, all kept to a very high standard of cleanliness. Dishwashing area under cover. Washing machine and dryers. Swimming pool. Boules. Table tennis. Play area. Reception sells snacks, drinks and gas. Internet access. Caravan storage. Wine tasting events and barbecues. Off site: The historic town of Airvault with good facilities is a 10-15 minute walk. Fishing 300 m. Riding 8 km.

At a glance

Welcome & Ambience	✓✓✓✓✓	Location	✓✓✓✓
Quality of Pitches	✓✓✓✓	Range of Facilities	✓✓✓✓

Directions

From D938 take D725 Airvault. On approaching village turn left over bridge. At T-junction at hilltop turn left, take second exit at roundabout and left at junction to site on left. Note: caravans not permitted in the village.

Charges 2003

Per person	€ 5.00 - € 6.00
child (under 7 yrs)	€ 2.00 - € 3.00
pitch	€ 7.50 - € 8.50
electricity (8A) and car on pitch	€ 9.00 - € 10.50

No credit cards.

Reservations

Contact site for details. Tel: 05 49 64 70 65. Email: camping@caravanningfrance.com

Open

1 April - 30 September.

FR86030 Camping Le Relais du Miel

Route d'Antran, 86100 Châtellerault (Vienne)

This site is being developed in the ten acre grounds of a rather grand house dating from Napoleonic times. Beside the River Vienne, it is surrounded by majestic old trees. Twin barns form two sides of a courtyard behind the house, one of which has already been converted very stylishly into reception, a high ceilinged function and games room. Beyond are an orchard and stone gateposts leading onto ground, previously the home farm, that now forms 80 large, flat pitches. The grass is gradually growing and over 1,000 trees and bushes have been planted, some now providing a little shade. All the 100-200 sq.m. pitches have electricity and water, 20 with drainage connections. You are welcome to stroll in the gardens and there is a gate in the walled grounds to the river bank where you may fish.

Facilities

First class toilet facilities have been created from three sets of outbuildings including washbasins in cabins, facilities for disabled people, dishwashing sinks, and a washing machine and dryer. Basic essentials and gas are kept. Bar and restaurant serving good value meals. Takeaway. Small snack bar with outdoor tables, sheltered by canopy, open in evenings in season. Swimming pool (15 x 7 m; not open all season). Playground. Tennis. Volleyball, basketball. Bicycle hire. Boules and games room with electronic games, pool and table tennis. Telescope. Torch useful. Off site: Riding 5 km. Golf 11 km. Supermarket 400 m. Futuroscope 16 km.

At a glance

Welcome & Ambience	✓✓✓✓	Location	✓✓✓✓
Quality of Pitches	✓✓✓✓✓	Range of Facilities	✓✓✓✓

Directions

Take exit no. 26 from the A10 autoroute (Châtellerault-Nord); site is signed just off the roundabout. From the N10 follow signs for Antran north of the town.

Latest charges

Per pitch incl. 2 persons, electricity and water	€ 19.00 - € 29.00
extra person over 5 yrs	€ 3.00 - € 5.00

Less 15% for 1 week, 20% for 2 weeks.

Reservations

Made with 10% deposit. Tel: 05 49 02 06 27. Email: camping@lerelaisdumiel.com

Open

15 May - 2 September.

FR86010 **Camping Le Petit Trianon**

Saint Ustre, 86220 Ingrandes-sur-Vienne (Vienne)

A family run site situated between Tours, Poitiers and Futuroscope, Le Petit Trianon has been a popular overnight stop reasonably close to the N10, one of the main routes to the southwest, for a good number of years. An original, albeit narrow, gateway leads into the campsite which consists of a slightly sloping meadow surrounded by trees in front of the château and a newer, large, more open field to one side, with a woodland area between. The 99 spacious, open but marked pitches are arranged to leave plenty of free space and there is shade in parts. All have electricity and 13 are fully serviced. Reception is housed in the château and this and the traditional, old outbuildings contain many of the main facilities, where several rooms can be heated, including the original toilet block. The pool area is located on the sunny side of a rather picturesque castled facade in which is a large, very cool reading room. Futuroscope at Poitiers is well worth at least a day's visit.

Facilities

The original toilet unit (looking a little dated and in need of some refurbishment) includes washbasins in cabins, some washbasin and shower combination units, baby baths, laundry with washing machines and dryer, and sinks for dishwashing. Smaller blocks have been added to serve the newer parts of the site and one contains facilities for disabled people. Motorcaravan service point. Shop with essentials and drinks (open certain hours). Takeaway cooked dishes. Heated swimming pool and paddling pools. Playground. Table tennis, minigolf, badminton, croquet, volleyball and boules. TV room with satellite, books and games. Bicycle hire. Local wine and cognac tastings on site and organised excursions. Caravan storage. Off site: Fishing 3 km. Restaurant 50 m. away with menu displayed on site.

At a glance

Welcome & Ambience	✓✓✓✓	Location	✓✓✓✓
Quality of Pitches	✓✓✓	Range of Facilities	✓✓✓✓

Directions

Ingrandes is signed from the N10 north of the town, which is between Dangé and Châtellerault. From autoroute A10 take exit 26 for Châtellerault-Nord and at roundabout follow signs for Tours to Ingrandes where site is signed.

Charges 2004

Per person	€ 6.60
child (0-6 yrs)	€ 1.10 - € 3.30
pitch	€ 3.95
serviced pitch	€ 6.60
electricity (5/10A)	€ 3.95 - € 4.35
vehicle	€ 3.75
dog	€ 2.10
local tax	€ 0.15

Less 10-20% for longer stays.

Reservations

Made with 25% deposit and fee (€ 12,50); min. 5 days in July/Aug. Tel: 05 49 02 61 47. Email: chateau@petit-trianon.fr

Open

20 May - 20 September.

FR86080 **Camping Caravaning Les Peupliers**

86700 Couhé (Vienne)

Family owned and run since 1968, Les Peupliers is located in a valley south of Poitiers. The site is arranged on the banks of a river (unfenced), the 130 pitches on both sides or around a fishing lake. On level grass, most are separated and all have electricity, while 55 are fully serviced. There is a good pool complex (open until mdinight) that includes impressive waterslides and new toboggans, a heated main pool, a paddling pool and a lagoon with two slides for younger children (under 10 yrs), plus water games. There is a local market for every day of the week (Chaunay, Lezay, Civray, Gencay, Rouillé or Vivonnet).

Facilities

The three toilet blocks are in Mediterranean style, with washbasins in cubicles and facilities for babies and disabled people. Dishwashing and laundry sinks. Washing machines and dryers. The newest block is in regular use, with the other two opened as the season progresses. Fridge rental. Small, well stocked shop. Snack bar, restaurant and bar with covered terrace and entertainment in peak season. Swimming pool complex (1/6-30/9). Playground. Fishing lake. Minigolf, table tennis and some pedaloes. Off site: Tennis court 800 m.

At a glance

Welcome & Ambience	✓✓✓	Location	✓✓✓
Quality of Pitches	✓✓✓	Range of Facilities	✓✓✓✓

Directions

Couhé is about 30 km. south of Poitiers on the N10. From the north, follow the signs for Couhé and the campsite, which is a short distance on the right.

Charges 2003

Per person	€ 5.50
child (2-10 yrs)	€ 3.50
pitch	€ 7.00
electricity (10/16A)	€ 3.00
electricity, water and drainage	€ 4.50

Less 30% in low season.

Reservations

Tel: 05 49 59 21 16. Email: info@lespeupliers.fr

Open

1 May - 30 September. Chalets for hire all year.

FR86040 Camping Le Futuriste

86130 St. Georges-les-Baillargeaux (Vienne)

On raised ground with panoramic views over the strikingly modern buildings and night-time bright lights that comprise the popular attraction of Futuroscope, Le Futuriste is a neat, modern site, open all year. It is ideal for a short stay to visit the park which is only 1.5 km. away (tickets can be bought at the site) but it is equally good for longer stays to see the region. With a busy atmosphere, there are early departures and late arrivals. Reception is open 08.00-22.00 hrs. There are 112 individual, flat, grassy pitches divided by young trees and shrubs which are beginning to provide some shelter for this elevated and otherwise rather open site (possibly windy). There are 28 pitches without electricity for tents, 22 with electricity and a further 62 with electricity, water, waste water and sewage connections. All are accessed via neat, level and firmly rolled gravel roads. The area has plenty of attractions and details are available from the enthusiastic young couple who run the site.

Facilities

Excellent, very clean sanitary facilities are housed in two modern blocks which are insulated and can be heated in cool weather. The facilities in the newest block are unisex. and include some washbasins in cabins and facilities for disabled people. Dishwashing and laundry sinks. Washing machine and dryer. Small shop (1/5-30/9) provides essentials (order bread the night before). New bar/restaurant. Snack bar and takeaway. Two outdoor pools, one with a slide and paddling pool (1/5-30/9). Free fishing in lake on site. Youth groups are not accepted. Off site: Bicycle hire 500 m. Golf 5 km. Supermarkets near.

At a glance

Welcome & Ambience	✓✓✓✓	Location	✓✓✓✓
Quality of Pitches	✓✓✓✓	Range of Facilities	✓✓✓✓

Directions

From either A10 autoroute or the N10, take Futuroscope exit. Site is located east of both roads, off the D20 to St Georges-Les-Baillargeaux. From all directions follow signs to St Georges. The site is on the hill; turn by the water tower and site is on the left.

Charges 2003

Per pitch incl. 1-3 persons	€ 12.75 - € 17.50
extra person	€ 1.65 - € 2.35
electricity (16A)	€ 2.35 - € 3.20
dog	€ 1.60
local tax	€ 0.07 - € 0.15
Camping Cheques accepted.	

Reservations

Phone bookings accepted for min. 2 nights.
Tel: 05 49 52 47 52. Email: d.Radet@libertysurf.fr

Open

All year.

Open all year. Panoramic view over the Futuroscope situated at 2 kms.
Heated swimming pool, pond, snack, bar, restaurant. Chalets for hire.
86130 St-Georges les Baillargeaux
Tel/Fax: 0033 549 52 47 52
www.camping-le-futuriste.fr

Loire Valley

FR86090 Camping du Parc de Saint-Cyr

86130 Saint-Cyr (Vienne)

This well organised, five hectare campsite is part of a 300 hectare leisure park, based around a large lake with sailing and associated sports, and an area for swimming (supervised July/Aug). Land-based activities include tennis, two half-courts, table tennis, fly fishing, badminton, pétanque, beach volleyball, TV room, and a well equipped fitness suite, all of which are free of charge. In high season there are extra free activities including a kids club, beach club, archery and an entertainment programme. Also in high season but charged for are sailing school, aquatic toboggan, windsurfing, canoe, kayak, water bikes and stunt bikes. Campers can also use the nine and 18 hole golf courses (with 20% discount for the 18 hole). If all this sounds a bit too exhausting, you could escape to the small, peaceful formal garden in the centre of the site. The campsite has around 179 tourist pitches and 11 mobile homes for rent. The marked and generally separated pitches are all fully serviced with electricity, water and drain.

Facilities

The main toilet block is modern and is supplemented for peak season by a second, recently refitted unit, which should prove adequate for demand, although they do attract some use by day-trippers to the leisure facilities. They include washbasins in cubicles, dishwashing and laundry sinks, washing machines and dryers, and facilities for babies and disabled persons. Shop, restaurant and takeaway (April - Sept). Playground on the beach. Bicycle hire. Barrier locked 22.00-07.00 hrs (€ 10 deposit for card).

At a glance

Welcome & Ambience	✓✓✓✓	Location	✓✓✓✓
Quality of Pitches	✓✓✓	Range of Facilities	✓✓✓✓

Directions

Saint Cyr is approx. midway between Châtellerault and Poitiers. Site is signed to the east of the N10 at Beaumont along the D82 towards Bonneuil-Matours, and is part of the Parc de Loisirs de Saint Cyr.

Charges 2003

Per pitch incl. electricity (10A),	
water and drainage	€ 6.00 - € 12.00
adult	€ 2.50 - € 5.00
child (1-7 yrs)	€ 1.50 - € 2.00
animal	free - € 1.50
local tax	€ 0.35

Reservations

Advisable for high season, made with fee (€ 7,62).
Tel: 05 49 62 57 22.
Email: contact@parcdesaintcyr.com

Open

1 April - 30 September.

Map 8

Burgundy is a wonderfully evocative region offering breathtaking chateaux and cathedrals, rolling hills and heady mountain views, vineyards and superlative cuisine, not to mention of course, a wide variety of world renowned wines.

Départements: 21 Côte d'Or, 58 Nièvre, 71 Saône-et-Loire, 89 Yonne

Major city: Dijon

In the rich heartland of France, Burgundy was once a powerful independent state and important religious centre. Its golden age is reflected in the area's magnificent art and architecture: the grand palaces and art collections of Dijon, the great pilgrimage church of Vézelay, the Cistercian Abbaye de Fontenay and the evocative abbey remains at Cluny, once the most powerful monastery in Europe.

However Burgundy is best known for its wine, including some of the world's finest, notably from the great vineyards of the Côte d'Or and Chablis, and also for its sublime cuisine. You'll also notice how driving through the country villages is like reading a wine merchant's list with plenty of opportunities for tasting and choosing your wine.

The area is criss-crossed by navigable waterways and includes the Parc Régional du Morvan; good walking country amidst lush, rolling wooded landscape.

Cuisine of the region

Many dishes are wine based, including *Poulet au Meursault* and *Coq au Chambertin*. Dijon is known for its *pain d'épice* (spiced honey-cake) and spicy mustard

Boeuf Bourguignon: braised beef simmered in a red wine-based sauce

Charolais (Pièce de): steak from Charolais cattle

Garbure: heavy soup, a mixture of pork, cabbage, beans and sausages

Gougère: cheese pastry based on Gruyère

Jambon persillé: parsley-flavoured ham, served cold in jelly

Matelote: fresh-water fish soup, usually based on a red wine sauce

Meurette: red wine-based sauce with small onions, used with fish or poached egg dishes

Places of interest

Autun: 12th century St Lazare cathedral

Beaune: medieval town; Museum of Burgundy Wine

Cluny: Europe's largest Benedictine abbey

Dijon: Palace of the Dukes, Fine Arts Museum, Burgundian Folklore Museum.

Fontenay: Fontenay Abbey and Cloister

Joigny: medieval town

Mâcon: Maison des Vins (wine centre)

Paray-le-Monial: Romanesque basilica, pilgrimage centre

Sens: historic buildings, museum with fine Gallo-Roman collections

Vézelay: fortified medieval hillside

tip

GET ON YOUR BIKE! BURGANDY HAS PLENTY OF LONG-DISTACE CANAL PATHS, GREAT FOR CYLING.

FR21010M Camping Municipal Louis Rigoly

Esplanade St Vorles, 21400 Châtillon-sur-Seine (Côte d'Or)

This well kept, small, hillside municipal site has 54 pitches. Mainly individual and separated, they are on fairly flat grass, 48 with electricity with mature trees providing shelter. Adjoining the site is the municipal swimming pool complex with both indoor and outdoor pools (on payment), and minigolf. There is no shop, but the town is close. The site, which has much transit trade, can become full by evening in season.

Facilities

The main toilet block at the lower end of the site is satisfactory. A smaller heated unit behind reception contains facilities for babies, a washing machine and dryer. Facilities for disabled visitors provided in a separate block. Snack bar July/Aug. Play area. Off site: Fishing or bicycle hire 1 km, riding 4 km.

At a glance

Welcome & Ambience	✓✓✓✓	Location	✓✓✓✓
Quality of Pitches	✓✓✓	Range of Facilities	✓✓✓

Directions

On northeast outskirts of town; site is signed from centre (steep hills approaching site, narrow roads).

Charges 2004

Per person	€ 2.80
pitch with electricity (4A)	€ 5.15 - € 7.30

No credit cards.

Reservations

Not officially made, but if you write shortly before your visit, they will reserve until 7 p.m. Tel: 03 80 91 03 05. Email: tourism-chatillon-sur-seine@wanadoo.fr

Open

1 April - 30 September.

FR21020M Camping Municipal Les Cents Vignes

10 rue Auguste Dubois, 21200 Beaune (Côte d'Or)

The Côte de Beaune, situated southeast of the Côte d'Or, produces some of the very best French wines. Beaune is also a city of art and has a charm all of its own and there are several 'caves' in the town just waiting to be visited. Les Cents Vignes is a very well kept site offering 116 individual pitches of good size, separated by neat beech hedges high enough to keep a fair amount of privacy. Rather over half of the pitches are on grass, ostensibly for tents, the remainder on hardstandings with electricity for caravans. A popular site, within walking distance of the town centre, it becomes full mid-June to early Sept. but with many short-stay campers there are departures each day and reservations can be made.

Facilities

Two modern, fully equipped and well constructed, sanitary blocks, one of which can be heated, should be large enough. Nearly all washbasins are in cabins. Dishwashing and laundry sinks. Washing machines. Shop, restaurant with takeaway (all 1/4-15/10). Playground. Sports area with tennis, basketball, volleyball, boules and table tennis. TV room. Barbecue area. Off site: Fishing or golf 4 km, bicycle hire 1 km. wind surfing 4 km.

At a glance

Welcome & Ambience	✓✓✓✓✓	Location	✓✓✓✓✓
Quality of Pitches	✓✓✓✓✓	Range of Facilities	✓✓✓✓

Directions

From autoroute exit 24 follow signs for Beaune centre on D2 road, camping signs to site in approx. 1 km. Well signed from other routes.

Charges 2003

Per person	€ 3.05
pitch with electricity (6A)	€ 7.20

Reservations

Made before 30 May without deposit. Tel: 03 80 22 03 91.

Open

15 March - 31 October.

FR21030M Camping Municipal Savigny-les-Beaune

Les Premiers Pres, 21420 Savigny-les-Beaune (Côte d'Or)

This popular site is ideally located for visiting the Burgundy vineyards, for use as a transit site or for spending time in the town of Beaune. During the high season it is full every evening, so it is best to arrive by 4 pm. The 90 level pitches are marked and numbered, with electricity and room for an awning. If reception is closed when you arrive, you find a pitch and report later, otherwise 'Madame' will allocate a place. Whilst the famed wine region alone attracts many visitors, Beaune, its capital, is unrivalled in its richness of art from times gone by. Narrow streets and squares are garlanded with flowers, cafés are crammed with tourists and overlooking the scene is the glistening Hotel Dieu.

Facilities

Well kept sanitary facilities are housed in a modern building behind reception. Additional WCs and water points are conveniently placed towards the middle of the site. Table tennis. Motorcaravan service point. Torch useful. Staff are pleasant and, if required, a bottle of local wine, soft drinks and ice can be purchased. Off site: Sunday market in the village.

At a glance

Welcome & Ambience	✓✓✓✓	Location	✓✓✓✓
Quality of Pitches	✓✓✓✓	Range of Facilities	✓✓✓

Directions

From A6 autoroute take exit 24 signed Beaune and Savigny-lès-Beaune onto D2. Turn right towards Savigny-lès-Beaune (3 km) and follow signs to site.

Charges 2003

Per person	€ 1.95
pitch with electricity	€ 6.15

Reservations

Not accepted. Tel: 03 80 26 15 06.

Open

1 May - 30 September.

FR21000 Camping Lac de Panthier

21320 Vandenesse-en-Auxois (Côte d'Or)

An attractively situated lakeside site in Bungundy countryside, Camping Lac de Panthier is divided into two distinct campsites. The first, smaller section houses the reception, shop, restaurant and other similar facilities. The second, larger area is 200 m. along the lakeside road and is where the site activities take place and the pool can be found. The 200 pitches (136 for touring units) all have electricity connections and are mostly on level grass, although in parts there are shallow terraces. The site's most obvious attraction is its proximity to the lake with its many watersports facilities. Used by tour operators. A 'Sites et Paysages' member.

Facilities

Four unisex toilet blocks (two for each site) also provide for babies and disabled people. Shop, bar and restaurant (all 15/5-22/9). Swimming pool complex with adults' pool, children's pool and water-slide (15/5-15/9). Watersports. Off site: Boat excursions from Pouilly en Auxois (8 km). Dijon, Autun and Beaune are also within easy reach.

At a glance

Welcome & Ambience	✓✓✓✓	Location	✓✓✓✓
Quality of Pitches	✓✓✓✓	Range of Facilities	✓✓✓✓

Directions

From the A6 join the A38 and immediately exit at junction 24. Take the N81 towards Arnay Le Duc (back over the A6), then almost immediately turn left on D977 for 5 km. Fork left again for Vandenesse en Auxois. Continue through village on D977 for 2.5 km, turn left again and site is on left.

Charges 2003

Per adult	€ 3.70 - € 6.10
child (under 7 yrs)	€ 1.80 - € 3.00
pitch	€ 4.10 - € 6.80
electricity (6/10A)	€ 4.00
dog	€ 1.50
local tax (over 17 yrs)	€ 0.30

Camping Cheques accepted.

Reservations

Contact site. Tel: 03 80 49 21 94.
Email: info@lac-de-panthier.com

Open

20 April - 29 September.

FR21040M Camping Municipal de Fouché

Rue du 8 Mai 1945, 21230 Arnay le Duc (Côte d'Or)

Useful as an overnight stop en-route to or from the Mediterranean or indeed for longer stays, this quite large but peaceful, lakeside site has good facilities and the added advantage of being open all year. It can be very busy during the school holidays, and is probably better visited outside the main season. There are 190 good sized pitches, on fairly level grass and all with electricity (some with water). This part of Burgundy is popular and Arnay le Duc itself is an attractive little town with an interesting history and renowned for its gastronomy, with many hotels and restaurants. The pitches, many hedged, offer a choice of shade or more open aspect.

Facilities

Two of the four sanitary blocks are reasonably modern and well maintained, including some British style WCs, washbasins in cabins, facilities for disabled visitors. Washing machines and dishwashing under cover. Shop in season (with bread) and snacks and drinks are served. TV/games room. Boules. Table tennis. Playground. Off site: Site is within walking distance of the town centre, which has an indoor swimming pool and tennis courts, etc.

At a glance

Welcome & Ambience	✓✓✓✓	Location	✓✓✓✓
Quality of Pitches	✓✓✓✓✓	Range of Facilities	✓✓✓✓

Directions

Site is on east side of town (well signed), 15 km. from A6 autoroute (exit at péage de Puilly en Auxois).

Charges 2004

Per unit incl. 2 persons	€ 8.50 - € 11.70
child (under 7 yrs)	€ 1.24 - € 1.60
electricity (10A)	€ 3.30
animal	€ 1.00
local tax (1/4-30/9) over 16 yrs	€ 0.30

Reservations

Advised; contact site. Tel: 03 80 90 02 23.
Email: camparnay@wanadoo.fr

Open

15 February - 15 November.

FR21050 Camping La Grappe d'Or

2 route de Volnay, 21190 Meursault (Côte d'Or)

Mersault, the capital of the great white wines of Burgundy, is southwest of Beaune and Camping La Grappe d'Or offers terraced pitches overlooking acres of vineyards. Most of the 118 touring pitches are flat, of varying sizes, and some have shade from mature trees. They all have electrical connections. There is an outdoor pool and flume and, during July and August, aqua gym and other water activities are organised. There is a fenced play area for youngsters and, just across the road from the entrance, there are two tennis courts for campers. A second part of the site is located 100 m. towards the village in the grounds of the owners' house. Here there are caravan holiday homes for rent as well as those used by tour operators. This is a reasonable campsite from which to enjoy some of the cycle/walking tours that take you around the local vineyards.

Facilities

Sanitary facilities are in three blocks with some washbasins in cabins. Child/baby room, facilities for visitors with disabilities, laundry and undercover dishwashing sinks. Shop, bar, restaurant, takeaway and swimming pool, all open from 15/5 - 15/9 although hours may vary. Play area, volleyball, tennis courts. Bicycle hire. Off site: Fishing 8 km, golf or riding 7 km. Indoor swimming pool 7 km.

At a glance

Welcome & Ambience	✓✓✓✓	Location	✓✓✓✓
Quality of Pitches	✓✓✓	Range of Facilities	✓✓✓✓

Directions

Site is north of Mersault. Take N74 from Beaune and follow the sign for Mersault; campsite is well signed from the town.

Charges 2004

Per unit incl. 2 persons	€ 11.50 - € 15.50
child (under 7 yrs)	€ 1.50 - € 1.90
electricity (15A)	€ 3.50
supplement for large	
motorcaravan in high season	€ 8.00

Reservations

Made with € 25 deposit plus € 5 fee.
Tel: 03 80 21 22 48.

Open

1 April - 15 October.

FR21060 Camping Les Bouleaux

21200 Vignolles (Côte d'Or)

Camping Les Bouleaux is an excellent little campsite located at Vignolles, northeast of Beaune. There are just 40 pitches, all with an electrical connection (long leads may be required on some pitches). The large flat pitches are attractively laid out and most are separated by hedges and trees giving some shade. Monsieur Rossignal takes great pride in his campsite, keeping the grounds and facilities exceptionally clean and tidy, and by planting bright flowers near the reception. Les Bouleaux makes a perfect overnight stop, especially as it's open throughout the year (including Christmas Day). The nearest shops and restaurants are 3 km. from the site – there are none on-site.

Facilities

An older unisex building provides Turkish style WCs, while the adjacent modern block houses British style WCs (no paper in either). Washbasins in cabins or communal; push-button controllable showers, excellent facilities for visitors with disabilities. Laundry and dishwashing sinks but no washing machines. The only water point is at the central toilet blocks - you probably need a short hose to fill fresh water containers. At present, motorcaravan's require an extra long hose or a portable container to fill onboard tanks (this may change in the near future). Gas exchange. Off site: Fishing 3 km. Golf 3 km. Riding 6 km. Bicycle hire 3 km.

At a glance

Welcome & Ambience	✓✓✓✓✓	Location	✓✓✓✓
Quality of Pitches	✓✓✓✓✓	Range of Facilities	✓✓✓

Directions

Vignolle is northeast of Beaune. Leave A6 autoroute at junction 24.1 south of Beaune. Turn right at roundabout, straight on at traffic lights (centre lane), then turn right at next roundoabout. Cross the autoroute, turn left at sign for Vignolle and follow the campsite signs.

Latest Charges

Per adult	€ 3.10
child (under 7 yrs)	€ 2.30
electricity (3/6A)	€ 1.90 - € 4.00
local tax	€ 0.08 - € 0.15

Reservations

Not usually required, but phone during July and August to confirm availability. Tel: 03 80 22 26 88.

Open

All year.

FR21070 Camping Municipal Les Grèbes

21330 Marcenay (Côte d'Or)

This attractive, peacefully located and very spacious lakeside site has 85 level, grassy pitches all with electricity hook-ups. They are arranged in small clearings with dividing shrubs and hedges. The stylish reception building has a small shop, a snack bar with drinks, a small library, some games machines and a pool table. The site has access via pedestrian gates onto the lakeside path, there is a small beach and marked swimming area and one can use non-powered boats or fish. The nearby Haut Fourneau is worth a visit.

Facilities

Two good quality modern sanitary units. The main one can be heated, the second at the rear of the site is open only for peak season. Both provide washbasins in cubicles and spacious hot showers. Good units for disabled people. Baby changing facility. Washing machine and dryer. Dishwashing facilities. Motorcaravan service point. Shop. Snackbar. Games room. Canoe hire. Playground. Volleyball, basketball and boules courts. Off site: Riding 500 m.

At a glance

Welcome & Ambience	✓✓✓✓	Location	✓✓✓✓
Quality of Pitches	✓✓✓✓	Range of Facilities	✓✓✓

Directions

Marcenay is about 35 km. east of Tonnerre. From Tonnerre take D965 east to Laignes, then D102 northeast to Marcenay, and follow signs to campsite and lake.

Charges 2003

Per person	€ 2.30
child (under 7 yrs)	€ 1.30
pitch and car	€ 4.30
electricity (6A)	€ 2.75

Reservations

Advised for July/Aug. No deposit required. Tel: 03 80 81 61 72.

Open

1 April - 15 September.

FR58010 Camping des Bains

15 avenue Jean Mermoz, 58360 St Honoré-les-Bains (Nièvre)

You are assured of a warm welcome at this attractive family run site, which is well situated for exploring the Morvan area. The spacious 120 level grassed pitches (all with electricity) are mostly separated by hedges with a large variety of mature trees offering shade next to the camping is the 'thermal spa' where there are opportunities to 'take the waters' for a three day session or a full blown cure of three weeks! Details are found at reception. There is an excellent restaurant almost opposite the campsite entrance. A 'Sites et Paysages' member.

Facilities

The two main sanitary units have mostly British style WCs, washbasins in separate cabins and ample hot showers (one block may be closed in low season). Dishwashing sinks, baby bath, laundry. Facilities for disabled people. Traditional family bar (1/6-30/9) also provides food and a takeaway service (1/6-15/9) with a separate slide and new paddling pool (15/6-15/9). Excellent play area and two small streams for children to fish. Table tennis. Minigolf. Entertainment weekly for children in July/Aug. Off site: Canal-side cycle route runs for 50 km. from Vandenesse (6 km). Bicycle hire or riding 500 m, fishing 5 km.

At a glance

Welcome & Ambience	✓✓✓✓	Location	✓✓✓✓
Quality of Pitches	✓✓✓✓	Range of Facilities	✓✓✓✓

Directions

From Nevers, travel east on D978; turn right onto D985 towards St Honoré-les-Bains, from where site is signed 'Camping des Bains', on entering town. Care is needed at narrow site entrance.

Charges 2003

Per unit incl. 2 persons	€ 14.50
extra person	€ 4.20
child (2- 7 yrs)	€ 2.75
electricity (6A)	€ 3.00
dog	€ 1.50
local tax	€ 0.30

Reservations

Write to site with deposit (€ 65) and fee (€ 12,20). Tel: 03 86 30 73 44. Email: camping-les-bains@wanadoo.fr

Open

1 May - 10 October.

FR58030 Castel Camping Manoir de Bezolle

58110 St Pereuse-en-Morvan (Nièvre)

Manoir de Bezolle is well situated to explore the Morvan Natural Park and the Nivernais area. It has been attractively landscaped to provide a number of different areas, some giving pleasant views over the surrounding countryside. Pitches of varying sizes are on level grass with shade, some with terracing and most have access to electricity. There are two small lakes, stocked with many fish for anglers. This site is good for families with a range of activities provided for them.

Facilities

Two main toilet blocks (opened as needed) provide washbasins in cabins, mostly British style WCs, bath, provision for disabled visitors and a baby bath. A fibreglass unit contains two tiny family WC/basin/shower suites for rent. A smaller, older block is by the pools. Laundry. Motorcaravan services. Shop (15/5-15/9; bread to order at other times). Bar and restaurant (15/5-15/9). Pizza and takeaway (main season only). Internet point. Two swimming pools with sunbathing terrace (1/6-15/9). Pony rides (June-Sept). Table tennis, minigolf. Fishing. Animation is organised in season.

At a glance

Welcome & Ambience	✓✓✓✓	Location	✓✓✓✓
Quality of Pitches	✓✓✓✓	Range of Facilities	✓✓✓✓

Directions

Site is between Nevers and Autun (mid-way between Châtillon-en-Bazois and Château-Chinon), just north of the D978 by the small village of St Péreuse-en-Morvan.

Charges 2003

Per pitch incl. 2 persons	€ 15.00 - € 21.00
extra person	€ 5.00 - € 6.00
child under 3 yrs	free - € 3.00
child 3-7 yrs	€ 3.00 - € 4.00
electricity (10A)	€ 4.00
animal	€ 2.00
local tax	€ 0.15

Camping Cheques accepted.

Reservations

Made with deposit (€ 45,70) and fee (€ 15,20). Tel: 03 86 84 42 55. Email: info@bezolle.com

Open

15 April - 30 September.

FR71020M Le Village des Meuniers

71520 Dompierre-les-Ormes (Saône-et-Loire)

In a tranquil setting with panoramic views, the neat appearance of the reception building sets the tone for the rest of this attractive site. It is an excellent example of current trends in French tourism development. The 116 terraced, grassy pitches, some with hardstanding, are all fairly level, each with electricity and ample water points. They all enjoy stunning views of the surrounding countryside – the Beaujolais, the Maconnais, the Charollais and the Clunysois. An extensive sunbathing area surrounds the attractively designed swimming pool complex. This is a superb site, tastefully landscaped, with a high standard of cleanliness in all areas. As the hedges and trees mature they will offer more shade. This is an area well worth visiting, with attractive scenery, interesting history, excellent wines and good food. Used by tour operators (12 pitches) and 17 chalets to rent.

Facilities

Sanitary facilities mainly in an unusual, purpose designed hexagonal block, with modern fittings, of high standard. Smaller unit in the lower area of the site, plus further toilets in the main reception building. Motorcaravan service point in car park. Café (high season). Bar, shop and takeaway (15/5-15/9). Swimming pool complex with three heated pools and toboggan run (from 1/6). Children`s activities organised in high season. Football. Minigolf. Off site: Fishing 1.5 km, riding 10 km. Village 500 m. for all services (banks and some shops, closed Sun/Mon).

At a glance

| Welcome & Ambience | ✓✓✓✓ | Location | ✓✓✓✓ |
| Quality of Pitches | ✓✓✓✓✓ | Range of Facilities | ✓✓✓✓ |

Directions

Town is 35 km. west of Macon. Follow N79/E62 (Charolles, Paray, Digoin) road and turn south onto D41 to Dompierre-les-Ormes (3 km). Site is clearly signed through village.

Charges 2003

Per person	€ 4.30 - € 5.80
pitch	€ 4.80 - € 6.40
electricity (15A)	€ 2.70
family rate (2 adults and children)	€ 17.00 - € 25.00

Reservations

Advised for July/Aug. Tel: 03 85 50 36 60. Email: levillagedesmeuniers@wanadoo.fr

Open

15 May - 15 September.

Le Village ★★★★ des Meuniers

CHALETS AND GITES OPENED ALL YEAR LONG
SWIMMING - POOL, MINIGOLF, WALKING PATHS

71 520 DOMPIERRE LES ORMES
Tél. (+33) 385 50 36 60
Fax : (+33) 385 50 36 61
@ : levillagedesmeuniers@wanadoo.fr
Website: villagedesmeuniers.com

Campsite opened from the 15th of May until the 15th of September

FR71010M Camping Municipal Mâcon

Route Nationale 6, 71000 Mâcon (Saône-et-Loire)

Always useful and well cared for, this site is worth considering as a stopover or for longer stays as it is close to the main route south. The 275 good sized pitches, all with electricity and some with fresh and waste water points, are on mown, flat grass, accessed by tarmac roads. There is a generally bright and cheerful ambience. A central play area is divided, part with a rubber base for toddlers and part with adventure equipment for 7-15 year-olds. The bar/restaurant is open all year and seems to be a favourite haunt for the locals at lunchtime. Gates closed 10.00-06.30 hrs. but large units note – the security barrier has a 3.8 m. height restriction so watch those top boxes and air-conditioners!

Facilities

Sanitary facilities in three modernised, well maintained units, are fully equipped with British and Turkish style WCs, and washbasins in cubicles. A fourth modern block is next to the swimming and paddling pools (for campers only). Facilities for disabled visitors. Dishwashing and laundry sinks. Washing machine and dryer. Some sanitary facilities closed out of peak season. Excellent motorcaravan service point (with Fiamma sewage couplings). Shop/tabac. Bar. Takeaway and restaurant (le Tipi) open midday and evenings. Good TV lounge. Playground. Off site: Swimming pool, sports stadium and supermarket nearby.

At a glance

| Welcome & Ambience | ✓✓✓✓✓ | Location | ✓✓✓✓ |
| Quality of Pitches | ✓✓✓✓ | Range of Facilities | ✓✓✓✓ |

Directions

Site is on northern outskirts of Mâcon on main N6, 3 km. from the town centre (just south of A40 autoroute junction).

Latest Charges

Per unit incl. 2 adults	€ 11.00
with electricity (5A)	€ 13.30
child (under 7 yrs)	€ 1.55
dog	€ 0.70
electricity 10A supplement	€ 2.65

Reservations

Not normally required. Tel: 03 85 38 16 22.

Open

15 March - 31 October.

FR71050 Camping Moulin de Collonge

71940 St Boil (Saône-et-Loire)

This well run, family site offers an 'away from it all' situation surrounded by sloping vineyards and golden wheat fields. It has an instant appeal for those seeking a quiet, relaxing environment. There are 57 level pitches, most with electrical hook-ups although long cables may be needed. Hanging flower arrangements are in abundance and, like the shrubs and grounds, are constantly attended by the proprietor and his family (M. Gillot`s other interest is the restoration of classic cars). Beyond the stream that borders the site are a pool, patio and a pizzeria (also open to the public all year). A new lake, 1.8 m. deep, has been created for leisure activities. The 'Voie Vert', a 40 km. track for cycling or walking starts near the site.

Facilities

Toilet facilities housed in a converted barn are tastefully decorated and well kept. Some washbasins are in cubicles, there are outside sinks for dishes and laundry. Washing machine and dryer under cover. Freezer for campers` use. Bread is delivered at 8.30 each morning. Ices and cool drinks can be purchased. Pizzeria. Swimming pool covered by plastic dome - some of the walls can be opened in good weather. Bicycle hire. Table tennis. Fishing. Pony trekking. Off site: Riding 4 km. Chateaux, wine route, churches.

At a glance

Welcome & Ambience	✓✓✓✓	Location	✓✓✓✓
Quality of Pitches	✓✓✓	Range of Facilities	✓✓✓✓

Directions

From Chalon-sur-Saône travel 9 km. west on the N80. Turn south on D981 through Buxy (6 km). Continue south for 7 km. to Saint-Boil and site is signed at south end of the village.

Charges 2003

Per person	€ 4.50 - € 5.50
child (under 7 yrs)	€ 2.29 - € 3.50
electricity	€ 3.00 - € 3.50

Less 20% outside July/Aug.
Camping Cheques accepted.

Reservations

Accepted - contact site. Tel: 03 85 44 00 40.

Open

1 March - 30 September.

FR71060 Camping Caravaning Château de Montrouant

71800 Gibles (Saône-et-Loire)

This is a small, pretty site beside a lake in the grounds of an imposing chateau, located in a steep valley in the rolling Charolais hills. There is ample shade from the many mature trees and the 45 pitches (12 used by tour operators) are on reasonably flat grassy terraces, mainly separated by small hedges. All have electrical connections. The overall appearance is attractive with some pitches overlooking the lake and some next to a field where ponies graze. This site is probably best for smaller units as the access roads are very steep and not in very good condition; caravans (and motorcaravans) are towed off site if required. The enthusiastic owner organises several unusual and interesting activities during the main season, including stone masonry, model boat building, walks, wine tours, etc. Good fishing is possible in the site`s lakes and is a feature of the site. Regrettably the season here is short and the site becomes quickly full mid-July - mid-Aug. and is very popular with the Dutch. The best times could be from late June - mid July or the second half of August. Motorcaravan owners should always check in advance as there may not be a suitable pitch. Used by a Dutch tour operator.

Facilities

The sanitary facilities, not too well designed and with maintenance that can be variable, are housed in a part of the château. They include washbasins in cabins. Dishwashing sinks. Washing machine and dryer. Very small open-air bar/restaurant for evening barbecues (only open certain evenings). Swimming pool with secluded sunbathing area, has been sympathetically landscaped. Half-court tennis. Fishing. Riding. Torches useful. Off site: Village of Gibles, with shops, restaurant, etc. is 2 km. Riding 10 km.

At a glance

Welcome & Ambience	✓✓✓✓✓	Location	✓✓✓✓
Quality of Pitches	✓✓✓	Range of Facilities	✓✓✓✓

Directions

Site is to the west of Mâcon and can be reached from the A6 (Macon Sud) via the N79 to Charolles (approx. 55 km). Take exit for Trivy - Dompierre-les-Ormes and D41 towards Montneland and Gibles.

Charges 2003

Per person	€ 4.70
child (under 7 yrs)	€ 3.00
pitch	€ 4.20
vehicle	€ 4.20
electricity (6A)	€ 4.20
dog	€ 3.00
local tax	€ 0.23

Special weekly charges. Camping Cheques accepted.

Reservations

Essential for high season (8/7-25/8) and made with 25% deposit. Tel: 03 85 84 54 30.

Open

1 June - 10 September.

FR71070 Castel Camping Château de L'Epervière

71240 Gigny-sur-Saône (Saône-et-Loire)

Peacefully situated on the edge of the little village of Gigny-sur-Saône, yet within easy distance of the A6 autoroute, this site nestles in a natural woodland area near the Saône river (subject to flooding in winter months). With 135 pitches, nearly all with electricity, the site is in two fairly distinct areas. The original part has semi-hedged pitches on part-level ground with plenty of shade from mature trees, close to the château and fishing lake – you may need earplugs in the mornings because of the ducks! The centre of the second area has a more open aspect, with large hedged pitches and mature trees offering shade around the periphery and central open grass area. A partly fenced road across the lake connects the two areas of the site (care is needed with children). The managers, Gert-Jan and Francois, and their team enthusiastically organise a range of activities for visitors that includes wine tastings in the cellars of the château and a Kids' Club in July/Aug. Used by tour operators (60 pitches). A member of 'Les Castels' group.

Facilities

Two well equipped toilet blocks, one beside the château and a newer one on the lower section include washbasins in cabins, dishwashing and laundry areas under cover. Washing machine and dryer. Shop providing bread and basic provisions (1/5-30/9). Tastefully refurbished restaurant in the château with a distinctly French menu (1/4-30/9). Second restaurant with more basic menu and takeaway service. A converted barn houses an attractive bar, large screen TV and games room. Unheated swimming pool (1/5-30/9), with many sunloungers, partly enclosed by old stone walls protecting it from the wind, plus a smaller indoor heated pool with jacuzzi, sauna and paddling pool. Well equipped play area. Outdoor paddling pool. Bicycle hire. Off site: Riding 15 km, golf 20 km.

At a glance

Welcome & Ambience	✓✓✓✓✓	Location	✓✓✓✓
Quality of Pitches	✓✓✓✓	Range of Facilities	✓✓✓✓✓

Directions

From N6 between Châlon-sur-Saône and Tournus, turn east on D18 (just north of Sennecey-le-Grand) and follow site signs for 6.5 km. From A6, exit Châlon-Sud from the north, or Tournus from the south.

Charges 2003

Per person	€ 5.10 - € 6.10
child (under 7 yrs)	€ 3.10 - € 4.10
pitch	€ 6.60 - € 9.20
dog	€ 2.10 - € 2.60
electricity (10A)	€ 3.10 - € 4.10

Camping Cheques accepted.

Reservations

Contact site. Tel: 03 85 94 16 90.
Email: domaine-de-leperviere@wanadoo.fr

Open

1 April - 30 September.

LES CASTELS ★★★★ Camping Qualité

Domaine du Château de l'Epervière

WELCOME IN THE HEART OF BURGUNDY

Domaine du Chateau de l'Epervière 71240 Gigny sur Saône
Tél : 03 85 94 16 90 Fax : 03 85 94 16 97
www.domaine-eperviere.com E-mail : domaine-de-leperviere@wanadoo.fr

169

FR71030M Camping Municipal Saint Vital

Rue des Griottons, 71250 Cluny (Saône-et-Loire)

Close to this attractive small town (300 metres walk) and next to the municipal swimming pool (free for campers), this site has 174 pitches. On gently sloping grass, with some small hedges and shade in parts, electricity is available (long leads may be needed). Some rail noise is noticeable during the day but we are assured that trains do not run 23.30-07.00 hrs. The town has the largest number of Roman houses in France, the National Stud farm, and don't miss the Cheese Tower for the best views of Cluny. The really excellent traffic free cycle path from Cluny to Givry is highly recommended.

Facilities

Two sanitary buildings provide British and Turkish style WCs, some washbasins in cubicles and controllable showers (no dividers). Dishwashing and laundry sinks. Washing machine and dryer. A rubbish recycling system operates. In high season, on Friday evenings, there is a presentation of local produce in the 'salle de reunion'. Off site: Fishing 100 m, bicycle hire 100 m. Wine routes, chateaux, churches.

At a glance

| Welcome & Ambience | ✓✓✓✓ | Location | ✓✓✓✓ |
| Quality of Pitches | ✓✓✓✓ | Range of Facilities | ✓✓✓ |

Directions

Site is east of town, by the D15 Azé/Blanot road.

Charges 2004

Per person	€ 3.30
child (under 7 yrs)	€ 1.90
pitch with electricity (6A)	€ 4.60

Reservations

Advised for high season. Tel: 03 85 59 08 34.

Open

1 May - 1 October.

FR71080 Camping de L'Etang Neuf

L'Etang Neuf, 71760 Issy-l'Évêque (Saône-et-Loire)

Overlooking a lake flanked by a forest on one side and a 19th century chateau on another, the tranquillity of this family managed site is a haven for relaxation. The 64 grass pitches, with electricity, are marked and separated by low hedges. There are some young trees offering a little shade. A separate area is set aside for tents. The children's play area is next to a fenced swimming pool and paddling pool. Many walks and cycle routes (all terrain) start at the site – free maps are provided.

Facilities

Two very clean sanitary blocks include British and Turkish style WCs and washbasins in cabins. Dishwashing and laundry sinks. Washing machine, ironing board and baby room. Separate shower and toilet rooms for disabled people are in the lower block. Motorcaravan service point. Bar/restaurant. Bread and croissants to order. Boules pitch. TV and games room. Table tennis. Volleyball. Off site: Just outside the site entrance is crazy golf. Nearest shop 1 km. in Issy l'Évêque. Riding 500 m.

At a glance

| Welcome & Ambience | ✓✓✓✓ | Location | ✓✓✓✓ |
| Quality of Pitches | ✓✓✓✓ | Range of Facilities | ✓✓✓✓ |

Directions

From D973 (Luzy - Bourbon-Lancy) turn left onto D25 (just west of Luzy) and continue for about 12 km. Turn right on D42 in centre of Issy l'Évêque, signed to campsite. Take care as the road narrows considerably as you approach the site entrance on the right.

Charges 2003

Per unit incl. 2 adults	€ 15.00
with 5A electricity	€ 18.00

Reservations

Advised for July and August. Tel: 03 85 24 96 05. Email: marc.pille@compaqnet.be

Open

1 May - 15 September.

FR71110 Camping du Lac

Le Fourneau, 71430 Palinges (Saône-et-Loire)

Camping du Lac is a very special campsite and it is all due to Monsieur Labille, its guardian. Firstly, he thinks of the campsite as his home and every visitor as his guest; secondly, the central amenity block is spotlessly clean; and thirdly, the campsite is next to a lake with a beach and safe bathing. Monsieur Labille provides tables and chairs for tent campers and he freezes bottles of water for cyclists to take away (free of charge). If you want to visit a specific place, then Monsieur knows exactly where you should go – he never recommends anything that he hasn't personally tried out. The campsite, owned by a municipality, comprises 46 good sized grass pitches, each with a small hardstanding. All the pitches have two electricity connections, and six have water and waste points.

Facilities

The central sanitary block provides showers, washbasins in cubicles, facilities for campers with disabilities and two family rooms. Washing machine and fridge for campers' use (free). Bread and croissants to order at reception. Boules. Play area. TV room. Sports field, lake beach and swimming adjacent. Bicycle and pedalo hire in July/Aug. Off site: Just outside the gates is a bar/snack bar serving very reasonably priced drinks, food and ice creams. Palinges is within walking distance, cycle and walk routes, museums, cruises on canals, chateaux, museographical complex.

At a glance

| Welcome & Ambience | ✓✓✓✓✓ | Location | ✓✓✓✓✓ |
| Quality of Pitches | ✓✓✓✓✓ | Range of Facilities | ✓✓✓✓ |

Directions

Palinges is midway between Montceau les Mines and Paray le Monial. From Montceau take N70, then turn left onto D92 to Palinges. Follow campsite signs. Site is also well signed from D985 Toulon-sur-Arroux to Charolles road.

Charges 2003

Per unit incl. 2 persons	€ 11.50
with electricity (10A)	€ 14.50
double axle caravan	€ 28.00

Reservations

Advised in July and August. Tel: 03 85 88 14 49.

Open

1 April - 30 September.

FR71090 Camping Intercommunal du Lac de Saint Point

71520 St Point (Saône-et-Loire)

Managed by a young husband and wife team, this site would make a convenient overnight stop. The area is renowned for its wine and cheese as well as Roman churches, abbeys and châteaux. There are 34 reasonably level touring pitches, mostly separated by low hedges, and 46 tent pitches on a sloping and partly terraced field behind. On-site activities include swimming in the lake (lifeguard on duty during July and August), with pedaloes for hire and fishing.

Facilities

Two sanitary blocks, one adjoining the reception and the other towards the back of the site up a slope, provide all the usual facilities and a washing machine. Shower and toilet/washbasin in separate cabins for campers with disabilities. Snacks are available in high season. Play area. Volleyball, basketball and badminton. Table tennis. Games room. Boules pitch. Mountain bike hire. Off site: Nearest shop 300 m. Tennis 4 km. Pony club 5 km. Organised walks on Wednesdays 4 km. Bicycle hire 4 km.

At a glance

Welcome & Ambience	✓✓✓	Location	✓✓
Quality of Pitches	✓✓	Range of Facilities	✓✓✓✓

Directions

Leave A6 at junction 29 and take the N79 as far as the Cluny exit. Bear left and follow the signs to St Point; campsite is on the outskirts of the village on the right.

Charges 2003

Per unit incl. 2 adults, 2 children	€ 11.00
with electricity	€ 14.00 - € 16.50
extra person	€ 1.50
extra child (up to 7 yrs)	€ 1.00
dog	€ 1.00

No credit cards.

Reservations

Advised in July/August. Tel: 03 85 50 52 31.
Email: camping.stpoint@wanadoo.fr

Open

1 April - 31 October.

Camping du lac de Saint-Point Lamartine ★★★

Very comfortable campsite
Near Beaujolais and Mâconnais vineyards,
Cluny (romanesque abbey)
An excellent location by a lake
Quiet, shady, family atmosphere
Bathing, fishing, hiking, Mountain biking,
playground, sportsground, games room, snack-bar...
Chalets for hire
Open 1st April - 31st October

Le Lac - 71520 Saint-Point
Tel: 0033 385 50 52 31 - Fax: 0033 385 50 51 92
E-mail: camping.stpoint@wanadoo.fr
http://perso.wanadoo.fr/camping.stpoint

Southern Burgundy

FR89060 Camping Les Ceriselles

Route de Vincelottes, 89290 Vincelles (Yonne)

A distinctive, modern site, Les Ceriselles was created in 1998 on land next to the Canal du Nivernais and is owned by a group of communities. A very level site, it has 84 pitches on grass, all with electricity, and 37 fully serviced. A covered terrace houses a small snack bar with a good range of snacks, takeaway and drinks. Staff live on site and the gates are locked at 22.00 -07.00 hrs. Cars are parked on the secure on-site car park and not on the pitches. Double axle caravans are not accepted. This good value site is just off the popular N6 route and ideal for exploring the Yonne valley and Auxerre region.

Facilities

Four small heated toilet blocks each provide 1 WC, 2 washbasins in cubicles and 2 showers per sex, with a unit for disabled visitors in block one (nearest reception). Chemical toilet disposal is via screw cap joints on the fully serviced pitches at present. Snack bar (all season, hours vary acc. to demand). Playground. Bicycle hire. Fishing. Boules. Off site: Supermarket and restaurant within walking distance. Cycle path along canal for 8 km. in either direction.

At a glance

Welcome & Ambience	✓✓✓✓	Location	✓✓✓✓
Quality of Pitches	✓✓✓✓	Range of Facilities	✓✓✓

Directions

Vincelles is about 10 km. south of Auxerre. From A6 take 'Auxerre Sud' exit and follow N65 towards Auxerre. After 4 km. turn south on N6 towards Avallon and after 10 km. turn left on D38. Site entrance is on left just before canal.

Charges 2003

Per person	€ 2.07
child (2-7 yrs)	€ 1.04
pitch	€ 5.74 - € 7.00
electricity (6A)	€ 1.75
animal	€ 0.80

Reductions for longer stays.

Reservations

Contact site. Tel: 03 86 42 39 39.
Email: lesceriselles@wanadoo.fr

Open

1 April - 30 September.

171

Map 9

Franche Comté

Located to the south of Alsace, the historic province of Franche Comté boasts a varied landscape ranging from flat plains to dense woodlands, rugged dramatic mountains and limestone valleys.

Départements: 25 Doubs, 39 Jura, 70 Haute-Saône, 90 Tre. de Belfort

Major city: Besançon

Franche Comté is really made up of two regions. The high valley of the Saône is wide, gently rolling farmland with a certain rustic simplicity, while the Jura mountains are more rugged with dense forests, sheer cliffs, craggy limestone escarpments and torrents of clear, sparkling water gushing through deep gorges. It is for this thrilling scenery that Franche Comté is best known. Nature lovers can climb, bike and hike in the mountains or explore the hills honeycombed with over 4,000 caves. The streams and lakes provide world-class fishing. The spa towns of Salins les Bains and Besançon offer relaxation and a chance to 'take the waters'.

The region has a rich architectural heritage dating from many different periods, including medieval abbeys and châteaux and a poignant chapel in memory of the war. Roman remains, fortresses perched on cliff tops and elegant spa towns can all be explored at leisure. The region's position, bordering Switzerland and close to Germany, is reflected in its culture and also the great diversity of architectural style in the many fine buildings.

Cuisine of the region

Freshwater fish such as trout, grayling, pike and perch are local specialities. The region has a rare wine known as *vin de paile* as well as *vin jaune* (deep yellow and very dry) and *vin du jura*, Jura wine.

Brési: water-thin slices of dried beef; many local hams

Gougére: hot cheese pastry based on the local *Comté* cheese

Jésus de Morteau: fat pork sausage smoked over pine and juniper

Kirsh: cherry flavoured liqueur

Pontarlier: aniseed liqueur

Poulet au vin jaune: chicken, cream and *morilles* (chestnuts) cooked in *vin jaune*

Places of interest

Arbois: Pasteur Family Home and Museum, Museum of Wine and Wine Growing

Belfort: sandstone lion sculpted by Bartholdi; Memorial and Museum of the French Resistance

Besançon: citadel with good views over the city

Champlitte: Museum of Folk Art

Dole: lovely old town, Louis Pasteur's birthplace

Gray: Baron Martin Museum

Luxeuil-les-Bains: Tour des Echevins Museum

Ornans: Gustave Courbet birthplace, museum

Ronchamp: Chapel of Notre-Dame du Haut de Ronchamp designed by Le Corbusier

Salins-les-Bains: Salt mines and tunnels

Sochaux: Peugeot Museum

Alan Rogers **tip**

THE 150 KM. TRAIL AROUND THE JURA LAKES OFFERS SPECTACULAR SCENERY AND POINTS OF INTEREST. OR SIMPLY SIT BACK AND ENJOY A CRUISE ALONG ONE OF THE MANY LAKES.

FR25030 Camping du Bois de Reveuge
25680 Huanne (Doubs)

As Bois de Reveuge was only opened in 1992, it still has a new look about it, in as much as there is little shade yet from the young trees. Being on a hillside, the pitches are on terraces with good views across the surrounding countryside and leading down to two lakes which may be used for fishing and canoeing. The site also has private use of a 10 hectare lake set in a park 10 km. away where there is a watersports school and boating opportunities. Tall trees have been left standing at the top of the hill 190 pitches available for tourers have a water supply as well as electricity (6A) and some are extra large (150 - 180 sq.m). There is a good solar heated swimming pool (15/5-15/9) which can be covered in cool weather and another pool with four water slides. Several supervisors are in attendance during the summer who, as well as acting as lifeguards, sometimes offer swimming lessons.

Facilities
Three modern sanitary blocks are nicely spaced around the site and have British and Turkish style WCs and washbasins mainly in cabins. Kiosk for basic food supplies (open all season) and restaurant/pizzeria with terrace (1/6-3/9). Swimming pools (19/4-20/9). Three children's play areas. High season `baby club` with a large tent for wet weather, large video screen and some music and other entertainment for adults. Bowling alley. Shooting range. Pony club. Groups may request activities such as orienteering. A package deal includes use of canoes as well as archery, fishing, bicycle hire and pedaloes.

Directions
Site is well signed from the D50. From A36 autoroute south of the site, take exit for Baume-les-Dames and head north on D50 towards Villersexel for about 7 km. to camp signs.

Charges 2003

Per unit incl. 2 persons	€ 17.00 - € 35.00
extra person	€ 3.00 - € 5.00
child (2-6 yrs)	€ 2.00 - € 4.00
animal	€ 2.00
Camping Cheques accepted.	

Reservations
Made with 30% deposit and fee (€ 20).
Tel: 03 81 84 38 60.
Email: info@campingduboisdereveuge.com

Open
19 April - 20 September.

At a glance
Welcome & Ambience	✓✓✓✓	Location	✓✓✓✓
Quality of Pitches	✓✓✓	Range of Facilities	✓✓✓✓

FR25000 Camping Le Val de Bonnal
Bonnal, 25680 Rougemont (Doubs)

This is an impressive, well managed site in a large country estate, harmoniously designed in keeping with the surrounding countryside, well away from main roads and other intrusions. Having said that, the site itself is very busy, with a wide range of activities and amenities. The 350 pitches, all of a good size and with electricity, are separated by a mixture of trees and bushes, carefully landscaped. Some of the newer pitches are less secluded, but the ambience generally is peaceful despite the size of the site (300 pitches in a large area) and its deserved popularity. The main attraction must be the variety of watersports on the three large lakes and nearby river which include swimming, pedaloes, and fishing as well as water skiing, windsurfing and canoeing. In fact, the range of activities available in high season is almost inexhaustible, not to say exhausting! Used by tour operators (150 pitches).

Facilities
Five clean toilet blocks include washbasins in cabins. Separate washing up blocks. Washing machines, ironing boards and sinks for laundry. Riverside restaurant, snack bar/takeaway, bar and terrace, shop (all 20/5-8/9), sympathetically converted from former farm buildings. New swimming pool complex features water slides. Well equipped children's play areas. Range of sport facilities including table tennis, boules, bicycle hire, and water sports, etc. Fishing on the river and lake. Off site: Golf 6 km. Day trips to Switzerland.

Directions
From Vesoul take D9 towards Villersexel. After approx. 20 km. turn right in the village of Esprels at sign for Val de Bonnal. Follow for 3.5 km. and site is on the left. From autoroute A36 take exit for Baume-les-Dames; go north on D50, then D486 to Rougemont and follow signs to site.

Charges 2003

Per pitch incl. 2 persons and electricity (5A)	€ 29.00
extra person	€ 7.00
child (3-8yrs)	€ 2.00
local tax	€ 0.30
Less 20% outside July/Aug.	

Reservations
Only made for pitches with electricity.
Tel: 03 81 86 90 87.
Email: val-de-bonnal@wanadoo.fr

Open
8 May - 8 September.

At a glance
Welcome & Ambience	✓✓✓✓	Location	✓✓✓✓
Quality of Pitches	✓✓✓✓	Range of Facilities	✓✓✓✓✓

FR25050M Camping Municipal de Saint Point-Lac

8 rue du Port, 25160 St Point-Lac (Doubs)

A good example of a municipal campsite in which the village takes a pride, this site is on the banks of a small lake with views to the distant hills. The 84 level, numbered pitches are on grass and 60 have electricity. It is worth making a detour from the Pontarlier - Vallorbe road or for a longer stay. The village shop and restaurant are an easy 200 m. walk from the site entrance.

Facilities

Good central sanitary block has British style WCs and free hot water. Hot snacks and takeaway in high season (July/Aug). Fishing. Off site: Bicycle hire 5 km.

At a glance			
Welcome & Ambience	√√√	Location	√√√√
Quality of Pitches	√√√	Range of Facilities	√√√

Directions

From north, take D437 south of Pontarlier and keep on west side of the lake to the second village (St Point-Lac); from south exit N57 at Les Hopitaux-Neufs and turn west to lake.

Charges 2003

Per pitch incl. 2 persons	€ 7.50 - € 9.00
with electricity (16A)	€ 11.50 - € 13.00
extra person	€ 2.00 - € 2.50
child (4-10 yrs)	€ 1.00 - € 1.25
animal	€ 1.00
local tax	€ 0.25

Reservations

Made with deposit (€ 45) and fee (€ 7,60). Contact site from 1 May, or the Mairie in writing only (postal address as above). Tel: 03 81 69 61 64. Email: camping-saintpointlac@wanadoo.fr

Open

1 May - 30 September.

FR39010 Camping La Plage Blanche

3 rue de la Plage, 39380 Ounans (Jura)

Situated in open countryside, along the banks of the River Loue, this site has 220 good sized, marked pitches on level ground, all with electricity. Trees provide both fully shaded and semi-shaded pitches. Approximately a kilometre of riverside and beach provide the ideal setting for children to swim and play safely in the gently flowing, shallow water – inflatables are popular and there is a canoe/kayak base. The site also has a swimming pool.

Facilities

Modern, well kept sanitary facilities in three unusual blocks include separate washing cabins. Dishwashing facilities are in blocks of 8 sinks. Launderette. Motorcaravan service area. Bar/restaurant with terrace (1/4-30/9). Pizzeria and akeaway (all season). TV room. Swimming pool and children's pool. Play area. River fishing. Table tennis. Off site: Bicycle hire 200 m. Riding 700 m. Golf 10 km.

At a glance			
Welcome & Ambience	√√√√	Location	√√√√
Quality of Pitches	√√√	Range of Facilities	√√√√

Directions

Ounans is 20 km southeast of Dole. From autoroute 36 from Besançon, take Dole exit and then D405 to Parcey. After Parcey take N5 to Mont Sous Vaudrey (8 km) then D472 towards Pontarlier to Ounans from where site is signed. From autoroute A9 take Dole exit and follow signs for N5, Poligny and Lons le Saunier. From Parcy follow directions above.

Charges 2003

Per person	€ 4.70
child (1-7 yrs)	€ 2.90
pitch	€ 5.90
electricity (6A)	€ 3.00
dog	€ 1.00
local tax	€ 0.15

Camping Cheques accepted.

Reservations

Made with deposit (€ 31) and fee (€ 8). Tel: 03 84 37 69 63. Email: reservation@la-plage-blanche.com

Open

1 April - 30 September.

FR39030 Camping Domaine de Chalain

39130 Doucier (Jura)

Doucier lies east of Lons-le-Saunier among the wooded hills of the Jura and rather away from the main routes. This large, park-like site (804 pitches) is on the edge of the Lac de Chalain surrounded on three sides by woods and some cliffs. Large areas are left for sports and recreation. The lake shelves gently at the edge but then becomes deep quite suddenly. Day visitors can be very numerous during fine weekends. The site also has an attractive, well equipped pool complex. The site is divided into two parts, one (nearer the lake) with larger pitches (costing more). You should find room in the other part, but for July and August, it is better to reserve to make sure. There are over 200 electrical connections, but little shade. Used by tour operators (100 pitches).

Facilities

Nine sanitary blocks, improved over the years, include washbasins with warm water (all in cabins). Showers are in separate blocks. One block can be heated with facilities for babies and disabled people. Washing machines. Shops (15/5-15/9). Bar, takeaway and snacks (1/5-20/9) and a community room. New pool complex with heated indoor pool, outdoor pools with slide, sauna and spa. Tennis, table tennis, minigolf and pedaloes for hire. Fishing. Bicycle hire. Animals and birds in enclosures. Cinema and organised activities, plus a disco for the young. Dogs are not permitted on the lake beach. Off site: Riding 2 km, golf 25 km.

At a glance

Welcome & Ambience	✓✓✓✓	Location	✓✓✓✓
Quality of Pitches	✓✓✓	Range of Facilities	✓✓✓✓

Directions

Site can only be approached via Doucier: from Switzerland via N5 (from Geneva), then the N78 and D39; from other directions via Lons-le-Saunier or Champagnole.

Charges 2003

Per unit incl. 3 persons acc.	
to location and services	€ 18.87 - € 32.13
extra adult	€ 6.22 - € 7.80
child (4-15 yrs)	€ 3.88 - € 4.69
electricity	€ 2.55
dog	€ 2.55
local tax	€ 0.26

Reservations

Made for min. 7 days with 30% deposit (min. € 61). Sat.-Sat. only in high season. Tel: 03 84 25 78 78. Email: chalain@chalain.com

Open

1 May - 20 September.

FR39040 Sunêlia La Pergola

39130 Marigny (Jura)

Close to the Swiss border and overlooking the sparkling waters of Lac de Chalain, La Pergola is a neat, tidy and terraced site set amongst the rolling hills of the Jura. Awaiting discovery as it is not on the main tourist routes, La Pergola is very well appointed, with 350 pitches, mainly on gravel and separated by small bushes, and all with electricity, water and drainage. Arranged on numerous terraces, connected by steep steps, some have shade and the higher ones have good views over the lake. A tall fence protects the site from the public footpath that separates the site from the lakeside but there are frequent access gates. The entrance is very attractive and the work that Mme. Gicquaire puts into the preparation of the flower-beds is very evident. The bar/restaurant terrace is beautiful, featuring grape vines for welcome shade and a colourful array of spectacular flowers leading on to a landscaped waterfall area next to the three swimming pools and entertainment area. English is spoken. Used by tour operators (120 pitches).

Facilities

The latest sanitary block serving the lower pitches is well appointed with private cabins. Slightly older blocks serve the other terraces. Visitors with disabilities are advised to select a lower terrace where special facilities are provided. Washing machines and dryers. Bar. Restaurant. Pool complex, two pools heated. Good play area and children's club. Table tennis and volleyball. Windsurfing, pedaloes and small boats for hire. Organised programme in high season includes cycle tours, keep fit sessions and evening entertainment with disco twice weekly. Off site: Riding 3 km.

At a glance

Welcome & Ambience	✓✓✓✓	Location	✓✓✓✓
Quality of Pitches	✓✓✓✓	Range of Facilities	✓✓✓✓✓

Directions

Site is 2.5 km. north of Doucier on Lake Chalain road D27.

Charges 2003

Per unit incl. 2 persons and electricity	€ 20.00 - € 35.00
extra person	€ 4.50 - € 5.50
child (2-6 yrs)	free - € 4.50
dog	€ 2.00
local tax	€ 0.35

Various special offers available.
Camping Cheques accepted.

Reservations

Made with deposit (€ 122) and fee (€ 27). Tel: 03 84 25 70 03. Email: contact@lapergola.com

Open

10 May - 21 September.

FR39050 Camping Fayolan

BP 52, 39130 Clairvaux-les-Lacs (Jura)

This modern site, backed by wooded hills, is situated on the shores of Le Petit Lac about a mile from the town of Clairvaux-les-Lacs amid the lakes and forests of the Jura. Here one can relax, enjoy the peaceful countryside, explore the interesting villages, historic towns and museums of the area by car or cycle or take to the water where you can swim, windsurf and canoe. The neat, tidy site is in two parts, with pitches from 80-100 sq.m. either on terraces overlooking the lake or on the flatter area near the shore. There are electrical connections for those who want them and 200 pitches also have water, drainage and sewage connections. The upper part has little shade until the young trees grow but there is some on the lower section. Used by tour operators (130 pitches).

Facilities

Four modern toilet units spread around the site have warm water from push-button taps in washbasins and showers and hot water in sinks. Shop. Restaurant. Two good attractive swimming pools (heated from mid-May), one with a slide, and smaller one for children (trunks, not shorts). Playground. Organised activities include archery, a fitness trail, walks, games, competitions, children's club and dancing. Fishing. Entertainment. Off site: Bicycle hire 800 m, riding 4 km.

At a glance			
Welcome & Ambience	✓✓✓	Location	✓✓✓✓
Quality of Pitches	✓✓✓✓	Range of Facilities	✓✓✓✓✓

Directions

Clairvaux-les-Lacs is on the N78 between Lons-le-Saunier and Morez. In Clairvaux follow signs for 'Lacs Campings' and Fayolan.

Charges 2003

Per unit incl. 2 persons	€ 9.98 - € 22.58
extra person	€ 4.42 - € 5.49
child (4-20 yrs)	€ 1.52 - € 5.39
electricity (6A)	€ 2.44 - € 2.74
serviced pitch	€ 3.81 - € 4.57
animal	€ 2.29
local tax	€ 0.31

Reservations

Made with 30% deposit and € 19 fee.
Tel: 03 84 25 26 19.
Email: Relais.Soleil.Jura@wanadoo.fr

Open

3 May - 15 September.

FR39060 Camping La Marjorie

640 Bvd. de l'Europe, 39000 Lons-le-Saunier (Jura)

La Marjorie is a spacious site set on the outskirts of the spa town of Lons-le-Saunier. It is a former municipal site with 200 level pitches. Mainly on hardstanding, they are separated by well trimmed hedges interspersed with tall trees which gives privacy plus a little shade at some part of the day. Bordering one area of the site are open fields and woodlands. All pitches have electricity and a few are fully serviced. The site is 2.5 km. from the centre of the town which is the capital town of the Jura region. There is a bicycle path from the site into town and a mountain bike track behind the site. English is spoken.

Facilities

Three well maintained toilet blocks, two modern and heated, have individual cubicles with washbasins and large showers. Baby baths, good facilities for disabled people, washing and ironing. Motorcaravan service point (charge). Small shop (15/6-31/8). Small bar with takeaway meals (all 15/6-31/8). TV room, table tennis, small play area, boule pitch, volleyball and football field. Archery, canoeing and riding can be arranged (fee). Off site: Local swimming pool 200 m. Restaurants 500 m. Golf 5 km. Caves and waterfalls 17 km.

At a glance			
Welcome & Ambience	✓✓✓✓	Location	✓✓✓✓
Quality of Pitches	✓✓✓✓	Range of Facilities	✓✓✓✓

Directions

Site is off the N83 Lons-le-Saunier - Besancon road. Approaching Lons on the D52 or the N78 or D471, site is signed from the first roundabout on the outskirts of the town. When approaching from Bescancon on N83, follow signs for Club Nautique on outskirts of Lons - this takes you under the N83 to the site.

Charges 2003

Per unit incl. 2 persons	€ 9.98 - € 13.50
with electricity (6A)	€ 11.05 - € 16.00
tent pitch incl. 2 persons	€ 8.50 - € 12.00
extra person	€ 2.38 - € 3.50
child (under 10 yrs)	€ 1.28 - € 2.00
dog	€ 1.00
double axle unit plus	€ 30.00
Less 10% for stays over 7 days.	

Reservations

Made with deposit (€ 130) and fee (€ 9,15).
Tel: 03 84 24 26 94.
Email: info@camping-marjorie.com

Open

1 April - 15 October.

FR70020M Camping International du Lac Vesoul

70000 Vesoul (Haute-Saône)

This is one of the better examples of a municipal site and is part of a leisure park around a large lake. A five kilometre path has been created around the lake for walking and cycling and there is a large open space for ball games or sunbathing, along with a good children's playground and bar/restaurant. A map at the entrance shows the water areas for swimming, boating and windsurfing. Watersports are organised by the Club Nautique Haut-Saonois Vesoul and there is also tennis, table tennis, archery, basketball and night-time carp fishing. The campsite does not have direct access to the lake as it is separated by a security fence, but access is possible at the site entrance. There are 160 good sized, level, grass pitches, all with electricity. Access is from hard roads and pitches are separated by shrubs and bushes. There is a large hard area in the centre of the site brightened by flowers and young trees.

Facilities

Three good quality toilet blocks, one heated, are well spaced around the site. They have a mix of British and Turkish style WCs and free, pre-mixed warm water from push-button taps in the washbasins and showers. Baby room. Facilities for disabled visitors. Washing machines and dryers.

At a glance

Welcome & Ambience	✓✓✓✓	Location	✓✓✓✓
Quality of Pitches	✓✓✓✓	Range of Facilities	✓✓✓

Directions

On road D457 to west of Vesoul on route to Besançon, well signed around the town.

Charges 2003

Per person	€ 3.00
child (under 7 yrs)	€ 1.30
pitch	€ 3.10
pitch with electricity (10A)	€ 5.10
vehicle	€ 2.10
dog	€ 1.60

No credit cards.

Reservations

Contact site. Tel: 03 84 76 22 86.

Open

1 March - 31 October.

FR90000 Camping L'Etang des Forges

11 rue Béthouart, 90000 Belfort (Tre. de Belfort)

Belfort (known as the City of the Lion) is a historic fortified town with much history. The region is well endowed with footpaths and cycle trails and this site would make a good base for a longer stay. There are also opportunities for ballooning and hang-gliding. Although 178 pitches are marked out, this very spacious site only uses 90 of them, and you should always be able to find room here. The pitches are all on level, mostly open ground divided by low bushes. A few trees around one end give a little shade to some pitches and there are electricity hook-ups to all pitches and a good supply of water taps. The reception building also contains a small shop and cafe.

Facilities

A single modern sanitary building (heated in cool weather) provides washbasins in cubicles, a suite for disabled people, dishwashing and laundry sinks, a washing machine and dryer. Motorcaravan service point. Outdoor swimming pool. Volleyball. Table tennis. Small playground. TV Room. Shop and cafe (117-31/8). Internet terminal. Off site: Large supermarket is on edge of town on the Mulhouse road.

At a glance

Welcome & Ambience	✓✓✓✓	Location	✓✓✓✓✓
Quality of Pitches	✓✓✓✓	Range of Facilities	✓✓✓✓

Directions

Site is northeast of town centre, adjacent to the lake and sports facilities (well signed).

Charges 2003

Per person	€ 3.10 - € 3.80
child (4-9 yrs)	€ 2.50 - € 3.10
pitch	€ 7.00 - € 8.00
electricity (6A)	€ 3.00
animal	€ 1.00 - € 1.50

Reservations

Not usually necessary. Tel: 03 84 22 54 92. Email: contact@campings-belfort.com

Open

14 April - 30 September.

Map 9

Deep valleys dividing mountain slopes, covered in lush alpine pastures and evergreen woods - this is the Savoy Alps bordering Switzerland. Further south you'll come across the Dauphine Alps which, although they can appear harsh and forbidding, offer spectacular scenery.

Savoy & Dauphiny Alps

Départements: 38 Isère, 73 Savoie, 74 Haute-Savoie

Major city: Grenoble

Lying between the Rhône Valley and the Alpine borders with Switzerland and Italy are the old provinces of Savoie and Dauphine. This is an area of enormous granite outcrops, deeply riven by spectacular glacier hewn and river etched valleys. One of the world's leading wintersport playgrounds there is also a range of outdoor activities in the summer. Despite development, great care has been taken to blend the old with the new and many traditional villages still retain their charm and historical interest. For many, it is an opportunity to escape the crowds and enjoy some clean air, unusual wildlife, stunning views, hidden lakes and sometimes isolated villages in spectacular mountain settings.

From Chambéry, north to the shores of Lac Léman (Lake Geneva) are many towns and villages that, since Roman times, have attracted visitors to take the waters. Aix-les-Bains, Evian and Annecy were three major lakeside spa resorts of the Victorians; while Chamonix and Grenoble attracted the 19th century travellers who pioneered modern skiing and 'alpinism'. To the north is the region of Chartreuse famous for its monastery and liqueur!

Cuisine of the region

Plat gratine applies to a wide varity of dishes, in the Alps this means cooked in breadcrumbs.

Farcement (Farçon Savoyard): potatoes baked with cream, eggs, bacon, dried pears and prunes

Féra: a freshwater lake fish

Fondue: hot melted cheese and white wine

Gratin Dauphinois: potato dish with cream, cheese and garlic

Gratin Savoyard: another potato dish with cheese and butter

Lavaret: a freshwater lake fish, like salmon

Longeole: a country sausage

Lotte: a burbot, not unlike an eel

Tartiflette: potato, bacon, onions and Reblochon cheese

Places of interest

Aix-les-Bains: spa resort on the Lac du Bourget, boat excursions to the Royal Abbey of Hautecombe

Albertville: 1992 Winter Olympics, museum, now has an active night-life!

Annecy: canal-filled lakeside town, 12th century château, old quarter

Bourg-St-Maurice: centre of Savoie café society

Chambéry: old quarter, Dukes of Savoie château, Savoie museum.

Chamonix: site of first Winter Olympics in 1924, world capital of mountain climbing

Evian-les-Bains: spa and casino on Lake Geneva

Grenoble: University city, Fort de la Bastille

Alan Rogers **tip**

WATCH THE FAMOUS CYCLE RACE, THE TOURS DE FRANCE, WHICH PASSES THROUGH THIS AREA IN JULY; AND HUSKY DOG TREKKING WHICH ALSO TAKES PLACE IN SUMMER.

FR38090M Camping Caravaning Belle Roche

38930 Lalley (Isère)

Belle Roche, a good, small municipal site, has extremely pleasant views all round and is a convenient overnight stop, or even for a longer stay. The level site is only a few years old, so is rather open at present with very little shade, but it is nonetheless neat and well maintained. There are 65 spacious pitches, many part grass with a gravel hardstanding. All have 16A electricity and there are ample water points. It is a convenient base for enjoying this scenic but relatively unknown Trièves part of the Isère.

Facilities

Two sanitary blocks provide some washbasins in private cabins. Facilities for disabled visitors. Laundry and dishwashing. Good motorcaravan service point. Bar and terrace serving simple, good value meals. Bread from reception. Swimming pool (19 x 12 m; June-Sept.) with large sunbathing area and sunbeds. Play area.
Off site: Village shop. Cycling, walking, climbing.

Directions

Follow N75 south from Grenoble (approx. 65 km.) turn left onto D66, signed Lalley and follow camping signs through the village. The campsite is on the right just beyond the village.

Charges 2003

Per unit incl. 2 persons	€ 10.90 - € 13.20
child (under 7 yrs)	€ 1.50
child (8 - 16 yrs)	€ 3.00

Camping Cheques accepted.

Reservations

Advised for July/Aug. Tel: 04 76 34 75 33.
Email: camping-belleroche@joliefrance.com

Open

1 May - 30 September.

At a glance

Welcome & Ambience	✓✓✓✓✓	Location	✓✓✓✓
Quality of Pitches	✓✓✓✓	Range of Facilities	✓✓✓✓

FR38010 Le Coin Tranquille

38490 Les Abrets (Isère)

Set in the Dauphiny countryside north of Grenoble, Le Coin Tranquille is truly a 'quiet corner', especially outside school holiday times, although it is still popular with families in high season. Les Abrets is well placed for visits to the Savoie regions and the Alps. It is a neat, tidy and well maintained site of 192 grass pitches (160 for touring units), all with electricity. They are separated by hedges of hydrangea, flowering shrubs and a range of trees to make a lovely environment doubly enhanced by the rural aspect and marvellous views across to the mountains. This is a popular site with a warm welcome, that makes a wonderful base for exploring the area, especially in low season– the Chartreuse caves at Voiron are well worth a visit. Used by tour operators (14 pitches). A 'Sites et Paysages' member.

Facilities

The central large sanitary block is of good quality and well kept, heated in low season. It includes washbasins in cabins, facilities for children and disabled people and a laundry room. Two other blocks on either edge of the site have been refurbished to a high standard. Busy shop. Excellent restaurant, open all year (closed two days weekly in low season) and attracting local clientele. Swimming pool and paddling pool (15/5-30/9; no bermuda shorts) with sunbathing areas. Play area. TV/video room with balcony, games room and quiet reading room. Supervised games for children, slide shows of the region's attractions and weekly entertainment for adults including live music (not discos) arranged in high season. Bicycle hire. Off site: Fishing 5 km. riding 6 km.

Directions

Site is northeast of Les Abrets. From the town take N6 towards Chambery, turning left after about 2 km (site signed) and site is about 1 km up a narrow road, on the right.

Latest Charges

Per pitch incl. 2 persons	€ 13.00 - € 24.00
extra person	€ 3.80 - € 6.00
child (2-7 yrs)	€ 2.20 - € 4.00
electricity (2/6A)	€ 1.30 - € 3.00

Camping Cheques accepted.

Reservations

Write with deposit (€ 107) and fee (€ 15,24).
Tel: 04 76 32 13 48.
Email: contact@coin-tranquille.com

Open

1 April - 31 October.

At a glance

Welcome & Ambience	✓✓✓✓✓	Location	✓✓✓✓
Quality of Pitches	✓✓✓✓✓	Range of Facilities	✓✓✓✓✓

Le Coin Tranquille - 38490 Les Abrets - www.coin-tranquille.com

FR38030 Camping La Cascade

Route de l'Alpe d'Huez, 38520 Bourg-d'Oisans (Isère)

La Cascade is close to and within sight and sound of the waterfall from which it takes its name. The friendly owners keep this very pleasant site neat and tidy. Bourg d'Oisans lies in the Romanche valley 725 m. above sea level surrounded by high mountains. It is a real sun trap and gets very hot in summer. The ski resorts of Alpe d'Huez and Les Deux Alpes are close by. The Alpe d'Huez road past the campsite with its 21 hairpin bends is revered by serious cyclists as it is often used as the 'king of the mountain' stage for the Tour de France. La Cascade has 133 individual pitches, 106 for touring units on mainly flat ground. Of varying but quite adequate size with electricity, many have little shade.

Facilities

Two heated sanitary blocks are of good quality with mainly British style toilets and washbasins in cabins. Washing machine. Bar and snack bar (1/7-31/8). Good sized, heated and sheltered swimming pool and paddling pool (15/5-30/9) surrounded by large, enclosed sunbathing area. Small playground. General room with TV. Games room. Table tennis, volleyball and boules. Evening entertainment and lots of activities organised in season. Off site: Supermarket 500 m. Bourg d'Oisans 1 km, with bars, restaurants, shops and banks etc. Ski resorts of Alpe d'Huez 13 km. and Les deux Alpes 25 km. Bicycle hire and riding 1 km, fishing 500 m.

At a glance

| Welcome & Ambience | ✓✓✓✓ | Location | ✓✓✓✓ |
| Quality of Pitches | ✓✓✓✓ | Range of Facilities | ✓✓✓✓ |

Directions

Leave Bourg d'Oisans on the N91 towards Briançon. Shortly after crossing the river, on a sharp right hand bend, turn left onto the D211, signed Alpe d'Huez. Site is on right in 400 m.

Charges 2004

Per unit incl. 2 persons	€ 14.80 - € 22.00
extra person (over 5 yrs)	€ 4.00 - € 5.50
electricity (16A)	€ 3.50
animal	free

Reservations

Essential for July/Aug; made for minimum 8 days with deposit (€ 64) and fee (€ 16). No reservations by phone. Tel: 04 76 80 02 42. Email: lacascade@wanadoo.fr

Open

20 December - 30 September.

FR38060 Camping Les Trois Lacs

La Plaine, 38460 Trept (Isère)

Les Trois Lacs is situated on the edge of three lakes in flat, open country in the north of Dauphine. It is a pleasant and relaxing base to enjoy either the countryside, the historic places of the region or the programme of leisure activities provided by the site. The land around the lakes has been well land-scaped with smooth lawns and a variety of shrubs and trees. The camping area is on one side of the largest lake with tall trees on one edge and views of distant mountains. The 166 good sized pitches, with 150 for tourists and 8 having water and a drain. They are in pairs between the hard access roads, each pair separated from the others by low hedges, but there is little shade. The smallest lake is kept for fishing and the others for boating and watersports with one section for swimming having a water slide (with lifeguard July/Aug).

Facilities

Good quality, fully equipped toilet blocks are in the centre of the camping area. Laundry room. Mobile shop calls in high season. Attractive bar/restaurant near reception serves drinks (all season) and simple snacks (June-Aug). Other snack bars are around the lakes. Two discos for teenagers and one for older people each week. Entertainment in July/Aug. Lakeside beach and water slide. Games room, tennis, table tennis, football, minigolf, beach volleyball, badminton, walking, and roller skating. Off site: Riding 500 m. Mountain bike hire 10 km. Shops at Trept 2 km.

At a glance

| Welcome & Ambience | ✓✓✓ | Location | ✓✓✓ |
| Quality of Pitches | ✓✓✓✓ | Range of Facilities | ✓✓✓✓ |

Directions

Leave N75 (Grenoble - Bourg-en-Bresse) road, at Morestel and travel west on D517. Site is well signed between Sablonnières and Trept.

Charges 2004

Per person	€ 3.00 - € 7.00
child (under 10 yrs)	free - € 3.50
pitch	€ 9.00 - € 17.00
animal	€ 2.00
electricity	free

Less 20% in low seasons.
Camping Cheques accepted.

Reservations

Made with deposit (€ 70) and fee (€ 15). Tel: 04 74 92 92 06. Email: les3lacs@free.fr

Open

1 May - 10 September.

FR38080 Camping Caravaning Au Joyeux Réveil

Le Château, 38880 Autrans (Isère)

The small town of Autrans is set on a plateau, 1,050 m. high, in the Vecors region. Au Joyeux Réveil is a simple site, run by a very friendly family (English spoken). It is ideally situated for any of the activities that this wonderful area has to offer – from walking, mountain biking and pot-holing in summer to downhill and cross-country skiing in winter, it is all there for you in magnificent scenery. The site is on the outskirts of the town, set below a ski jump and short lift. The 111 pitches, 80 for touring are mainly on grass, reasonably level with small trees giving only a little shade. All have electricity and are in a sunny location with fantastic views over the surrounding wooded mountians. The D531 road and then the D106 look a little daunting on the map but they are good roads with reasonable gradients.

Facilities

The new toilet block is very well appointed, with under-floor heating and all the expected facilities. Another new building houses a bar with terrace, snack bar/takeaway (July and August). Small, kidney-shaped swimming pool with sunbathing area and a large paddling pool with toboggan for children. Small play area and large chess table. TV room. Off site: Short ski-lift is near the site and a shuttle bus runs regularly the 5 km. to the longer runs. Fishing, bicycle hire or riding 300 m.

At a glance

| Welcome & Ambience | ✓✓✓✓✓ | Location | ✓✓✓✓ |
| Quality of Pitches | ✓✓✓ | Range of Facilities | ✓✓✓✓ |

Directions

Exit autoroute A48, north west of Grenoble at junction 13 (going south) or 3A (going north). Follow N532 to Sassenage, turn west onto D531 to Lans en Vercors. At the roundabout turn right on D106 signed Autrans. On entering village turn right at roundabout and very shortly right again. Site is on your left.

Charges 2003

Per unit incl. 1 or 2 persons	€ 14.00 - € 17.00
extra person	€ 4.30
child (under 6 yrs)	€ 3.10
electricity (4/10A)	€ 3.00 - € 3.80
local tax	€ 0.15

Winter prices - apply to site.
Camping Cheques accepted.

Reservations

Write to site with 20% deposit and € 12 fee.
Tel: 04 76 95 33 44.
Email: camping-au-joyeux-reveil@wanadoo.fr

Open

All year excl. Oct. and Nov.

FR38040 Camping La Rencontre du Soleil

Route de l'Alpe d'Huez, 38520 Bourg-d'Oisans (Isère)

This part of the Isère is an attractive and popular region with some exceptional scenery for which this site proves a good base from which to explore. Pleasant, friendly and family run, it nestles between two impressive mountain ranges, at the base of France's largest National Park, Le Parc des Ecrins. Only 2 km. from Bourg d'Oisans, a regular staging point for the Tour de France, it offers some serious and exciting cycling. The site has 73 level, hedged pitches, most of average size, with mature trees offering good shade. Electricity is available. Canoeing, rafting, riding and many other activities are possible nearby. The site is used by tour a operators (20 pitches). A 'Sites et Paysages' member.

Facilities

A large heated toilet block provides all the usual amenities, all of high quality and extremely clean and well maintained. Washing machine and dryer. Motorcaravan service point. Bread to order. Restaurant and takeaway (all season). Sitting room with TV and children's play room adjoining. Small, sheltered swimming pool (all season). Play area. Programme of activities in high season includes walking, mountain biking and a mini-club for children. Off site: Supermarket 1 km. towards Bourg d'Oisans. Fishing 1 km. Bicycle hire 1.2 km. Canoeing, rafting, riding, hiking and climbing nearby. Cable car at Alpe d'Huez. Some skiing normally possible until mid-July at Les Deux Alpes (16 km.).

At a glance

| Welcome & Ambience | ✓✓✓✓✓ | Location | ✓✓✓✓ |
| Quality of Pitches | ✓✓✓✓ | Range of Facilities | ✓✓✓✓ |

Directions

Leave Bourg d'Oisans on the N91 towards Briancon. Shortly after crossing the river, on a sharp right hand bend, turn left on D211 signed Alpe d'Huez. Site is on left just beyond Camping la Piscine. Entrance is on a sharp bend - take care.

Charges 2003

Per unit incl. 2 persons	€ 14.30 - € 22.40
incl. 3 persons	€ 15.85 - € 24.65
extra person	€ 4.80 - € 5.45
child (2-5 yrs)	€ 3.25 - € 3.85
electricity (2/10A)	€ 2.90 - € 4.00
dog	free - € 0.80
local tax	€ 0.30

Camping Cheques accepted.

Reservations

Advised in high season with 20% deposit and fee (€ 15.25). Tel: 04 76 79 12 22.
Email: rencontre.soleil@wanadoo.fr

Open

11 May - 15 September.

FR38100 Camping Belledonne

Rochetaillée, 38520 Bourg-d'Oisans (Isère)

This extremely neat site, run by the Arnaud family takes its name from the nearby Belledonne mountain range, and one of the six valleys of the Oisan area. All are impressive, but there is something rather magnificent about the views surrounding this site; furthermore it enjoys sunshine for most of the day. Access roads throughout are tarmac and each of the 150 grassy pitches, 105 for touring, are not only level and well drained, but also generously sized, with electricity. The site is divided into six areas, each named after one of the local valleys. High hedges and abundant mature trees provide ample privacy and shade. Next to this is an attractive pool complex, comprising two swimming pools, one paddling pool and sunbathing space surrounded by well tended gardens and grass spaces. All in all this is a friendly and well run site (English spoken), suitable for relaxing or as a base for exploring the interesting countryside around. There is some noise from the nearby road. A 'Sites et Paysages' member.

Facilities

Two sanitary blocks include washbasins in cabins, a mixture of British and Turkish style toilets, washing up sinks, laundry, baby changing rooms and facilities for disabled visitors. Shop. Bar/restaurant (all season). Takeaway. TV room. Swimming and paddling pools. Tennis. Volleyball. Small play area and a large grass meadow with comprehensive fitness course. Bicycle hire.

At a glance

Welcome & Ambience	✓✓✓✓	Location	✓✓✓✓✓
Quality of Pitches	✓✓✓✓	Range of Facilities	✓✓✓✓

Directions

From Grenoble take N85 to Vizille, then N91 towards Bourg d'Oisans. Branch left on D526 and site is approx. 250 m. on right.

Charges 2003

Per pitch incl. 2 persons	€ 14.40 - € 20.90
extra person	€ 3.80 - € 5.40
child (under 7 yrs)	€ 2.60 - € 3.60
electricity (3/6A)	€ 2.70 - € 3.70
dog	€ 0.90

Reservations

Made with € 14 fee; contact site. Tel: 04 76 80 07 18. Email: belledon@club-internet.fr

Open

24 May - 13 September.

FR38110 Camping Le Champ du Moulin

Bourg d'Arud, 38520 Venosc (Isère)

With steep-sided mountains on all sides, Le Champ du Moulin nestles comfortably on the floor of the narrow Vénéon valley. Even though the bustling town of Le Bourg d'Oisans is only a 15 minute drive away, this peaceful campsite is enjoyed by visitors in both winter and summer. When we visited in early spring, it proved to be a good base for skiing. A cabin chairlift near the entrance transports visitors to Les 2 Alpes. This renowned resort lies out of sight over a sharp rise and offers miles of ski runs in season and extensive glacier skiing in summer. Watching over the site is the more traditional village of Venosc which clings to the hillside a short walk away. Its church, narrow streets, old buildings and notable craft shops are a delightful alternative to the more recently developed glitzy ski towns. On site, generous pitches and large trees are features to note. However, when the mountain snows starts to melt in late May/early June, the River Vénéon adjacent to the site changes from its winter trickle to an impressive torrent. Parents with small children need to be especially vigilant. With its location on the edge of the Ecrins National Park, this is a peaceful location with stunning mountain scenery and miles of marked cycling and walking trails. It is not really a suitable site for teenagers seeking late-night revelry and nightly disco dancing.

Facilities

A well heated toilet block is welcome after a day of winter sport, and clothes soon dry on the racks provided. Excellent baby room. Laundry. Motorcaravan service point. Chalet restaurant/bar with very good home cooking at easy-on-the-pocket prices. Small shop sharing reception with bread each morning. Play area. TV room. Computer room with internet access. Fishing. Off site: Municipal heated outdoor pools and flume next door open in summer, together with a playground, tennis courts and tree-top adventure park. White water rafting, paragliding, bungee jumping and hill walking available nearby. Discounted ski passes. Riding 0.5 km, golf 3 km (both summer only).

At a glance

Welcome & Ambience	✓✓✓✓	Location	✓✓✓✓
Quality of Pitches	✓✓✓✓	Range of Facilities	✓✓✓✓

Directions

From Grenoble, leave on the southeast side of the city following signs for Oisans. At Bourg d'Oisans (40 km), go through village following signs for Les 2 Alpes and Briancon. After 3 km. turn right at sharp ben for Venosc. In 8 km. along the twisting valley road, pass the bottom ski station on the left. Site is on right after 400 m.

Charges 2003

Per unit incl. 1 or 2 persons	€ 12.00 - € 17.50
child (3-7 yrs)	€ 2.20 - € 2.80
electricity (3/10A)	€ 2.50 - € 8.00
dog	€ 0.50 - € 1.00
local tax	€ 0.25

Less 10% for 14 nights, 15% for 21 nights. Special ski arrangements.

Reservations

Made with deposit and € 13 booking fee. Tel: 04 76 80 07 38. Email: christian.avallet@wanadoo.fr

Open

15 December - 30 September.

FR38120 Camping du Bontemps

38150 Vernioz (Isère)

This spacious, attractive and well cared for site is enhanced by a wide variety of coniferous and deciduous trees planted by the dedicated owner nearly 30 years ago. The 200 large, level and grassy pitches are arranged in groups, partly separated by neat hedges, all with water and electricity. Seven pitches are used for mobile homes and chalets and a group at the back is used by weekenders. The shop, bar/restaurant, landscaped swimming pool and superb children's play pool, including toboggan, mushrooms and fountain are conveniently placed near to the entrance. The large sports area and excellent activity hall are off to one side minimising noise problems. There is a field and stable for horses, a small river and fishing lake adjacent to the site. This is an excellent site for both short and long stays.

Facilities

The excellent two main toilet blocks and the smaller block near the pool are modern, kept very clean and contain all the necessary facilities. There is an extensive list of activities for all the family (high season). Shop. Bar/restaurant (all season). Swimming pools (June-30 Sept). Several play areas. Minigolf. Table tennis. Tennis. Badminton, archery, volleyball and football. Riding. Electronic games. Two motorhome service points. Off site: The small village of Vernioz (shops, restaurant and bar) 2 km. Historic old market town of Vienne 20 km. City of Lyons. Bicycle hire 7 km. Golf 20 km.

At a glance

Welcome & Ambience	✓✓✓✓✓	Location	✓✓✓✓
Quality of Pitches	✓✓✓✓	Range of Facilities	✓✓✓✓

Directions

Exit A7 south of Lyons at junction 11. Continue south for about 7 km. on the N7. Just north of Auberives turn left on D37 and follow campsite signs for 7 km. Entrance is on the right just beyond Vernioz.

Charges 2003

Per adult	€ 5.00
child (under 7 yrs)	€ 2.50
pitch	€ 6.50 -€ 9.00
electricity (6A)	€ 2.50
dog	€ 2.00

Reservations

Essential in high season, contact site. There are usually a few spaces available each day for overnight stops, but arrive early. Tel: 04 74 57 83 52. Email: info@campinglebontemps.com

Open

1 April - 30 September.

FR73010 Camping Le Bois Joli

73130 St Martin-sur-la-Chambre (Savoie)

If you are looking for somewhere different off the beaten track where time can pass you by, or happen to be passing through on the N6 from Albertville to Modane and the Fréjus tunnel to Italy, this could be a good stopping place. Le Bois Joli (roughly speaking, 'pretty woodland', which it certainly is) is in wooded country in a most peaceful situation. Numerous trees provide good shade to all the pitches, although the natural layout of the site may not suit those who prefer uniformity and order. A minor road divides the site into two section, both with touring pitches. The 116 irregular shaped pitches vary in size from small to very large, some are grassy but most stony and some slope. They are in terraced clearings and all have electricity but water points are few and far between. There are two special pitches with water and drain for motorhomes. Access to some pitches is not easy. Every effort has been made to disturb the natural habitat as little as possible. The Savoie region is probably better known for its winter activities, but the beauty of the landscape and variety of plants existing beneath the winter snow means it is well worth visiting in the summer.

Facilities

Two sanitary blocks, one refurbished and one with a newly built addition, provide basic facilities and the supply of hot water may be inadequate at peak times. British and Turkish style toilets, a room for disabled people, baby room, laundry and dishwashing sinks. Kiosk with terrace for drinks, takeaway food and basic food supplies. Bar (May to Sept) and rest room offering local cuisine from time to time and continental breakfasts daily (July/Aug). Heated swimming pool. Two play areas. Archery and table tennis. Very few organised activities. Off site: Several shops in Arves, 1 km. Fishing 2 km. Riding 4 km. Bicycle hire 10 km. Many mountain walks.

At a glance

Welcome & Ambience	✓✓✓✓	Location	✓✓✓✓
Quality of Pitches	✓✓✓	Range of Facilities	✓✓✓✓

Directions

Leave A43 autoroute at exit 26 signed La Chambre. At roundabout turn right on D927 and shortly, at next roundabout, turn left on D213 signed St Arve. In a few hundred metres turn right opposite the railway station (site signed). Site is just over 1 km. on the left.

Charges 2003

Per unit incl. 2 persons	€ 10.00 - € 13.00
extra person	€ 3.05 - € 3.40
child (under 7 yrs)	€ 1.55 - € 2.30
electricity (2-10A)	€ 2.30 - € 3.05
animal	€ 0.95
local tax	€ 0.17

No credit cards.

Reservations

Write to site. Tel: 04 79 56 21 28. Email: camping-le-bois-joli@wanadoo.fr

Open

1 April - 30 September.

FR73020 Camping Caravaneige Le Versoyen

Route des Arcs, 73700 Bourg-St Maurice (Savoie)

Bourg-St-Maurice is on a small, level plain at an altitude of 830 m. on the River Isère, surrounded by high mountains. For many years a winter ski resort, it now caters for visitors all year round. The Parc national de la Vanoise is near, along with a wealth of interesting places. Le Versoyen itself attracts visitors all year round (except for a month when they close). The site's 200 unseparated, flat, grass pitches are marked by numbers on the tarmac roads and all have electrical connections. Trees typically seen at this altitude give shade in some parts, although most pitches have almost none. Duckboards are provided for snow and wet weather and hardstanding pitches are available for motorcaravans. This is a good base for winter skiing, summer walking, climbing, rafting or canoeing, or for car excursions.

Facilities

Two acceptable toilet blocks can be heated, although the provision may be hard pressed in high season. British and Turkish style WCs. Laundry. Motorcaravan service facilities. Heated restroom with TV. Small bar with takeaway in summer. Free shuttle to funicular railway. Off site: Commercial centre 500 m. away provides a variety of shops. Fishing or bicycle hire 200 m. Tennis and swimming pool 500 m. (free for campers during 7/8). Riding 1 km. Bourg-St-Maurice 1.5 km. Les Arcs (15 minutes by funicular railway) with ski lifts, some for bikes, to wonderful mountain tracks for bikes and ramblers (15 km). Cross country ski track (up to 30 km. in winter) just behind the site.

At a glance

Welcome & Ambience	✓✓✓✓	Location	✓✓✓✓
Quality of Pitches	✓✓✓	Range of Facilities	✓✓✓

Directions

Site is 1.5 km. east of Bourg-St-Maurice on CD119 Les Arcs road.

Charges 2003

Per unit incl. 2 person	€ 10.20 - € 13.68
extra person	€ 3.50 - € 4.74
child 3-7 yrs	€ 1.50 - € 3.10
child 7-13 yrs	€ 3.40 - € 4.70
electricity (4-12A)	€ 4.20 - € 7.50
cyclist or hiker's tent incl. 1 person	€ 9.20 - € 12.18
dog	€ 1.00
local tax	€ 0.17

Reservations

Write to site with deposit (€ 30) and fee (€ 10). Tel: 04 79 07 03 45. Email: leversoyen@wanadoo.fr

Open

All year except 7/11- 14/12 and 2/5-15/5.

FR73030 Camping Les Lanchettes

73210 Peisey-Nancroix (Savoie)

This site is in the beautiful Vanoise National Park and at 1,470 m. is one of the highest campsites in this guide. The steep climb to the site, not recommended for underpowered units, through spectacular scenery is well worth the effort. This natural site is terraced and has 90 good size, reasonably level and well drained, grassy/stony pitches. With 80 used for touring units, all have electricity. Because it is very cold in winter and quite cold on some spring and autumn evenings (warm bedding necessary) there are no outside taps. In winter about 30 of the pitches at the bottom of the site are unused as they become part of a cross country ski run. For those who love mountains, wonderful scenery, flora and fauna and for those wanting a walking/biking summer holiday, from novice to expert, this is the site for you. In winter it is ideal for the serious skier being close to the famous resort of Les Arcs.

Facilities

Comprehensive facilities are all in the basement of the house, very cosy in winter. The large, open entrances are closed during cold weather and when the evenings are cold allowing the building to be heated. Motorcaravan service point. Restaurant with takeaway (July/Aug. and mid Dec-mid April). Playground. Club/TV room. Large tent/marquee used in bad weather for a meeting place and as a dormitory by those with small tents. In winter a small bus runs to all the hotels, bars, ski tows etc and calls at the campsite. Accompanied walks (one free) in the National Park. Off site: Village of Peisey-Nancroix with a few restaurants, bars and shops 3 km. Les Arcs winter sports centre 6 km. Riding next to site. Outdoor swimming pool and bicycle hire 6 km. Golf and indoor pool 8 km. Wide range of footpaths and mountains bike rides in the valley and mountains around. Some of the chair lifts carry bikes up to the walking/bike tracks high up in the mountains, the descent is breathtaking. The roads around are ideal for the serious road cyclist.

At a glance

Welcome & Ambience	✓✓✓✓✓	Location	✓✓✓✓
Quality of Pitches	✓✓✓✓	Range of Facilities	✓✓✓✓

Directions

From Albertville take N90 towards Bourg-St-Maurice, through Moûtiers and Aime and approx. 5 km. further turn right, signed Landry and Peisey-Nancroix. Follow road down and then up a reasonably wide, steep, winding hill (with a few hairpin bends) for 10 km. Site is on right about 1 km. beyond Nancroix.

Latest Charges

Per unit incl. 2 persons	€ 10.80 - € 11.90
extra person	€ 3.70 - € 4.00
child (2-7 yrs)	€ 2.30 - € 2.50
electricity (3-10A)	€ 2.90 - € 7.30
Camping Cheques accepted.	

Reservations

Contact site. Tel: 04 79 07 93 07. Email: lanchettes@free.fr

Open

15 Dec - 15 Oct.

FR74010 Camping Les Deux Glaciers

Route des Tissiéres, Les Bossons, 74400 Chamonix (Haute-Savoie)

A pleasant and well kept, small mountain site for summer or winter use, Les Deux Glaciers lies between the two glaciers and is close to the well known resort of Chamonix. There are 135 individual pitches on terraces or single plots, levelled out of quite steeply rising ground, with electricity available in all areas. Access may be difficult for large outfits. The site is quietly situated with fine views of the surrounding high mountains but, being a northern slope, it loses the sun a little early and can be quite cold at night. It is pleasantly laid out with different trees and floral displays in their season. With a good position and commendable amenities and welcome, the site becomes full for much of July/Aug. They are not keen on reservations but may make some for British visitors, so try. In season, if not reserved, arrive early.

Facilities

Two small, clean sanitary blocks, both heated in cool weather, have modern facilities, at least half the washbasins in cabins. Facilities for disabled visitors. Washing machine and drying room. Snack restaurant (high season). Mobile traders call in season. General room (for winter use only). Table tennis. Off site: Village shop 500 m. Fishing, bicycle hire or riding within 2 km, golf 4 km. Chamonix, ski lifts, funicular railway and walks varying from a stroll to full mountain hikes.

At a glance

| Welcome & Ambience | ✓✓✓✓ | Location | ✓✓✓✓ |
| Quality of Pitches | ✓✓✓ | Range of Facilities | ✓✓✓✓ |

Directions

From west turn right off N506 on second road for Les Bossons, which takes you direct to site. From east turn right at sign for Les Bossons, then left at T-junction and pass under the main road to the site, on the right in few hundred metres.

Latest Charges

Per unit incl. 2 persons	€ 11.60
extra person	€ 4.40
child (under 7 yrs)	€ 2.20
electricity (2-10A; higher in winter)	€ 2.20 - € 6.40
local tax	€ 0.23

No credit cards.

Reservations

May be possible - see text. Tel: 04 50 53 15 84. Email: glaciers@clubinternet.fr

Open

All year.

FR74060 Camping La Colombière

St Julien-en-Genevois, 74160 Neydens (Haute-Savoie)

La Colombière, a small family owned site is on the edge of the small residential village of Neydens, a few minutes from the A40 autoroute and only a short drive from Geneva. It is an attractive, site with only 107 pitches, all reasonably level and separated by fruit trees, flowering shrubs and hedges. There are views to the east and west of the mountain ridges. M. Bussat owns a small vineyard close to the site, has the wine made in Switzerland and sells it by the glass or bottle in the restaurant (a very nice rosé). One of France's long-distance footpaths (GR65) passes close to the site. The village of Neydens is the first stage for pilgrims from Northern Europe on the route to Santiago de Compostella on their way to cross the Pyrénées at St Pied de Port. The site has a dormitory with seven beds for pilgrims or for anyone else who may need a bed, for example, motorcyclists or a family en-route south. Neydens makes a good base for visiting Geneva and the Lac Leman region. It is a very pleasant, friendly site where you may drop in for a night stop – and stay for several days! English is spoken. A 'Sites et Paysages' member.

Facilities

Three good sanitary blocks (one can be heated) include washbasins in cubicles, a baby room and facilities for disabled people. Motorcaravan service point. Fridge hire. Gas supplies. Very good bar/restaurant (all season) and terrace overlooking the heated pool (15/5-15/9). Low season organised visits of discovery, in high season one daily event including organised mountain walks and guided cycle tours (bicycle hire on site). Archery, volleyball and boules competitions. Playground. French country music evenings. Off site: Fishing or riding 1 km, golf 5 km. Geneva, the Lake and beautiful surrounding area.

At a glance

| Welcome & Ambience | ✓✓✓✓✓ | Location | ✓✓✓✓ |
| Quality of Pitches | ✓✓✓✓ | Range of Facilities | ✓✓✓✓ |

Directions

Take exit 13 from A40 autoroute south of Geneva, and then N201 towards Annecy. Turn into village of Neydens and follow campsite signs.

Charges 2004

Per unit incl. 2 persons	€ 14.00 - € 22.00
electricity (5/6A)	€ 3.50
child (2-7 yrs)	€ 3.00 - € 4.00
dog	€ 1.70

Camping Cheques accepted.

Reservations

Write to site. 8 days or more in high season gives free bicycle hire for 1 person, for 1 day. Less than 3 days - fee of € 15.24. Tel: 04 50 35 13 14. Email: la.colombiere@wanadoo.fr

Open

10 April - 30 September.

FR74030M Camping Belvédère

8 route du Semnoz, 74000 Annecy (Haute-Savoie)

Annecy is an attractive town in a beautiful setting at the head of the lake of the same name. The old centre is intersected by flower decked canals and also has historical interest. There is much to see and do in this region in both summer and winter, with Geneva near and the high Alps. Le Belvédère, as its name implies, overlooks the lake and is the nearest campsite to the town which can be reached by a quiet footpath. There are good part hardstanding terraces, with electricity, water and drain, for 80 caravans and 50 grass pitches for tents. Space may be limited if the site is busy. One small area is reserved for groups. Tall pines and a steep hillside provide a backdrop to the site to the west and small trees provide decoration without giving much shade. This site is ideally placed for visiting Annecy but it is not suitable for large units.

Facilities

Three modern toilet blocks are situated around the site and were clean when we visited. One is heated in cold weather, with a washroom for visitors with disabilities. Laundry facilities. Small shop, bar and restaurant (from June). Games room. Good playground. Swimming is possible in the lake. Bicycle hire. Communal area for barbecues. Other commercial sporting activities can be booked from the site. Off site: Boat launching 600 m. Lakeside beach 800 m. Many other activities on and around Lake Annecy.

At a glance

Welcome & Ambience	✓✓✓✓	Location	✓✓✓✓
Quality of Pitches	✓✓✓✓	Range of Facilities	✓✓✓✓

Directions

Leave autoroute A41 at Annecy Sud and take N508 towards Albertville and drive around the town. Just after some traffic lights descend a hill and look out for the 'H' and 'Silence' signs for the hospital. Very soon after, on a left hand bend, turn right up the hill, signed Le Semnoz. Keep right at the fork. Take care at next junction. You must not take the right hand road which is signed Belvédère as this leads to a very steep hill back down to the lake. Turn left, signed Camping Belvédère, and you will shortly come to the site.

Charges 2003

Per unit incl. 2 persons and tent	€ 9.90 - € 13.00
caravan incl. 2 persons	€ 13.75 - € 17.55
extra person	€ 3.80 - € 4.60
child (2-10 yrs)	€ 2.30 - € 2.75
electricity (10A)	€ 2.30

Reservations

Necessary for July/Aug. - write to Mairie d'Annecy, BP 2305, 74011 Annecy. Tel: 04 50 45 48 30. Email: camping@ville-annecy.fr

Open

6 April - 15 October.

FR74040 Camp de la Ravoire

Bout-du-Lac, route de la Ravoire, 74210 Doussard (Haute-Savoie)

De la Ravoire is a quality site, some 800 m. from Lake Annecy, noted for its neat and tidy appearance and the quietness of its location in this popular tourist region. The 112 numbered pitches, on well mown grass and separated by small shrubs, have some shade, although there are trees on the lake side of the site. The 90 pitches for touring units (21 with water and drain) have electricity connections. Those looking for a quiet campsite in this most attractive region without the 'animation' programmes that so many French sites feel are necessary will find this a peaceful base, although disco noise from a site by the lake may drift across under some weather conditions. Used by a tour operator (18 pitches).

Facilities

The very good central toilet block includes washbasins in cabins, facilities for disabled people, and a laundry room with washing machines, dryers and irons. Bar and snack bar. Shop. Outdoor pool with separate water slide and paddling pool. Good young children's play area. Sports areas. Off site: Fishing, boat launching, bicycle hire 1 km, riding 6 km, golf 8 km. Good restaurant on the lakeside where the camp road leaves the main road, with others near, plus shops in Doussard village and Annecy.

At a glance

Welcome & Ambience	✓✓✓✓✓	Location	✓✓✓✓
Quality of Pitches	✓✓✓✓	Range of Facilities	✓✓✓✓

Directions

Site is signed from the N508 Annecy - Albertville road, just north of Bout-du-Lac. At traffic lights in Bredannaz turn right and then immediately left. Site is on the left in about 1 km.

Charges 2004

Per unit incl. 2 adults and electricity (5A)	€ 27.20
child under 10 yrs	€ 2.55
child 10-15 yrs	€ 3.80
electricity (10/15A)	€ 2.00 - € 3.10
motorcaravan services	€ 10.00

Plus local tax. Less 20% outside July/Aug.

Reservations

Essential for July/Aug; made for min. 10 days. Tel: 04 50 44 37 80. Email: info@camping-la-ravoire.fr

Open

15 May - 15 September.

FR74100 Village Camping Europa

1444 Route Albertville, 74410 St Jorioz (Haute-Savoie)

You will receive a friendly welcome at this quality, family run site. The flowers, shrubs, trees (giving some shade) and grassy pitches are lovely, in fact everything is neat and tidy. Of the 210 medium to large size, level pitches, 110 are for touring, all have electricity close by and a few have water and drain. The static units are separated from the touring section by high hedges giving the impression that you are on a small site. Europa should suit those families who like to make their own entertainment although there are some activities for children and a weekly soirée (high season) and it is a good base from which to tour the beautiful lake Annecy area. They may be some noise from the adjacent main road.

Facilities

Two good toilet blocks, the one nearest the tourers recently modernised to a very high standard. They have all necessary facilities, including some large cubicles with both showers and washbasins. Motorcaravan service point. Good bar and restaurant (1/6-31/8) offering a wide range of dishes and menus. Swimming pool complex comprising reasonably sized, heated swimming pool, paddling pool, jacuzzi, 5 slides and a cascade (jacuzzi, slides and cascade from mid June; entry bracelet € 2 per week). Volleyball. Basketball. Football. Bicycle hire. Internet access. Barrier card deposit € 20. Off site: Fishing 300 m. Boat launching 500 m. Riding 3 km. Lakeside beach 2 km. Golf 8 km. 40 km long lakeside bike ride. Lake Annecy and all its activities.

Directions

From Annecy take N508 signed Albertville. Site is well signed on the right between Saint-Jorioz and Duingt.

Charges 2003

Per unit incl. 2 persons	€ 14.20 - € 22.80
with 6A electricity	€ 17.40 - € 26.00
extra person	€ 3.40 - € 5.30
child (2-6 yrs)	€ 2.30 - € 4.20

Reservations

Made with deposit (€ 94) and fee (€ 16).
Tel: 04 50 68 51 01.
Email: info@camping-europa.com

Open

8 May - 15 September.

At a glance

Welcome & Ambience	✓✓✓✓	Location	✓✓✓✓
Quality of Pitches	✓✓✓✓	Range of Facilities	✓✓✓✓

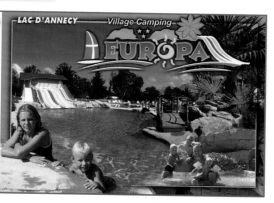

Village Camping EUROPA

Charming site, 400 meters from the lake of Annecy – 1 heated swiming pool, 1 water complex (with 5 water slides, waterfalls, children's games, jacuzzi, lagoon) – Restaurant with specialities of the Savoy region Quality installations – Chalets and mobile homes to let – Bikes for hire – Situated next to a cycling track.

Village Camping EUROPA
1444, route d'Albertville 74 410 ST – JORIOZ
Tel. 33 (0) 4 50 68 51 01 Fax. 33 (0) 4 50 68 55 20
E-mail : info@camping-europa.com
www.camping-europa.com

FR74110 Camping Le Taillefer

1530 Route de Chaparon, 74210 Doussard (Haute-Savoie)

This excellent, small site is family run and friendly. It is only 1.5 km. from Lake Annecy, yet it offers a quiet, very relaxing and beautiful environment all at a very good price. The views over the lakeside mountains are stunning. This site is terraced and abounds with flowers, shrubs and small trees. It only has 32 average to good sized, grassy, level and sunny pitches, 28 with electricity. Those at the bottom of the site are reserved for tents. In high season the site is quiet as there are no organised events, although there are plenty on and around the lake close by.

Facilities

The modern toilet block with ample separate facilities for ladies and men is near reception and has all the necessary facilities including for disabled visitors. Very small shop selling bread, drinks and ices etc. Small bar in high season. Playground. Small club/TV room. Torches needed - no site lighting. Off site: Nearby village of Doussard has several shops, medical services and a bank. Lake Annecy with beaches, restaurants, snack bars, fishing and many water sports. Minigolf, bicycle hire, boat launching, small nature reserve (all on Lake Annecy). Golf 5 km. Riding 7 km. 20 km cycle ride by the lake.

Directions

From Annecy take N508 signed Albertville. At traffic lights in Breddanaz turn right and then immediately left for 1.5 km. and site is on the left. Do not turn in by reception, as this is a dead end. Wait in road until directions are received.

Charges 2004

Per unit incl. 2 persons	€ 11.50 - € 12.80
extra person	€ 2.80
child (under 10 yrs)	€ 2.20
electricity (6A)	€ 3.20

Reservations

Made with € 30 booking fee. Tel: 04 50 44 30 30.

Open

1 May - 30 September.

At a glance

Welcome & Ambience	✓✓✓✓	Location	✓✓✓✓
Quality of Pitches	✓✓✓✓	Range of Facilities	✓✓✓

FR74130 **Camping de la Plage**

304 rue de la garenne, 74500 Amphion-les-Bains (Haute-Savoie)

This very good, family run site is small, quiet and friendly. It has a very long season and is only a few hundred metres from Lake Geneva and the village of Amphion making it an excellent centre to relax and explore this wonderful region. Madame Frossard loves gardening and the site does her credit with its flowers, trees, hedges and beautifully mown grass. The 53 pitches, only a few used by mobile homes, are level, medium to large and separated by trees. They all have water points, drains and electricity. In addition to the very small pool on the site, there is a super water sports centre in the adjacent park (with a large pool, paddling pool, diving pool, wave pool and a giant slide), plus an excellent playground and plenty of space to enjoy.

Facilities

The ample facilities are comprehensive and first class, with fully controllable showers, washbasins in cabins, facilities for children and disabled people, sinks for dishwashing and laundry. One toilet block is heated off season. Washing machine, dryer and iron. Small bar and takeaway in high season. Small heated swimming pool, covered in cool weather and with invigorating pressure jets. Small young children's playground. Table tennis, boules. TV room. Well equipped exercise room. Off site: Lake Geneva with beaches, restaurants, snack bars, fishing and many water sports and ferry to Annecy - from 300 m. Small shops, restaurants and supermarket within walking distance in village of Amphion les Bains. Hypermarket 1 km. Golf 3 km.

Directions

Site is between Thonon les Bains and Evian les Bains. Turn off the N5 at Amphion les Bains (at roundabout with statue and fountains) and follow site signs - site in a few hundred metres.

Charges 2003

Per unit incl. 2 persons	€ 16.00 - € 21.00
child (under 8 yrs)	€ 3.00
electricity (2-6A)	€ 1.52 - € 3.80

Reductions for long stay in low season.

Reservations

Essential in high season and made with 25% deposit and € 11 booking fee. Tel: 04 50 70 00 46. Email: info@camping-dela-plage.com

Open

All year excl. 3 Nov - 24 Dec.

At a glance

Welcome & Ambience	✓✓✓✓✓	Location	✓✓✓✓✓
Quality of Pitches	✓✓✓✓	Range of Facilities	✓✓✓✓

FR74070 **Camping Caravaning L'Escale**

74450 Le Grand-Bornand (Haute-Savoie)

You are assured a good welcome from the Baur family at this beautifully maintained, picturesque site. Situated at the foot of the Aravis mountain range, beside the picture postcard ski resort of Le Grand-Bornand, L'Escale has wonderful views and is clearly popular all year round. The 149 fairly sunny pitches are of average size, clearly marked with a part grass, part gravel surface and separated by trees and shrubs. All have electricity and 80 pitches are fully serviced. The village (200 m.) has all the facilities of a major resort with ongoing activity for summer or winter holidays. In summer a variety of well signed footpaths provide forest or mountain walks of all degrees of difficulty. In winter the area provides superb facilities for down-hill and cross-country skiing and après-ski entertainment. La Maison du Patrimoine is a must to visit. A 'Sites et Paysages' member.

Facilities

The toilet blocks (some heated when cold) have all the necessary facilities. Two chalet buildings provide further facilities. Facilities can be under pressure during peak periods. Below the main building is a large drying room with sinks, tumble dryer and washing machines. Separate room for skis and boots. Play area. Tennis and table tennis. Torches are advisable. A new complex with interconnected indoor and outdoor pools and paddling pools, bar/restaurant and reception is planned. Off site: The village (5 minutes walk) has excellent cultural and leisure activities, including shops, bars, restaurants, municipal pool complex, archery, paragliding, hang-gliding, 150 km. of signed walks, organised activities for children and adults and, in winter, ice skating and ice hockey. Bicycle hire 200 m. Riding and golf 3 km. Festival des Mômes (The Kids' Festival) 22-23 Aug.

Directions

Probably the best access is via Annecy following the D16 and D909 roads towards La Clusaz. Shortly before La Clusaz, at St Jean-de-Sixt, turn left on D4 signed Le Grand Bornand. Site is signed on the right, just before entering the village.

Charges 2003

Per unit incl. 1 or 2 persons	€ 13.20 - € 15.50
extra person	€ 3.90 - € 4.50
electricity (2-10A)	€ 3.10 - € 7.90
animal	€ 1.80
local tax	€ 0.40

Camping Cheques accepted.

Reservations

Made with deposit (€ 71) and fee (€ 10). Tel: 04 50 02 20 69. Email: contact@campinglescale.com

Open

All year excl. Oct and Nov.

At a glance

Welcome & Ambience	✓✓✓✓✓	Location	✓✓✓✓✓
Quality of Pitches	✓✓✓✓	Range of Facilities	✓✓✓✓✓

travel service
TO BOOK THIS SITE
0870 405 4055
Expert Advice & Special Offers

FR74090 Camping Le Plan du Fernuy

Route des Confins, 74220 La Clusaz (Haute-Savoie)

The pretty little village of La Clusaz (pop. 1,800) is 32 km. east of Annecy at 1,200 m. above sea level in the heart of the Savoie Alps. Le Plan du Fernuy, 2 km. east of the village lies just to the north of the Avaris mountain range in a peaceful, scenic location. The neat, rectangular site has 53 of its 80 pitches available for tourists. Of reasonable size, all with electricity connections and 22 fully serviced, the pitches are arranged in rows on either side of hard access roads with good mountain views. Although surrounded by trees, there is little shade. The site's crowning glory is an excellent indoor heated pool with large windows looking out on to the mountains and sunbeds beside them. Reception is at the front of the pool building and, although the pool is not supervised, it can be seen from here. This is good ski-ing (free ski bus) in winter and walking country in summer with other sporting opportunities nearby. The pleasant owners speak good English.

Facilities

The large apartment building at entrance houses very good sanitary provision on the ground floor and is heated in cool weather. Some washbasins are in cabins. Baby room. Facilities for disabled visitors. Separate rooms for dishwashing and laundry with washing machine and dryer. Motorcaravan service point. Pleasant bar provides snacks, takeaway, basic food supplies, video games and a TV room. Heated indoor pool around 13 x 7 m. in size with separate paddling pool. Ski excursions organised. Off site: Shops and restaurants in village.

At a glance

Welcome & Ambience	✓✓✓✓	Location	✓✓✓✓
Quality of Pitches	✓✓✓✓	Range of Facilities	✓✓✓✓

Directions

From Annecy take D909 to La Clusaz and turn towards Les Confins for site after 2 km. (well signed). It is best to avoid using D909 from Flumat particularly with caravans or motorhomes.

Charges 2003

Per pitch incl. 2 persons	€ 16.00 - € 18.00
with electricity (4-13A)	€ 21.00 - € 24.50
extra person	€ 5.50
child (2-7 yrs)	€ 4.00
animal	€ 1.50
local tax	€ 0.40

Winter prices are higher.

Reservations

Advised for mid-July - mid-Aug. and winter. Tel: 04 50 02 44 75. Email: leplan.du.fernuy@wanadoo.fr

Open

8 June - 19 September and 20 December - 28 April.

Map 10

Atlantic Coast

Endless shimmering beaches, huge sand dunes, watersports aplenty, fragrant pine forests, the fine wines of Bordeaux, and the chic city of Biarritz: it's easy to see the allure of the Atlantic Coast.

The coastal départements of the official region of Aquitaine, stretching from Bordeaux in the north to the Pyrénées and the Spanish border are included in our 'tourist' region: 33 Gironde, 40 Landes, 64 Pyrénées Atlantiques

The Atlantic Coast stretches north from Biarritz to Arcachon. The most notable features are the uninterrupted line of vast sandy beaches, over 100 miles long, and the endless pine woods in the hinterland - this is Europe's largest man-made forest. There are also many lakes to see, ideal for watersports activities.

The département of the Gironde covers the area from the Bassin d'Arcachon, famed for its oysters and Europe's highest sand dune, to the Gironde estuary and Bordeaux. The vineyards of Bordeaux are world famous and especially well known for their Medoc, Sauternes, and St Emilion wines.

The Pays Basque area in the southwest corner is much influenced by Spain. The most famous Basque towns are Biarritz, Bayonne and the picturesque old port of St-Jean-de-Luz. Further inland and nearer the Pyrénées is the attractive town of St-Jean-Pied-de-Port on the pilgrims' route to northern Spain and Santiago de Compostela, close to the forest of Iraty with its lakes and ski runs.

Cuisine of the region

Seafood is popular, local specialities include carp stuffed with foie gras and mullet in red wine

Cèpes: fine, delicate mushrooms; sometimes dried

Chorizos: spicy sausages

Chou farci: stuffed cabbage, sometimes *aux marrons* (with chestnuts)

Foie Gras: specially prepared livers of geese and ducks, seasoned and stuffed with truffles

Gâteau Basque: shallow custard pastry with fillings

Jambon de Bayonne: raw ham, cured in salt and sliced paper thin

Lamproie: eel-like fish with leeks, onions and red Bordeaux wine

Places of interest

Bayonne: old streets and fortifications; Basque Museum

Bordeaux: 14,000 piece Bohemian glass chandelier in foyer of the Grand Theatre, 29 acre Esplanade des Quinconces

Pau: famous motor racing circuit on (closed) public highway; stadium for the Basque game of *pelota*

St Emilion: visit the castle ramparts or drink premier cru St Emilion at pavement cafés

St Jean-de-Luz: seaside resort and fishing village

St Jean-Pied-de-Port: ancient city with citadel, bright Basque houses in steep streets

TOUR THE VINEYARDS OF THE BORDEAUX REGION AND SAMPLE THE LOCAL WINES. THERE ARE PLENTY TO VISIT INCLUDING THOSE AT MÉDOC, ST-ÉMILION, AND SAUTERNES.

FR33020 Camping Caravaning Fontaine–Vieille

4 boulevard du Colonel Wurtz, 33510 Andernos-les-Bains (Gironde)

Fontaine-Vieille is a large, traditional type of site that recently celebrated its 50th anniversary. The site stretches along the eastern edge of the Bassin d'Arcachon under light woodland in the residential area of the small town of Andernos. Popular with the French, it has 800 individual pitches, some with views and 600 with electricity. On flat grassy ground, they are marked by stones in the ground or young trees. A beach runs alongside the tidal Bassin which can be used for boating when the tide is in. When it is out, there is sand and mud but it is claimed that swimming in the channels is still possible.

Facilities

Seven sanitary blocks of rather unusual design provide an adequate number of hot showers, plus facilities for people with disabilities and children. Shop (15/5-15/9). Bar with terrace. Restaurant with takeaway (all season). Communal barbecue (only gas individual barbecues may be used). Swimming pool complex. Four tennis courts. TV room. Two play areas for little ones and adventure area for older children. Minigolf. Boats, sailboards for hire. Bicycle hire. Sports are organised. Caravan storage. Off site: Riding 5 km. Golf 3 km. Town shops near.

At a glance

| Welcome & Ambience | √√√√ | Location | √√√√ |
| Quality of Pitches | √√√ | Range of Facilities | √√√√ |

Directions

Turn off D3 at southern end of Andernos towards Bassin at camp sign.

Charges 2003

Per unit incl. 2 persons	€ 13.00 - € 20.00
with electricity (5A)	€ 16.00 - € 24.00
extra person	€ 3.00 - € 5.00
child (2-7 yrs)	€ 2.00 - € 3.00
local tax	€ 0.30
animal	€ 2.00 - € 3.00

Reservations

Made for any length with deposit (€ 80) and fee (€ 20). Tel: 05 56 82 01 67.

Open

1 April - 30 September.

FR33050 Camping Les Ourmes

Avenue du Lac, 33990 Hourtin (Gironde)

Located only 500 metres from the largest fresh water lake in France, only ten minutes drive from the beach and with its own pool, this is essentially a holiday site. Its 270 pitches, marked but in most cases not actually separated, are arranged amongst tall pines and other trees which give good shade. All have electricity connections. The site's amenities are arranged around a pleasant entrance courtyard with an evening entertainment programme in season. This site has a busy, cosmopolitan feel, with visitors of many different nationalities.

Facilities

Three recently refurbished toilet blocks are of a good standard including some washbasins in cabins. Washing machine in each block and dryer, with hot water taps for washing up. Small shop (1/6-15/9). Bar/restaurant with outdoor tables serving takeaway snacks and a range of reasonably priced meals (1/7-31/8). Medium sized swimming pool and new paddling pool (1/5-15/9). Separate large leisure area with play area, volleyball and basketball courts and table tennis tables (under cover). TV, games rooms. Boules. Off site: Watersports and fishing possible on the lake, with bicycle hire, tennis and riding within 500 m.

At a glance

| Welcome & Ambience | √√√√ | Location | √√√√ |
| Quality of Pitches | √√√ | Range of Facilities | √√√√ |

Directions

Follow Route du Port (Ave du Lac) from the town centre and site is signed on left.

Charges 2003

Per unit incl. 2 persons	€ 11.00 - € 16.90
incl. electricity	€ 14.00 - € 19.90
extra person (over 2 yrs)	€ 1.80 - € 3.00
dog	€ 1.20 - € 1.50
local tax (over 10 yrs)	€ 0.50

No credit cards.

Reservations

Necessary in high season. Tel: 05 56 09 12 76. Email: lesourmes@free.fr

Open

1 April - 30 September.

FR33110 Airotel Camping de la Côte d'Argent

33990 Hourtin-Plage (Gironde)

Spread over 20 hectares of undulating sand-based terrain and in the midst of a pine forest, this large site is well placed and well equipped for leisurely family holidays. It also makes an ideal base for walkers and cyclists, with over 100 km. of cycle lanes leading through the Medoc countryside. Hourtin-Plage is a pleasant invigorating resort on the Atlantic coast and a popular location for watersports enthusiasts, or those who prefer spending their days on the beach. More appealing though may be to stay on site, for Côte d'Argent's top attraction is its pool complex with wooden bridges connecting the pools and islands, on which there are sunbathing patios and play areas. There are 750 touring pitches which are not clearly defined and in the trees, some on soft sand-based ground. The site is well organised and ideal for children, although it can be noisy at night in high season. There are 48 hardstandings for motorcaravans outside the site, providing a cheap stop-over, but with no access to site facilities.

Facilities

Five very clean sanitary blocks of various ages include provision for disabled visitors. Plenty of laundry machines. Motorcaravan service points. Large supermarket. Restaurant, takeaway and pizzeria bar. Four swimming pools, waterslides and flumes. Two tennis courts. Pool tables. Four play areas. Mini-club and organised entertainment in season. Charcoal barbecues are not permitted. Off site: Walkway to the beach.

At a glance

Welcome & Ambience	✓✓✓✓	Location	✓✓✓✓
Quality of Pitches	✓✓✓	Range of Facilities	✓✓✓✓✓

Directions

Turn off D101 Hourtin-Soulac road 3 km. north of Hourtin. Then join D101E signed Hourtin-Plage. Site is 300 m. from the beach.

Charges 2003

Per unit incl. 2 persons	€ 19.00 - € 28.00
tent incl. 2 persons	€ 15.00 - € 25.00
extra person	€ 3.00 - € 5.00
child (2-10 yrs)	€ 2.00 - € 4.00
electricity (6A)	€ 5.00
dog	€ 2.00 - € 4.00
local tax	€ 0.50

Camping Cheques accepted.

Reservations

Necessary for July/August. Tel: 05 56 09 10 25.
Email: info@camping-cote-dargent.com

Open

15 May - 18 September.

FR33090 Camping Le Pressoir

Petit Palais et Cornemps, 33570 Lussac (Gironde)

Buried in the famous wine producing countryside of the Lussac, Pomerol and St Emilion area north of Bordeaux, Le Pressoir is surrounded by fields of vines. With a manicured entrance featuring attractive trees, shrubs and flowers, together with preserved equipment from its former role as a wine farm, it is a neat site with good quality facilities. The 100 large pitches are arranged on either side of a gravel road leading up a slight hill and many are shaded by attractive trees. They are over 100 sq.m. and equipped with electricity (blue EC plugs) and interspersed with five Trigano type tents for hire. The old barn has been converted into a stylish bar and a really charming, separate restaurant. A quiet, family site, Le Pressoir provides a comfortable base for a holiday in this area famous for good food and wine.

Facilities

Very good fully equipped toilet facilities in purpose built block near the farmhouse include hair and make-up area for ladies, facilities for disabled visitors, and washing machine. Bar. Restaurant (all season). Swimming pool (14 x 7 m; 15/5-15/9, no bermuda shorts). Playground with timber equipment. Petanque, volleyball and table tennis. Gates locked 22.00 - 08.00 hrs. Off site: Tennis nearby. Fishing 5 km. Riding and bicycle hire 10 km.

At a glance

Welcome & Ambience	✓✓✓✓	Location	✓✓✓✓✓
Quality of Pitches	✓✓✓✓	Range of Facilities	✓✓✓✓

Directions

From N89 Bordeaux - Périgueux turn at Saint Médard de Guizières towards Lussac on the D21. Site is signed here and also from Lussac.

Charges 2004

Per person	€ 6.00
child (2-6 yrs)	€ 3.50
pitch	€ 6.90
with 6A electricity	€ 9.90

Camping Cheques accepted.

Reservations

Contact site. Tel: 05 57 69 73 25.
Email: camping.le.pressoir@wanadoo.fr

Open

April - 3 October.

FR33080 Domaine de la Barbanne

Route de Montagne, 33330 St Emilion (Gironde)

La Barbanne is a pleasant, friendly, family-owned site in the heart of the Bordeaux wine region, only 2.5 km. from the famous town of St Emilion. With 160 pitches, the owners have transformed it into a carefully maintained, well equipped site. The original parts of the site bordering the lake have tarred roads, good shade and pleasant surroundings, whilst the newer area has younger trees, some shade and gravel access roads. The pitches are being re-numbered and are all large, level and grassy with dividing hedges and electricity connections. La Barbanne has an attractive entrance and reception area with ample space for parking or turning. The site owners run a free minibus service three times a day to St Emilion and also organise excursions to local places of interest, including Bordeaux. A `Sites et Paysages` member.

Facilities

Two toilet blocks, the original one fully refurbished, the other in the newer area being very modern. Most washbasins are in private cabins. Visitors with disabilities are well catered for. Motorcaravan service point. Small, well stocked shop. Bar with terrace, takeaway and restaurant (1/7-31/8). Two landscaped swimming pools, one heated with cork-screw water slide (15/4-20/9). Fully enclosed play area with seats for parents and an organised children`s club (from 1/7). Tennis, boules, volleyball, table tennis and minigolf. The lake provides superb free fishing, pedaloes, canoes and lakeside walks. Bicycle hire. Off site: St Emilion and shops 2.5 km. Riding 8 km.

At a glance

Welcome & Ambience	✓✓✓✓	Location	✓✓✓✓✓
Quality of Pitches	✓✓✓✓	Range of Facilities	✓✓✓✓

Directions

At St Emilion take D122 for 2.5 km. Turn right just before Montagne and site is on left after 400 m. Caravans and motorhomes are forbidden through the village of St Emilion. They must approach the site by taking the D243 from Libourne or from Castillon on the D936 via D130/D243.

Latest charges

Per person	€ 3.50 - € 5.50
child (under 7 yrs)	€ 2.00 - € 4.20
pitch	€ 5.50 - € 7.00
animal	free - € 1.40
electricity (6A)	€ 3.00 - € 4.00

Camping Cheques accepted.

Reservations

Made for min. 4 days. Tel: 05 57 24 75 80. Email: barbanne@wanadoo.fr

Open

1 April - 20 September.

FR33120 Camping La Cigale

Route de Lège, 33740 Arès (Gironde)

La Cigale is an attractive little site with charm and ambience where the owners extend a very warm welcome. Small and beautifully maintained, it is set amid pine trees and M. Pallet`s floral displays. The 95 pitches, most with electricity and of 100 sq.m. in size, are level and grassy, divided by hedges and flower borders. The majority have shade from the pine trees. There are two small swimming pools in a pleasant setting and under the ample shade of a large plane tree, where drinks, meals and snacks are served on the bar terrace. This is an exceptional area for cycling, with designated routes. Across the bay lies bustling Arcachon and the enormous Dune de Pilat, easily reached by ferry from Cap Ferret. Used by tour operators (18%).

Facilities

The central, flower-bedecked, unisex toilet block includes a family room with two showers, facilities for disabled visitors and a laundry with a washing machine and dryer. All is meticulously maintained. Motorcaravan services. Simple shop. Bar terrace with meals and snacks. Pizza take-away at front of the site. Two small swimming pools. Small play area. Full-time entertainers for children and adults in July/Aug. Free donkey cart rides every Sunday. Off site: Site is convenient for a wide choice of beaches. Fishing and riding 1 km. Village centre 800 m.

At a glance

Welcome & Ambience	✓✓✓✓✓	Location	✓✓✓✓
Quality of Pitches	✓✓✓✓	Range of Facilities	✓✓✓✓

Directions

Leave Bordeaux ring-road at exit 10 (D213) or exit 11 (D106) and continue on good roads direct to Arès. Turn into Arès following road to church square. Turn right following signs for Lège/Cap Ferret. Site is 800 m. on left.

Charges 2003

Per unit incl. 1 or 2 persons	€ 16.00 - € 22.00
extra person	€ 4.00 - € 4.30
child (7 yrs)	€ 2.50 - € 2.60
electricity (4/6A)	€ 4.30
local tax	€ 0.17

Reservations

Advised for July/Aug. and made with deposit (€ 79) and fee (€ 16). Tel: 05 56 60 22 59. Email: campinglacigaleares@wanadoo.fr

Open

15 May - 15 September.

FR33130 Camping Caravaning Les Grands Pins

33680 Lacanau-Océan (Gironde)

This Atlantic coast holiday site with direct access to a fine sandy beach, is on undulating terrain amongst tall pine trees. A large site, it provides 570 pitches, with about 44 private and rental mobile homes, leaving around 525 pitches of varying sizes for touring units. The site is well served by tarmac access roads, and although not noticeably divided, one half of the site is a traffic free zone (except for arrival or departure day, caravans are placed on the pitch, with separate areas outside the zone for car parking). There is a good number of tent pitches, those in the centre of the site having some of the best views, and especially useful for tenters are safety deposit and fridge boxes which are available for rent. The large sandy beach is a 350 m. stroll from the gate at the back of the site.

Facilities

Five toilet blocks include washbasins in cubicles, dishwashing and laundry sinks, a dog and wetsuit washing area, baby room and facilities for disabled people (not all units are open in low season). Well equipped launderette. Motorcaravan services. Good sized supermarket, surf boutique. Bar, restaurant and snack bar with takeaway. Heated swimming pool (20 x 10 m, from 1/5 with lifeguard in July/Aug) with large paved sunbathing surround. Jacuzzi. Free fitness activities (aquagym, etc). Games room. Gym. Tennis (charge in July/Aug). Two playgrounds. Bicycle hire. Organised activities for children (July/Aug). Entrance barrier with keypad access. Only gas barbecues are permitted. Off site: Fishing, golf, riding and bicycle hire 5 km.

At a glance

Welcome & Ambience	✓✓✓✓	Location	✓✓✓✓✓
Quality of Pitches	✓✓✓	Range of Facilities	✓✓✓✓

Directions

From Bordeaux take N125/D6 west to Lacanau, continue on D6 to Lacanau Ocean. At second roundabout, take second exit: Plage Nord and follow signs to camps sites. Les Grand Pins is signed to the right at the far end of the road. If approaching from northern France you could use the ferry from Royan to Le Verdon.

Charges 2003

Per caravan pitch incl. 2 persons and electricity	€ 23.00 - € 33.00
tent pitch incl. 2 persons and electricity	€ 23.00 - € 29.00
extra person	€ 6.50 - € 9.00
child (2-12 yrs)	free - € 4.00
dog	€ 3.00 - € 4.00

Reservations

Essential for high season, made with deposit and fee. Discounts for early booking. Tel: 05 56 03 20 77. Email: reception@lesgrandspins.com

Open

1 May - 15 September

FR33140 Camping Le Grand Pré

Route de Casteljaloux, 33430 Bazas (Gironde)

In a rural position, this is a developing site where the owners stated phiolosophy of tranquility in nature is realised. There are only 30 grass pitches at present, which are separated by low shrubs and bushes, some of which have yet to mature. All have electricity hook-ups water and drainage. Reception facilities and a bar are in a very tastefully converted old barn, where you may have breakfast or collect bread if ordered the day before. There is a traffic free footpath direct from the site to the town, which we can recommend. The fortified town is notable for the magnificent Cathedral (illuminated at night), the annual festival of the Bazardais cattle, the bonfires of St Jean, and the weekly Saturday market, and is on the Pilgrims Route. The year 2004 will see the completion of a cycle path from Bazas to the Atlantic coast (on 80 km. of old railway track). Reservation is advisable for July and August.

Facilities

The single, high quality toilet block should be adequate for current demand, but will be supplemented by more units as the site expands. It includes open and cubicle washbasins, washing machine and dryer, dishwashing and laundry sinks, an excellent baby room, and full facilities for disabled persons. Motorcaravan service point. Unusual swimming pool and paddling pool. Sunbathing area. Small playground. Volleyball, boules. Library with some English books. B&B nearby at the Château.

At a glance

Welcome & Ambience	✓✓✓✓✓	Location	✓✓✓✓
Quality of Pitches	✓✓✓✓	Range of Facilities	✓✓✓✓

Directions

Bazas is around 55 km. southeast of Bordeaux, and 15 km. south of Langon. From Bazas centre take the D655 east towards Casteljaloux, and the site entrance is about 1 km. on your right (well signed).

Charges 2003

Per unit incl. 1 or 2 persons	€ 7.65 - € 18.30
incl. 3 persons	€ 9.20 - € 21.35
extra person over 10 yrs	€ 2.30 - € 3.82
electricity (6-16A)	€ 3.10 - € 4.60
dog	free - € 1.53
Discounts for longer stays	

Reservations

Advisable for July and August. Tel: 05 56 65 13 17. Email: legrandpre@wanadoo.fr

Open

1 April - 31 October.

FR33150M Camping Municipal Les Gabarreys

Route de la Rivière, 33250 Pauillac (Gironde)

An attractive, small site with well tended flower beds, Les Gabarreys is surrounded by the many vineyards of the Médoc region (reception can provide a good map). An excellent site, it has 59 pitches, 41 with hardstanding for caravans or motorcaravans (so pegging out awnings could be a problem), 14 grass pitches for tents and four mobile homes, all with electric hook-ups (some may require long leads). The site is popular with the grape pickers in September, but the warden always keeps some pitches for tourists.

Facilities

Two immaculate toilet blocks provide open and cubicle washbasins and excellent facilities for disabled people. Motorcaravan services. General room with satellite TV, fridge-freezer and a small library. Minigolf (free) and volley-ball.

At a glance

Welcome & Ambience	✓✓✓✓	Location	✓✓✓✓
Quality of Pitches	✓✓✓✓	Range of Facilities	✓✓✓

Directions

Pauillac lies on the western side of the Gironde estuary, NNW of Bordeaux. From Bordeaux take the D1 to St Laurent, then the D206 to Pauillac. At roundabout turn right to Pauillac Guais, then straight ahead at next roundabout and turn right just before the Maison du Tourisme. Site is 800 m. on the left. Alternatively if approaching from the north, you could use the ferry from Royan to Le Verdon, or Blaye to Lamarque (cheaper).

Charges 2003

Per unit incl. 1 or 2 persons	€ 7.65 - € 18.30
incl. 3 persons	€ 9.20 - € 21.35
extra person over 10 yrs	€ 2.30 - € 3.82
electricity (6-16A)	€ 3.10 - € 4.60
dog	free - € 1.53

Reservations

Advisable for July, August, September.
Tel: 05 56 59 10 03.
Email: camping.les.gabarreys@wanadoo.fr

Open

4 April - 11 October.

FR33210 Sunêlia La Pointe du Medoc

Route de la Pointe de Grave, 33123 Le Verdon-sur-Mer (Gironde)

La Pointe du Medoc, part of the Sunelia group, was established four years ago close to the tip of the Medoc peninsula and it benefits from some excellent, modern amenities. This site has 260 pitches, with around half taken by mobile homes or chalets. It is situated roughly equi-distant between the sandy Atlantic beach (accessed by a pleasant walk through the forest opposite the site) and that of the Gironde estuary, both around one km away. Pitches are generally large (100-150 sq.m.). Some are in full sun (the site lost many trees in the great storm of 1999) but those towards the rear of the site offer much more shade. All are equipped with electricity, and many have water and drainage. A little used railway line passes by the front of the site, as well as the main road to Le Verdon. The site is well located for excursions to the Medoc chateaux or marshland.

Facilities

Two modern toilet blocks are maintained to a high standard, with good hot showers and washbasins in private cabins. Pleasant bar and restaurant with takeaway. Heated swimming pool with small waterfalls, split-level paddling pool. Massage room. Beach volleyball. Minigolf. Multi-sport terrain. Bicycle hire. Communal barbecue area. Wide range of organised entertainment and imaginative children's club in high season. Off site: Sea fishing 1 km. Riding 5 km.

At a glance

Welcome & Ambience	✓✓✓✓	Location	✓✓✓✓
Quality of Pitches	✓✓✓✓	Range of Facilities	✓✓✓✓✓

Directions

Site is on the RN215 just south of Le Verdon and can be accessed either from the south (Bordeaux or the Blaye ferry), or from the north using the regular Royan-Pointe de Grave car ferry.

Charges 2003

Per unit incl. 2 persons and electricity (6A)	€ 12.00 - € 20.00
extra person (over 1 yr)	€ 2.00 - € 5.00
Camping Cheques accepted.	

Reservations

Essential for high season - contact site.
Tel: 05 56 73 39 99.
Email: info@camping-lapointemedoc.com

Open

3 April - 30 September

FR33230 Camping Caravaning Le Truc Vert

Route du Truc-Vert, Cap Ferret Océan, 33950 Lège (Gironde)

Relaxing amidst the tall pines of this 10 hectare hillside site is pleasant, but if you are looking for more activity there are many cycle ways and walks around the site to enjoy. There are over 400 pitches (280 with electricity) with trees giving shade. Some pitches are level but for many you will need levelling blocks. Some of the site roads are very steep so care is needed. The entrance area is decked with flowers and a blaze of colour when in bloom and very welcoming. There are tables and chairs outside the reception and bar where you can sit in the evening sun. This is a very pleasant place to stay either to relax or enjoy the local area. Care needs to be taken while travelling on the main roads through the woods as the occasional wild boar ventures out onto the roads. The beach is only 600 metres (with lifeguard coverage).

Facilities

Seven toilet blocks spread well around the site offer satisfactory facilities with showers and washbasins in cubicles, facilities for disabled people (although some may find the roads on site very steep). Motorcaravan service area. Laundry and dishwashing. Bar and restaurant. Supermarket. Play area. TV/games room. Various activities on site, evening entertainment in season. Off site: Fishing 300 m. Beach 300 m. Riding 500 m.

At a glance

Welcome & Ambience	✓✓✓✓✓	Location	✓✓✓✓✓
Quality of Pitches	✓✓✓✓	Range of Facilities	✓✓✓✓

Directions

From Bordeaux take D106 heading for Lège Cap Ferret. Just before village sign for Le Petit Piquey turn right (large billboard for the site above hedge) and follow through the residential area and woods for about 4 km. site on your left.

Charges 2003

Per person (over 2 yrs)	€ 3.00 - € 4.20
pitch	€ 12.00 - € 17.90
electricity (5A)	€ 3.05
local tax	€ 0.42

Reservations

Contact site. Tel: 05 56 60 89 55.
Email: camping.truc-vert@worldonline.fr

Open

20 April - 30 September.

FR33220 Sunêlia Le Petit Nice

Rout de Biscarosse, 33115 Pyla-sur-Mer (Gironde)

Le Petit Nice is a traditional seaside site, just south the great Dune de Pyla (Europe's largest sand dune, and a genuinely remarkable sight). It is a friendly, if relatively unsophisticated, site with direct (steep) access to an excellent sandy beach. The 225 pitches are for the most part terraced, descending towards the sea. Many are quite small, with larger pitches generally occupied by mobile homes. For this reason it is likely to appeal more to campers and those with small motorcaravans and very small caravan. Most pitches are shaded by pine trees but those closest to the sea are unshaded. Unusually, the site also has a private hang-gliding and paragliding take-off strip (very popular activities here).

Facilities

Two refurbished toilet blocks include washbasins in cubicles, baby rooms and facilities for disabled people. New, very smart bar/restaurant. Well stocked shop. Ggames room. Attractive swimming pool with small slide, children's pool and jacuzzi. Tennis, table tennis and boules court.

At a glance

Welcome & Ambience	✓✓✓	Location	✓✓✓✓✓
Quality of Pitches	✓✓	Range of Facilities	✓✓✓✓

Directions

The site is on the D218 (Arcachon - Biscarosse) south of the Dune de Pyla and is the fifth site you pass after the Dune.

Charges 2003

Per adult	€ 3.50 - € 6.00
child	€ 2.00 - € 4.00
pitch	€ 13.00 - € 26.00
electricity	€ 3.00 - € 5.00

Reservations

Essential in high season. Tel: 05 56 22 74 03.

Open

1 April - 30 September.

the travel service
TO BOOK THIS SITE
0870 405 4055
Expert Advice & Special Offers

FR33240 **Camping Airotel de L'Océan**

33680 Lacanau (Gironde)

Its location on the Atlantic coast, only 600 metres from a lovely sandy beach makes this site extremely popular. Set in 10 hectares of wooded sand dunes, the site offers the total holiday experience with over 500 pitches set amongst pine trees with areas for peace and quiet and areas for those who want to be on top of it all. The pitches are quite spacious, some level and others requiring blocks. At the time of our visit everywhere was very dry and there was very little grass. There is a large swimming pool complex, a bar and disco (in a soundproof building). Lacanau-Océan has many weekend visitors from Bordeaux and is popular for surfing.

Facilities

Six toilet blocks provide spacious facilities including washbasins in cabins, a room for disabled visitors in each block (although the site is quite hilly in places), baby rooms, washing machines and dishwashing. Motorcaravan service point. Supermarket. Bar, restaurant and takeaway. Large leisure pool complex. Various sports facilities. Fitness gym. TV and games rooms. Internet access. Bicycle hire. Barbecue area. Off site: Beach 600 m. Shops 1 km. Many cycle routes through the woods.

At a glance

Welcome & Ambience	✓✓✓✓	Location	✓✓✓✓✓
Quality of Pitches	✓✓✓✓	Range of Facilities	✓✓✓✓

Directions

From Bordeaux take D106 then onto D3 to Royan and through the wooded areas of the Atlantic coast. At Lacanau join D6 to Lacanau Ocean. At roundabout before village turn right and site is 800 m. on the right.

Latest charges

Per unit incl. 2 persons	€ 11.00 - € 14.00
with electricity	€ 14.00 - € 17.00
extra person	€ 4.20 - € 7.00
child (under 12 yrs)	free - € 5.50
dog	free - € 4.00

Reservations

Made with 25% deposit and € 28 fee.
Tel: 05 56 03 24 45.

Open

1 May - 30 September.

FR33320 **Camping Talaris Vacances**

Route de l'Océan, 33680 Lacanau (Gironde)

This is a typically French campsite where the owner is anxious to welcome more British visitors. It is located near a large lake and just 6 km. from the Atlantic coast at Lacanau Océan, so there are opportunities for swimming in either lake or sea, for surfing, water-skiing or sailing. There are plenty of cycle tracks and horse riding is available nearby. On site, there is plenty going on for youngsters – the many activities take place in front of the bar, restaurant and swimming pool area, so it is probably not the place for parents to relax! However, the part of the campsite allocated to the 150 tourist pitches is amongst mature trees (mainly oak, silver birch and the inevitable pines) at the far end of the site, so is surprisingly peaceful and relaxed. Some 100 mobile homes and chalets are available for rent, grouped in another part of the site.

Facilities

Two similar almost identical toilet blocks, one serving mainly the area occupied by tour operators providing activity holidays for young people, but the one in the camping/caravanning area is adequate for the needs, with pre-set showers and washbasins in cubicles. Dishwashing and laundry sinks under cover. Washing machines and dryers. The hot water supply was a little unreliable when we stayed. Baby room and facilities for disabled people. Shop (July/Aug). Bar/restaurant and takeaway (1/5-13/9). Swimming pools (1/5-13/9). Off site: Lake 1 km. Sea beach 6 km.

At a glance

Welcome & Ambience	✓✓✓✓	Location	✓✓✓✓
Quality of Pitches	✓✓✓	Range of Facilities	✓✓✓✓

Directions

From Bordeaux, take N125/D6 west to Lacanau and continue on D6 towards Lacanau Océan. Site is on right in about 7 km.

Charges 2003

Per unit incl. 2 persons	€ 15.60 - € 23.00
extra person	€ 3.20 - € 4.80
child (3-10 yrs)	€ 2.20 - € 3.10
animal	€ 2.90
electricity (6A)	€ 3.90

Reservations

Contact site. Tel: 05 56 03 04 15.
Email: talarisvacances@free.fr

Open

1 May - 13 September.

FR33310 Yelloh! Village Le Panorama

Grande Dune du Pyla, route de Biscarrosse, 33260 Pyla sur Mer (Gironde)

Many campsites set amongst pine trees have a rather untidy look, but Panorama is different. Here the entrance is very inviting with well tended flower beds and a pleasant, airy reception. From the entrance there is a climb up to the pitches, passing the swimming pool and play area. The touring pitches are set amongst the tall pines, all with electricity, and they outnumber the mobile homes. There are many activities and entertainments organised in high season, even classical concerts. A track leads down to the beach with a staircase. A Yelloh Village member.

Facilities

The toilet blocks, of varying ages and quality, (one block has recently been renovated) are clean and well maintained with free hot showers, baby rooms and facilities for disabled people. Fridge hire. Laundry facilities. Motor-caravan service point. Bar/restaurant with panoramic view of the ocean is a sight worth seeing. Attractive pool area with three heated swimming pools and jacuzzi (1/5-30/9). Adjacent play area. Tennis. Minigolf and table tennis. Organised entertainment in high season, for all ages. Off site: Riding 1 km. Golf 10 km.

At a glance

Welcome & Ambience	✓✓✓✓✓	Location	✓✓✓✓✓
Quality of Pitches	✓✓✓✓	Range of Facilities	✓✓✓✓

Directions

The new D259, signed from the N250 to Biscarrosse and Dune du Pilate, just before La Teste, avoids Pyla-sur-Mer. At the roundabout at end of new road, turn left on D218 coast road. Site is 4 km. on right.

Charges 2004

Per pitch incl. 2 persons	€ 15.00 - € 33.00
child (under 12 yrs)	€ 1.00 - € 2.50
electricity (3-10A)	€ 3.00 - € 5.00

Reservations

Made with deposit (€ 120) and fee (€ 30).
Tel: 05 56 22 10 44.
Email: mail@camping-panorama.com

Open

1 May - 30 September.

FR40020 Camping Les Chênes

Bois de Boulogne, 40100 Dax (Landes)

Dax is not a place that springs at once to mind as a holiday town but, as well as being a 'spa', it has a comprehensive programme of events and shows during the summer season. Les Chênes is well established site, popular with the French, situated on the edge of town amongst park-land (also near the river) and close to the spa for the thermal treatments. The 183 touring pitches are of two types, some large and traditional with hedges, water and electricity connections, and others more informal, set amongst tall pines with electricity if required. This is a reliable, well run site, with a little of something for everyone, but probably most popular for adults taking the 'waters'.

Facilities

There are two very different toilet blocks, one new and very modern with heating, washbasins in cubicles, facilities for disabled people and good provision for babies and young children. The older block has been refurbished. Laundry room. Ample laundry and dishwashing sinks. Reasonably well stocked shop also providing takeaway food (3/4-30/10). Unusual and attractive swimming and paddling pools (1/5-18/8). Good play area. Large field suitable for ball games, table tennis and boule pitch. Bicycle hire. Mini-club for children (July/Aug). Occasional special evenings for adults with meals and dancing. Charcoal barbecues are not permitted. Off site: Restaurant opposite the site entrance. Fishing 100 m, riding and golf 300 m. Beaches 28 km.

At a glance

Welcome & Ambience	✓✓✓✓	Location	✓✓✓
Quality of Pitches	✓✓✓✓	Range of Facilities	✓✓✓✓

Directions

Site is west of town on south side of river, signed after main river bridge and at many junctions in town – Bois de Boulogne (1.5 km). In very wet weather the access road to the site may be flooded (but not the site).

Charges 2003

Per pitch incl. 1 or 2 persons and electricity (5A)	€ 13.00 - € 21.00
with water and drainage	€ 15.00 - € 17.50
extra person	€ 4.10 - € 7.00
child (0-12 yrs)	€ 2.00 - € 3.50
animal	€ 1.70

Reservations

Made with deposit (€ 46) and fee (€ 7,62); contact site. Tel: 05 58 90 05 53.
Email: camping-chenes@wanadoo.fr

Open

27 March - 6 November.

Atlantic Coast

Great on-line holiday deals *alanrogersdirect*.com

FR40040 Yelloh! Village La Paillotte

40140 Azur (Landes)

La Paillotte, in the Landes area of southwest France, is a site with a character of its own. The campsite buildings (reception, shop, restaurant, even sanitary blocks) are all Tahitian in style, circular and constructed from local woods with the typical straw roof (and layer of waterproof material underneath). Some are now being replaced but still in character. It lies right beside the Soustons lake, 1.5 km. from Azur village, and has its own sandy beach. This is particularly suitable for young children because the lake is shallow and slopes extremely gradually. For boating the site has a small private harbour where you can keep your own non-powered boat (of shallow draught). All 310 pitches at La Paillotte are marked, individual ones and are mostly shady with shrubs and trees planted. The 150 pitches for touring units vary in price according to size, position and whether they are equipped with electricity, water, etc. La Paillotte is an unusual site with its own atmosphere which appeals to many regular clients. Used by tour operators (45 pitches). Member 'Yelloh Village'.

Facilities

Circular rustic-style toilet blocks are rather different from the usual campsite amenities, but are modern and fully tiled. They include individual washbasins, partly enclosed, some toilets and basins en-suite and separate 'mini' facilities for children. Outside washing-up sinks. Washing machines and dryers. Motorcaravan service points. Shop (1/6-6/9). Good restaurant with pleasant terrace overlooking the lake and bar (all 12/5-10/9). Takeaway (high season). New swimming pool complex (from 1/5). Sports, games and activities organised for children and adults. 'Mini-club' room, with 'mini' equipment. TV room, library. Bicycle hire. Table tennis. Sailing, rowing boats and pedaloes for hire. Torches useful. Dogs are not accepted. Off site: Riding 5 km, golf 10 km. Atlantic beaches 10 km.

At a glance

Welcome & Ambience	✓✓✓✓	Location	✓✓✓✓✓
Quality of Pitches	✓✓✓✓	Range of Facilities	✓✓✓✓✓

Directions

Coming from the north along N10, turn west on D150 at Magescq. From south go via Soustons. In Azur turn left before church (site signed).

Charges 2004

Per unit incl. 2 persons	
with 10A electricity	€ 15.00 - € 34.00
with electricity and water	€ 17.00 - € 36.00
pitch by the lake	€ 20.00 - € 42.00
extra person (over 3 yrs)	€ 3.00 - € 6.50
local tax	€ 0.40

Reservations

Advised for high season; made for Sat. to Sat. only 2/7- 27/8, with deposit (€ 38.11 per week) and fee (€ 25). Tel: 05 58 48 12 12. Email: info@paillotte.com

Open

April - September.

FR40030 Les Pins du Soleil

Départementale 459, 40990 St Paul-lès-Dax (Landes)

This site will appeal to families, particularly those with younger children, or those who prefer to be some way back from the coast within easy reach of shops, cultural activities, etc. and well placed for touring the area. Dax is a busy spa town with many attractions. The site has 145 good sized pitches, 99 for touring units of which 59 have electricity and drainage. Although new, the site benefits from being developed in light woodland so there is a fair amount of shade from the many small trees. A range of excursions is possible by bus to St Sebastian, Lourdes, etc. English is spoken. The nearby Calicéo aquatic centre is recommended.

Facilities

Modern sanitary facilities include facilities for babies, disabled visitors and laundry. Small supermarket. Bar. Takeaway (from June). Attractive, medium sized swimming pool with café (both 2/6-15/9). Playground and children's mini-club in high season. Volleyball, table tennis and bicycle hire. Off site: Fishing 1 km. Riding 3 km. Bus to the thermal baths.

At a glance

Welcome & Ambience	✓✓✓✓	Location	✓✓✓
Quality of Pitches	✓✓✓	Range of Facilities	✓✓✓✓

Directions

Approaching from west on N124, avoid bypass and follow signs for Dax and St Paul. Almost immediately turn right at roundabout onto D459 and follow signs. Site is a little further along on the left. It is also well signed from the town centre, north of the river.

Charges 2003

Per pitch incl. 2 persons	€ 8.00 - € 16.00
with electricity, water, drainage	€ 15.00 - € 21.00
extra person	€ 6.00
child (4-10 yrs)	€ 3.50
animal	€ 1.50
local tax	€ 0.27

Less for stays over 21 nights.
Camping Cheques accepted.

Reservations

Made with deposit (€ 35) and fee (€ 6).
Tel: 05 58 91 37 91. Email: pinsoleil@aol.com

Open

7 April - 27 October.

FR40050 Sunêlia Le Col-Vert

Lac de Leon, 40560 Vielle-St Girons (Landes)

This extensive but natural site edges a nature reserve and stretches for one kilometre on a narrow frontage along the Lac de Léon, a conservation area. This makes it particularly suitable for those who want to practise water sports such as sailing and windsurfing. Bathing is also possible as the lake bed shelves gently making it easy for children. The site has a supervised beach, sail-boarding courses are arranged and there are boats and boards for hire. There are some 800 pitches in total, the 380 pitches for touring units being flat and covered by light pinewood, most with good shade and many along the lake side. They are of around 100 sq.m, only partly separated and some 120 have water and electricity points. Much 'animation' is organised in season: children's games, tournaments, etc. by day and dancing or shows in the evenings. Used by tour operators (80 pitches).

Facilities

Of the four toilet blocks, one is heated in low season. Mostly British WCs, washbasins in cabins. Dishwashing sinks (mainly cold water but with hot tap to draw from). Washing machines, dryer and dishwasher. Good facilities for disabled people. Motorcaravan services. Shops (15/4-15/9). Good bar/restaurant by the lake (open to all). Simple takeaway. Two pools (all season and supervised), one open air with whirlpool and one covered and heated. Sunbathing areas. Playground. TV room, table tennis, amusement machines. Sports area with boules, tennis and volleyball. Fitness centre and sauna. Two jogging tracks. Safety deposit boxes. An overall charge is made for the leisure activities but this excludes certain facilities, eg. riding, bicycle hire, sauna, tennis, minigolf. Fishing (lessons for children). Riding. Sailing school (15/6-15/9). Several areas for barbecues.
Off site: Walking and cycle ways in the forest. Golf 10 km. Atlantic beaches 5 km.

At a glance

Welcome & Ambience	✓✓✓✓	Location	✓✓✓✓✓
Quality of Pitches	✓✓✓	Range of Facilities	✓✓✓✓✓

Directions

Site is off D652 Mimizan-Léon road, 4 km. south of crossroads with D42 at St Girons. Road to lake and site is signed at Veille.

Charges 2003

Per unit incl. 2 persons acc to season, type and location	€ 10.50 - € 40.90
extra person	€ 2.00 - € 5.50
child (3-13 yrs)	€ 1.50 - € 4.50
electricity (3/10A)	€ 3.50 - € 5.00
dog	€ 1.00 - € 2.50
local tax	€ 0.50

Camping Cheques accepted.

Reservations

Any length with UK £42 deposit per week booked and £25 fee. Tel: 05 58 42 94 06.
Email: contact@colvert.com

Open

1 April - 26 September.

the travel service TO BOOK THIS SITE 0870 405 4055 Expert Advice & Special Offers

FR40060 Camping Eurosol

Route de la Plage, 40560 Vielle-St Girons (Landes)

The sandy beach 700 metres from Eurosol has supervised bathing in high season. The site also has its own swimming pool with paved sunbathing areas which are planted with palm trees giving quite a tropical feel. The site itself is on undulating ground amongst mature pine trees giving good shade and the pitches on the slopes are mainly only suitable for tents. The 417 pitches for touring units are numbered (although with nothing to separate them, there is little privacy) and 259 have electricity with 120 fully serviced (86 with mobile homes). A family site with entertainers who speak many languages, many games and tournaments are organised and a beach volleyball competition is held each evening in front of the bar.

Facilities

There are four main toilet blocks all refurbished to include washbasins in cabins. Two smaller blocks have facilities for babies and disabled people. Motorcaravan service point. Fridge rental. Well stocked shop (11/5-21/9). Bar, restaurant and takeaway (all 1/7-31/8). Raised deck area and a stage for live shows (mainly performed by the very versatile staff) arranged in July/Aug. and finishing by midnight. Swimming pool. Tennis. Multi-sport court for basketball, handball and football. Charcoal barbecues are not permitted.
Off site: Riding school opposite. Fishing 700 m.

At a glance

Welcome & Ambience	✓✓✓✓	Location	✓✓✓✓
Quality of Pitches	✓✓✓	Range of Facilities	✓✓✓✓✓

Directions

Turn off D652 at St Girons on D42 towards St Girons-Plage. Site is on left before coming to beach (4.5 km).

Charges 2003

Per unit incl.1 or 2 persons	€ 10.00 - € 19.50
with electricity	€ 12.50 - € 25.50
with water and drainage	€ 12.50 - € 28.50
extra person (over 4 years)	€ 4.00
dog	€ 2.50
local tax	€ 0.22 - € 0.44

Reservations

Made for min. 1 week with deposit (€ 95) and fee (€ 25). Tel: 05 58 47 90 14.
Email: contact@camping-eurosol.com

Open

8 May - 18 September.

FR40100 Camping du Domaine de la Rive

Route de Bordeaux, 40600 Biscarosse (Landes)

Set in pine woods, La Rive has a superb beach-side loaction on Lac de Sanguient. It provides mostly level, numbered and clearly defined pitches of 100 sq.m. all with electricity connections. The swimming pool complex is wonderful, with various pools linked by water channels and bridges, the four-slide pool having a wide staircase to the top to speed up enjoyment. There is also a jacuzzi, paddling pool and two large, unusually shaped swimming pools, all surrounded by paved sunbathing areas and decorated with palm trees. An indoor pool is planned. The beach is excellent, shelving gently to provide safe bathing for all ages. There are windsurfers and small craft can be launched from the site's slipway. This is a friendly site with a good mix of nationalities.

Facilities

Five modern, very good quality toilet blocks have washbasins in cabins and mainly British style toilets. Visitors with disabilities well catered for in three blocks. Baby baths. We found the facilities very clean. Motorcaravan service point. Well stocked shop with gas (15/5-15/9). Bar serving snacks and takeaway. Games room adjoining. Restaurant with reasonably priced family meals (1/6-15/9). Swimming pool complex supervised July/Aug (15/5-15/9). Play area. Two tennis courts. Bicycle hire. Hand-ball or basketball court, table tennis, boules, archery and football. Fishing. Water skiing. Watersports equipment hire. Tournaments in various sports are arranged in June-Aug. Discos and karaoke evenings organised outside bar with stage and tiered seating. Mini-club for twice daily. Charcoal barbecues not permitted on pitches (central area available). Caravan storage. Off site: Riding 5 km. Golf 10 km.

At a glance

Welcome & Ambience	✓✓✓✓	Location	✓✓✓✓
Quality of Pitches	✓✓✓✓	Range of Facilities	✓✓✓✓✓

Directions

Take D652 from Sanguinet to Biscarosse and site is signed on the right in about 6 km.

Latest charges

Per pitch incl. 2 persons and electricity (6A)	€ 20.00 - € 30.00
with water and drainage	€ 23.00 - € 33.00
extra person	€ 3.40 - € 5.00
child (3-10 yrs)	€ 2.30 - € 3.50
boat	€ 3.70 - € 5.50
dog	€ 2.10 - € 3.30
local tax	€ 0.25 - € 0.50

Camping Cheques accepted.

Reservations

Advised for July/Aug; write or fax site. (deposit €100). Tel: 05 58 78 12 33. Email: info@camping-de-la-rive.fr

Open

1 April - 30 September.

FR40070 Camping Lous Seurrots

Contis Plage, 40170 St Julien-en-Born (Landes)

Lous Seurrots is only a short 300 metre walk from the beach and parts of the site have views across the estuary. There are 610 pitches, mainly in pine woods on sandy undulating ground. They are numbered but only roughly marked out, most have good shade and over 80% have electrical hook-ups. The site's pool complex is in a superb setting of palm trees and flower beds and the paved sunbathing areas have wonderful views out to the estuary and the sea. For all its size, Lous Seurrots is a family site with the emphasis on peace and tranquillity (no discos). Used by tour operators.

Facilities

Six well kept, modern toilet blocks cope very well and include some washbasins in cabins, and some showers with washbasins. Baby rooms and good facilities for disabled people. Numerous laundry and dishwashing sinks and washing machines. Motorcaravan service point. Large well stocked shop (1/6-15/9). Bar, takeaway and restaurant (15/5-15/9). Swimming pool complex (15/5-30/9), four pools and a jacuzzi with keep fit classes held every morning in July/Aug. Tennis, table tennis, archery, volleyball and minigolf. Canoeing. Bicycle hire. Fishing. Mini-club for younger children. Evening entertainment twice weekly in high season in open-air auditorium. Only gas barbecues are permitted. Off site: Riding 3 km.

At a glance

Welcome & Ambience	✓✓✓✓	Location	✓✓✓✓
Quality of Pitches	✓✓✓	Range of Facilities	✓✓✓✓✓

Directions

Turn off D652 on D41 (15 km. south of Mimizan) to Contis-Plage and site is on left as you reach it.

Charges 2003

Per unit incl. 2 adults	€ 17.00 - € 25.00
extra person	€ 4.00 - € 6.00
child (3-7 yrs)	free - € 5.00
electricity (6A)	€ 4.00
animal	€ 3.00
local tax	€ 0.44

Reservations

Made with deposit (€ 46) and fee (€ 18,29). Tel: 05 58 42 85 82. Email: info@lous-seurrots.com

Open

1 April - 30 September.

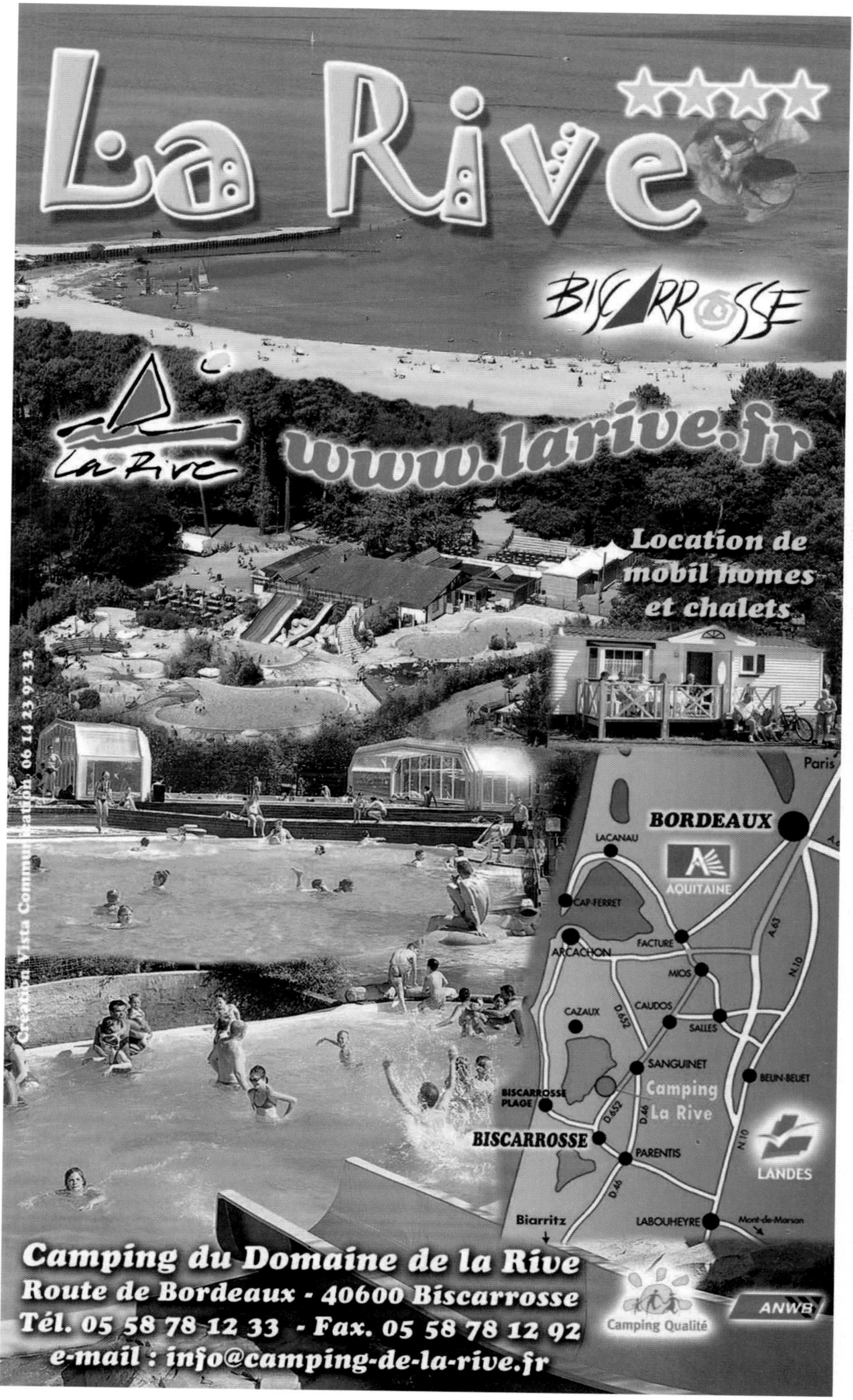

La Rive

★★★★

BISCARROSSE

La Rive

www.larive.fr

Location de mobil homes et chalets

Création Vista Communication 06 14 23 92 32

Paris

LACANAU

BORDEAUX

AQUITAINE

CAP-FERRET

FACTURE

ARCACHON

MIOS

CAUDOS

CAZAUX

SALLES

SANGUINET

BELIN-BELIET

BISCARROSSE PLAGE

Camping La Rive

BISCARROSSE

PARENTIS

LANDES

Biarritz

LABOUHEYRE

Mont-de-Marsan

Camping du Domaine de la Rive
Route de Bordeaux - 40600 Biscarrosse
Tél. 05 58 78 12 33 - Fax. 05 58 78 12 92
e-mail : info@camping-de-la-rive.fr

Camping Qualité

ANWB

FR40120N Domaine Naturiste Arnaoutchot

40560 Vielle-St Girons (Landes)

'Arna' is a large naturist site with extensive facilities and direct access to the beach. Even with 500 pitches, its layout in the form of a number of sections, each with its own character, make it quite relaxing and very natural. These sections amongst the trees and bushes of the Landes provide a variety of reasonably sized pitches, most with electricity, although the hilly terrain means that only a limited number are flat enough for motorcaravans. The centrally located amenities are extensive and of excellent quality. The site has the advantage of direct access to a large, sandy naturist beach, although access from some parts of the site may involve a walk of perhaps 600-700 m. The 'Arna Club' provides more than 30 activities and workshops (in the main season). English is spoken. There are chalets, mobile homes, caravans and tents for rent. The site is used by a tour operator (20 pitches). Green Key award. Member 'France 4 Naturisme'.

Facilities

Sanitary facilities include not only the usual naturist site type of blocks with communal hot showers, but also a number of tiny blocks with one hot shower, WC and washbasin each in an individual cabin. All blocks have been upgraded to provide fully tiled, modern facilities, one block is heated in low season. Laundry. Motorcaravan service point. Large supermarket and a range of other shops. Bar/restaurant, pizzeria and tapita (fish) bar. Pizza delivery to pitches or to telephone point on beach. Heated indoor swimming pool with solarium, whirlpool and slide. Outdoor pool and terraced sunbathing area. Health centre with sauna, steam, whirlpool and massage treatments. Arna Club (main season) including riding, archery, golf practise, tennis, petanque, swimming, rambling, cycling, sailing school, handicrafts, excursions and special activities for children. TV, video and games rooms. Cinema. Library. Hairdresser and chiropodist. Cash point. Internet point. Bicycle hire. Fishing on site. Torches useful. Barbecues are not permitted. Off site: Riding and golf 5 km.

Directions

Site is signed off D652 road at Vielle-Saint-Girons - follow D328 for 3-4 km.

Charges 2003

Per unit incl. 2 persons	€ 13.00 - € 31.00
extra person (over 3 yrs)	€ 2.00 - € 6.50
electricity (3A)	€ 3.50
animal	€ 1.20 - € 2.80
local tax	€ 0.50

Deposit on arrival for accommodation € 50. Special offers available. Camping Cheques accepted.

Reservations

Made with 25% deposit and fee (€ 30).
Tel: 05 58 49 11 11. Email: contact@arna.com

Open

1 April - 26 September.

At a glance

Welcome & Ambience	✓✓✓✓	Location	✓✓✓✓
Quality of Pitches	✓✓✓	Range of Facilities	✓✓✓✓✓

FR40110 Camping Caravaning Sen Yan

Le Village Tropical, 40170 Mézos (Landes)

This exotic family site is about 12 kilometres from the Atlantic coast in the Landes forest area and set just outside the village. There are 310 pitches marked with hedges, 190 with electricity, and with ample water points. Some mobile homes and tour operator pitches are in a separate 'village'. The reception, bar and pool area is almost tropical with the luxuriant greenery of its banana trees, palm trees, tropical flowers and its straw sunshades. Activities and evening entertainment include a disco twice a week in high season.

Facilities

Three toilet blocks with good quality fittings have showers and washbasins in cabins and some British style WCs. The newest block is especially suitable for low season visitors, with a special section for babies, plus facilities for disabled people. Shop (from 15/6). Bar, restaurant and snacks (1/7-31/8). Swimming pools (1/6-30/9), one of which can be covered. Archery. Practice golf. Only gas barbecues are permitted. Off site: Fishing 500 m. Rding 6 km.

Directions

From N10 take exit 14 (Onesse-Laharie), then D38 Bias/Mimizan road. After 13 km. turn south to Mézos from where site is signed.

Latest charges

Per pitch incl. 2 persons	€ 11.90 - € 17.00
with 5A electricity	€ 14.00 - € 20.00
extra person	€ 3.90
child (under 7 yrs)	€ 2.90
twin axle caravan plus	€ 15.25

Reservations

Made with deposit (€ 84) and fee (€ 26).
Tel: 05 58 42 60 05. Email: reception@sen-yan.com

Open

1 June - 15 September.

At a glance

Welcome & Ambience	✓✓✓✓	Location	✓✓✓✓
Quality of Pitches	✓✓✓✓	Range of Facilities	✓✓✓✓✓

FR40090M Camping Municipal Lou Broustaricq

Route de Langeot, 40460 Sanguinet (Landes)

This municipal site has all the appearance and atmosphere of a privately run enterprise. It has 590 pitches (of which 220 are for tourers) on flat ground in woodland, mostly shaded by high trees. Some pitches are now separated by newly planted shrubs and trees. Caravan pitches are 110 sq.m. with hardstanding (20 for motorcaravans), electricity and water, pitches for tents average 100 sq.m. A path of about 200 m. leads to the big lake (no cars this way, but access for cars with boats 2 km). A very reliable site, there is always a chance of finding space. There may be some aircraft noise at times from a nearby army base. The site is used by two French tour operators.

Facilities

Eight unisex toilet blocks (one modern block heated in winter) have washbasins in cabins and facilities for disabled people and babies. The older blocks are now looking a little tired and cleaning can be variable. Washing machines and dryers. Supermarket and other shops by entrance (mid June-mid Sept) and a bar, restaurant, snack bar and takeaway (July/Aug). Swimming pool complex with sunbathing areas, with new slide and extra pools (mid-June - mid-Sept, lifeguards in July/Aug). Two tennis courts. Bicycle hire. Minigolf, table tennis, volleyball, basketball. Playgrounds. Tournaments are organised in season. Area for barbecues. Entrance barrier (€ 15 deposit for card, or € 50 for card and pool bracelet).

Directions

Turn to northwest off the D46 at site sign, 1 km. northeast of Sanguinet.

Charges 2003

Per unit incl. 1 or 2 persons	€ 9.00 - € 24.70
extra person	€ 1.70 - € 2.80
electricity (6/10A)	€ 2.70 - € 4.00
animal	€ 1.50 - € 2.20

Reservations

Made for any length with deposit (25%) and fee (€25). Tel: 05 58 82 74 82. Email: loubrousta@wanadoo.fr

Open

All year.

At a glance

Welcome & Ambience	✓✓✓✓	Location	✓✓✓✓
Quality of Pitches	✓✓✓✓	Range of Facilities	✓✓✓✓

FR40160 Camping Les Vignes

Route de la Plage du Cap de L'Homy, 40170 Lit-et-Mixe (Landes)

Les Vignes is a large holiday site close to the Atlantic coast with 450 pitches, of which 250 are occupied by a mix of mobile homes, bungalows and tents, most of which are for rent. The 157 tourist pitches are relatively level on a sandy base, all serviced with electricity and water, some with waste water drains. The site's amenities, including a supermarket, restaurant and bar, are located at the entrance to the site. The rather stylish swimming pool complex includes a six lane water slide. A wide range of activities is provided and during July and August a great variety of entertainment options for both adults and children, some of which take place in the new entertainment 'Big Top'.

Facilities

Four virtually identical sanitary units (not all open in low season) provide combined washbasin and shower cubicles, dishwashing and laundry sinks, washing machines and dryers, facilities for babies and disabled people. Large supermarket (15/6-10/9). Restaurant and bar (15/6-10/9). Takeaway (July/Aug). Swimming pool complex (1/6-15/9). Tennis. Table tennis. Golf driving range. Minigolf. Volleyball, basketball. Pétanque. Kids club and playground. Bicycle hire. Barrier closed 23.00-07.00 hrs. Off site: Golf course, canoeing, kayaking, surfing, riding. Many cycle tracks.

Directions

Lit-et-Mixe is on the D652 20 km. south of Mimizan. Turn west on D88 1 km. south of town towards Cap de l'Homy for 1.5 km. where site entrance is on left.

Charges 2003

Per pitch incl. 2 persons (10A electricity and water incl.)	€ 14.50 - € 33.00
extra person (over 5 yrs)	€ 4.00 - € 5.00
child (under 5 yrs)	€ 1.50 - € 3.00
animal	€ 3.00

Reservations

Advisable for high season, made with deposit and fee. Tel: 05 58 42 85 60. Email: contact@les-vignes.com

Open

1 June - 15 September.

At a glance

Welcome & Ambience	✓✓✓✓	Location	✓✓✓✓
Quality of Pitches	✓✓✓	Range of Facilities	✓✓✓✓

FR40130 Camping de la Côte

40660 Messanges (Landes)

A peaceful family site, surrounded by pine forests near the beaches of the Landes, has large, level pitches edged with newly planted trees and shrubs. Many of the 142 touring pitches are set among trees that provide shade, 118 have electricity connections and 12 also have water and drainage. The beach and the dunes are 20 minutes walk. M. and Mme. Moresmau are very proud of their site and do their uptmost to maintain a quiet family atmosphere with customers who return year after year.

Facilities

Two modern toilet blocks built in the Landes style are of excellent quality and very well maintained. Facilities include washbasins in cabins, a baby room and provision for disabled people. Washing machines and dryer with sinks for laundry and dishes. Motorcaravan service point. Reception sells bread and milk, a few basic supplies and gas (1/7-31/8). Takeaway pizza (July/Aug). Barbecues only permitted at designated areas. Games room, play area, football, volleyball, table tennis and boules. Mobile homes to rent. Off site: Fishing and riding within 1 km. Bicycle hire 1.5 km. Golf 2 km. Supermarket and Vieux-Boucau near.

At a glance

| Welcome & Ambience | ✓✓✓✓ | Location | ✓✓✓✓ |
| Quality of Pitches | ✓✓✓✓ | Range of Facilities | ✓✓✓ |

Directions

Site is signed off the D652, 1.5 km. north of Vieux-Boucau.

Charges 2003

Per unit incl. 2 persons	€ 8.40 - € 11.50
extra person	€ 2.30 - € 2.90
child (under 7 yrs)	€ 1.60 - € 2.10
electricity (6/10A)	€ 2.20 - € 3.90
water and drainage	€ 2.00 - € 3.00

Reservations

Advised and made with deposit (€ 60).
Tel: 05 58 48 94 94. Email: lacote@wanadoo.fr

Open

1 April - 30 September.

FR40190 Camping Airotel Saint Martin

Avenue de l'Océan, 40660 Moliets-Plage (Landes)

A family site aimed mainly at couples and young families, Airotel St Martin has a small number of mobile homes (77) compared to the number of touring pitches (583). First impressions are of a neat, tidy, well cared for site with direct access to the beach. The pitches are mainly typically French in style with low hedges separating them plus some shade. There is also a 'free and easy' area under tall trees. Electric hook ups are 5-10A and a number of pitches also have water and drainage. Entertainment in high season is low key. Daytime competitions and a 'mini-club' are organised. The occasional evening entertainment is well away from the pitches with no discos or karaoke.

Facilities

The six toilet blocks are of a high standard and very well maintained with washbasins in cabins, large showers, baby rooms and facilities for disabled customers. Motorcaravan service point. Washing machines and dryers. Fridge rental. Very good supermarket and various bars, restaurants and takeaways are at the entrance, owned by the site and mostly open all season. Attractive new indoor pool, jacuzzi and sauna (charged for in July/Aug) is open all season. Large outdoor pool area with pools, jacuzzi and paddling pool (mid June - mid Sept). Multi sports pitch. Small play area. Internet access. Off site: Tennis and golf 700 m. Riding 7 km. This is an excellent area for cycling.

At a glance

| Welcome & Ambience | ✓✓✓✓✓ | Location | ✓✓✓✓ |
| Quality of Pitches | ✓✓✓✓✓ | Range of Facilities | ✓✓✓✓ |

Directions

From the N10 take D142 to Lèon, then D652 to Moliets-et-Mar. Follow signs to Moliets-Plage, site is well signed.

Latest charges

Per unit incl. 1 or 2 persons	€ 16.00 - € 24.50
with electricity (5/10A)	€ 18.00 - € 27.50
100 sq.m. pitch	€ 21.00 - € 32.00
with electricity	€ 20.00 - € 33.00

Prices are for reserved pitches.

Reservations

Contact site. Tel: 05 58 48 52 30.
Email: contact@camping-saint-martin.fr

Open

Easter - 15 October.

FR40140 Camping Caravaning Lou P'tit Poun

110 avenue du Quartier Neuf, 40390 St Martin de Seignanx (Landes)

The manicured grounds surrounding Lou P'tit Poun give it a well kept appearance, a theme carried out throughout this very pleasing site. It is only after arriving at the car park that you feel confident it is not a private estate. Beyond this point the site unfolds to reveal an abundance of thoughtfully positioned shrubs and trees. Behind a central sloping flower bed lies the open plan reception area. The avenues around the site are wide and the 168 pitches are spacious. All have electricity (6/10A), 30 are fully serviced and some are separated by low hedges. The jovial owners not only make their guests welcome, but extend their enthusiasm to organising weekly entertainment for young and old during high season. A 'Sites et Paysages' member.

Facilities

Two unisex sanitary blocks, maintained to a high standard and kept clean, include washbasins in cabins, a baby bath and provision for disabled people. Dishwashing sinks and laundry facilities with washing machine and dryer. Motorcaravan service point. Café, bread and ices (1/7-31/8). Swimming pool (1/6-15/9). Play area. Games room, TV. Half court tennis. Table tennis. Bicycle hire. Caravan storage. Off site: Fishing and riding 7 km. Golf 10 km. Bayonne 6 km. Sandy beaches of Basque coast ten minute drive.

At a glance

Welcome & Ambience	✓✓✓✓✓	Location	✓✓✓✓
Quality of Pitches	✓✓✓✓✓	Range of Facilities	✓✓✓✓

Directions

Leave A63 at exit 6 and join N117 towards Pau. Site is signed at Leclerc supermarket. Continue on N117 for approx. 5.5 km. and site is then clearly signed on right.

Latest charges

Per pitch incl. 1 or 2 persons	€ 9.00 - € 20.00
with 4A electricity	€ 11.50 - € 23.50
extra person	€ 4.00 - € 5.50

No credit cards.

Reservations

Made with deposit (€ 46) and fee (€ 15,24).
Tel: 05 59 56 55 79. Email: ptitpoun@club-internet.fr

Open

1 June - 15 September:

FR40170 Haven Camping La Réserve

Gastés, 40160 Parentis-en-Born (Landes)

La Resérve was featured in this guide until it was sold a few years ago; it has now been taken over by Haven Europe. A big site set in a pine wood, it has access to a large lake with a beach and small harbour (beaches are nearby). The lake shelves very gradually so provides good bathing for children and good facilities for windsurfing and sailing; powered boats for water skiing are also for hire. The 700 numbered pitches (200 for touring) are of above average size (mostly 120 sq.m.), set on mainly flat ground and marked by stones in the ground. Most have electricity. Much organised entertainment and sports activities for children and adults in the Haven Europe tradition. On the downside, we were not impressed by the reception given to our inspectors. However, Haven Europe management have addressed this issue and we are assured that our readers will not encounter the same indifference.

Facilities

Five toilet blocks, with en-suite facilities in one, include washbasins in cabins. Washing machines; when visited they were in need of maintenance – this is being addressed. Well stocked supermarket. Restaurant and large bar where entertainment is organised all season. Heated swimming pool, another unheated outdoor pool, with water slides and paddling pool (lifeguards on duty). Children's club. Two tennis courts (floodlit in the evening), minigolf, table tennis and volleyball. Boat hire, windsurfing courses and water skiing. TV room. Fishing. Bicycle hire. Dogs not accepted.

At a glance

Welcome & Ambience	✓✓✓✓	Location	✓✓✓✓
Quality of Pitches	✓✓✓	Range of Facilities	✓✓✓✓✓

Directions

Turn west off D652 Gastes - Mimizan road 3 km. south of Gastes by camp sign.

Charges 2003

Per pitch incl. up to 6 persons	€ 10.00 - € 31.00
with electricity	€ 11.00 - € 37.00

Reservations

Accepted at any time for min. 4 days; no booking fee. Contact site or Haven Europe in the UK on.
Tel: 0870 242 7777 for information or reservation.
Tel: 05 58 09 74 79. Email: lareserve@haven.fr

Open

30 April - 19 September.

FR40180 Camping Le Vieux Port

Plage sud, 40660 Messanges (Landes)

The area to the north of Bayonne is heavily forested and a number of very large campsites are attractively located close to the superb Atlantic beaches. Le Vieux Port is probably the largest and certainly one of the most impressive of these. A well established destination appealing particularly to families with teenage children, this lively site has no fewer than 1,406 open pitches of mixed size, most with electrical hook-ups and some with water and drainage. Sprawling beneath the pines, the camping area is well shaded and pitches are generally of a good size, attractively grouped around the toilet blocks. At least a third of the site is taken up with mobile homes and there are a large number of tour operators here (30%). The heated swimming pool complex is exceptional, boasting five outdoor pools and three large water slides. There is also a heated indoor pool. At the back of the site a path leads across the dunes to a superb beach. A little train also trundles to the beach on a regular basis in high season (small charge). All in all, a lively site with a great deal to offer an active family.

Facilities

Nine well appointed toilet blocks are all of modern design and well maintained. Facilities for disabled people. Motorcaravan service point. Good shopping facilities, including a well stocked supermarket and various smaller shops. Several restaurants (including takeaway service) and bars (all open all season). Large swimming pool complex (no bermuda shorts). Three tennis courts, two football pitches, a multi-sport pitch, minigolf etc. Bicycle hire. Well run and popular riding centre. Large animation team organise a wide range of activities in high season including discos and karaoke evenings. Only communal barbecues are allowed.

At a glance

| Welcome & Ambience | ✓✓✓ | Location | ✓✓✓✓✓ |
| Quality of Pitches | ✓✓✓✓ | Range of Facilities | ✓✓✓✓✓ |

Directions

Leave RN10 at Magescq exit heading for Soustons. Pass through Soustons following signs for Vieux-Boucau. Bypass this town and site is clearly signed to the left at second roundabout.

Charges 2003

Per unit incl. 2 persons	€ 12.00 - € 27.00
child (under 10 yrs)	€ 1.80 - € 3.50
electricity (6/8A)	€ 2.70 - € 6.50

Reservations

Essential in high season. Tel: 05 58 48 22 00. Email: levieuxport@wanadoo.fr

Open

1 April - 30 September.

FR40200 Yelloh! Village Le Sylvamar

Avenue de l'Océan, 40530 Labenne Océan (Landes)

Camping Village Sylvamar is less than one km. from the long sandy beach of Labenne Ocean. The large, light and airy reception area with its internet access point is very welcoming. The 500 pitches (320 for touring units) are level, numbered and mostly separated by low hedges. Many have water and drains and there is welcoming shade. The pool complex is absolutely superb, set in a sunny location. There are pools of various sizes with inflatable boats and rubber rings provided. There is ample room for sunbathing and all is overlooked by the bar/restaurant and its terrace. A Yelloh! Village member.

Facilities

Four modern toilet blocks with good quality fittings have washbasins in cabins, and facilities for babies and disabled visitors. Washing machines at each block. No shop on site but a large supermarket is only 500 m. Bar/restaurant (all season) sells bread and takeaway and has a comprehensive menu. Play area for young children. Mini-club in July/Aug. Fitness centre. Tennis. Bicycle hire. Table tennis. Badminton. Library. Extensive entertainment programme for all ages, incl. evening shows in the outdoor amphitheatre. Fridge hire. Barbecues not permitted (communal ones provided).

At a glance

| Welcome & Ambience | ✓✓✓✓ | Location | ✓✓✓✓ |
| Quality of Pitches | ✓✓✓✓ | Range of Facilities | ✓✓✓✓✓ |

Directions

Labenne is on the N10. In Labenne, head west on D126 signed Labenne Océan; site is on right in 4 km.

Charges 2004

Per unit incl. 2 persons, electricity	€ 12.00 - € 28.00
extra person (over 7 yrs)	€ 3.00 - € 6.00
dog	free - € 4.00

Reservations

Made with deposit (€ 130), fee (€ 30) and cancellation insurance (€ 16). Tel: 05 59 45 75 16. Email: camping@sylvamar.fr

Open

17 April - 25 September.

FR64010 Europ Camping

Ascarat, 64220 St Jean-Pied-de-Port (Pyrénées-Atlantiques)

Europ Camping is a neat and orderly, family run site with wonderful views of the vine-covered closer hills and the distant high Pyrénées. Each of the 93 pitches is clearly marked and separated by shrubs and all have electricity, water and drainage. The area is good for walking or mountain biking and there is rafting on a local river. The site is only 20 km. from the forest of Iraty with its lakes and ski-runs, and the Spanish border on the route de St Jacques-de-Compostelle, is 8 km.

Facilities

The central, modern and well appointed toilet block includes washbasins in cubicles and facilities for disabled visitors. Two washing machines, dryer. Laundry and dishwashing sinks (with excellent supply of hot water) outside, but all under cover. Motorcaravan service point. Small shop. Bar/restaurant with reasonably priced meal of the day and takeaway. Swimming pool with paddling pool and sauna. Play area. Volleyball and petanque. Barbecue area. Off site: St Jean-Pied-de-Port 2 km. Tennis near, fishing 200 m. Bicycle hire 2 km. Riding 10 km.

Directions

Site is 2 km. northwest of St Jean-Pied-de-Port in the hamlet of Ascarat and is signed from the D918 Bayonne road.

Charges 2004

Per person	€ 5.40
child (under 7 yrs)	€ 2.70
pitch and car	€ 7.50
electricity (6A)	€ 3.80
local tax	€ 0.25

Reservations

Made in writing with 30% deposit and € 21,34 fee. Tel: 05 59 37 12 78.

Open

Easter - 30 September.

At a glance

Welcome & Ambience	✓✓✓	Location	✓✓✓✓
Quality of Pitches	✓✓✓✓	Range of Facilities	✓✓✓✓

FR64060 Camping Le Pavillon Royal

Avenue du Prince de Galles, 64210 Bidart (Pyrénées-Atlantiques)

Le Pavillon Royal has an excellent situation on raised ground overlooking the sea, with good views along the coast to the south and to the north coast of Spain beyond. Beneath the site – and only a very short walk down – stretches a wide sandy beach. This is the Atlantic with its breakers and a central marked-out section of the beach is supervised by lifeguards (mid-June - 25 Sept). There is also a section with rocks and pools. If the sea is rough, the site has a large swimming pool and sunbathing area. The site is divided up into 303 marked, level pitches, many of a good size. Connected by asphalt roads, all have electricity and most are serviced with electricity, water and drainage. Much of the campsite is in full sun, although one area is shaded. Reservation in high season is advisable.

Facilities

The toilet blocks are of highest quality with mainly British style WCs, washbasins in cabins, sinks and baby baths and good units for disabled people, all thoroughly cleaned twice daily. Washing facilities are closed at night except for night units. Washing machines and dryers. Motorcaravan services. Well stocked shop (including gas). Restaurant with takeaway (all season). Swimming and paddling pools. Sauna. General room, TV room and games room with table tennis, also used for films. Fishing. Surf school. Dogs are not accepted. Barrier card with deposit (€ 20). Off site: Bicycle hire 3 km. Rding 1 km.

Directions

Don't go into Bidart as the site is on the Biarritz side. From the north, keep on main N10 bypassing Biarritz, then turn sharp back right on D911 (last possible road leading to Biarritz). After 600 m. turn left at camp sign (easy to miss). From A63 autoroute take C4 exit.

Charges 2003

Per unit incl. 2 persons, electricity and water	€ 23.00 - € 35.00
tent pitch incl. 1 or 2 persons	€ 17.00 - € 27.00
child (under 4 yrs)	€ 6.00 - € 6.50
local tax	€ 0.50

Reservations

Made for exact dates with deposit and fee. Tel: 05 59 23 00 54. Email: info@pavillon-royal.com

Open

15 May - 25 September.

At a glance

Welcome & Ambience	✓✓✓✓	Location	✓✓✓✓✓
Quality of Pitches	✓✓✓✓	Range of Facilities	✓✓✓✓✓

FR64090 Camping Airotel La Chêneraie

Chemin Cazenave, 64100 Bayonne (Pyrénées-Atlantiques)

La Chêneraie is only 8 km. from the coast at Anglet with its long sandy beach and large car park, but with the calm and tranquillity of this site you would think you were much further away from all the hustle and bustle of the coast. The distant views of the Pyrénées all add to the feeling of peace. The 210 pitches are arranged on neat grass, with most partially divided by trees and shrubs, so quite well shaded. Many have electricity connections, some with water and drainage. One area is very sloping but it has been terraced to give level pitches. Wooded walks lead to a small lake which can be used for inflatables or fishing (no swimming). A tour operator uses 20 pitches. English is spoken.

Facilities

The large, central sanitary block includes washbasins in cabins, with three smaller blocks around the site providing additional facilities. In high season these facilities may be under pressure and maintenance and cleaning could be variable. Dishwashing and laundry sinks. Washing machine and dryers, baby baths, and facilities for disabled people. Shop, restaurant with all day snacks and takeaway (all main season). Medium sized swimming pool open June - end August (longer if the weather is good). Playground. Tennis courts (free outside July/Aug). TV room. Table tennis. Off site: Bicycle hire 5 km. Riding 6 km. Golf 7 km.

At a glance

| Welcome & Ambience | ✓✓✓✓ | Location | ✓✓✓✓ |
| Quality of Pitches | ✓✓✓ | Range of Facilities | ✓✓✓✓ |

Directions

Site is 4 km. northeast of Bayonne just off main N117 road to Pau, signed at traffic lights. From new autoroute A63 take exit 6 marked 'Bayonne St Esprit'

Charges 2004

Per person	€ 3.70 - € 4.40
child (under 10 yrs)	€ 2.15 - € 2.75
pitch	€ 9.45 - € 11.43
with water and electricity	€ 13.75 - € 18.00
tent pitch	€ 7.65 - € 8.85
local tax	€ 0.20

Less 10-20% outside 1/6-1/9. No credit cards.

Reservations

Made for min. 1 week with deposit (€ 62) and fee (€ 15,24). Tel: 05 59 55 01 31.

Open

Easter - 30 September (full services 1/6-15/9).

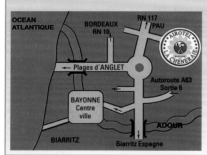

BAYONNE **Airotel La Chêneraie** ★★★★

Camping Caravaning
Tel. 0033 559 55 01 31
Fax: 0033 559 55 11 17
★
SWIMMING POOL ON SITE
Beaches only a few minutes'drive - Tennis
Archery - Entertainment - Fishing
Fully equipped
BUNGALOWS - CHALETS
MOBILHOMES for hire.
View of Pyrénées

FR64080 Camping Les Tamaris Plage

Quartier Acotz, 64500 St Jean-de-Luz (Pyrénées-Atlantiques)

This is a small, pleasant and well kept site. It is situated well outside the town but just across the road from a sandy beach with 79 numbered pitches, 45 with electricity, including some mobile homes and bungalows. They are of very good size and separated by hedges, on slightly sloping ground with some shade. It becomes full for nearly all July and August with families on long stays, so reservation then is advisable. There is no shop, but bread is available daily across the road.

Facilities

Single toilet block of superb quality and unusual design and should be ample provision for the site. Washbasins and showers in private cabins, mainly British style WCs, dishwashing sinks, facilities for disabled people and washing machine. New covered terrace with views of the sea. TV room for adults and children's room with TV and games. Playground. Off site: Fishing 30 m. Bicycle hire and golf 4 km. Riding 7 km.

At a glance

| Welcome & Ambience | ✓✓✓✓ | Location | ✓✓✓✓✓ |
| Quality of Pitches | ✓✓✓✓ | Range of Facilities | ✓✓✓ |

Directions

Proceed south on N10 and 1.5 km. after Guethary. Take first right (before access to the motorway and Carrefour centre) and follow camp signs.

Latest charges

Per unit (100 sq.m. pitch) incl.	
2 persons and electricity (5A)	€ 21.00 - € 27.50
tent pitch (80 sq.m.) incl.	
2 persons	€ 16.50 - € 23.00
extra person (over 2 yrs)	€ 3.50 - € 5.00
dog	€ 2.30

Reservations

Made with 20% deposit and fee (€ 18.30). Tel: 05 59 26 55 90. Email: tamaris1@clubinternet.fr

Open

1 April - 30 September.

FR64110 Camping du Col d'Ibardin

64122 Urrugne (Pyrénées-Atlantiques)

This family owned site at the foot of the Basque Pyrénées is highly recommended and deserves praise. It is well run with emphasis on personal attention, the smiling Madame, her staff and family ensuring that all are made welcome and is attractively set in the middle of an oak wood. Behind the forecourt, with its brightly coloured shrubs and modern reception area, various roadways lead to the 193 pitches. These are individual, spacious and enjoy the benefit of the shade (if preferred a more open aspect can be found). There are electricity hook-ups and adequate water points. From this site you can enjoy the mountain scenery, be on the beach at Socoa within minutes or cross the border into Spain approximately 14 km. down the road. Used by tour operators (20 pitches).

Facilities

Two toilet blocks, one rebuilt to a high specification, are kept very clean. WC for disabled people. Dishwashing facilities in separate open areas. Laundry unit with washing machine and dryer. Motorcaravan service point. Small shop selling basic foodstuffs and gas, with orders taken for bread (1/5-15/9). Catering and takeaway service in July/Aug. Bar and occasional evening entertainment which includes Flamenco dancing. Swimming pool and paddling pool. Children's playground and club with adult supervision. Tennis courts, boules, table tennis, video games. Bicycle hire. Off site: Fishing 5 km. Riding 2 km. Golf 7 km. Large supermarket and shopping centre 5 km.

At a glance

Welcome & Ambience	✓✓✓✓	Location	✓✓✓✓
Quality of Pitches	✓✓✓✓	Range of Facilities	✓✓✓✓

Directions

Leave A63 autoroute at St Jean-de-Luz sud, exit no. 2 and join the RN10 in the direction of Urrugne. Turn left at roundabout (signed Col d'Ibardin) on the D4 and site is on right after 5 km. Do not turn off to the Col itself, but carry on towards Ascain.

Latest charges

Per unit incl. 2 persons	€ 12.00 - € 18.00
extra adult	€ 2.60 - € 4.00
child (2-7 yrs)	€ 1.55 - € 2.50
electricity (4/10A)	€ 2.75 - € 4.85
animal	€ 1.00 - € 1.60
local tax	€ 0.25

No credit cards.

Reservations

Are accepted - contact site. Tel: 05 59 54 31 21. Email: info@col-ibardin.com

Open

1 April - 30 September.

Camping Caravaning
Du Col D'Ibardin

Open 01 April – 30 September
Swimming pool ● Tennis ● Bar ● Children's Pool and Club
Launderette ● Hot Water ● Snacks ● Playground ● Bicycle Hire
● Little farm with animals for children
● Mobil-homes to rent

Tel: (0033) (0)559.54.31.21
Fax: (0033) (0)559.54.62.28
Site: www.col-ibardin.com
E-mail: info@col-ibardin.com

64122 URRUGNE
PAYS BASQUE

FR64040 Camping Des Gaves

64440 Laruns (Pyrénées-Atlantiques)

Des Gaves is a clean, small and well managed site, open all year, with very friendly owners and staff. It is set high in Pyrennean walking country on one of the routes to Spain. Laruns is only 25 km. from the Spanish border. There are 101 pitches including 50 level touring pitches of which 38 are fully serviced, numbered and separated (the remainder are used for seasonal units). The river runs alongside the site (well fenced) and fishing is possible. There are also five delightful wooden chalets to rent.

Facilities

The very clean toilet block has been refurbished, can be heated in cool weather and has modern fittings. Washbasins for ladies in curtained cubicles and one shower in ladies' suitable for showering children. Dishwashing and laundry sinks. Laundry room. No shop but baker calls daily (July/Aug). Small bar with large screen TV, pool and video games (July/Aug). Larger bar with table tennis tables. Small play area. Boules. Volleyball. Fishing. Card operated barrier (€ 20 deposit). Off site: Bicycle hire 800 m.

At a glance

| Welcome & Ambience | ✓✓✓✓ | Location | ✓✓✓✓ |
| Quality of Pitches | ✓✓✓✓ | Range of Facilities | ✓✓✓✓ |

Directions

Take N134 from Pau towards Olorons and branch left on D934 at Gan. Follow to Laruns and just after town, turn left following signs to site.

Charges 2003

Per person	€ 2.90 - € 3.51
child (under 10 yrs)	€ 1.83 - € 2.29
pitch with electricity (3-10A)	€ 6.86 - € 13.11

Reservations

Advised for July/Aug. and winter sports season. Tel: 05 59 05 32 37. Email: campingdesgraves@wanadoo.fr

Open

All year.

FR64230M Camping Municipal de Mosqueros

64270 Salies de Bearn (Pyrénées-Atlantiques)

In scenic surroundings convenient for the A64, this three star municipal site is worthy of its grading and is attractively located in a parkland one km. from the pretty little town of Salies de Béarn. It has an immaculate appearance, welcoming wardens and very clean facilities. Tarmac roads lead from the entrance barrier (locked at night), past reception to spacious, numbered pitches. Most have electricity, many have water connections and all are separated by tall shrubs and hedges giving privacy. Salies de Béarn, with its old houses overhanging the river and its thermal baths, is only minutes away.

Facilities

The fully equipped toilet block is in a central position and maintained to a high standard. Dishwashing and laundry area with sinks, washing machine, dryer and iron. TV and recreation room. Swimming pool. Off site: Tennis court next to site. Golf and riding 2 km.

At a glance

| Welcome & Ambience | ✓✓✓✓ | Location | ✓✓✓✓ |
| Quality of Pitches | ✓✓✓✓ | Range of Facilities | ✓✓✓ |

Directions

Site is well signed in the town and is on the D17 Bayonne road, west of the town.

Latest charges

Per person	€ 2.45
child (1-7 yrs)	€ 1.50
caravan pitch with electricity (10A)	€ 7.40

Reservations

Advisable for July/Aug. Contact site. Tel: 05 59 38 12 94.

Open

15 March - 15 October.

FR64210M Camping Municipal Chibaou-Berria

64500 St Jean-de-Luz (Pyrénées-Atlantiques)

The first impression of this large site beside the beach is one of neatness. From the entrance tarmac roads lead to spacious pitches which are divided by hedges with plenty of room for awnings. Pitches to the left hand side beyond reception are placed at different levels, whilst those to the right have a sea view. There are 221 pitches in all, all with electrical hook-ups. There is direct access to the beach for surfing and windsurfing. Nearby are discos, tennis courts and often Basque folk festivities.

Facilities

Toilet facilities, spotlessly clean when visited, include some showers with washbasins and individual wash cabins. Toilets are a mix of British and Turkish style. Dishwashing sinks in open position. Laundry facilities including washing machines and ironing room.

At a glance

| Welcome & Ambience | ✓✓✓✓ | Location | ✓✓✓✓ |
| Quality of Pitches | ✓✓✓✓ | Range of Facilities | ✓✓✓ |

Directions

From A63 autoroute (St Jean de Luz Nord) take N10 towards Bayonne, then take second left signed Acotz Campings. Site signed in about 1 km. From north, 1.5 km. after Geutherey on N10 take right at Carrefour supermarché, signed 'Plages'.

Latest charges

Per person	€ 4.90
child (under 10 yrs)	€ 2.70 - € 2.80
pitch with electricity	€ 7.80
Local tax incl.	

Reservations

Contact site. Tel: 05 59 26 11 94.

Open

1 June - 15 September.

FR64070 Camping Le Ruisseau

Route d'Arbonne, 64210 Bidart (Pyrénées-Atlantiques)

This pleasant, busy site, just behind the coast, is about 2 km. from Bidart and 2.5 km. from a sandy beach. It has two swimming pools – one 1,100 sq.m. pool complex with slides on the main site and an indoor heated pool on the newer area opposite. There is also a little lake, where boating is possible, in the area at the bottom of the site which has a very pleasant open aspect and now includes a large play area. Pitches on the main campsite are individual, marked and of a good size, either on flat terraces or around the lake. The terrain is wooded so the great majority of them have some shade. There are 330 here with a further 110 on a second area where shade has developed and which has its own good toilet block. Electrical connections are available throughout. Animation is provided in the main season, with organised day-time sports and evening entertainment nightly in season. The site is popular with tour operators and the site has a number of its own mobile homes.

Facilities

Toilet facilities (unisex) consist of two main blocks and some extra smaller units. With washbasins in cabins, they are regularly refurbished and maintained. Washing machines. Shop. Large self-service restaurant with takeaway and separate bar with terraces, and TV. Outdoor swimming pools and indoor pool. Sauna and solarium. Large play area. Two tennis courts (free outside July/Aug). Volleyball, table tennis. Fitness track. TV and games rooms. Minigolf. Fitness room. Bicycle hire. Surf board hire. Off site: Riding and golf 2 km.

At a glance

Welcome & Ambience	✓✓✓✓	Location	✓✓✓✓
Quality of Pitches	✓✓✓	Range of Facilities	✓✓✓✓✓

Directions

Site is east of Bidart on a minor road towards Arbonne. From A63 autoroute take Biarritz exit (4), turn towards St Jean-de-Luz and Bidart on N10. At second roundabout, turn left and follow camp signs for 1.5 km.

Charges 2004

Per unit incl. 2 persons	€ 15.00 - € 23.00
extra person	€ 4.30 - € 5.35
child (under 7 yrs)	€ 2.15 - € 3.00
electricity	€ 2.90 - € 3.80
dog	free - € 1.50
local tax	€ 0.50

Reservations

Made for exact dates, for min. a week or so in main season, with deposit (€ 53,36), fee (€ 9,45) and cancellation insurance (€ 2,74). Tel: 05 59 41 94 50. Email: francoise.dumont3@wanadoo.fr

Open

15 May - 12 September, with all amenities.

FR64140 Sunêlia Bérrua

Rue Berrua, 64210 Bidart (Pyrénées-Atlantiques)

Berrua Village Camping, set only one kilometre from the sea, is an ideal location for visiting the beaches here in southwest France. A neat and tidy site, it has 270 level pitches (120 for touring units) set amongst trees. Most have electricity and some are fully serviced. The swimming pool is a little on the plain side but has sunbeds for sunbathing and a paddling pool. There is some animation organ-ised in high season for both adults and children, for example guided walks, dances, sporting competi-tions, bingo and karaoke. A member of the Sunêlia group.

Facilities

Toilet facilities are good (unisex) consisting of two blocks with washbasins in cabins, baby rooms, facilities for disabled visitors, washing machines and dishwashing sinks (cold water only). Motorcaravan service point. Shop (July/Aug). Bar/restaurant and takeaway (15/4-15/9). Swimming pool. Games room. Play area (3-10yrs only). Bicycle hire. Archery and boule. Off site: Fishing 1 km. Golf and riding 3 km.

At a glance

Welcome & Ambience	✓✓✓✓	Location	✓✓✓✓
Quality of Pitches	✓✓✓✓	Range of Facilities	✓✓✓✓✓

Directions

From A63 exit 4, take N10 south towards St Bidart. At roundabout after the 'Intermarche' turn left. Site is on the left after 800m (well signed).

Charges 2003

Per unit incl. 2 persons	€ 13.50 - € 22.50
extra person	€ 2.80 - € 5.00
child (2-10 yrs)	€ 1.90 - € 3.00
electricity (6A)	€ 2.50 - € 3.80
animal	free - € 3.00
Camping Cheques accepted.	

Reservations

Contact site. Tel: 05 59 54 96 66. Email: contact@berrua.com

Open

6 April - 5 October.

213

Map 11

The Dordogne is a historical region of great beauty, full of pretty golden-stoned villages and ancient castles. Home to delicacies such as foie gras, truffles and walnuts, plus Roquefort cheese and Cognac, it is one of the gastronomic centres of France.

We have used départements from these official regions to form 'The Dordogne'.
Aquitaine: 24 Dordogne, 47 Lot-et-Garonne
Midi-Pyrénées: 12 Aveyron, 46 Lot
Poitou-Charentes: 16 Charente

The Dordogne's history goes back many thousands of years when man lived in the caves of Périgord and left cave paintings at sites such as Les Eyzies and Lascaux. Aquitaine was ruled by the English for 300 years following the marriage of Eleanor of Aquitaine to Henry Plantagenet, who became King of England in 1154.

The villages and castles of the area bear evidence of the resulting conflict between the French and English, and today add charm and character to the countryside. Monpazier is the best example of the 'bastides' (fortified towns) and is set in a diverse region of mountains, vineyards, and fertile river valleys. The rolling grass-lands and dense forests include the beautiful valleys of the Dordogne and Vézère.

South of the cultivated fields and cliff-side villages beside the river Lot lie the higher, stony lands of the Quercy Causse and the rocky gorges of the Rivers Aveyron and Tarn. Centred around Millau, there are tortuous gorges and valleys, spectacular rivers, underground caves and grottes, and thickly forested mountains.

Cuisine of the region

Local specialities include the fish dishes: carp stuffed with foie gras, mullet in red wine and *besugo* (sea bream), plus *cagouilles* (snails from Charentes)

Cassoulet: a hearty stew of duck, sausages and beans

Cèpes: fine, delicate mushrooms; sometimes dried

Chou farci: stuffed cabbage, sometimes aux marrons (with chestnuts)

Confit de Canard (d'oie): preserved duck meat

Foie Gras: specially prepared livers of geese and ducks, seasoned and stuffed with truffles

Magret de canard: duck breast fillets

Mouclade: mussels cooked in wine, egg yolks and cream, served with Pineau des Charentes

Places of interest

Agen: rich agricultural area, famous for its prunes

Angoulême: Hill-top town surrouded by ramparts, cathedral, Renaissance château

Cognac: the most celebrated *eau de vie* in the world, cellars, Valois Castle

Cordes: medieval walled hilltop village

Monflanquin: well preserved fortified village

Rocamadour: cliffside medieval pilgrimage site

Saint Cirq-La Popie: medieval village perched on a cliff

Sarlat: Saturday market

Alan Rogers tip

LEARN HOW TO COOK THE REGION'S SPECIALITIES AT ONE OF THE MANY COOKERY COURSES OPEN TO VISITORS. ASK THE LOCAL TOURIST OFFICE FOR DETAILS.

FR12150 Camping Marmotel

12130 St Geniez-d'Olt (Aveyron)

The road into Marmotel passes various industrial buildings and is a little off-putting – persevere, they are soon left behind. The campsite itself is a mixture of old and new. The old part provides many pitches with lots of shade and separated by hedges. The new area is sunny until the trees grow. These pitches each have a personal sanitary unit, with shower, WC, washbasin and dishwashing. New and very well designed, they are reasonably priced for such luxury. All pitches have electricity. A lovely new restaurant with terrace overlooks new heated swimming and paddling pools which have fountains, a toboggan and sun beds on either grass or the tiled surrounds. The bar/reception area is also new with comfortable seating and internet access.

Facilities
Good sanitary facilities include baby baths and facilities for disabled visitors. Washing machines. Bar/restaurant and takeaway (all season). Swimming pools. Fishing. Bicycle hire. Tennis. Small play area. Entertainment for all ages in July/Aug. including a disco below the bar, cinema screen, karaoke, dances and a mini club for 4-10 yr olds. Off site: Large supermarket 500 m. Riding 500 m. Bicycle tours and canoe trips on the Lot and rafting on the Tarn are organised.

At a glance
Welcome & Ambience	✓✓✓✓	Location	✓✓✓✓
Quality of Pitches	✓✓✓	Range of Facilities	✓✓✓✓

Directions
Heading south on A75 (free) take exit 40 and signs for St Geniez d'Olt. Site is at west end of village, signed onto D19 to Prades d'Aubrac, then 500 m. on left.

Charges 2004
Per unit incl. 1 or 2 persons, 10A electricity	€ 16.50 - € 28.00
child under 3 yrs	€ 2.00 - € 3.00
animal	€ 1.00 - € 1.50
Less 30% outside July/Aug.	

Reservations
Made with deposit (€ 100) and fee (€ 15).
Tel: 05 65 70 46 51. Email: info@marmotel.com

Open
1 May - 19 September.

FR12120 Camping du Rouergue

Avenue de Fondiès, 12200 Villefranche-de-Rouergue (Aveyron)

A spacious, well appointed and shady site in the Vallée de L'Aveyron, Camping du Rouergue is next to the municipal sports facilities and run by the Rouergue Tourisme Service. The site has 98 grassy individual pitches of varying sizes, served by tarmac roads, and virtually all serviced with electricity, water and waste water drain. There are reduced rates for campers at the municipal swimming pool and shops and restaurants are within walking distance along the riverside foot and cycle path. Villefranche-de-Rouergue is one of the larger bastide towns of the region and is on the pilgrim route to Santiago de Compostela. The site is also ideally placed for exploring the many other historical bastides of the Rouergue and Aveyron.

Facilities
The modern spacious sanitary unit includes mainly washbasins in cubicles, dishwashing and laundry sinks and facilities for baby changing and for disabled persons. With two identical sections to the block, only one is open during low season. Motorcaravan service point outside campsite entrance. TV room. Well equipped children's playground.

At a glance
Welcome & Ambience	✓✓✓✓	Location	✓✓✓✓
Quality of Pitches	✓✓✓✓	Range of Facilities	✓✓✓

Directions
Villefranche de Rouergue is about midway between Cahors and Rodez. Site is 1 km. southwest of town on D47 towards Monteils, follow signs from D911 to campsite and 'stade'.

Charges 2003
Per pitch incl. 2 persons	€ 10.50 - € 13.50
child (4-10 yrs)	€ 1.50
electricity (16A)	€ 2.50

Reservations
Advisable for high season, made with 20% deposit.
Tel: 05 65 45 16 24. Email: infos@villefranche.com

Open
20 April - 30 September.

FR12040 Camping Les Tours

12460 St Amans-des-Cots (Aveyron)

This is an impressive campsite set in beautiful countryside very close to the Truyère Gorges, Upper Lot valley and the Aubrac Plateau. Efficiently run, it is situated on the shores of the Lac de la Selves providing 275 pitches. Of around 100 sq.m. and with electrical connections, some border the lake, the rest are terraced and hedged with views of the lake. About 100 pitches also have individual water points. The site has a spacious feel, enhanced by the thoughtfully planned terraced layout, and seemed to be in an excellent state of repair and very clean. The owner and his staff are friendly and helpful. Used by tour operators (70 pitches). There is some up and down walking to the facilities, especially from the upper terraces.

Facilities

Four good toilet blocks including two excellent new ones, one of an unusual round design, are fully equipped including individual washing cubicles and are more than adequate for number of campers. Attractive central complex housing the amenities. Restaurant, bar. Swimming pools (650 and 40 sq.m.). Shop (with gas), Takeaway. Modern play area. Volleyball, tennis courts, football area and table tennis under cover. Varied programme of daytime and evening activities, with mini-club, archery and tree climbing (all supervised). Lake activities include canoeing, pedaloes, windsurfing, water ski-ing and provision for launching small boats. Internet terminal. Off site: Riding and golf 8 km.

At a glance

Welcome & Ambience	✓✓✓✓	Location	✓✓✓✓✓
Quality of Pitches	✓✓✓✓	Range of Facilities	✓✓✓✓✓

Directions

Take D34 from Entraygues-sur-Truyère to St Amans-des-Cots (14 km.). In St Amans take the D97 to Colombez and then the D599 to Lac de la Selves (site is signed). Site is 5 km. from St Amans. Alternatively, if using autoroute A75, take St Flour exit and follow D921 south for 41 km. Go 1.5 km. past Lacalm and turn right on D34 signed St Amans-des-Cots. Follow signs for 23 km.

Charges 2004

Per unit incl. 2 persons	€ 20.80 - € 26.50
extra person	€ 4.40 - € 5.50
child (under 7 yrs)	€ 3.00 - € 3.80
electricity (6A)	€ 2.40 -€ 3.00

Less 10-20% outside July/Aug.

Reservations

Made and are advisable for July/Aug. - write for details. Tel: 05 65 44 88 10.
Email: camping-les-tours@wanadoo.fr

Open

22 May - 5 September.

FR1210M Camping Municipal du Lauradiol

12460 Campouriez (Aveyron)

A strikingly neat and pretty little site, tucked into a wooded gorge in the Aveyron hills, Lauradiol is alongside the La Selves river (fishing possible), 500 m. from the Cambeyra barrage. The 34 pitches, 21 with electricity, are arranged on flat grass, neatly separated by trim hedges. Many are quite large, although those actually along the river bank are somewhat smaller. There is quite good shade from a variety of trees. Surprisingly for such a small site, there is even a swimming pool, plus paddling pool, and a well kept tennis court – both free to campers. There is not much else by way of facilities, but there are several villages within 5 or 6 km. for restaurants, shopping, etc.

Facilities

The toilet block was recently refurbished and very clean when inspected. It includes washbasins in private cabins and a room for disabled visitors (WC, basin and shower). Swimming pool. Tennis

At a glance

Welcome & Ambience	✓✓✓	Location	✓✓✓✓
Quality of Pitches	✓✓✓✓	Range of Facilities	✓✓✓✓

Directions

Site is between Entraygues sur Truyère and Campouriez on the D34 at the hamlet of Lauradiol, about 5 km. from Entraygues. Site entrance is by the river bridge at junction of D34 and D572.

Charges 2003

Per caravan incl. electricity and 3 or 4 persons	€ 14.50
tent incl. 1 or 2 persons	€ 10.00

No credit cards.

Reservations

Advised for July/Aug. Write or phone La Mairie de Campouriez. Tel: 05 65 44 53 95.

Open

20 June - 10 September.

FR12050 Camping Les Terrasses du Lac

Route du Vibal, 12290 Pont-de-Salars (Aveyron)

At an altitude of some 2,000 ft. on the plateau of Le Lévézou, this outlying site enjoys attractive views over Lac de Pont de Salars. The site seems largely undiscovered by the British, perhaps as it is only open for a short season. A terraced site, it provides 180 good sized, level pitches, 130 for touring, with or without shade, all with electricity. Some pitches have good views over the lake which has direct access from the site at two places – one for pedestrians and swimmers, the other for cars and trailers for launching small boats. This site is well placed for excursions into the Gorges du Tarn, Caves du Roquefort and nearby historic towns and villages. Although there are good facilities for disabled visitors, the terracing on the site may prove difficult.

Facilities

Four toilet blocks of varying ages include some washbasins in private cabins, plus dishwashing areas under cover and laundry facilities. Fridge hire. Shop. Large bar/restaurant with a lively French ambience serving full meals in high season and snacks at other times, with takeaway in high season (all 1/7-31/8). Heated swimming pool (200 sq.m.) and children's pool (1/6-30/9). Solarium. Playground. Volleyball, pétanque, table tennis, billiards. Games and TV rooms. Entertainment and activities organised in high season. Barbecue area. Off site: Tennis 3 km. Riding 5 km. Golf 20 km.

At a glance

| Welcome & Ambience | ✓✓✓✓✓ | Location | ✓✓✓✓ |
| Quality of Pitches | ✓✓✓✓ | Range of Facilities | ✓✓✓✓ |

Directions

Using D911 Millau - Rodez road, turn north at Pont de Salars towards the lake on the D523. Follow camp signs. Ignore first site and continue following lake until Les Terraces (approx. 5-6 km).

Charges 2003

Per pitch incl. 2 persons	€ 11.00 - € 18.00
child (2-7 yrs)	€ 3.00
electricity (6A)	€ 3.30 - € 4.50

Reservations

Made with deposit (€ 61) and fee (€ 15,24). Tel: 05 65 46 88 18. Email: terrasses12@aol.com

Open

1 June - 30 September.

In overhanging of the lake, discover an exceptional place for your relaxation and your escape. Chalets and Mobile homes to rent. A 200 m² heated swimming pool. Free activities

LES TERRASSES DU LAC ★★★★

Route de Vibal 12 290 PONT DE SALARS
Tel : 0033 565 46 88 18
Fax : 0033 565 46 85 38
w w w . t e r r a s s e s . f r . s t
T E R R A S S E S 1 2 @ a o l . c o m

FR12070 Camping La Grange de Monteillac

12310 Séverac-l'Eglise (Aveyron)

La Grange de Monteillac is a modern, well equipped site in the beautiful, well preserved small village of Sévérac L'Église. A spacious site, it provides 105 individual pitches, 70 for touring, on gently sloping grass, separated by flowering shrubs and young trees offering little shade. All pitches have access to electricity (6A, long leads may be required), water and drains. They include 35 chalets, mobile homes and tents for rent in separate areas. The friendly owner and his welcoming staff will advise about the visits to a château evening with candlelight banquet, an angora farm, and a local pottery that are run weekly in main season. An evening stroll around this delightful village is a must, and Sévérac Le Château (21 km) and the many other pretty towns and villages should satisfy all needs.

Facilities

The toilet block is modern, spacious and clean, with all washbasins in cubicles. Facilities for babies and disabled people. Dishwashing and laundry sinks. Washing machine and dryer. Shop at reception (1/7-31/8). Poolside restaurant/snack-bar serving pizzas, grills etc. and takeaway in high season. Music or groups feature in the bar (July-Aug). Two swimming pools (1/6-15/9). Pool/bar/restaurant/music room some way from touring area. Large well equipped playground plus plenty of grassy space for ball games. Organised Children's club, bicycle hire and archery lessons. Off site: Shops in village 1.5 km. Fishing 2 km. Riding 9 km.

At a glance

| Welcome & Ambience | ✓✓✓ | Location | ✓✓✓✓ |
| Quality of Pitches | ✓✓✓ | Range of Facilities | ✓✓✓✓ |

Directions

Site is on the edge of Sévérac L'Église village, just off N88 Rodez - Sévérac Le Château road. From A75 use exit 42.

Charges 2003

Per unit incl. 2 persons and electricity	€ 20.00
extra person	€ 3.50
child (under 7 yrs)	€ 2.80
dog	€ 1.30

Less 30% outside July/Aug.

Reservations

Contact site. Tel: 05 65 70 21 00. Email: info@la-grange-de-monteillac.com

Open

1 May - 15 September.

FR12010 Camping Val de Cantobre

12230 Nant-d'Aveyron (Aveyron)

This pleasant terraced site has been imaginatively and tastefully developed by the Dupond family over a 25 year period. In particular, the magnificent carved features in the bar create a delightful ambience, complemented by a recently built terrace. True, the ground is hard in summer but reception staff supply robust nails if your awning pegs prove a problem. Most of the 200 pitches (all with electricity and water) are peaceful, generous in size and blessed with views of the valley. The pools have a new surround, bedecked by flowers and crowned by a large urn which dispenses water into the paddling pool. But it is the activity programme that is unique at Val de Cantobre, supervised by qualified instructors, some arranged by the owners and some at a fair distance from the site. Passive recreationists appreciate the scenery, especially Cantobre, a medieval village that clings to a cliff in view of the site. Nature lovers will be delighted to see the vultures wheeling in the Tarn gorge alongside more humble rural residents. Butterflies in profusion, orchids, huge edible snails, glow worms, families of beavers and the natterjack toad all live here. It is easy to see why – the place is magnificent. Although tour operators occupy around 40% of the pitches, the terrace design provides some peace and privacy, especially on the upper levels and a warm welcome awaits from the Dupond family.

Facilities

The fully equipped impressive toilet block is beautifully appointed with a huge indoor dishwashing area. Shop, although small, offers a wide variety of provisions; including many regional specialities (comparing well with local shops and markets). Attractive new bar, restaurant, pizzeria and takeaway facility. Some steepish up and down walking from furthest pitches to some facilities). Three adjoining swimming pools. Around 15 types of activity including river rafting, white water canoeing, rock climbing or jumps from Millau's hill tops on twin seater steerable parachutes. All weather sports pitch. Fishing. Torch useful.

At a glance

| Welcome & Ambience | ✓✓✓✓✓ | Location | ✓✓✓✓✓ |
| Quality of Pitches | ✓✓✓✓ | Range of Facilities | ✓✓✓✓ |

Directions

Site is 4 km. north of Nant, on D991 road to Millau. From Millau direction take D991 signed Gorge du Dourbie.

Charges 2004

Per unit incl. 2 persons and 4A electricity	€ 19.00 - € 29.00
extra person (4 yrs and over)	€ 4.00 - € 7.00
dog	free - € 2.00

Camping Cheques accepted.

Reservations

Made for any length with 25% deposit, fee (€ 18,29) and optional cancellation insurance. Tel: 05 65 58 43 00. Email: info@valdecantobre.com

Open

18 May - 15 September, with all facilities.

FR12170 Sunêlia Le Caussanel

12290 Canet de Salars (Aveyron)

This large, extremely spacious site on the banks of Lac de Pareloup is greatly improved. It is ideal, in low season, for those seeking a tranquil holiday in a beautiful region of France or in high season, for those seeking an active holiday. It has 235 large, fairly level, grassy pitches, with 169 for touring. Most have 6A electricity (a few have 10A) but very long leads may be necessary, and 33 have water and a drain. The pitches are defined by a tree or boulder in each corner and offer little privacy but many have wonderful views over the lake. Most pitches have little shade with only a few having good shade. Although the pool and paddling pool behind reception are quite small, the adjacent lake offers a large area, 1 km. long, for swimming and all the usual watersports. One tour operator takes 20 pitches.

Facilities

Five well cleaned, modern toilet blocks have all the necessary facilities. Motorcaravan service point (€ 3) at entrance. Shop (limited hours in low season). Bar. Restaurant and takeaway (July/Aug). Swimming pool and paddling pool (from June). Very large play area. Boules. Tennis. Football. Volleyball. Large room for table tennis. TV room and clubhouse. Extensive programme of family events (July/Aug). Fishing. Bicycle hire (July/Aug). Motor boat launching. Various water sports (July/Aug) and swimming in adjacent lake. Internet access. Off site: Cycle and footpaths around the lake. Many other marked walks and cycle rides. Shops, banks, restaurants, etc. 8 km. Riding 10 km. Golf 30 km. Canoeing, rafting, paragliding and windsurfing.

At a glance

| Welcome & Ambience | ✓✓✓✓ | Location | ✓✓✓✓ |
| Quality of Pitches | ✓✓✓✓ | Range of Facilities | ✓✓✓✓✓ |

Directions

From D911 Rodez - Millau road, just east of Pont de Sellars, turn south on D993 signed Salles-Curan. In about 6 km. at crossroads turn right on D538 signed Le Caussanel. Very shortly turn left and carry straight on to site.

Charges 2003

Per unit incl. 2 persons	€ 11.50 - € 19.20
extra person	€ 4.40 - € 5.10
child (2-7 yrs)	€ 3.20 - € 3.70
electricity	€ 2.80
water and drain	€ 2.20

Reservations

Essential in high season, made with deposit (€ 90) and fee (€ 10). Tel: 05 65 46 85 19. Email: lecaussanel@wanadoo.fr

Open

28 June - 30 August.

FR12020 Camping Caravaning Les Rivages

Avenue de l'Aigoual, route de Nant, 12100 Millau (Aveyron)

Les Rivages is a large site on the outskirts of the town. It is well organised and well situated, being close to the high limestone Causses and the dramatic gorges of the Tarn and Dourbie, the latter of which runs past the back of the site. Smaller pitches, used for tents and small units, abut a pleasant riverside space suitable for sunbathing, fishing or picnics. Most of the 314 pitches are large, 100 sq.m. or more, and well shaded. A newer part of the site (on the right as you enter) has less shade but pitches are larger. All pitches have electricity, and 100 have water and drainage. The site offers a very wide range of sporting activities close to 30 in all (see facilities). Millau is a bustling and pleasant town. Don't miss the night markets, but don't eat before you get there – there are thousands of things to taste, many of them grilled or spit roasted. The gates are shut 10 pm. - 8 am, with night-watchman.

Facilities

Four well kept modern toilet blocks have all necessary facilities. A special block for children includes baby baths, small showers, children's toilets as well as ironing facilities. Shop for most essentials (20/5-15/9). Terrace restaurant and bar overlooking a good-sized main swimming pool and children's pool (from 10/5). Play area. Much evening entertainment, largely for children, along with child-minding and a mini-club. Tennis (indoor and outdoor). Squash (can be viewed from the bar). Table tennis. Floodlit petanque. Many river activities, walking, bird watching and fishing. Off site: Rafting and canoeing arranged. Bicycle hire 1 km, riding 10 km, golf 40 km. Hypermarket in Millau.

At a glance

Welcome & Ambience	✓✓✓✓✓	Location	✓✓✓✓✓
Quality of Pitches	✓✓✓✓	Range of Facilities	✓✓✓✓

Directions

From Millau, take D991 road south towards Nant. Site is about 400 m. on the right.

Charges 2004

Per pitch incl. 2 persons	€ 15.50 - € 24.00
with electricity (6A)	€ 15.50 - € 24.00
with water and drainage	€ 17.50 - € 26.00
extra person (over 3 yrs)	€ 3.00 - € 4.50
pet	free - € 3.00
local tax (15/6-15/9)	€ 0.30

Reservations

Advisable for July/Aug. with deposit (€ 61) and fee} (€ 15,24). Tel: 05 65 61 01 07.
Email: campinglesrivages@wanadoo.fr

Open

1 May - 30 September.

Airotel Les Rivages ★★★★
camping • caravaning • mobil-home • tentes

GORGES DU TARN • MILLAU • AVEYRON
Avenue de l'Aigoual - 12100 MILLAU - France
Tél. 00 33 (0)5 65 61 01 07 • Fax 00 33 (0)5 65 59 03 56

www.campinglesrivages.com
e-mail : campinglesrivages@wanadoo.fr

FR12000 Camping Caravaning de Peyrelade

Route des Gorges du Tarn, 12640 Rivière-sur-Tarn (Aveyron)

Situated at the foot of the Tarn gorges on the banks of the river, this attractive site is dominated by the ruins of the Château de Peyrelade. Bathing from the pebble beach is safe and the water is clean. The 130 touring pitches are terraced, level and shady with electricity hook-ups (long leads may be required for riverside pitches) and nearby water points. The site is ideally placed for visiting the Tarn, Jonte and Dourbie gorges, and centres for rafting and canoeing are a short drive up the river. Other nearby attractions include the Caves of Aven Armand, the Chaos de Montpellier, Roquefort (of cheese fame) and the pleasant town of Millau. Many of the roads along and between the Gorges are breath-taking for passengers, but scary for drivers who don't like looking down!

Facilities

The two toilet blocks have been refurbished. Young children are catered for, also people with disabilities. Washing machines and dryer. Bar, restaurant, pizzeria and takeaway services (all from 1/6). Children's paddling pool and attractively designed swimming pool (proper swimming trunks, no shorts). Good playground. Games room and mini-club. Fishing. Off site: Bicycle hire 100 m, riding 3 km. Facilities in the adjacent leisure centre can be booked at reception at reduced charges. Millau nearby with hypermarket, shops and night markets but note road to/from Millau can be jammed at peak hours.

At a glance

Welcome & Ambience	✓✓✓✓	Location	✓✓✓✓
Quality of Pitches	✓✓✓✓	Range of Facilities	✓✓✓✓

Directions

Take autoroute A75 to Séverac. From N9 Séverac - Millau road, turn east from Aguessac on D907 (follow Gorges du Tarn signs). Site is 2 km. past Rivière sur Tarn, on the right - the access road is quite steep.

Latest Charges

Per unit incl. 2 persons	€ 13.00 - € 18.00
extra person	€ 3.00 - € 4.00
child (under 5 yrs)	€ 2.00 - € 2.50
dog	€ 1.50
electricity (6A)	€ 3.00
local tax	€ 0.15

Reservations

Made with deposit (€ 70) and fee (€ 15,24).
Tel: 05 65 62 62 54.
Email: campingpeyrelade@wanadoo.fr

Open

15 May - 15 September.

FR12080 Camping Club Les Genêts

Lac de Pareloup, 12410 Salles Curan (Aveyron)

This family run site is on the shores of Lac de Pareloup and offers both family holiday and watersports facilities. The 162 pitches include 102 grassy, mostly individual pitches for touring units. These are in two areas, one on each side of the entrance lane, and are divided by hedges, shrubs and trees. Most have electricity and many also have water and waste water drain. The site slopes gently down to the beach and lake with facilities for all watersports including waterskiing. A full animation and activities programme is organised in high season, and there is much to see and do in this very attractive corner of Aveyron. Used by tour operators (40 pitches). A 'Sites et Paysages' member.

Facilities

Two main sanitary units include washbasins in cubicles and a suite for disabled people. Refurbishment of the older unit is planned, whilst the other unit is new. Baby room. Dishwashing and laundry sinks. Laundry room. Very well stocked shop. Bar and restaurant. Snack bar serving pizzas and other snacks in main season. Swimming pool and spa pool (both 1/6-15/9; unsupervised). Playground. Minigolf, volleyball and boules. Bicycle hire. Red Indian style tee-pees. Hire of pedaloes, windsurfers and kayaks. Fishing licences available.

At a glance

Welcome & Ambience	✓✓✓✓	Location	✓✓✓✓
Quality of Pitches	✓✓✓	Range of Facilities	✓✓✓✓✓

Directions

From Salles-Curan take D577 for about 4 km. and turn right into a narrow lane immediately after a sharp right hand bend. Site is signed at junction.

Charges 2003

Per unit incl. 1 or 2 persons and 6A electricity	€ 11.00 - € 26.00
lakeside pitch	€ 11.00 - € 34.00
extra person	€ 4.00 - € 6.00
child (under 2 yrs)	free
pet	€ 3.00 - € 4.00

Plus local tax. Refundable deposits for barrier card € 20 and for pool bracelet € 8 per person.

Reservations

Advised for July/Aug. and made with deposit (€ 155) and fee (€ 29). Tel: 05 65 46 35 34.
Email: contact@camping-les-genets.fr

Open

25 May - 15 September.

FR16050M Camping Municipal de Cognac

Boulevard de Châtenay, route de Ste Sévère, 16100 Cognac (Charente)

If you are a lover of brandy this area is a must, with abundant vineyards and little roadside chalets offering tastings of Pineau (a Cognac based aperitif) and a vast range of Cognacs. This municipal site by the Charente river is convenient as a night stop or longer stay to visit the area, and for sleeping off the effects of the 'tastings' – you probably won't even notice the slight noise from the nearby road! The 175 large pitches, with electricity (5/6A), are neatly laid out and separated by shrubs and trees. The famous Cognac Houses (Pineau, Hennessy, Martell, Remy Martin, etc.) and the Cognac Museum may be visited. There is public transport to the town centre (daily July/Aug; Saturdays only at other times).

Facilities

Two fairly modern toilet blocks have mixed British and Turkish style WCs, including children's toilets, washbasins in cabins, dishwashing and laundry sinks and a washing machine. Cleaning can be variable. Motorcaravan services. Small swimming pool on site (municipal pool nearby). Snack bar and entertainment (1/7-15/9). Fishing. Volleyball. Table tennis. Play area on grass. Off site: Riverside walks. Restaurants, bars and shops in the town (2.3 km). Bicycle hire 2 km, riding 6 km, golf 5 km.

At a glance

Welcome & Ambience	✓✓✓	Location	✓✓✓✓
Quality of Pitches	✓✓✓	Range of Facilities	✓✓✓✓

Directions

Site is signed from N141 (Saintes - Angoulême). Follow signs for town centre. Site is north of the town beside the river on the D24 to Boutiers and Ste Sévère.

Charges 2003

Per pitch incl. 2 persons	€ 10.00 - € 11.00
extra person	€ 2.00 - € 3.00
Less for stays over 3 days.	

Reservations

Write for more information to Office de Tourisme de Cognac, 16 Rue du 14 Juillet, 16100 Cognac.
Tel: 05 45 36 55 36. Email: camping@cc-cognac.fr

Open

1 May - 15 October.

FR16060 Camping Marco de Bignac

Lieudit 'Les Sablons', 16170 Bignac (Charente)

The small village of Bignac is set in peaceful countryside not too far from the N10 road, north of Angoulême. The Marshall family have worked hard to improve this tranquil site which is arranged along one side of an attractive lake on a level, grassy meadow. The 89 pitches are marked at each corner by a tree so there is shade, and electricity is available. At the far end of the site is a hedged swimming pool and plenty of space for ball games. The lake shores are home to ducks and the lake itself is used for fishing and small boats. The reception office is part of the owner's home and near to it is a bar and restaurant with tables outside. This site is popular with British visitors and is a peaceful, location for couples or young families. There is no noisy entertainment and all activities are free.

Facilities

Two traditional French style toilet blocks have functional facilities all in cabins opening from the outside. Dishwashing or laundry sinks at either end of each block. Washing machine. Bar and snack bar (1/6-31/8; closed Mon. until high season). Essentials kept in the bar and baker calls daily (high season). Swimming pool (15/6-31/8, unsupervised). Football field, badminton, tennis, table tennis, pedaloes, minigolf a boule pitch (boules provided) and fishing, all free. Library. Play area. Pets corner. Special evenings, outings and competitions organised in high season. A torch may be useful. Off site: Local markets. Riding 5 km.

At a glance

Welcome & Ambience	✓✓✓✓	Location	✓✓✓✓✓
Quality of Pitches	✓✓✓✓	Range of Facilities	✓✓✓✓

Directions

From N10 south of Poitiers, 14 km. north of Angoulême, take D11 west to Vars and Basse. Where you turn right onto D117 to Bignac. Site is signed at several junctions and in village (Camping Bignac).

Charges 2003

Per pitch incl. 2 persons	€ 12.00 - € 16.00
extra person	€ 2.00 - € 4.00
child (2-7 yrs)	free - € 2.50
electricity (3/6A)	€ 2.50 - € 4.00

Reservations

Made with deposit (€ 30 per week).
Tel: 05 45 21 78 41.

Open

15 May - 15 September.

FR16030M **Camping Municipal Le Champion**

16230 Mansle (Charente)

Le Champion is a convenient stop-over from the N10 or a good base to explore the northern Charente area. Beside the Charente river, the site has a cool, relaxing atmosphere created by its attractive location. The site, with 120 average sized, separated pitches, is mostly open with little shade. All pitches have electricity and water points. Two privately owned restaurants are at the site entrance. One is attractively canopied and has 'al fresco' facilities and snack bar priced food. Information about opportunities for cycling, walking, canoeing or fishing is available from the local Syndicat d'Initiative (500 metres). There is some road noise from the N10.

Facilities

The main modern sanitary block is well maintained and provides some washbasins in cabins and facilities for disabled people. Dishwashing and laundry areas and a small washing machine. An additional smaller, older block is in the tenting area at the rear of the site. Motorcaravan service point at entrance. Minigolf. Off site: Town and shops 200 m. Swimming pool in town (discount for campers), recreational area next to the site.

At a glance

Welcome & Ambience	✓✓✓✓	Location	✓✓✓✓
Quality of Pitches	✓✓✓	Range of Facilities	✓✓✓

Directions

Site is well signed off the N10 (in the town of Mansle), 30 km. north of Angoulême.

Charges 2003

Per adult	€ 2.00
child (under 7 yrs)	€ 1.00
caravan or tent	€ 1.70
motorcaravan incl. 2 persons	€ 10.00
vehicle	€ 1.70
electricity (16A)	€ 2.50

No credit cards.

Reservations

Bookings accepted without deposit, although not usually necessary. Tel: 05 45 20 31 41.

Open

15 May - 15 September.

An arboresque 2 hectare campsite situated on the banks of the river 'Charente'. 120 flat sites separated by smal hedges. Mobile homes to rent.

Open from 15ᵗʰ May to 15ᵗʰ September.

Leisure : Children's park, fishing, mini-golf, snack-bar, restaurant, canoe/kayak base near-by.

★ ★ ★

Camping Municipal " Le Champion "

Rue de Watlington 16230 Mansle - mairie.mansle@wanadoo.fr
Tel: (+33) 05.45.20.31.41 or 05.45.22.20.43 - Fax: (+33) 05.45.22.86.30

FR24000 Camping La Tuilière

St Rémy-sur-Lidoire, 24700 Montpon Ménestérol (Dordogne)

La Tuilière is a traditional and spacious site, run by a family with lots of activities for children. With a small lake, 100 pitches are arranged on a gently sloping hillside. Most pitches are reasonably level with some shade and 75 have electricity connections, although long leads may be needed. The entrance building houses a small reception. The small unfenced lake, where there is play equipment, can be used for fishing and water games. This is a typical French site with very friendly owners (who encourage British rallies). St Rémy is in the western Dordogne (less crowded with tourists), not far from Ste Foy la Grande, and well positioned to visit the wine areas of St Emilion, Pomerol and Bergerac.

Facilities

Two modern toilet blocks are very clean and include some washbasins in cubicles. Baby room and unit for disabled visitors. Laundry facilities. Small shop and attractively furnished bar/restaurant for lunches and evening meals (all 1/7-31/8), overlooking the swimming pool and paddling pool. Jacuzzi. Good play area and tennis court. Archery, minigolf, table tennis and pool tables. Dances, tournaments and karaoke nights arranged in July/Aug. Off site: Supermarket 5 km. Riding 3 km. Bicycle hire.

At a glance

Welcome & Ambience	✓✓✓✓✓	Location	✓✓✓✓✓
Quality of Pitches	✓✓✓✓	Range of Facilities	✓✓✓✓

Directions

From the north on D708 Montpon-Ménestérol to Ste Foy-la-Grande road, site is 5 km. south of Montpon on the right. From the south site is 1.5 km. north of St Rémy on the D708 (on the left).

Charges 2003

Per person	€ 2.50 - € 3.10
pitch with electricity (5/10A)	€ 5.90 - € 7.60
Less 20% in low season.	

Reservations

Made with € 10 deposit. Tel: 05 53 82 47 29. Email: la-tuiliere@wanadoo.fr

Open

1 June - 15 September.

FR16020 Castel Camping Les Gorges du Chambon

Eymouthiers, 16220 Montbron (Charente)

A welcoming and friendly, family site in pretty, rolling Périgord Vert countryside, Gorges du Chambon is arranged around a restored Charente farmhouse and its outbuildings. It provides an attractive, spacious setting with 120 large, marked pitches with electrical connections. On gently sloping grass and enjoying extensive views over the countryside, the pitches are arranged in two circular groups with a sanitary block at the centre of each. The site also offers canoe hire on the river and a footpath has been created to the river with two beaches where swimming is possible. A converted barn provides an interesting gallery arrangement in the restaurant/bar. The site owners are very helpful.

Facilities

Traditional style, unisex blocks include washbasins in private cabins, facilities for disabled people, a baby bath, laundry sinks, washing machine and tumble dryer, and good dishwashing rooms. Reception stocks some basic supplies and bread can be ordered the day before. Bar and restaurant (good food, well priced), plus takeaway including pizzas (all season). Swimming pool (18 x 7 m) and children's pool. Play area. Games room, TV and table tennis. Tennis, archery and minigolf, Bicycle and canoe hire. Animation is organised in July/Aug. including a children's club, youth disco and teenagers' corner. Dogs are not accepted. Off site: Fishing and riding within 200 m. Golf 4 km. Visits are organised to local producers and day trips (low season).

At a glance

Welcome & Ambience	✓✓✓✓✓	Location	✓✓✓✓✓
Quality of Pitches	✓✓✓✓	Range of Facilities	✓✓✓✓

Directions

From N141 Angoulême - Limoges road at Rochefoucauld take D6 to Montbron village. Follow D6 in direction of Piegut-Pluviers and site is signed down country road past holiday complex.

Charges 2004

Per person	€ 3.50 - € 5.60
child (1-7 yrs)	free - € 2.60
pitch with electricity (6A)	€ 8.20 - € 10.20
vehicle	€ 1.50 - € 2.10
Camping Cheques accepted.	

Reservations

Necessary for July/Aug; contact site quoting Alan Rogers. Tel: 05 45 70 71 70. Email: gorges.chambon@wanadoo.fr

Open

10 April - 25 September.

FR24330 Camping de L'Etang Bleu

24340 Vieux-Mareuil (Dordogne)

Set halfway between the historic towns of Perigueux and Angoulême, this tranquil countryside site in a mature woodland setting has recently been acquired by enthusiastic British owners Mark and Jo Finch. The site has 169 pitches, with 108 available to touring units. The remainder are taken up by two small tour operators and site owned mobile homes and ready erected tents for rent. The pitches are of a good size, flat and grassy, with mature hedging and trees providing privacy and plenty of shade. All pitches have water and 90 have electricity. At the bottom of the site is a fishing lake stocked with carp (no permit required), and various woodland walks start from the campsite grounds. The bright and cheerful 'bistro bar' provides good value food and drinks, and becomes a focal point for evening socialising on site. This site is ideal for couples or families with young children who are looking for a quiet and relaxing holiday away from the hustle and bustle of the busiest tourist areas, but still within reach of some of the area's major towns.

Facilities

Two modern, clean and well maintained toilet blocks provide mostly British style toilets, washbasins (some in cubicles), showers, facilities for babies and disabled people. Laundry. Dishwashing facilities. Small playground with paddling pool. Swimming pool (20m x 10m) with sun terrace and loungers. Pleasant bar and terrace with 'bistro' food (all season), Takeaway. Small shop (items not stocked can be ordered on request). Table tennis, boules. Canoe and bicycle hire. Various entertainments, sporting activities and excursions organised in high season. (Floodlit tennis court, minigolf and adventure type playground are planned for summer 2004). Off site: Restaurant - Auberge de L'Etang Bleu - next to campsite, small supermarket, post office etc. in Mareuil (7 km).

At a glance

Welcome & Ambience	✓✓✓✓	Location	✓✓✓✓
Quality of Pitches	✓✓✓✓	Range of Facilities	✓✓✓✓

Directions

From Angoulême take D939 south, from Perigueux take D939 north. From either direction after about 45 km. Vieux Mareuil is signed on north side of the road. Turn on D93, and follow narrow road through village. Just after village site is signed on right. Follow signs down long drive to site. Note: American-style motorhomes and larger caravans may find it easier to access site by taking the D708 Mareuil - Nontron road, and turning south on the D93, avoiding the narrow access roads in Vieux Mareuil village.

Charges 2003

Per adult	€ 3.50 - € 5.00
child (2-7 yrs)	€ 2.00
pitch with electricity (10/16A)	€ 7.50 - € 11.00
pet	€ 3.00

Less 30% in low seasons.

Reservations

Advisable for high season. Tel: 05 53 60 92 70.

Open

1 April - 30 September.

FR24010 Castel Camping Château Le Verdoyer

Champs Romain, 24470 St Pardoux (Dordogne)

Le Verdoyer is a Dutch, family-owned site developed in the park of a restored château. We particularly like this site for its beautiful buildings and lovely surroundings. It is situated in this lesser known area of the Dordogne sometimes referred to as the Périgord Vert, with its green forests and small lakes. The 37 acre estate has two such lakes, one in front of the Château for fishing and one accessed by a footpath, with sandy beach and safe swimming area. There are 150 marked, level, terraced pitches (some a little rocky). Mostly of a good size (100-150 sq.m), all have electricity, with a choice of wooded area or open field, where hedges have been planted and have grown well; 120 are 'confort' pitches with more planned. There is a swimming pool complex and in high season activities are organised for children (5-13 yrs) but there is definitely no disco! The courtyard area between reception and the bar is home to evening activities, and provides a pleasant place to enjoy drinks and relax. The Château itself has rooms to let and its excellent lakeside restaurant is also open to the public. Used by a Dutch tour operator (15 pitches).

Facilities

Recently completely renewed, three very well appointed toilet blocks include washbasins in cabins, facilities for disabled people and baby baths. Serviced launderette. Motorcaravan service point. Fridge rental. Multi-purpose shop with gas. Bar with snacks and takeaway facilities. Good value bistro serves meals in July/Aug. Restaurant open to public. Two pools (25 x 10 m. and 10 x 7 m; the smaller one can be covered in low season) and paddling pool. Children's play areas. All-weather tennis court. Volleyball, basketball and badminton. Table tennis. Minigolf. Bicycle hire (tennis and bicycles free in low season). Small library. Off site: Riding 3 km.

At a glance

Welcome & Ambience	✓✓✓✓✓	Location	✓✓✓✓✓
Quality of Pitches	✓✓✓✓	Range of Facilities	✓✓✓✓

Directions

Site is 2 km. from the Limoges (N21) - Chalus (D6bis-D85) - Nontron road, 20 km. south of Chalus and is well signed from the main road. Site is on the D96 about 4 km. north of village of Champs Romain.

Charges 2003

Per unit incl. 2 persons and electricity (5/10A)	€ 18.00 - € 29.00
extra adult	€ 5.00 - € 6.00
child (under 4 yrs)	free
dog	free - € 3.00

Between 5/7-23/8 stay 14 nights, pay for twelve. Camping Cheques accepted.

Reservations

Write to site. Tel: 05 53 56 94 64. Email: chateau@verdoyer.fr

Open

10 April - 16 October.

FR24250 Camping Les Tourterelles

24390 Tourtoirac (Dordogne)

This is a site with its own equestrian centre that will appeal to lovers of the countryside, in an area that is ideal for walking or horse riding. The adjacent riding stables with 30 horses is run by the owner's daughter Angélique. There are 125 pitches in total, but the site has some chalets, bungalows and mobile homes which leaves around 87 grassy pitches for tourists. These are on several different levels most with good shade from mature trees, and all have electricity.

Facilities

Three good, fully equipped toilet blocks, one new provides a baby unit. Laundry. Bread can be ordered. Bar/restaurant serving good value meals, with takeaway. Freezer pack service. Swimming pool (20 x 10 m.) and paddling pool. Riding. Tennis, volleyball, badminton, table tennis. Animation programme in main season. Off site: Shop at Tourtoirac (1 km), supermarket at Excideuil. Fishing 1km.

At a glance

Welcome & Ambience	✓✓✓✓	Location	✓✓✓✓
Quality of Pitches	✓✓✓✓	Range of Facilities	✓✓✓✓

Directions

On D704 just after Cherveix-Cubas turn right on D5 to Tourtoirac. Turn right in village and fork left on D73 (Coulaures) to site in 1 km.

Charges 2003

Per adult	€ 3.80
pitch with electricity (6A)	€ 10.75 - € 12.35

Low season discounts for over 55's. No credit cards.

Reservations

Advised for July/Aug; contact site. Tel: 05 53 51 11 17. Email: les-tourterelles@wanadoo.fr

Open

30 April - 30 September

FR24280 Camping de Barnabé

Rue des Bains, 24750 Perigeux (Dordogne)

A memorable site in a unique setting, Barnabé has a special ambience. A distinctive 1936 Art Deco style building houses the reception, bar, restaurant and games room, complete with an attractive terrace overlooking the River L'Isle, in the style of the old 'Cafe de Paris'. The bar has its own Wurlitzer juke box, and you will find pool tables, pinball and table football in the old ballroom. This site has 56 pitches all with electricity. Pitches are in four areas, with 42 pitches on one side of the river. The other 14 are in an annexe on the opposite side. Pedestrian access between the two parts is provided by an old fashioned, passenger operated ferry boat. The entrance and access roads are a little narrow.

Facilities

Six sanitary buildings around the site (one on the far side of the river). Not modern, but functional, simple and clean with spacious shower cubicles. Unisex facilities, with both British and Turkish style toilets (no paper). One heated block is open in winter. Off site: Périgeux town centre 2 km.

At a glance

Welcome & Ambience	✓✓✓	Location	✓✓✓✓
Quality of Pitches	✓✓✓	Range of Facilities	✓✓✓✓

Directions

Approaching from the west of town, at N2089 and N221 roundabout, take exit for 'centre ville'. Follow under bridge and up hill. Keep right and turn right at lights. From the east side follow signs for 'Brive', cross the river, and after 1.5 km. at lights mentioned above - turn left. Site is signed after 400 m. to the right.

Charges 2003

Per person	€ 3.40
pitch incl. electricity (4/6A)	€ 5.30 - € 7.70

Reservations

Contact site for details. Tel: 05 53 53 41 45.

Open

All year.

FR24160 Camping Le Grand Dague

Atur, 24750 Périgueux (Dordogne)

This good quality site is only a few miles from Périgueux and yet in an extremely rural and tranquil setting. The site is spacious, clean and attractive and 68 of the 93 pitches are for touring units, all with electricity and divided by tall, mature hedging. Several large, open grassy areas provide plenty of space for youngsters, and along with a range of play equipment, make this an ideal site for young families. The Dutch owners have a passion for motorcycling, the 'Harley Davidson' themed campsite bar bearing witness to this! There are no tour operators. A 'Sites et Paysages' member.

Facilities

Excellent sanitary facilities are housed in a centrally located unit, part of which is heated for use in colder months. Mostly unisex facilities include washbasins in cubicles, a baby room and facilities for people with disabilities. Small shop for essentials (15/6-30/9). Attractive restaurant, bar and takeaway (all from June). Swimming pool, water slide and paddling pool (from early May). Football, volleyball, badminton, petanque, minigolf and table tennis. Play area. Fishing. Bicycle hire. Off site: Riding 5 km, golf 10 km.

At a glance

Welcome & Ambience	✓✓✓✓	Location	✓✓✓
Quality of Pitches	✓✓✓✓	Range of Facilities	✓✓✓✓

Directions

From either N89 Périgueux bypass or Périgueux town centre take the D2 towards Atur. At village turn east on minor road (turn is fairly sharp) for 3km to site.

Charges 2003

Per person	€ 4.25 - € 5.75
pitch with electricity (6A)	€ 8.20 - € 10.50

Reservations

Contact site. Tel: 05 53 04 21 01. Email: info@legranddague.fr

Open

Easter - 30 September.

FR24300 Camping La Rivière Fleurie

St Aulaye de Breuilh, 24230 St Antoine de Breuilh (Dordogne)

This quiet and pleasant campsite is close to the vineyards of Pomerol and St Emilion, and not far from the extensive shopping of St Foy la Grande and Bergerac. The 60 pitches are all spacious, divided by shrubs, and maturing trees are beginning to provide shade on many. All pitches have electricity. There are no tour operators, but 8 pitches are used for site owned mobile homes, and there are also studio apartments to let throughout the year. The site has a tranquil and peaceful ambience, suitable for anyone looking for a quiet and relaxing holiday.

Facilities

Sanitary facilities are plentiful and modern. Bar and terrace restaurant serving a range of basic meals. Swimming pool (100 sq.m) and toddlers' pool. Football, volleyball, table tennis, table football and TV room. Weekly 'soirées' where the owners host an evening of French food and entertainment. Bicycle hire. Canoe trips arranged. Off site: Municipal tennis court adjacent (free to campers). Fishing 100 m. Riding 4 km. Bicycle hire 8 km.

At a glance

| Welcome & Ambience | ✓✓✓✓ | Location | ✓✓✓✓ |
| Quality of Pitches | ✓✓✓✓ | Range of Facilities | ✓✓✓✓ |

Directions

Site is in the hamlet of St Aulaye, about 3 km. south of the D936 Bordeaux - Bergerac road. Site is signed at two points off the D936 down local roads, one 6 km. east of Lamothe-Montravel, the other at the western end of St Antoine de Breuilh. Follow 'camping' signs along either road until you come to the river, and site is 500 m.

Charges 2003

Per unit incl. 2 persons	€ 16.00 - € 28.00
extra person	€ 3.00 - € 7.50
child (under 4 yrs)	free
animal	€ 3.00
electricity (4/10A)	free

Reservations

Advised for July/August. Deposit of 30% (sterling cheques accepted as deposit). Tel: 05 53 24 82 80. Email: info@la-riviere-fleurie.com

Open

1 April - 30 September.

FR24060 Camping Le Paradis

St Léon-sur-Vézère, 24290 Montignac (Dordogne)

Le Paradis is an exceptionally attractive riverside site, halfway between Les Eyzies and Montignac. Well placed for exploring the Dordogne and its prehistoric grottos and other sites, the site is very well kept and laid out with mature shrubs and bushes of different types. It has 200 individual pitches of good size on flat grass, divided by trees and shrubs (139 for touring units). All have electricity, most also have water and drainage, and there are some special pitches for motorcaravans. Canoeing on the Vézère river starts from steps which give comfortable access to the riverside, adjacent to a small beach. The site welcomes a good quota of British and Dutch clients, many through a tour operator. Organised games, competitions and evening events are aimed at maintaining a true French flavour. English is spoken. This is a site of real quality, which we thoroughly recommend.

Facilities

Two unisex toilet blocks are of outstanding quality and fully equipped. They can be heated, have baby baths and toilets, extensive laundry facilities and even outside showers for swimmers. Well stocked shop (with gas). Restaurant with extensive choice of menu with good takeaway service. Very good pool complex heated in low season, with a large deep pool (25 x 10 m), a smaller shallower one (17 x 7 m), plus a paddling pool. Two tennis courts. Football, BMX track, volleyball, table tennis and pool activities. Canoe hire. Fishing. Bicycle hire. Well designed playground. Off site: Riding 2 km. Various trips organised to surrounding area.

At a glance

| Welcome & Ambience | ✓✓✓✓ | Location | ✓✓✓✓ |
| Quality of Pitches | ✓✓✓✓ | Range of Facilities | ✓✓✓✓✓ |

Directions

Site is 12 km. north of Les Eyzies and 3 km. south of St Léon-sur-Vézère, on the east side of the D706.

Charges 2003

Per person	€ 4.76 - € 6.80
pitch	€ 7.49 - € 10.70
electricity (6A)	€ 3.00
local tax (1/7-31/8)	€ 0.24

Low season reductions. 10% discount for pensioners in low seasons. Camping Cheques accepted.

Reservations

Made for any length with deposit (€ 80) and fee (€ 20). Tel: 05 53 50 72 64. Email: le-paradis@perigord.com

Open

1 April - 25 October.

FR24180 Camping Caravaning Saint Avit Loisirs

Le Bugue, 24260 St Avit-de-Vialard (Dordogne)

Although St Avit Loisirs is set in the middle of rolling countryside, far from the hustle and bustle of the main tourist areas of the Dordogne, the facilities are first class, providing virtually everything you could possibly want without the need to leave the site. This makes it ideal for families with children of all ages. The site is divided into two sections. One smaller part is dedicated to chalets and mobile homes, whilst the main section of the site contains 199 flat and mainly grassy pitches, all a minimum of 100 sq.m and with electricity, arranged in cul-de-sacs off a main access road. Tour operator tents and mobile homes (with lots of British visitors) occupy around half the pitches, leaving 99 for touring units. Three modern unisex toilet blocks provide high quality facilites, but could possibly become over-stretched (particularly laundry and dishwashing sinks) in high season. The café (highly recommended), shop and bar open onto a large terrace with pergola and hanging baskets, which overlooks the excel-lent pool complex. In high season a variety of activities and entertainments are organised – tourna-ments, aquagym, bingo and even weekly films in English. The site is ideally situated for visits to Les Eyzies and Lascaux as well as many other places of interest in the Dordogne region. English is spoken.

Facilities

Modern toilet blocks include washbasins in cabins, full laundry facilities and baby changing areas. Well stocked shop, bar, restaurant, good-value cafeteria and takeaway are housed in a recently built, but traditional-style stone building. Outdoor swimming pool (200 sq.m), children's pool, water slide, 'crazy river' and heated indoor pool with jacuzzi and adjacent fitness room. Disco behind bar, sound-proofed. Table tennis. Floodlit minigolf and boules area and dirt bike track. Good quality tennis court, volleyball and extensive play area. Canoe trips on the Dordogne, and other sporting activities organised. Good walks direct from the site. Off site: Sarlat and Perigeux within range for markets and hypermarkets.

At a glance

Welcome & Ambience	✓✓✓✓✓	Location	✓✓✓
Quality of Pitches	✓✓✓✓	Range of Facilities	✓✓✓✓✓

Directions

Site is 6 km. north of Le Bugue. From D710 Le Bugue - Perigueux road, turn west on C201 (about 2.5 km. from Le Bugue), toward St Avit de Vialard. Follow road around and through hamlet of St Avit, bearing right - site is about 1.5 km. past here, on the right. Note: the road to St Avit is narrow and bumpy in places.

Charges 2004

Per person	€ 3.50 - € 7.50
child (under 4 yrs)	free
pitch with electricity (6A)	€ 9.00 - € 15.00
with water and drainage	€ 11.50 - € 18.00
dog	€ 2.00 - € 3.70
local tax	free - € 0.30

Reservations

Made with deposit (€ 46 per week) and fee (€ 15). Tel: 05 53 02 64 00.
Email: contact@saint-avit-loisirs.com

Open

1 April - 30 September.

FR24290 Camping Le Moulin du Bleufond

Ave. Aristide Briand, 24290 Montignac (Dordogne)

Built on flat ground around a 17th century mill, this converted and improved former municipal site has its own pool as well as adjacent town facilities for various sports. The 84 pitches (66 for touring units) are marked and divided by mature hedges, all have electricity and most have some shade. Some pitches are quite small, so it is best to ensure when booking that you ask for one of the larger ones (in excess of 100 sq.m). Owners of the very largest caravans or motorhomes may need to think again. Montignac is at the head of what is to become a World Heritage site – the Vezère valley houses some of the planet's most important prehistoric caves and grottoes, with the Lascaux complex only minutes away. Although the original cave is now closed to the public, the replica Lascaux II is nearby. A third major cave system was discovered recently. The site is separated from the river by a reasonably quiet road, but there is a sizeable bank for fishing. This is an ideal base from which to visit a fascinating and beautiful part of the Perigord.

Facilities

Modern, clean sanitary facilities are well cared for by the energetic new owners and can be heated. Bread and a few essentials available at reception. Bar, snack bar and terrace restaurant (all season). Heated swimming pool (140 sq.m) and paddling pool. Games room with table football, pool, table tennis and giant TV screen. Canoe trips and bicycle hire can be arranged. Musical evenings weekly in high season. Off site: Shops, supermarkets, bars and a range of interesting restaurants in the town.

At a glance

Welcome & Ambience	✓✓✓✓	Location	✓✓✓✓✓
Quality of Pitches	✓✓✓	Range of Facilities	✓✓✓✓

Directions

Site is just south of Montignac town centre, on D65 to Sergeac. Just after the stone bridge on one way system in centre of the town turn sharp right (allow for a wide sweep!) The site is 750 m. on the left.

Charges 2003

Per person	€ 3.30 - € 4.26
child (3-8 yrs)	€ 2.13 - € 2.28
pitch with electricity (-10A)	€ 6.30 - € 8.10
animal	€ 1.52

10% discount for senior citizens in low season (for advance bookings).

Reservations

Advised for July/Aug with 30% deposit (no booking fee). Tel: 05 53 51 83 95.
Email: le.moulin.du.bleufond@wanadoo.fr

Open

1 April - 15 October.

FR24170 Camping Le Port de Limeuil

24480 Allés-sur-Dordogne (Dordogne)

At the confluence of Dordogne and Vézère rivers, opposite the picturesque village of Limieul, this delightful family site exudes a peaceful and relaxed ambience. There are 90 marked, grassy, and flat pitches, some very spacious and all with electricity connections. The buildings are in traditional Périgourdine style and surrounded with flowers and shrubs – it is a very pretty site – and the young French owners have been steadily developing the facilities. A sports area on a large open grassy space between the river bank and the main camping area adds to the feeling of space, and provides an additional recreation and picnic area (there are additional unmarked pitches for tents and camper vans along the bank here). This is an ideal location for visiting the west central part of the Dordogne département, and is recommended for long stays. It is used fairly unobtrusively by a tour operator.

Facilities

The two toilet blocks are very well appointed. Friendly bar/restaurant with snacks and takeaway (all 25/5-5/9). Swimming pool with jacuzzi, paddling pool and children's slide (1/5-15/9). Badminton, football, boules and volleyball. Mountain bike hire. Canoe hire - launched from the site's own pebble beach. Off site: The pretty, medieval village of Limeuil is only 200 m. Riding 1 km, golf 10 km.

At a glance

Welcome & Ambience	✓✓✓✓	Location	✓✓✓✓✓
Quality of Pitches	✓✓✓✓	Range of Facilities	✓✓✓✓

Directions

Site is about 7 km south of Le Bugue. From D51/D31E Le Buisson to Le Bugue road turn west onto D51 towards Limeuil. Just before you cross the bridge into the village of Limeuil, turn left (site signed here), across another bridge. Site is about 100 m. along this road on the right.

Charges 2004

Per pitch incl. 2 persons	€ 19.30
extra person	€ 4.80
child (under 10 yrs)	€ 3.50
electricity (5A)	€ 3.10
dog	€ 2.00
local tax	free - € 0.30

Reservations

Advised for mid July - end Aug. Tel: 05 53 63 29 76. Email: didierbonvallet@aol.com

Open

1 May - 30 September.

FR24240 Camping Les Bo–Bains

24150 Badefoils-sur-Dordogne (Dordogne)

Offering a limited number of touring pitches, but a good range of facilities and activities, Les Bo-Bains is a well kept site in an attractive location alongside the Dordogne river. The flat, grassy and larger than average pitches are all set along the river bank (families with young children need to consider this), and are divided by hedges, shrubs and bushes of different types. All pitches have electricity, with water taps and drainaway points between each pair. River bathing is possible, although in places the current can be quite strong. Canoeing can be arranged from reception and there are places to launch one's own small craft. The site welcomes a good quota of French and Dutch clients, but not many British as yet. Mobile homes and chalets are available to rent.

Facilities

The two main toilet blocks are of good quality with baby rooms and laundry facilities. Small shop. Bar (open all season) and restaurant with a choice of menu and comprehensive takeaway service (15/5-15/9). Swimming pool complex with a main pool (18 x 9 m), another shallower one (5 x 5 m), plus two slides and landing pool (14 x 7 m). Several small play areas. TV room. Multi-gym. Small football field. Minigolf, archery, boules, trampoline, volleyball, badminton, table tennis and basketball courts. Children's club. Games, competitions and evening events. Quad bike and bicycle hire. Tennis. Riding. Canoeing excursions. Off site: The small village of Badefols is within easy walking distance, and has a restaurant, bar, tobacconist and an historic château.

At a glance

Welcome & Ambience	✓✓✓	Location	✓✓✓✓
Quality of Pitches	✓✓✓✓✓	Range of Facilities	✓✓✓✓

Directions

Site is on D29 Bergerac - Sarlat road, about 4 km. east of Lalinde, on the north side of the road.

Charges 2003

Per pitch incl. 2 persons and electricity (5A)	€ 16.00 - € 28.00
extra person over 4 yrs	€ 3.00 - € 7.50
animal	free - € 3.00

Reservations

Advised for July and August. Made for any length with deposit (30% - minimum € 45) and booking fee (€ 16). Tel: 05 53 73 52 52.

Open

15 April - 30 September.

FR24100 Sunêlia Le Moulinal

24540 Biron (Dordogne)

A lakeside site with a wide range of activities, not only does Le Moulinal provide a good base for exploring the southern Dordogne, but it also has extensive wooded grounds to explore with picnic areas. Of the 280 grassy pitches, only around 40 are available for touring units, and these are spread amongst the site's own mobile homes, chalets and some tour operator tents. All pitches are flat, grassy and have electricity (3/6A), but vary considerably in size from 75 sq.m. to over 100 sq.m. The five-acre lake has a sandy beach and is suitable for boating (canoes available), swimming and fishing. Ambitious, well organised animation is run throughout the season – including a 'baby club' (ages 2-6 yrs), tennis, mountain biking, canoeing, riding, archery, rock climbing, potholing and craft activities (all charged), and children's activities, sports tournaments, discos and fishing (free of charge). The site is also popular with tour operators (80 pitches), although the owner has reduced their presence.

Facilities

Toilet facilities, built to harmonise with the surroundings, include British and Turkish style toilets (most in one block), some washbasins in cabins, and dishwashing sinks. Facilities for disabled people and babies. Laundry with washing machines and dryers. Motorcaravan service point. Excellent restaurant serving regional meals. Bar serving snacks and light meals (all season). Snack bar/takeaway on the other side of the lake. Large, heated swimming pool with jacuzzi and children's pool. Rustic play area on grass. Volleyball, table tennis, football and hockey. Bicycle hire. Excursions organised on foot, on horseback, by car or bicycle. Full programme of evening entertainment in high season.

At a glance

Welcome & Ambience	✓✓✓✓✓	Location	✓✓✓✓
Quality of Pitches	✓✓✓✓	Range of Facilities	✓✓✓✓✓

Directions

Site is 53 km southeast of Bergerac. From D104 Villeréal - Monpazier road take the D53/D150 south to Lacapelle Biron. Just before Lacapelle Biron turn right onto the D255 towards Dévillac, (site is well signed here), and site is 1.5 km along on the left.

Charges 2003

Per standard pitch incl. 2 persons	€ 12.00 - € 29.00
with services	€ 19.00 - € 39.00
pitch near lake with electricity	€ 17.00 - € 37.00
extra person	€ 3.00 - € 8.20
child (2-7 yrs)	free - € 7.80
animal	free - € 3.00
local tax	€ 0.08 - € 0.16

Low season offer - 14 nights for price of 10.

Reservations

Made with deposit (€ 92) and for high season, fee (€ 28). Tel: 05 53 40 84 60.
Email: lemoulinal@perigord.com

Open

5 April - 14 September with all services.

FR24040 Castel Camping Le Moulin du Roch

Route des Eyzies, D47, 24200 Sarlat (Dordogne)

Set on natural sloping woodland in the grounds of a former water mill, the Dutreux family have ensured that Le Moulin du Roch is an attractive and well run family campsite. The site has 199 pitches, of which 91 are available for touring units. Pitches are mostly flat (some slope slightly) and grassy, and all have electricity. Pitches on the upper levels have plenty of shade, whilst those on the lower level near the amenities and the fishing lake are more open. Entertainment and activities are organised from June to September, with something for everyone from craft workshops and sports tournaments to canoeing and caving for the more adventurous. An excellent multi-lingual children's club runs in July and August. Walking and cycle routes lead from the site through surrounding woodland.

Facilities

Three modern toilet blocks provide excellent facilities. Washing machines and dryers. Shop (18/5-7/9) stocks a good range of groceries and fresh food, and is very reasonably priced. Bar with terrace, takeaway and superb restaurant (all 1/5-19/9, closed Mondays). Newly built swimming pool with adjoining paddling pool (1/5-19/9). Fishing lake (carp and roach - no charge), tennis, table tennis, boules area, volleyball, playground, discos twice weekly in high season. Animals are not accepted. Off site: Medieval town of Sarlat with all amenities is 10 km. Bicycle hire and riding both 10 km, golf 15 km.

At a glance

Welcome & Ambience	✓✓✓✓✓	Location	✓✓✓✓
Quality of Pitches	✓✓✓✓	Range of Facilities	✓✓✓✓✓

Directions

Site is on south side of the D47, 10 km. from Sarlat and 11 km. from Les Eyzies.

Charges 2004

Per pitch incl. 2 persons	€ 13.00 - € 24.00
with electricity (6A)	€ 17.00 - € 28.00
with full services	€ 13.00 - € 28.00
extra person	€ 3.00 - € 7.20
child (4-9 yrs)	free - € 2.60

Camping Cheques accepted.

Reservations

Essential from June - August, with deposit (20%) and fee (€ 19 in July/Aug). Tel: 05 53 59 20 27.
Email: moulin.du.roch@wanadoo.fr

Open

1 May - 14 September.

FR24080 Camping Caravaning Le Moulin de David

Gaugeac, 24540 Monpazier (Dordogne)

Owned and run by a French family who continually seek to improve it, this pleasant and attractive site is one for those who enjoy peace, away from the hustle and bustle of the main Dordogne attractions, yet sufficiently close to them to be accessible. Set in a 14 ha. wooded valley, it has 160 pitches (all with electricity) split into two sections; 106 are for tourers – 35 below the central reception complex in a shaded situation, and 73 above on partly terraced ground with varying degrees of shade. Spacing is good and there is no crowding. The site has been attractively planted with a variety of shrubs and trees, and combined with the small stream that runs through the centre, they create a beautiful and tranquil setting. There is a delightful wooded walk via a long distance footpath (GR36) to Château Biron, about 2-3 km distance, and the Bastide town of Monpazier is also within walking distance (2 km). A 'Sites et Paysages' member.

Facilities

All three sanitary blocks are of a good standard, including washbasins in cabins, facilities for disabled visitors and babies in each. Adequate dishwashing and laundry sinks. Laundry room. Good shop. Bar/restaurant with shaded patio and takeaway. Swimming pool and paddling pool, plus freshwater pool with waterslide. Play area. Boules, half-court tennis, table tennis, volleyball, basketball, trampolining and football area. Library. Bicycle hire. Events, games and canoe trips organised (1/7-31/8).

At a glance

Welcome & Ambience	✓✓✓✓	Location	✓✓✓✓✓
Quality of Pitches	✓✓✓✓✓	Range of Facilities	✓✓✓✓✓

Directions

From Monpazier take D2 Villeréal road. Take third turn left (after 2 km), signed to site and 'Gaugeac mairie'. Site is about 500 m. along this road on the left.

Charges 2003

Per person (over 2 yrs)	€ 3.65 - € 6.40
pitch	€ 5.00 - € 12.00
electricity (3/10A)	€ 3.35 - € 5.65
Camping Cheques accepted.	

Reservations

Advisable for Jul/Aug, with deposit (€ 61 per week reserved) and fee (€ 19). Tel: 05 53 22 65 25. Email: courrier@moulin-de-david.com

Open

15 May - 11 September.

FR24110 Camping Caravaning Aqua Viva

Route Sarlac-Souillac, Carsac-Aillac, 24200 Sarlat (Dordogne)

This shaded woodland site is ideally situated for visits to Rocamadour and Padirac, as well as the medieval town of Sarlat, only 7 km away. The site is divided into two sections, separated by a small access road. Pitches are flat, divided by shrubs, and vary from average to large size. Many have shade from the numerous trees (the shadier pitches tend to have less grass and more sand!). All have electricity. A wide range of organised activities run all season, making this site popular with families, especially those with pre-teen and younger teenage children. English is spoken. There are no tour operators, but the site attracts a good mixture of nationalities, resulting in a very 'international' ambience.

Facilities

Each part of the site has a central, modern toilet block, with facilities for disabled people, laundry and baby areas. Bar and restaurant/takeaway with terrace. Shop selling good range of groceries. Heated swimming pool and children's pool. Small fishing lake. High quality minigolf. Half tennis court, ping pong tables, volleyball and badminton nets. Good under 7's play park. Floodlit boules pitch and multi-sports court. Bicycle hire. Off site: Arial woodland assault course 500 m. Riding and golf 5 km.

At a glance

Welcome & Ambience	✓✓✓✓✓	Location	✓✓✓✓
Quality of Pitches	✓✓✓	Range of Facilities	✓✓✓✓✓

Directions

Site is 7 km. from Sarlat on south of the D704 (Sarlat - Souillac). From Souillac, the access road is just around a left hand bend, and is not easy to see. If you miss the turn there is a roundabout in 1 km.

Charges 2003

Per person	€ 3.10 - € 6.20
pitch with electricity (3/10A)	€ 7.70 - € 14.00

Reservations

Made with 50% deposit and fee. Tel: 05 53 31 46 00. Email: aqua_viva@perigord.com

Open

Easter - Last Saturday in September.

FR24030 Camping Les Périères

Route St Nathalène, 24203 Sarlat (Dordogne)

Les Périères is a good quality small site in an attractive setting within walking distance of the beautiful medieval town of Sarlat. The 100 pitches arranged on wide terraces around the semi-circle of a fairly steep valley, overlooking central leisure area that includes indoor and outdoor pools and tennis courts. The pitches are of a very good size, all equipped with electricity, water and drainage and many have dappled shade from the numerous walnut trees on the site (the walnuts can be bought in the campsite shop). Reservations are advised for high season, when the site becomes busy, although a few pitches are made available on a 'first come first serve basis'. The site has a refreshingly spacious and open feel, quite free from overcrowding, even at busy times.

Facilities

The toilet blocks of varying styles and sizes should be quite sufficient, including washbasins in cabins, facilities for disabled visitors, a good baby bathroom in one block and washing machines and dryers. Motorcaravan service point. Small shop. Pleasant bar. Small snack bar/takeaway (July/August). Outdoor swimming pool (no shorts) and paddling pool and heated indoor spa pool and sauna. Two tennis courts. Table tennis (indoors or out), football pitch and fitness track with exercise halts. Stone cottages to rent. No electric barbecues allowed. Off site: Bicycle hire 1 km, fishing 5 km, riding or golf 7 km.

At a glance

Welcome & Ambience	✓✓✓✓	Location	✓✓✓✓✓
Quality of Pitches	✓✓✓✓	Range of Facilities	✓✓✓✓

Directions

Site is on the east side of Sarlat, on the D47 to Ste Nathalene. (Negotiating Sarlat town centre is best done outside of peak hours.

Charges 2003

Per unit incl. 2 persons	€ 18.20 - € 24.60
with electricity (6A)	€ 22.00 - € 28.50
child (under 7 yrs)	€ 3.70

Credit cards accepted with 2% fee.

Reservations

Advised for high season and made for min. 1 week with deposit (€ 100 p/week) and fee (€ 15). Tel: 05 53 59 05 84. Email: les-perieres@wanadoo.fr

Open

Easter - 30 September.

Camping Les Périères

24200 SARLAT, DORDOGNE - PÉRIGORD

The 4-star site in a natural amphitheatre of woods and meadows. A peaceful oasis in the heart of Black Périgord, yet only half a mile from the medieval town and gastronomic centre of Sarlat.

**LARGE INDIVIDUAL PITCHES
EXCELLENT TOILET BLOCKS
SWIMMING POOLS, one covered and heated
SAUNA - TENNIS COURTS
VOLLEYBALL - TABLE TENNIS
LOUNGE BAR - SHOP - LIBRARY**

FR24220 Camping Domaine des Chênes Verts

Route de Sarlat, 24370 Calviac en Périgord (Dordogne)

This peaceful countryside family campsite is set in a beautiful area of the Dordogne valley, and is complemented by the renovated Périgordian farm buildings which house the amenities at the centre of the site. The spacious grounds which contain many trees provide 143 pitches on either side of the main buildings, of which 63 are for touring units. Most of the good sized, grassy pitches are shaded, and all are separated by hedging. There is electricity to all pitches, and water points nearby. The majority of pitches are level but some are gently sloping. The owners, who speak some English, are very helpful and friendly, and in high season they organise a range of entertainments and activities from wine tasting to canoeing expeditions, and of course the obligatory boules tournaments.

Facilities

Two fully equipped unisex toilet blocks include washbasins in cabins, dishwashing and laundry areas. Washing machine. Shop (1/07-30/08, but bread, milk etc available in reception in low season). Motorcaravan service point. Fridge hire. Gas supplies. Bar, restaurant and takeaway (15/6-15/9). Medium sized swimming pool with large sunbathing area (15/6-15/9), covered, heated pool (1/4-20/9) and a paddling pool. Play area. Large open grass area for ball games, volleyball, basketball and tennis courts. TV and games room. Off site: Forest walks and cycle tracks lead from the site.

At a glance

Welcome & Ambience	✓✓✓✓	Location	✓✓✓✓
Quality of Pitches	✓✓✓✓	Range of Facilities	✓✓✓✓

Directions

From D704 Sarlat - Gourdon road turn east on D704A towards Souillac and Calviac (this turn is 3.5 km. from Sarlat). Site is about 5 km. along this road on the left.

Latest charges

Per person	€ 3.60 - € 4.50
child (under 7 yrs)	€ 2.00 - € 2.50
pitch with electricity (6A)	€ 8.40 - € 10.50

Reservations

Advised in July/Aug. Tel: 05 53 59 21 07. Email: chenes-verts@wanadoo.fr

Open

1 May - 28 September.

FR24090 Camping Soleil Plage

Vitrac, 24200 Sarlat (Dordogne)

This spacious site is in one of the most attractive sections of the Dordogne valley, right on the riverside. The site has 199 pitches, divided into two sections, of which around 114 are for touring units. The smaller section surrounds the main reception and other facilities, which are housed in a renovated Périgordin farmhouse, whilst the larger section of the site is about 250 m. from the reception and pool areas, and offers river bathing from a sizeable pebble bank. All pitches are bounded by hedges and are of good size, and in the larger section there are a few giant pitches for large families. Most pitches have some shade. Various activities are organised in high season including walks and sports tournaments, and canoe hire is available from the site. A weekly 'soirée' usually involves a barbecue or paella, with wine and a band – worth catching! The site is increasingly popular, though in late August it begins to empty, but reservations are essential for July - early Aug. Used by tour operators (50 pitches).

Facilities

Toilet facilities are provided by two modern unisex blocks. Washing machines. Motorcaravan service point. Friendly bar with extensive and good value takeaway menu, refurbished restaurant serving excellent Périgourdine menus, and well stocked shop (all 12/5-15/9). Very impressive swimming pool complex includes main pool, paddling pool, spa pool and two water slides. Tennis court, devilish minigolf, table tennis, volleyball and football pitches. TV room. Playground. Fishing. Canoe and kayak hire. Off site: Bicycle hire 2 km, golf 1 km, riding 5 km.

At a glance

Welcome & Ambience	✓✓✓✓✓	Location	✓✓✓✓✓
Quality of Pitches	✓✓✓✓✓	Range of Facilities	✓✓✓✓

Directions

Site is 8 km. south of Sarlat. From D703 Vitrac - Carsac-Aillac road turn southeast at golf course (site signed). Follow road to T-junction, turn right at and follow road around to the left. Site is just after corner.

Charges 2004

Per person	€ 4.00 - € 6.40
child (2-10 yrs)	€ 2.40 - € 3.70
pitch with electricity	€ 8.50 - € 14.00

Reservations

Made for exact dates: min. 1 week with deposit (€ 65) and fee (€ 35); send for booking form.
Tel: 05 53 28 33 33. Email: soleil.plage@wanadoo.fr

Open

1 May - 30 September.

Soleil Plage
CAMPING CARAVANING ★★★★
CHALETS - CANOES

Into the PERIGORD along the RIVER DORDOGNE between SARLAT and DOMME the very picturesque site of

SOLEIL PLAGE ★★★★

Lieu-Dit Caudon, VITRAC
24200 SARLAT
Tel: 0033 553.28.33.33
Fax: 0033 553.28.30.24
www.CAMPING-SOLEILPLAGE.fr

FR24230 Camping Le Moulin de Paulhiac

24520 Daglan (Dordogne)

Daglan is a very pretty well restored village that is becoming something of a tourist centre for this quieter area of the Dordogne. The friendly Armagnac family are justifiably proud of their well-kept and attractive site, built in the grounds of an old mill. The 150 numbered pitches (98 for touring) are separated by hedges and shrubs, all have electricity, and there is plenty of shade. Many pitches are next to a stream that runs through the site, and joins the River Ceou along its far edge. A tent field slopes gently down to the river, which is well marked and quite shallow. This site will appeal especially to families with younger children. Used by a tour operator (50 pitches).

Facilities

Two clean toilet blocks provide modern facilities, including those for disabled. Well-stocked shop - including home-grown walnuts (delicious!). Good value restaurant and takeaway. Modern pool complex (no bermuda style shorts) with a main pool, covered by a sliding roof in low season (15 x 7.5 m), two small pools and two slides. Volleyball, table tennis, badminton and boules. Bicycle hire. Canoe trips are organised. Regular evening activities organised. Children's club. Off site: Municipal tennis courts adjoining.

At a glance

Welcome & Ambience	✓✓✓✓✓	Location	✓✓✓✓
Quality of Pitches	✓✓✓✓	Range of Facilities	✓✓✓✓✓

Directions

Site is 17 km south of Sarlat, and is on the east side of the D57, about 3.5 km north of the village of Daglan.

Charges 2003

Per person	€ 5.75
pitch with electricity (6A)	€ 11.50
30% Low season reductions.	

Reservations

Any length with deposit (€ 72) and fee (€ 8).
Tel: 05 53 28 20 88.
Email: Francis.Armagnac@wanadoo.fr

Open

15 May - 15 September.

(233)

FR24150 Camping Les Deux Vallées

24220 Vézac (Dordogne)

This site is enviably situated almost under the shadow of Beynac castle in the heart of the Dordogne. There are 88 flat marked touring pitches, including a newly established and more open section. Many pitches are of a good size, some generous, and are divided by trees and shrubs, all with electricity. There is plenty of shade and the general feel is of unspoilt but well managed woodland. There is a small fishing lake on site, and it is only a short distance to the Dordogne river for bathing or canoeing. The site is being steadily upgraded with more pitches planned by its Dutch owners, who provide a friendly welcome. The site is popular with Dutch visitors, but English is spoken. A single track railway runs along the eastern boundary of the site (trains are relatively infrequent). This site would be ideal for those wanting a quiet and relatively inexpensive base from which to visit the Dordogne region.

Facilities

The main unisex toilet block is modern and very clean, and gives an ample provision, with good access for disabled people. A second smaller recently refurbished block can be heated for off-season use. Shop and bar/restaurant (both 1/06-30/9) serving good value snacks and more ambitious meals to take away, eat inside or on the terrace. Good sized pool (1.6 m. deep) and children's pool (from mid May). Bicycle hire. Volleyball, basketball, small minigolf, boules area, table tennis, table football. Quiz nights and barbecues are a regular feature in the main season. Off site: Riding 2 km, golf 8 km.

At a glance

Welcome & Ambience	✓✓✓	Location	✓✓✓✓
Quality of Pitches	✓✓✓	Range of Facilities	✓✓✓✓

Directions

Site is on the northwest side of the D57 Beynac-et-Cazenac - Sarlat road, about 8 km from Sarlat and 2 km. from Beynac. From Beynac follow D57, pass under railway bridge and then take second turni left (site signed). Go across a level crossing, follow road around and take first turn left. Site is about 200 m. From Sarlat this turn will be on your right, just past a detatched stone house.

Charges 2003

Pitch	€ 4.00 - € 6.50
Per person over 3 yrs	€ 3.00 - € 5.00
electricity (6A)	€ 3.00
animal	€ 0.60 - € 1.00
local tax	€ 0.30
No credit cards.	

Reservations

Advised for July/Aug. and made with deposit (€ 100) and fee (€ 15). Tel: 05 53 29 53 55. Email: les2v@perigord.com

Open

All year.

Camping Les Deux Vallées

OPEN ALL YEAR

Our small and friendly Dutch owned 3 star campsite nestles in the heart of the glorious Dordogne Valley. With all the top class facilities you would expect at a price you thought was a thing of the past. Situated just 500m from the river and within gentle cycling distance of five of the region's major Châteaux "Les Deux Vallees" is the ideal base to explore the delights of this wonderful area. Low season and long stay discounts. Special rates for Rallies. Accommodation Rental. And above all a holiday you will remember with pleasure.

Annemarie & Ruel, Kathalÿn & Maartje,
Les Deux Vallées, 24220 Vezac, France
Phone: 00 33 553 29 53 55. Fax: 0033 553 31 09 81
E-mail: les2v@perigord.com - Web Site: www.les-2-vallees.com

FR24320 Camping Les Peneyrals

Le Poujol, St Crépin-Carlucet, 24590 Salignac - Eyvigues (Dordogne)

Set within easy reach of all the attractions of the Périgord region, M. and Mme. Havel have created an attractive and friendly family campsite. Set on a wooded hillside, with flowers in abundance (thanks to the dedication of Mme. Havel's mother), the site has 199 pitches, of which 87 are available for touring units. The pitches at the bottom of the hill tend to be quieter as they are further from the main facilities, but are all level and grassy (some on terraces), with electricity, and most have some shade. An attractive bar and restaurant with terrace overlook the excellent pool complex and sunbathing areas. At the bottom of the campsite is a small fishing lake with carp (no charge to fish), and in July and August, activities are organised including archery, various sports tournaments, aqua gym, discos and a children's club. The site is used fairly unobtrusively by two tour operators (71 pitches).

Facilities

Two modern, unisex toilet blocks provide good quality facilities, including provision for babies and disabled visitors. Motorcaravan service point. Good value shop, restaurant and takeaway. Pool complex with two large pools (one heated), paddling pool and four water slides with splash pool. Bicycle hire. Minigolf, tennis court (charged). Football. Badminton, volleyball and table tennis. Play area. Off site: Supermarkets, banks, etc. in Sarlat (11 km).

At a glance

Welcome & Ambience	✓✓✓✓✓	Location	✓✓✓✓
Quality of Pitches	✓✓✓✓	Range of Facilities	✓✓✓✓✓

Directions

Site is 11 km. north of Sarlat. From D704 (Sarlat - Montignac) turn east on D60 towards Salignac-Eyvigues. After 4 km. turn south on D56 towards St Crépin-Carlucet. Site is 500 m. along this road.

Charges 2003

Per person	€ 4.20 - € 6.40
pitch with electricity (5/10A)	€ 7.90 - € 12.60

Reservations

Advised for July and August, with deposit (€ 70) and booking fee (€ 17). Tel: 05 53 28 85 71. Email: camping.peneyrals@wanadoo.fr

Open

15 May - 12 September.

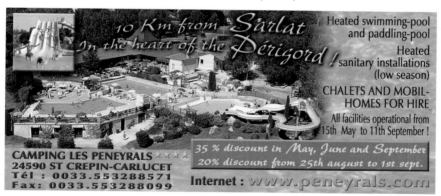

Heated swimming-pool and paddling-pool

Heated sanitary installations (low season)

CHALETS AND MOBIL-HOMES FOR HIRE

All facilities operational from 15th May to 11th September !

35 % discount in May, June and September
20% discount from 25th august to 1st sept.

CAMPING LES PENEYRALS ★★★★
24590 ST CREPIN-CARLUCET
Tél : 0033.553288571
Fax: 0033.553288099
Internet : www.peneyrals.com

FR24310 Camping Caravaning La Bouquerie

24590 St Geniès-en-Périgord (Dordogne)

La Bouquerie is a lively site, situated within easy reach of the main road network in the Dordogne, but without any associated traffic noise. The main complex is based around some beautifully restored traditional buildings. It includes a bar and restaurant overlooking the pool complex, with a large outdoor terrace. Only 37 of the 185 pitches are used for touring units, Of varying size (80-120 sq.m.), these are flat and grassy, some with shade, and all have electrical connections. The rest of the pitches are taken up by site owned mobile homes and two tour operators. In high season the site offers a range of tournaments and sporting activities (aqua-gym, archery, canoeing, walks etc) as well as a children's club. There are plans to improve the lake at the foot of the site. La Bouquerie is ideally situated for exploring the Périgord region, and has something to offer families with children of all ages.

Facilities

The three unisex toilet blocks contain a mixture of new and older facilities, but are all very clean and well maintained. Two blocks provide facilities for disabled visitors and baby rooms. Covered laundry area with washing machines and covered drying lines. Shop (15/05-15/09) for bread, milk, papers and a range of groceries, as well as takeaway food. Bar and restaurant (both 15/05-15/09). Pool complex (all season) with paddling pool. Fishing in lake. Bicycle hire. Off site: Shops and restaurants etc in the nearby village.

At a glance

Welcome & Ambience	✓✓✓✓	Location	✓✓✓✓
Quality of Pitches	✓✓✓	Range of Facilities	✓✓✓✓✓

Directions

Site is signed just off D704 Sarlat - Montignac road, 500 m. north of junction with D64 St Geniès road. Turn off D704 at sign and take first left to site.

Charges 2004

Per person	€ 4.60 - € 6.50
pitch with electricity	€ 9.30 - € 12.00
Less 20-30% outside 5 July - 25 Aug.	

Reservations

Advised for high season. Tel: 05 53 28 98 22. Email: labouquerie@wanadoo.fr

Open

Easter - 28 September.

235

FR24340 Camping Le Val de la Marquise

24260 Campagne (Dordogne)

This recently refurbished campsite, set between the tourist centres of Le Bugue and Les Eyzies, is in an ideal situation from which to explore the châteaux and prehistoric sites of the Périgord region. The 131 touring pitches are flat, grassy and all of a good size (mostly over 110 sq.m.). The pitches are divided by shrubs, and some have shade from mature trees, whilst others are more open. Most have electricity. The site has a good quality bar and snack bar with takeaway, and receptions stocks a range of basic groceries including bread made freshly on site every day. Weekly entertainment and excursions are organised in high season, but the site retains a relaxed peaceful air and is an ideal retreat after a busy day of sightseeing in the area.

Facilities

The central, very clean toilet block provides first-rate facilities, including controllable showers, washbasins in cubicles, laundry and dishwashing sinks and a baby bath. A smaller block near reception houses facilities for disabled visitors (no ramp but only a half inch step into the building) and washing and drying machines. Bar (1/6-15/9) and snack bar/takeaway (15/7-15/8) with terrace. Swimming pool with sun terrace and paddling pool. Small fishing lake (free). Chalets to rent. Off site: Bars and restaurants in the village of Champagne (500 m).

At a glance

Welcome & Ambience	✓✓✓	Location	✓✓✓✓
Quality of Pitches	✓✓✓✓	Range of Facilities	✓✓✓✓

Directions

Site is 28 km. west of Sarlat, and 4 km. southeast of Le Bugue. Take D703/D706 Le Bugue - Les Eyzies road. At village of Champagne take D35 heading east towards St Cyprien (there is a peculiar 'Y' junction where the D703, D706 and D35 meet). Site is about 500 m. along the D35 on the right.

Charges 2003

Per unit incl. 6 persons	€ 4.20 - € 7.00
extra person	€ 3.10 - € 4.40
child (2-10 yrs)	€ 2.10 - € 3.00
electricity (15A)	€ 3.00
animal	€ 1.05 - € 1.50

Reservations

Advised for July/Aug. with deposit (€ 31 per week) and fee (€ 16). Tel: 05 53 54 74 10. Email: val-marquise@wanadoo.fr

Open

4 April - 15 October.

FR24350 Camping Le Moulin de la Pique

24170 Belves (Dordogne)

Set in the grounds of converted former mill and iron foundry, this impressive and well managed site offers something for every member of the family. The 135 touring pitches are flat, grassy and extremely spacious (most well over 100 sq.m.) and most have electricity (6A), water and drainage. Some pitches border the lake which can be used for both fishing and boating. The 11th century fortified town of Belvès is only 2 km. away and the campsite is well located for access to the many other attractions of the Dordogne valley. Daily entertainment and activities is organised and there is even a 'fossil field', where children can become amateur archaeologists, digging for genuine fossils. Discounted golf, canoeing, bike hire and horse riding can be arranged through the campsite reception. Used by one UK tour operator (55 pitches).

Facilities

Three modern toilet blocks provide good quality unisex facilities. Baby baths and changing. Facilities for disabled visitors. Dishwashing and laundry sinks. Washing and drying machines. Bar and restaurant, snack bar and shop (open all season), Swimming pool (heated), paddling pool, four water slides with separate landing pool. Playing field, football field. Volleyball. Table tennis.Tennis. Boules. Minigolf. Various play areas. TV and games room. Toddler's playroom. Library. Internet access. Mobile homes to rent. Off site: Bars, restaurants and shops in the village of Belvès (2 km).

At a glance

Welcome & Ambience	✓✓✓✓	Location	✓✓✓✓
Quality of Pitches	✓✓✓✓✓	Range of Facilities	✓✓✓✓✓

Directions

Site is 35 km. southwest of Sarlat. From Siorac-en-Périgord, take D710 south (signed Belvès and Fumel). After about 4.5 km. at roundabout, continue straight ahead on D710 (signed Fumel) and site is about 2.5 km along on the left hand side.

Charges 2003

Per person (over 3 yrs)	€ 5.20 - € 7.30
pitch	€ 12.00 - € 14.00

Reservations

Advised for July/Aug. with 50% deposit. Tel: 05 53 29 01 15. Email: info@rcn-lemoulindelapique.fr

Open

20 April - 11 October.

FR24360 Camping Le Mondou

24370 St. Julien de Lampon (Dordogne)

This quiet little Dutch owned site mid-way between Sarlat and Souillac is ideally situated for visiting a wide range of attractions in the Dordogne and Lot departments. It is set amongst countryside at the edge of the small village of St Julien, and only 2 km. from the Dordogne river. The 62 grassy pitches are of medium size (tending to be long and narrow rather than square), divided by shrubs, and with some shade from a variety of trees. All have electricity. The friendly and helpful owners – John and Lia, organise regular evening entertainments during high season, and work hard to ensure that everyone enjoys their stay at Le Mondou.

Facilities

Two sanitary blocks provide basic facilities, including facilities for disabled visitors, baby baths, washing machine, ironing board and iron. Terrace bar and snack bar with reasonably priced menu. Large swimming pool with sun terrace and children's paddling pool. Rustic style children's play area and large playing field. Boules pitch, volleyball/badminton net. Off site: Bar, restaurant and small shop in the village of St Julien-de-Lampon about 1 km. away.

At a glance

| Welcome & Ambience | ✓✓✓✓ | Location | ✓✓✓✓ |
| Quality of Pitches | ✓✓✓ | Range of Facilities | ✓✓✓✓ |

Directions

Site is 12 km. southwest of Souillac. From D703 Sarlat-Souillac road turn south across the river at Rouffillac, signed towards St. Julien-de-Lampon. On entering village of St Julien turn left on the D50, signed Mareuil and Le Roc. Follow road (it is narrow in one or two places), and just at the end of the village site is signed at a right turn. Follow for 500 m. to site on the right.

Charges 2003

Per person	€ 4.00
child (under 7 yrs)	€ 1.70
pitch	€ 4.00
electricity (6A)	€ 2.45

Reservations

Advised for July/August. Tel: 05 53 29 70 37. E-mail: lemondou@camping-dordogne.info

Open

1 May - 15 October.

FR46040 Camping Moulin de Laborde

46700 Montcabrier (Lot)

The watermill and its outbuildings at Moulin de Laborde have been sympathetically developed and provide for the site facilities with a courtyard and terrace. Bordered by woods, hills and a small river, there are 90 pitches of at least 100 sq.m on level grass. Well marked out by shrubs and trees, all have electricity. A gate at the back of the site leads walkers onto a 'Grand Randonée'. The Château of Bonaguil and towns of Fumel and Villefranche du Perigord are close. The friendly Dutch owners speak good English and French.

Facilities

The good toilet block has well designed showers and washbasins in cabins. Covered area provides sinks for dishwashing and laundry. Unit for disabled people. Washing machine and dryer. Shop stocks basics and gas (all season). Small bar, restaurant and takeaway. Swimming pool with sunbathing area and paddling pool (1/5-15/9). Play area. Small lake for recreation with rafts and rowing boats. Volleyball, badminton court, boules, recreation room and table tennis. Mountain bike hire. Fishing. Rock climbing and archery lessons. Live music one evening a week. Dogs are not accepted. Off site: Riding 5 km, golf 8 km, tennis near and canoeing on the Lot.

At a glance

| Welcome & Ambience | ✓✓✓✓ | Location | ✓✓✓✓ |
| Quality of Pitches | ✓✓✓✓ | Range of Facilities | ✓✓✓✓ |

Directions

Site is near Montcabrier, which is just south of the D673, 12 km. from Fumel. Follow D673 north for 1 km. towards Gourdon, and site is on the left.

Charges 2003

Per person	€ 5.50
child (under 7 yrs)	€ 2.75
pitch	€ 7.00
electricity (6A)	€ 2.25
local tax	€ 0.30

No credit cards.

Reservations

Write to site with deposit (€ 7 per night booked). Tel: 05 65 24 62 06. Email: moulindelaborde@wanadoo.fr

Open

1 May - 15 September.

FR46050 Camping Le Rêve

46300 Le Vigan (Lot)

Le Rêve is a very peaceful site situated in the heart of rolling countryside where the Perigord runs into Quercy. Le Rêve continues to impress us with its tranquillity and the young Dutch owners are keen to develop the site in such a way that this will not be lost. The 56 touring pitches are all of good size, with access to electricity, and divided by shrubs. A few of the pitches are situated at the edge of the forest, and provide plenty of shade. Plenty of large grassy areas give lots of space for children to play, and make this site particularly suitable for young families.

Facilities

The modern toilet block includes a heated enclosed area for cooler weather. Washbasins in cabins, special cubicles for disabled people and a baby room. Washing machine and dryers. Small shop for basics (bread, milk etc.), pleasant bar, restaurant and takeaway (all open all season). Small, clean, solar heated swimming pool and large paddling pool with 'mushroom' fountain. Play area. Boules. Bicycle hire. Table tennis and volleyball. Off site: Fishing 5 km, riding 2 km.

At a glance

Welcome & Ambience	✓✓✓✓	Location	✓✓✓
Quality of Pitches	✓✓✓✓	Range of Facilities	✓✓✓✓

Directions

From N20 Souillac-Cahors road take D673 3 km. south of Payrac. After 2 km. site is signed down small lane on west side of the road. Turn here, and follow signs for another 2.5 km. to site.

Charges 2003

Per person	€ 4.00
child (under 7 yrs)	€ 2.20
pitch	€ 6.00
electricity (6A)	€ 2.50

Less 20-30% outside July/Aug. No credit cards.

Reservations

Advised for high season and made for any length with deposit (€ 70) and fee (€ 5). Tel: 05 65 41 25 20. Email: info@campinglereve.com

Open

25 April - 15 September.

FR46030 Camping Les Pins

46350 Payrac-en-Quercy (Lot)

Camping Les Pins is suitable for a Dordogne holiday or overnight stop on way south. It is named after its magnificent pine trees and also has impressive views. There are 125 clearly marked, level pitches (100 sq.m), of which 55 are for touring units (some mobile homes on site). Many pitches are shady although there is a fair number of sunny places, and all have electricity, most also with water and drainage. There is a bar and a good value restaurant with reasonably imaginative menus. The site is used by tour operators.

Facilities

Three toilet blocks, two recently modernised, are well maintained and include washbasins in cabins and good baby bath facilities. Dishwashing and laundry sinks, washing machines and dryers (with plenty of drying lines). Motorcaravan service point. Shop (1/6-31/8). Refurbished bar/restaurant with terrace and views of the swimming pool. Good takeaway (1/6-31/8). Swimming pool (15 x 17 m.), three water slides and smaller paddling pool (15/5-15/9). Tennis court. Table tennis, pétanque and volleyball. TV and library. Some entertainment in season, including weekly family discos. English is spoken. Off site: Fishing 7 km, riding 10 km.

At a glance

Welcome & Ambience	✓✓✓✓	Location	✓✓✓✓
Quality of Pitches	✓✓✓✓	Range of Facilities	✓✓✓✓

Directions

Site entrance is on western carriageway of the N20 just south of Payrac-en-Quercy, 16 km. from Souillac.

Latest charges

Per person	€ 4.88
child (under 7 yrs)	€ 3.05
pitch	€ 7.32
with electricity (6A)	€ 9.91
local tax	€ 0.30

Less 30% outside 15/6-1/9.

Reservations

Made for min. 1 week with deposit (25%) plus fee (€ 15,24). Tel: 05 65 37 96 32. Email: info@les-pins-camping.com

Open

1 April - 30 September.

FR46010 Camping Domaine de la Paille Basse

46200 Souillac-sur-Dordogne (Lot)

Lying some 8 km. from Souillac, this family owned, high quality site is easily accessible from the N20 and well placed to take advantage of excursions into the Dordogne. It is part of a large 'Domaine' of 80 hectares, which is available to campers for walks and recreation. The site is quite high up and there are excellent views over the surrounding countryside. The 250 pitches are in two main areas – one is level in cleared woodland with good shade, and the other on grass in open ground without shade. Numbered and marked, the pitches are a minimum 100 sq.m. and often considerably more. About 80 have individual electricity, water and drainage, and electricity is available to all the others. Activities and entertainment are organised in season (animation was of a very high standard when we stayed). For good reason, the site can get very busy in high season and is popular with tour operators (20%), but there is more space available from mid August.

Facilities

The main toilet facilities are in three different sections, all centrally located close to reception (there is also a small night unit at one end of site). All have modern equipment and are kept very clean. Laundry facilities. Shop for essentials. Good restaurant, bar with terrace and takeaway. Crêperie. Good swimming pool complex, with main pool (25 x 10 m), second one (10 x 6 m) and paddling pool (unheated). Solarium. Sound-proofed disco room (twice weekly in season). TV rooms (with satellite). Cinema room below the pool area. Archery, tennis (charged), football, volleyball and table tennis. Playground. Off site: Golf 4 km.

At a glance

Welcome & Ambience	✓✓✓✓	Location	✓✓✓✓
Quality of Pitches	✓✓✓✓	Range of Facilities	✓✓✓✓

Directions

From Souillac take D15 road leading northwest towards Salignac-Eyvignes and after 6 km. turn right at camp sign and follow steep and narrow approach road for 2 km.

Charges 2003

Per person	€ 5.60
child (under 7 yrs)	€ 3.60
pitch	€ 8.70
electricity (3A)	€ 3.60
local tax	€ 0.20

Less 20% outside 15/6-1/9.
Camping Cheques accepted.

Reservations

Advised mid-July - mid-Aug. and made for min. 1 week with deposit and € 18,29 booking fee. Tel: 05 65 37 85 48. Email: paille.basse@wanadoo.fr

Open

15 May - 15 September.

Le Domaine de la Paille Basse, half way between Rocamadour and the caves of Lascaux, is an excellent base for excursions enabling you to visit the highlights of two régions. Situated at the top of a hill, La Paille Basse is a restored medieval village in the heart of 200 acres of wooded land. La Paille Basse has carefully combined architectural beauty and modernity, fitting its facilities within the original buildings.

Castel Camping La Paille Basse
★★★★
46200 Souillac
Tel: 0033 565 37 85 48
Fax: 0033 565 37 09 58
LES CASTELS

FR46080 Camping Château de Lacomté

46500 Carlucet (Lot)

Château de Lacomté is the closest site in this guide to Rocamadour; just a 15 minute drive along a back road. A little further on is the Gouffre de Padirac with its underground rivers and concretions. The site is run by an English family, Sheila and Stuart Coe and their children, who have worked hard developing the site and provide a warm welcome. The restaurant and bar make up part of the converted outbuildings of the château. The views from the terrace over mature woodland are memorable, and the pool and terrace are beautifully lit at night. The Coes try to retain as much of the meadowland as possible for wildlife and flowers. The main camping field is quietly located down a slope to one side of the bar area. The first section contains pitches marked out on slightly sloping ground, most with flat areas, and six with hardstanding. The majority of pitches on this upper terrace have good shade, although most pitches on the extensive lower field are still relatively open. All pitches have electricity, water and drainage. The site is very popular with British visitors and it is advisable to reserve if you want one of the best places. Perhaps a little more out of the way than other Dordogne sites and out of season you may have to travel to the nearest town for bread and other supplies. A new and novel service, aimed at people with large motorhomes, cyclists and backpackers, offers the use of a small car included in the cost of the pitch (drivers over 25 yrs). A 'Freedom' pitch including the car, two persons and 10A electricity costs € 43.25 per day.

Facilities

The good, clean toilet block is well equipped. Laundry facilities. Fridge hire. Small shop (15/6-15/9). Restaurant (with a good reputation). Bar. Large swimming pool (from 1/6) with paddling area. Playground, tennis court and table tennis. Torches useful. Off site: Fishing 6-10 km. Close to Gramat and Cahors for supermarkets and other shops.

At a glance

| Welcome & Ambience | ✓✓✓✓ | Location | ✓✓✓✓ |
| Quality of Pitches | ✓✓✓✓ | Range of Facilities | ✓✓✓✓ |

Directions

From A20 take exit 56, at second roundabout take third exit onto D807 direction Gramat. After approx 1.5 km. take D32 direction Rocamadour/Carlucet. After 2.5 km. left fork and follow signs to site. If approaching from Gramat direction (N140, D807) do not turn left at Le Bastit onto D50, but continue for 5 km, and turn left onto D32. The D50 is totally unsuitable for all types of caravan.

Charges 2003

Per person	€ 5.80
child (1-12 yrs)	€ 3.35
pitch with electricity	€ 11.65

Less 20-35% in low seasons.

Reservations

Made with 25% deposit and fee (€ 7,62).
Tel: 05 65 38 75 46.
Email: chateaulacomte@wanadoo.fr

Open

15 May - 15 October.

FR46110 Camping du Port

46600 Creysse (Lot)

Set off the beaten track this small, unassuming riverside campsite provides an unusual combination of peace and tranquility alongside a range of sporting activities to occupy even the most adventurous of people. Pitches are mostly flat, and of a large size (100 sq.m plus), with plenty of shade from the abundant trees, but no dividing hedges or fences. 70 of the 100 touring pitches have electricity. The far side of the site slopes down to the picturesque Dordogne river, providing a launching area for canoes, and a small gravel 'beach'. The campsite owner runs daily activities including canoeing, caving, climbing, abseiling, cycling, walking and woodland assault course through the trees, all under qualified supervision. On-site entertainments include regular paella, 'moules and frites' and bbq evenings, live musical entertainment and open air cinema screenings (July/Aug). Despite all these activities the campsite retains a very rural 'a la ferme' ambience, and is ideal for anyone seeking a restful time away from the hustle and bustle of the larger sites along the Dordogne.

Facilities

Central toilet block contains a mix of older and more modern facilities, which are a little basic, but well cleaned, and would appear more than adequate for the number of pitches. Toilets are mostly British style, washbasins both open and in cubicles, showers pre-set pushbutton type. Dishwashing and laundry sinks, washing machine. Small shop with reasonable range of groceries, bread, camping gas etc. Open air bar and terrace, small snack bar/takeaway. Attractive swimming pool with sun terrace (no paddling pool). All facilities open 1/5-30/9, but may be limited in low season. Mobile homes to rent. Off site: Bar/restaurant in the pretty medieval village of Creysse, about 500 yds away, providing a varied menu including 'a la carte'.

At a glance

| Welcome & Ambience | ✓✓✓✓ | Location | ✓✓✓✓ |
| Quality of Pitches | ✓✓✓✓ | Range of Facilities | ✓✓✓✓ |

Directions

Site is approximately 15 km. east of Souillac. From the village of Martel on the D703 take the D23 south to Creysse. The site is signposted on the left just before you enter the village.

Charges 2003

Per person	€ 3.60
child under 7 yrs	€ 2.60
pitch with electricity (6A)	€ 6.10
animal	€ 0.50
local tax	€ 0.20

Reservations

Not required. Tel: 05 65 32 27 59.
Email: circal@wanadoo.fr

Open

1 May - 30 September.

FR47010 Camping Caravaning Moulin du Périé

47500 Sauveterre-la-Lemance (Lot-et-Garonne)

Set in a quiet area and surrounded by woodlands this peaceful little site is well away from much of the tourist bustle. Its 125 grass pitches, divided by mixed trees and bushes, are reasonably sized and extremely well kept, as indeed is the entire site. All pitches have electricity and most enjoy good shade, with younger trees and shrubs rapidly filling out in the new area. The picturesque old mill buildings, adorned with flowers and creepers, now home to the restaurant etc. and the food is to be recommended as is the owner's extensive knowledge of wine that he is pleased to share with visitors. The attractive front courtyard is complemented by an equally pleasant terrace at the rear. A quiet, friendly site with regular visitors – reservation is advised for July/Aug. A 'Sites et Paysages' member.

Facilities

Three clean, modern and well maintained toilet blocks incorporate facilities for disabled visitors, babies and laundry. Motorcaravan service facilities. Shop for essentials (with gas). Bar/reception and restaurant (including takeaway). Two small, clean swimming pools (no bermuda-style shorts) overlook a shallow, spring water lake, ideal for inflatable boats and paddling. Bordering the lake, a large grass field is popular for football and volleyball. Boules, table tennis, outdoor chess. New children's playground and trampoline. Small, indoor play area. Bicycle hire. In season various activities, on and off site are arranged; including canoeing, riding, wine tasting visits, sight seeing trips plus weekly barbecues and gastronomic meals. Winter caravan storage. Off site: Fishing 1 km. Small supermarket in village and larger stores in Fumel.

Directions

Sauveterre-la-Lémance lies by the Fumel - Périgueux (D710) road, midway between the Dordogne and Lot rivers. From D710, cross railway line, straight through village and turn left (northeast) at far end on C201 minor road signed Château Sauveterre, Loubejec and site. Site is 3 km. up this road on right.

Charges 2003

Per unit incl. 2 persons	€ 11.60 - € 19.80
with electricity (6A)	€ 15.05 - € 23.25
extra person	€ 3.75 - € 5.90
child (under 7 yrs)	€ 1.60 - € 3.15
animal	€ 1.90 - € 3.60

Camping Cheques accepted.

Reservations

Advised for July/Aug. and made with deposit (€ 130) and fee (€ 18). Tel: 05 53 40 67 26. Email: moulinduperie@wanadoo.fr

Open

6 May - 25 September.

At a glance

Welcome & Ambience	✓✓✓✓✓	Location	✓✓✓✓
Quality of Pitches	✓✓✓✓	Range of Facilities	✓✓✓✓

FR47030 Castel Camping Le Château de Fonrives

Rives, 47210 Villeréal (Lot-et-Garonne)

This is one of those very pleasant Dordogne sites set in pretty part-farmed, part-wooded countryside, close to the delightful old town of Villeréal. The neat, orderly site is a mixture of hazelnut orchards, woodland with lake, château (mostly 16th century) and camping areas. An attractive avenue leads to the barns adjacent to the château which have been tastefully converted (the restaurant particularly so). There are 200 pitches, 140 for touring units. All have electricity, 60 have water taps and they are of 100-150 sq.m. in size. Pitches near the woodland receive moderate shade, but elsewhere there is light shade from hedges and young trees. Some 'wild' camping is possible in one or two areas. The lake can be used for fishing or boating.

Facilities

Two main sanitary units are clean and adequate including washbasins in well appointed cabins and some private bathrooms (for hire by the week). Facilities for children and babies. Laundry rooms. Motorcaravan services. Shop. Elegant restaurant, plus bar, snacks and takeaway meals (all 10/6-10/9). Covered swimming pool (no bermuda style shorts) with water slides and paddling pool. Play areas. Small field for volleyball and football. Reading room. Minigolf. Tennis. Bicycle hire. Activities organised for children and adults in season, including excursions and walks. Caravan storage. Off site: Riding 8 km.

At a glance

Welcome & Ambience	✓✓✓✓	Location	✓✓✓✓
Quality of Pitches	✓✓✓✓	Range of Facilities	✓✓✓✓

Directions

Site is about 2 km. northwest of Villeréal, on the Bergerac road (D14/D207).

Charges 2004

Per unit incl. 2 persons	€ 16.00 - € 23.00
extra person	€ 4.00
child (under 7 yrs)	€ 2.00
electricity (4-10A)	€ 3.00 - € 5.50

Reservations

Advisable for July/Aug. Tel: 05 53 36 63 38. Email: chateau.de.fonrives@wanadoo.fr

Open

4 May - 14 September.

FR47100M Camping Municipal Tonneins

47400 Tonneins (Lot-et-Garonne)

Close to the River Garonne, this small site has a rather formal charm with neat flower beds, well mown lawns and a generally extremely well cared for appearance. With a small reception, the Guardien based on site and a security barrier, it only has 40 pitches (a few occupied by seasonal units) plus a meadow for additional camping. All with electricity, the pitches are of a reasonable size, partly separated by hedges and shrubs. The site is on the southern outskirts of the town with a fair choice of shops, restaurants, etc, and only a 15 minute drive from the charming old riverside town of Port St Marie. There is some road and rail noise at times. This is a good stopping off point.

Facilities

Sanitary facilities, very clean when seen in high season, provide British style WCs, washbasins in cabins and dishwashing sinks (H&C) under cover. Purpose built and roomy but of fairly old design, they are adequate rather than luxurious. Washing machine. No proper chemical disposal point. Ice and cold drinks available. Under cover area with fridge and freezer and tables and chairs. Small play area, sandpit and table tennis. Torch useful.

At a glance

Welcome & Ambience	✓✓✓✓	Location	✓✓✓✓
Quality of Pitches	✓✓✓✓✓	Range of Facilities	✓✓✓

Directions

Take either exit 5 from autoroute to Marmande then the N113 south or exit 6 to Aiguillon (avoid town) and follow N113 north. Site off N113 just south of Tonneins.

Charges 2003

Per unit incl. 1 person	€ 5.10
incl. 2 persons	€ 7.24
extra person	€ 2.35
electricity (15A)	€ 3.00
local tax	€ 3.00

Reservations

Contact site. Tel: 05 53 79 02 28.

Open

1 June - 30 September.

242

FR47050 Camping Moulin de Campech

47160 Villefranche-de-Queyran (Lot-et-Garonne)

This site is run by Sue and George Thomas along with Sue's parents, Dot and Bob Dunn. A cheery welcome and a free drink awaits you and a determination to ensure that you enjoy your stay. A fabulous view also awaits as you descend the drive from the entrance. The trout lake with graceful weeping willows feeds under the restored mill house which is home to the owners, the main administration area alongside and the bar and restaurant. Enjoy the fare produced by Sue on the pretty terrace as the trout jump (fresh trout is a menu option). The river continues through one side of the site. Children will need supervision around the lake and at the pool which is on an elevated area above the mill house. The 60 pitches are mostly divided by hedges, with electricity available (long leads may be necessary in places).

Facilities

The single, rather ordinary toilet unit has modern fittings, can be heated and includes both British and Turkish style WCs, some washbasins in cubicles with hot water, or open washbasins (cold only in men's section). Covered dishwashing and laundry sinks (H&C). Two washing machines and a dryer. Bar and restaurant. Terraced swimming pool and baby pool. Open grassy area for volley-ball and other games. Table tennis and baby-foot in tent outside. Board games, boules and small library. Barbecue and gourmet nights organised in high seaosn. Fishing (discounted rate for campers). Torch useful. Off site: Watersports, bicycle hire, golf or riding 10 km. Markets every day in villages and towns around the region.

At a glance

Welcome & Ambience	✓✓✓✓✓	Location	✓✓✓✓
Quality of Pitches	✓✓✓✓	Range of Facilities	✓✓✓✓

Directions

Take A10 south to Bordeaux. Join A62 for Toulouse and take exit 6 for Damazan. Follow D8 to Mont de Marsan, at Cap du Bosc turn right onto D11 for Casteljaloux. The site is 10 km. on the right and signed.

Charges 2004

Per person	€ 3.45 - € 4.85
child (under 7 yrs)	€ 2.60 - € 3.50
pitch	€ 6.80 - € 8.50
electricity (2/6A)	€ 2.30 - € 3.80
dog	€ 2.40

Reservations

Advised for July/Aug. Tel: 05 53 88 72 43. Email: campech@wanadoo.fr

Open

1 April - 24 October.

Limousin & Auvergne

These two quiet and deeply rural provinces are right in the centre of France and are surrounded by the tourist regions of the Loire Valley, the Dordogne and the Auvergne. Unknown to many, it is often 'forgotten territory' but by some it's considered close to paradise.

We have combined two official regions: Limousin with départements 19 Corrèze, 23 Creuse, 87 Haute-Vienne; and Auvergne, 03 Allier, 15 Cantal 43 Haute-Loire, 63 Puy-de-Dôme. Also included is 48 Lozère, part of the offical region of Languedoc-Roussillon

This is the home of Limoges porcelain and Aubosson tapestry, of exceptional Romanesque and Gothic Churches and fairytale Renaissance châteaux. Limousin is an unspoilt, thinly populated region on the western side of the Massif Central. With hills and gorges and lush green meadows, numerous ancient village churches dot the landscape as well as more imposing abbey churches and fortresses. The many lakes and rivers of the Limousin provide endless possibilities for canoeing, sailing, wind-surfing and other watersports. To the south, fortified cities cling to mountain sides, home to many religious events and legends.

The Auvergne, set in the heart of the Massif Central was formed by a series of volcanic eruptions and is a dramatic region of awe-inspiring non-active volcanoes, lakes, sparkling rivers, green valleys and forests. There are also numerous under-ground streams that have carved out extensive and fantastic cave systems, for which the region is famous. It is a wonderful destination for nature lovers, those who enjoy active outdoor pursuits or for people who want to relax at spa resorts.

Cuisine of the region

Limousin is known for a thick soup called *bréjaude* and its beef, which is extremely tender and full of flavour. Local specialties in the Auvergne include ham and andouille sausages, stuffed cabbage, and bacon with lentil and *cèpes* (mushrooms). Le Puy is famed for its lentils and *Vereine du Velay* – yellow and green liqueurs made from over 30 mountain plants.

Aligot: purée of potatoes with Tomme de Cantal cheese, cream, garlic and butter

Friand Sanflorin: pork meat and herbs in pastry

Jambon d'Auvergne: a tasty mountain ham

Perdrix à l'Auvergnate: partridge stewed in white wine

Potée Auvergnate: a stew of vegetables, cabbage, pork and sausage

Places of interest

Aubusson: long tradition of tapestry making, Hotel de Ville tapestry collections

Clermont-Ferrand: old city centre, 11th and 12th century Notre Dame du Port Basilica, 13th century cathedral; known as *ville noire* for its houses built in local black volcanic rock

Limoges: porcelain, enamel and faience work, château, church of St Michel-de-Lions, cathedral of St Etienne

Vichy: spa, natural spring park

tip

FOR THOSE FASCINATED BY CREEPY CRAWLIES, TAKE A TRIP TO THE PARC DES ABEILLES AND THE CITÉ DES INSECTES - A GREAT DAY OUT FOR CHILDREN!

FR03170M Camping Municipal Dompierre-sur-Besbre

03290 Dompierre-sur-Besbre (Allier)

An immaculate site with a cosmopolitan clientele, this very attractive, floral site has level, individually hedged, grassy pitches. It is located next to the municipal sports fields, and within easy walking distance of the town centre and supermarket (700 m). There are 70 pitches, some very large, with only a few long stay units, leaving about 65 for tourists; 60 have electricity and most have full service facilities. The warden is very proud of his efficiently run, value for money site. The Canal Latéral de la Loire is good for boating – do visit the nearby vertical boat lift.

Facilities

The toilet block is kept very clean and includes some washbasins in curtained cubicles for ladies, Turkish and British style WCs, dishwashing and laundry sinks plus a washing machine. Excellent motorcaravan service point. New facilities are under construction. Off site: The Vallée de la Besbre has a wealth of activities, with tennis and a swimming pool close by. Several rivers and small lakes nearby are suitable for fishing. Cycle tracks and footpaths, and equestrian centres in the area.

At a glance

Welcome & Ambience	✓✓✓✓	Location	✓✓✓
Quality of Pitches	✓✓✓✓	Range of Facilities	✓✓✓

Directions

Site is southeast of town centre just before the junction of N79 and D55, close to the river bridge

Charges 2003

Per adult	€ 1.85
child (5-14 yrs)	€ 1.00
pitch	€ 1.40
motorcaravan	€ 1.70
electricity (10A)	€ 1.60

Reservations

Advised for high season. Tel: 04 70 34 55 57.

Open

15 May - 15 September.

FR03010 Camping de la Filature

Ile de Nieres, 03450 Ebreuil (Allier)

Near to the spa town of Vichy and beside a fine fly fishing river that borders the Massif Central region, this site makes a good base to explore the Auvergne. Developed on the site of a spinning mill (hot water is still produced by wood burning – note the chimney), this rural setting is home to peacocks (including some white ones). It has an individuality that is unusual in French sites which is being perpetuated by its English owners. There are 80 spacious, grassy pitches, most with shade from mature trees and many directly on the river bank. In summer the river is clean, shallow and pleasant to play in. There is a deeper swimming area 500 m. away. Most pitches have electricity. The area is ideal for walking and cycling, especially mountain biking. Bird watching and wild flowers are additional attractions.

Facilities

Very clean sanitary facilities are in individual cubicles in pleasantly decorated buildings. Fully equipped, they include mostly British type toilets, bathroom, a washing machine and ironing facilities. Small shop for essentials (1/5-30/9). Baker calls. Bar (1/6-30/9). Excellent takeaway (1/6-30/9). Barbecues and pizza nights organised in high season. River bathing and fishing. Children's play area. Bicycle hire. Minigolf, table football, table tennis. Off site: Riding, canoeing and tennis nearby.

At a glance

Welcome & Ambience	✓✓✓✓✓	Location	✓✓✓✓
Quality of Pitches	✓✓✓✓✓	Range of Facilities	✓✓✓✓

Directions

Site is well signed from exit 12 of A71 autoroute to Clermont Ferrand in the direction of Ébreuil. It is about 6 km. from the A71 and 1 km. west of Ébreuil beside the river on the D915 towards the Chouvigny gorges.

Charges 2004

Per unit incl. 2 persons	€ 15.00
extra adult	€ 4.00
child (under 16 yrs)	€ 2.00
electricity (3/6A)	€ 2.00 - € 3.00

Discounts in low season.

Reservations

Made with deposit (€ 30 per week of stay or full amount if stay costs less). Tel: 04 70 90 72 01. Email: camping.filature@libertysurf.fr

Open

31 March - 1 October.

FR03050 **Camping Caravaning La Petite Valette**

Sazeret, 03390 Montmarault (Allier)

Originally a working farm, La Petite Valette has been transformed by its hard working Dutch and German owners into a very attractive and peaceful campsite. There are 55 level grassy pitches of average size, many with rural views, each with an electricity point and separated by flowering bushes and trees, which gives some shade. A small lake in one of the lower fields is stocked with fish for anglers. Ponies and small livestock (rabbits, chickens and ducks) keep the farm feeling alive and restaurant tables in the cottage garden overflowing with flowers provide a tranquil atmosphere. The countryside is ideal for cycling and there are many interesting old villages nearby.

Facilities

Toilet facilities are housed in original outbuildings, each block having very good quality, modern fittings. A large separate room has full facilities for disabled people, families and babies. Laundry. Bread can be ordered. Meals and snacks served in the farmhouse restaurant (to order only). Takeaway service. New swimming and paddling pools, with sunbathing areas. Small fenced play area with seating. Table tennis in one of the barns, mountain bike hire and organised activities in July/Aug. Off site: Tennis, riding and sailing in the area. Montmarault 4 km. for shopping needs.

At a glance

| Welcome & Ambience | ✓✓✓ | Location | ✓✓✓✓ |
| Quality of Pitches | ✓✓✓ | Range of Facilities | ✓✓✓✓ |

Directions

From N79 Montmarault - Moulins road, turn right at first roundabout onto D46 signed St Pourcain. Turn left at next roundabout onto unclassified road signed Deux-Chaises and La Valette. After 2.5 km. turn left at site sign (La Valette) and site is approx. 1 km.

Charges 2003

Per adult	€ 3.75 - € 4.54
child (0-8 yrs)	€ 2.68 - € 3.76
pitch with electricity (6A)	€ 8.80 - € 9.85
surcharge for one night stay	€ 4.00 - € 5.50

For one night stay 1/7-31/8, plus 10%.

Reservations

Essential for July/Aug. and made with 50% deposit. Tel: 04 70 07 64 57. Email: la.petite.valette@wanadoo.fr

Open

1 April - 30 October.

FR15010 **Camping Le Belvédère du Pont de Lanau**

15260 Neuvèglise (Cantal)

This is a very steeply terraced, family run site in the picturesque southern Auvergne. Of the 120 pitches around 100 are for touring. The highest pitches, affording wonderful views, have no electricity and are only suitable for tents. The lower pitches have 6A electricity and some pitches have a sink, draining board and barbecue. The pitches are of good size and separated by conifers and pines, offering good shade and privacy. The site roads are steep and have sharp bends and access may be difficult for large units. Some pitches are some distance from the toilet blocks and access may involve a large number of steep steps. The nearby lake is good for fishing and water sports but swimming is not allowed. The site has its own small pool and terrace but little space for children to play. There are many places of interest in the area, including the Viaduc de Garabit (built by Eiffel), the Cantal Mountains and Salers (one of the most beautiful villages in France). It is an excellent region for walking, cycling, mountain biking and bird watching. There are beautiful wild flowers in the spring and wonderful autumn colours. This is not an ideal site for those who are not physically fit.

Facilities

Two toilet blocks have fairly modern equipment, including some basins in cabins. Baby room. Good facilities for disabled people. Sauna. Washing machine and dryer. Good motorcaravan service point. Spacious bar/restaurant/TV room provides meals and takeaways all season. Small shop in high season. Organised activities for all the family in July/Aug. Off site: Fishing, boat launching 500 m. Bicycle hire 5 km. Riding 20 km.

At a glance

| Welcome & Ambience | ✓✓✓✓ | Location | ✓✓✓✓ |
| Quality of Pitches | ✓✓✓ | Range of Facilities | ✓✓✓✓ |

Directions

Site is 5 km. north of Chaudes-Aigues on D921 St Flour - Rodez road. Turn west at site sign, entrance is just beyond the Belvédère Centre de Vacance.

Charges 2003

Per unit incl. 1 or 2 adults	€ 10.70 - € 16.70
with electricity (6A)	€ 12.40 - € 19.10
with elecrtricity, sink and barbecue	€ 13.90 - € 21.40
extra adult	€ 2.15 - € 3.20
child (4-9 yrs)	€ 1.70 - € 2.40

Reservations

Advised in high season. Tel: 04 71 23 50 50. Email: Belvedere.Cantal@wanadoo.fr

Open

1 April - 15 October.

FR15030 Camping Caravaning Le Val Saint Jean

15200 Mauriac (Cantal)

La Val Saint-Jean is part of a typical, newly developed 'Centre de Loisirs' which the French do so well, set beside a lake in the heart of the département of Cantal. The campsite is situated at a height of 700 m. and provides 100 generously sized touring pitches (with electricity), terraced with good views and organised for the maximum of privacy, on a hill above the lake. The site is well planned so that you are never far from a sanitary block and it has an impressive number of good quality facilities. Most of the activities are situated by the lake where you can use all the facilities of the leisure club (high season) including cycling, canoeing, kayaking and pedalos. The lake has a sandy beach and an area for swimming. There is a large swimming pool, plus one for children on the campsite with sunbathing areas (free to campers). Both the pool and the lake have lifeguards most of the time in high season and they can get very busy in the main season. This less well known region is well worth exploring and the local gastronomy can be experienced in the village of Mauriac with its attractive architecture typical of the area.

Facilities

The two toilet blocks (4 and 6 years old) are well equipped with hot water throughout, providing some washbasins in cabins, dishwashing sinks and a laundry room with washing machine and dryer. Facilities for people with disabilities. Limited shop. Bar, snack bar and restaurant (all May - Sept). Swimming and paddling pools (1/6-15/9). Play area, playing field and table tennis. Watersports. Fishing. Activities organised for children (8-16 yrs) in July/Aug. Off site: Nine-hole golf course next to site. Mauriac village 600 m. Riding 2 km.

At a glance

Welcome & Ambience	✓✓✓✓	Location	✓✓✓✓✓
Quality of Pitches	✓✓✓✓	Range of Facilities	✓✓✓✓

Directions

From Clermont-Ferrand take RN89 towards Bordeaux, then D922 towards Bort-les-Orgues and Mauriac. Site is well signed in Mauriac.

Charges 2003

Per unit incl. 2 persons	€ 9.00 - € 16.00
extra adult	€ 3.00 - € 5.00
child under 10 yrs	free - € 2.50
child 10-18 yrs	€ 3.00 - € 4.00
dog	€ 1.50
electricity (10A)	€ 3.00
Plus local tax.	

Reservations

Contact site. Tel: 04 71 67 31 13.
Email: sogeval@wanadoo.fr

Open

24 April - 15 September.

Camping Val St-Jean ★ ★ ★
Mauriac   Auvergne

Tel: 0033 471 67 31 13 - Fax: 0033 471 68 17 34
E-mail: SOGEVAL@wanadoo.fr
Website: www.camping-massifcentral.com

FR19050 Camping La Rivière

Route de Brive, 19270 Donzenac (Corrèze)

The Corrèze is not nearly as well known as the Dordogne to the immediate south, but it is, in fact, a beautiful area which is deserving of more attention. Donzenac itself is an attractive small town with a variety of shops, restaurants, etc. This former municipal site is situated on the outskirts, somewhat less than a mile from the centre (an uphill walk). The site is quite small with 77 fairly large pitches on level grass, the majority with electricity and many with shade from tall trees. It is next door to the town tennis courts and swimming pool (July/Aug. only; free to campers).

Facilities

Modernised sanitary facilities are very good and include a laundry room. Small takeaway. Baker calls at site in July/Aug. Table tennis, boules and minigolf. Fishing. Bicycle hire. Off site: Riding 4 km, golf 10 km

At a glance

Welcome & Ambience	✓✓✓✓	Location	✓✓✓✓
Quality of Pitches	✓✓✓✓	Range of Facilities	✓✓✓

Directions

Site is signed 'Village de Vacances', off the D920 at the bottom of the hill 2 km. south of Donzenac (7 km. north of Brive).

Charges 2003

Per person	€ 3.50 - € 3.90
child	€ 2.00 - € 2.40
pitch	€ 4.10
electricity (5A)	€ 2.50
dog	€ 1.00
local tax	€ 0.40

Reservations

Probably unnecessary, but if in doubt phone. Tel: 05 55 85 63 95.

Open

1 April - 30 September.

FR19070 Camping Chateau de Gibanel

St Martial Entrayguis, 19400 Argentat (Corrèze)

This slightly terraced campsite is located in a beautiful estate, dominated by the 16th century château, on the banks of a very clean lake in this lesser known part of the Dordogne valley. Boats of up to 10 hp can be used on the lake for watersports and fishing. The very friendly family (English spoken) have ensured that everything is of a very high standard. Nearly all of the 250 grassy pitches are used for touring units. All have electricity and are separated by a variety of mature trees giving varying amounts of shade. Some have an ideal position alongside the lake. Many of the trees have low branches making access to most pitches difficult for large motorcaravans. The attractive bar, restaurant and disco in the château is set well away from the pitches and the swimming pool and good sized paddling pool, with large sunbathing terrace, are alongside the spacious and well equipped play area.

Facilities

Four modern, spacious and very clean toilet blocks include many large cubicles with a shower and washbasin making them ideal for families. Washing machine and dryer. Small shop for basics (all season). Bar, restaurant and takeaway (July/Aug). Wide range of family activities in July/Aug, including weekly dance evenings, folklore events, watersports, walking and cycling, Bicycle hire (July/Aug). TV room, Table tennis. Boules. Volleyball. Bus stop on site in July/Aug. Off site: Argentat with its interesting old town, shops, restaurants etc. 5 km.

At a glance

Welcome & Ambience	✓✓✓✓✓	Location	✓✓✓✓
Quality of Pitches	✓✓✓✓	Range of Facilities	✓✓✓✓

Directions

Site is 5 km. northeast of Argentat. Take D18, signed Eggletons, and after 4 km, alongside the lake, fork right at site sign. Follow lane down to site.

Charges 2003

Per person	€ 3.60 - € 4.50
child (under 7 yrs)	€ 1.80 - € 2.25
pitch	€ 4.00 - € 5.00
electricity (6A)	€ 2.70

Reservations

Essential in high season. Tel: 05 55 28 10 11. Email: contact@camping-gibanel.com

Open

1 June - 15 September.

FR19060 **Camping Le Mialaret**

Route d'Egletons, 19160 Neuvic (Corrèze)

Mialaret is 4 km. from the village of Neuvic and only 6 km. from the river Dordogne. It is set in the grounds of a 19th century château, now a hotel with a good reputation for fresh lobster and with a special evening menu for campers. Most pitches are set in a sunny, gently sloping meadow type situation. Some are level and separated by small bushes, most have electricity. In low season there are cooking courses with the chefs of the hotel, also at that time of the year the owner has time to take customers on a conducted tour of the estate in his 4x4 vehicle. Entertainment in high season is quite low key with a mini club, some games, tournaments or an evening sing-along around a campfire, also musical evenings by both professionals and of the do-it-yourself type.

Facilities

Three refurbished sanitary blocks give an adequate provision, one heated. Washbasins in cabins and adjustable showers. baby baths, facilities for disabled people, washing machines and dishwashing sinks. Motorcaravan service point. Shop at reception with bread daily. Bar with snacks and takeaway. Dinner at the hotel at special rate for campers. Play areas. Tennis. Fishing. Volleyball, football. Bicycle hire. The swimming pool is virtually a national monument as it is an original art-deco example. Unfortunately no paddling pool but a swimming pool is planned. Off site: Village with shops and lake 4 km. Golf 4 km. Canoeing, cycling and riding trips organised.

At a glance

Welcome & Ambience	✓✓✓✓	Location	✓✓✓✓
Quality of Pitches	✓✓✓	Range of Facilities	✓✓✓✓

Directions

From Clermont-Ferrand take N89 southwest, and at Ussel take D962 to Neuvic. In Neuvic follow signs for Egleton and signs for site. Site is 4 km. on right. Note: the D991 Egleton - Neuvic road is only suitable for cars and small motorcaravans.

Charges 2003

Per person	€ 4.50 - € 5.50
child (2-8 yrs)	free - € 3.00
pitch	€ 4.50 - € 6.50
electricity (6A)	€ 2.00 - € 3.00
local tax	€ 0.30

Camping Cheques accepted.

Reservations

Contact site. Tel: 05 55 46 02 50.
Email: info@lemialaret.com

Open

1 April - 31 October.

Camping Cheque
Elected Topcamping 2003

Close to the Gorges de la Dordogne and the lake of Neuvic (410 ha), you'll discover our heaven on earth. A 44 ha estate nestled in the midst of 2000 ha of unspoilt forest. We offer lodging à la carte :

★★★★ campsite, fully equipped bungalow-tents, chalets or hotelrooms. Art deco pool (300 m"), tennis, 2 fishing ponds, mountainbike & hikingtrails, miniclub & minifarm. Gastronomic restaurant & brasserie/pizzeria. Golf, horseriding, water/jetski & kano/kayak at 6 km. Discover the spirit of nature at Mialaret.

www.lemialaret.com   info@lemialaret.com

Domaine de Mialaret
Route d'Egletons - 19 160 NEUVIC (Corrèze) - Tel : 05.55.46.02.50 - Fax : 05.55.46.02.65

249

FR23010 Camping Le Château de Poinsouze

Route de la Châtre, B.P. 12, 23600 Boussac-Bourg (Creuse)

Le Château de Poinsouze is a recently developed site with 136 pitches arranged on the open, gently sloping, grassy park to one side of the château's main drive – a beautiful plane tree avenue. It is a well designed, high quality site. The 112 touring pitches, some with lake frontage, all have electricity , with water, waste water and sewage connections to many. The château (not open to the public) lies across the lake from the site. Exceptionally well restored outbuildings on the opposite side of the drive house a new restaurant, other facilities and the pool area. The site has a friendly family atmosphere, there are organised activities in main season including dances, children's games and crafts, family triathlons, and there are marked walks around the park and woods. All facilities are open all season, though times may vary. This is a top class site with a formula which should ensure a stress-free, enjoyable family holiday. Boussac (2.5 km) has a market every Thursday morning. The massive 12/15th century fortress, Château de Boussac, is open daily all year.

Facilities

The high quality, double glazed sanitary unit is entered via a large utility area equipped with dishwashing and laundry sinks, foot-pedal operated taps, sinks accessible for wheelchair users, drinks machine and two smaller rooms with washing machines, dryer and ironing. Four spacious rooms are very well equipped including some washbasins in cubicles, baby baths, changing mats and child's WC, and two suites for disabled people. Good motorcaravan service point. Well stocked shop. Takeaway, Comfortable bar with games, TV and library room above. New restaurant. Well fenced swimming pool with slide, children's pool (children wear colour coded bracelets, deposit required). Fenced playground designed with safety in mind. Table tennis, petanque, pool table and table football games. Bicycle hire. Free fishing in the lake (if you put the fish back); boats and lifejackets can be hired. Football, volleyball, basketball, badminton and other games. Dogs are not accepted in high season (11/7-21/8).

At a glance

Welcome & Ambience	✓✓✓✓✓	Location	✓✓✓✓✓
Quality of Pitches	✓✓✓✓	Range of Facilities	✓✓✓✓

Directions

Site entrance is 2.5 km north of Boussac on D917 (towards La Châtre).

Charges 2003

Per pitch incl. 2 persons	€ 12.00 - € 19.00
with electricity (6A)	€ 19.00 - € 25.00
with electricity (10A) and full services	€ 21.00 - € 26.00
extra adult	€ 3.50 - € 5.50
child (2-7 yrs)	€ 2.00 - € 4.00
electricity 10-25A	€ 2.00 - € 4.50
dog (low and mid-season only)	€ 3.00

Camping Cheques accepted.

Reservations

Advisable during July/Aug; made with 30% deposit and € 18,29 fee. Tel: 05 55 65 02 21.
Email: info.camping-de.poinsouze@wanadoo.fr

Open

15 May - 12 September.

Centre of France

Château de Poinsouze
★★★★

LES CASTELS

Camping Cheque

New Family Campsite. Calm & Nature. Exceptional fully enclosed sanitary facilities. Heated swimming pool. Chalets & mobil-homes for hire. Gites all year long.
Route de la Châtre 23600 Boussac-Bourg - Tel: 0033 555 65 02 21 - Fax: 0033 555 65 86 49
info.camping-de.poinsouze@wanadoo.fr / www.camping-de-poinsouze.com

FR43020 Camping du Puy-en-Velay

Avenue d'Aiguilhe, 43000 Le Puy-en-Velay (Haute-Loire)

This very popular urban site is within ten minutes walk of the old town with its very interesting old centre and is well worth the trip. The Office de Tourisme is on the southern side in Place du Breuil. It has a good security barrier and a warden who speaks good English and lives on site. Tarmac roads lead to 80 grassy pitches with electricity, including five with water and a drain. A motorcaravan service point is adjacent with its own security barrier – apply to campsite reception for a barrier key to use the services, or for an overnight stop (reception opens 08.00 - 21.00 hrs). Access is good and early arrival is advised.

Facilities

The main sanitary unit, recently refurbished and extended, includes some washbasins in cubicles. Facilities for disabled persons. Dishwashing and laundry sinks. An older unit at the rear of the site is only used in peak season. The facilities may be stretched in high season. Motorcaravan service point - see above. A room by reception has tourist information and a TV. Table tennis, boule, volleyball and badminton. Off site: Indoor pool and tennis adjacent. Baker and small supermarket 5 minutes walk. Several other shops, bar and restaurants close by.

At a glance

Welcome & Ambience	✓✓✓✓	Location	✓✓✓✓
Quality of Pitches	✓✓✓	Range of Facilities	✓✓✓

Directions

Site is northwest of the town centre, close to where N102 crosses the River Borne, and the Rocher St Michel d'Aiguilhe (a church on a rocky pinnacle). Site is well signed from around the town. Large blues 'Aire de Service' sign at entrance.

Charges 2003

Per unit incl. 2 persons	€ 7.95
extra adult	€ 2.25
child (2-10 yrs)	€ 1.12
electricity (6A)	€ 2.90
local tax	€ 0.15

Aire de service € 5,29 + € 0,30 p/person p/night. Services only € 2,59. No credit cards.

Reservations

Contact site for details. Tel: 04 71 09 55 09.

Open

Mid-April - 1 October.

FR43030 Camping du Vaubarlet

Vaubarlet, 43600 Ste Sigolène (Haute-Loire)

This peacefully located, spacious riverside family site has 131 marked, level, grassy and open pitches, with only those around the perimeter having shade and all having electricity. With 102 pitches for tourists, the remainder are occupied by site owned tents or mobile homes. Those who really like to get away from it all can use a small 'wild camping' area on the opposite side of the river with its own very basic facilities. This area is reached either by footbridge or a separate road access. The main site is separated from the river (unfenced) by a large field used for sports activities. This is also an attractive site for those seeking a quieter late break in September when it can be warm and sunny and with the pool, rooftop sun-deck, delightful modern bar with covered terrace all open. Tourist attractions in and around the region include a textile museum in Sainte Sigolène, an 'escargot' farm in nearby Grazac, the stunning scenery, chateaux and churches of the Haute-Loire, and the annual medieval festival in Le Puy each September. A 'Sites et Paysages' member.

Facilities

Two toilet units have British and Turkish style WCs, some washbasins in cubicles for ladies, baby room, laundry with washing machine and dryer and dishwashing sinks. Two new family bathrooms (WC, basin, shower) behind the bar, are also suitable for disabled people. Basic sanitary unit and campers' kitchen with cooker in 'wild' area. Small shop (bread to order). Takeaway in main season. Bar. Fenced swimming pool with children's pool. Bicycle hire. Table tennis, boule, volleyball and space for ball games. Playground. Organised activities in main season include camp fire and music evenings, canoe lessons for children, pony riding and mini-motorbike motocross (possibly noisy). Trout fishing (licenses available). Birdwatching, walking. Barbecues on loan. Off site: Two supermarkets and other shops in Ste Sigolène (6 km). Riding 15 km. Three golf courses around 30 km.

At a glance

Welcome & Ambience	✓✓✓✓✓	Location	✓✓✓✓
Quality of Pitches	✓✓✓✓	Range of Facilities	✓✓✓✓

Directions

Site is 6 km. southwest of Ste Sigolène on the D43 signed Grazac. Turn off this road by river bridge and follow signs.

Charges 2003

Per unit incl. 2 persons	€ 15.00
extra person	€ 3.00
child (2-7 yrs)	€ 2.00
electricity (6A)	€ 3.00
pet	€ 1.00

Less 15% outside July/Aug. Camping Cheques accepted.

Reservations

Advised for high season and made with 25% deposit and fee (€ 19,82). Tel: 04 71 66 64 95. Email: camping@vaubarlet.com

Open

1 May - 30 September.

FR48000 Camping Caravaning Le Champ d'Ayres

Route de la Brèze, 48150 Meyrueis (Lozère)

The road to Meyrueis is not for the faint-hearted, although we managed in quite a large motorhome with only a few stretches being a little on the narrow side. Le Champ d'Ayres is a traditionally French style site with a modern feel to it, set in the heart of the Cevennes. Very neat, tidy and well kept, it is run by a young family with young families in mind (teenagers might be bored). The site is slightly sloping with 70 grass pitches, the majority hedged with well trimmed bushes and most with some shade. All have electricity but may require long leads. The area is surrounded by mountains and gorges but the river Jonte is not a canoeing river (a trip to the Tarn would be needed). The Gorges de Jonte has an observatory from which vultures can be observed flying the thermals. Being very central there are many attractions in the area – wild horses have been introduced on the causses a few miles to the north, the observatory at the top of Mt Aigoual is well worth a visit and there are many caves in the region.

Facilities

The central toilet block, kept very clean, includes mainly British style WCs and some washbasins in cabins. Family sized shower room, room with facilities for disabled visitors and baby room. Laundry and dishwashing sinks. Washing machine and dryer. Reception incorporates a small bar (15/6-15/9) which also sells ices and bread. Takeaway (15/6-15/9). Swimming and paddling pools (20/5-15/9). Play area on grass (5-10 yrs), small games room, table tennis, basketball, netball and a boules pitch. In July/Aug activities are arranged for children, also paella evenings with music and activities such as walking and caving. Off site: The pretty small town of Meyrueis has many good shops and restaurants. Fishing 100 m. Riding 300 m. Bicycle hire 500 m.

At a glance

Welcome & Ambience	✓✓✓✓✓	Location	✓✓✓✓
Quality of Pitches	✓✓✓✓	Range of Facilities	✓✓✓✓

Directions

From N9 at Aquessac (5 km. north of Millau) take D907 signed Gorge du Tarn. At Rozier turn right on D996 signed Meyrueis and Gorges de la Jonte. In Meyrueis follow signs for Château d'Ayres and campsite signs. Site is 500 m east of the town.

Charges 2003

Per unit incl. 2 persons	€ 10.00 - € 14.00
extra person	€ 2.50 - € 3.30
child (under 7 yrs)	€ 1.60 - € 2.30
electricity (6A)	€ 2.50
local tax	€ 0.25

Reservations

Contact site. Tel: 04 66 45 60 51.
Email: campinglechampdayres@wanadoo.fr

Open

1 April - 30 September.

FR48060 Camping Les Terraces du Lac de Naussac

Lac de Naussac, 48300 Langogne (Lozère)

The Lac de Naussac is the largest in the Lozère and this site has direct access to the lake. There are 180 grassy pitches many with panoramic views over the lake and surrounding hills. There is a small pool and various other leisure amenities including tennis and bike hire. The lake offers a wide range of water based activities, notably sailing and fishing. This is superb walking country and the long distance Stevenson trail passes close by at Langogne.

Facilities

The 3 sanitary blocks are modern and well maintained. Bar, restauraurant, take away in adjacent hotel. Lively 'animation' programme in peak season. Play area. Off site: Langogne (shops, restaurants, Stevenson trail etc.) 2 km. Golf (9 hole) 3 km. Riding 3 km.

At a glance

Welcome & Ambience	✓✓✓	Location	✓✓✓✓
Quality of Pitches	✓✓✓	Range of Facilities	✓✓✓

Directions

Leave the N88 (Le Puy - Mende) road shortly after passing through Langogne. Turn right towards the Lac de Naussac and the site is clearly marked.

Charges 2003

Per pitch incl. 2 persons	€ 11.50 - € 14.50
extra person	€ 3.50
child (2-6 yrs)	€ 1.50
electricity	€ 2.50
animal	€ 0.50

Camping Cheques accepted.

Reservations

Contact site. Tel: (0)4 66 69 29 62.
Email: naussac@club-internet.fr

Open

1 April - 30 September.

FR63050 **Camping La Ribeyre**

Jassat, 63790 Murol (Puy-de-Dôme)

About a kilometre from the centre of Murol, La Ribeyre has a charm about it which is quite unique. The owners, Mme Pommier and her two sons, originally farmers, have put much personal effort in constructing the site, its buildings and the pool. There is an extremely friendly atmosphere here. Many young trees have been planted to add to those already on site and a man-made lake at one end provides facilities for water sports. There is a picturesque reception area, with a fountain and tastefully laid-out floral decorations. The site now provides 400 level, grassy pitches, of which 300 have electricity (6A) and 110 have individual electricity, water and drainage. Although not normally advertised, there are 10A outlets for those who ask. The surrounding area is very much worth a visit. From mountains rising to over 6,000 ft, to lakes, cavernes and many local craft centres, this site is a superb centre. It is only 5 or 6 km. from St Nectaire, about 10 km. from Besse and about 20 km. from Le Mont Dore, which is a starting point for the Puy de Sancy, the highest peak in the area. This is a wonderful walking and cycling area and the flowers in May and June are a joy to behold.

Facilities

Six excellent, very clean modern toilet blocks provide British and Turkish style WCs and some washbasins in cubicles. Snack bar in peak season (20/6-1/9). Heated swimming pool 200 sq.m.(1/5-1/9). TV and games room. Tennis, volleyball and fishing. New play area. Small campsite lake provides swimming, canoeing and surf boarding (lifeguard in July/Aug). Off site: Bicycle hire 1 km. Riding 300 m. fishing, boating and sailing at Lac Chambon 3 km. Further shops and restaurants at Murol, 1 km.

At a glance

Welcome & Ambience	✓✓✓✓✓	Location	✓✓✓✓
Quality of Pitches	✓✓✓✓	Range of Facilities	✓✓✓✓

Directions

From A75 autoroute, take exit 6, signed St Nectaire and carry on to Murol. Several sites are signed as you go into the town. Turn left and then, opposite Syndicat d'Initiative, turn right. La Ribeyre is the second site on the left, just after the entrance to Jassat and is well marked on left.

Charges 2003

Per unit incl. 2 adults	€ 12.30 - € 16.90
child (under 5 yrs)	€ 2.56 - € 3.80
electricity (6A)	€ 3.60 - € 4.20
local tax	€ 0.19 - € 0.38

No credit cards. Camping Cheques accepted.

Reservations

Contact site. Tel: 04 73 88 64 29.
Email: laribeyre@free.fr

Open

1 May - 15 September.

FR63040 Château Camping La Grange Fort

Les Pradeaux, 63500 Issoire (Puy-de-Dôme)

This site has good, modern facilities, yet is oozing with character. It is very popular with the Dutch. The 15th century castle is impressive, more British in style than the usual French château. The new reception is well stocked with tourist information. The restaurant in the castle, (once the kitchen and dining hall) has great atmosphere and offers a simple daily menu. The cosy bar still has the old stable stalls and hay racks. The 120 pitches are of average size on grass, connected by rather narrow roads and with limited play space for children. Some of the smaller pitches are in sunny fields around the castle, others in bays with hedges and trees. All have electrical hook-ups (most new connections). There are pleasant walks in the extensive grounds. You are assured a warm welcome at this Dutch owned site.

Facilities

The main toilet facilities are modern and heated but hot water is only available morning and early evening. Both ladies and men have baby rooms, the men's also has facilities for disabled visitors and a 'hydra shower'. Dog shower. Laundry room. Reception has a few groceries (bread to order). Restaurant (1/5-15/9), bar (15/6-15/9) and takeaway (1/5-15/9). Indoor pool with sliding glass doors, sauna and massage table (15/4-15/10). Two outdoor pools (15/6-1/10) with grass sunbathing areas. Play area and games room. Tennis, minigolf, table tennis, volleyball, football field and boules. Organised activities in season include archery, canoeing, riding and cycling (horses and bikes provided). Off site: Fishing 250 m. Riding 8 km.

At a glance

Welcome & Ambience	✓✓✓✓✓	Location	✓✓✓✓
Quality of Pitches	✓✓✓	Range of Facilities	✓✓✓✓

Directions

From A75 autoroute take exit 13 at Issoire. Travel east on D996 to Parentignat and in village turn right (D999) and after 200 m. right again on D34 signed Nonette. Site is 3 km.

Charges 2003

Per adult	€ 5.25
child (under 7 yrs)	€ 3.00
electricity (6A)	€ 2.50
Camping Cheques accepted.	

Reservations

Contact site for details. Tel: 04 73 71 02 43.
Email: chateau@grangefort.com

Open

10 April - 15 October.

FR63070 Camping Le Pré Bas

Lac Chambon, 63790 Murol (Puy-de-Dôme)

In the heart of the Parc des Volcans d'Auvergne, beside Lac Chambon, Le Pre Bas is especially suitable for families with younger children and those seeking the watersports opportunities that the lake provides. Large, level, grassy pitches are divided up by mature hedging and trees and, with 63 mobile homes for rent, around 120 pitches are available for tourists, all with electricity. A gate leads to the lakeside, where in the high season there is windsurfing, pedaloes, canoes or fishing, and 50 m. away is a beach with supervised bathing. The site has a new pool complex with heated swimming pools (one covered), a large slide and a paddling pool.

Facilities

There is one large, newly refurbished central toilet building with four smaller units spread around site. Including washbasins in cubicles, facilities for disabled guests and dishwashing sinks. Laundry room. Baby room. Motorcaravan service point. Snack bar with a small terrace (10/6-10/9 and some weekends in low season). Well fenced, swimming pool complex (10/6-10/9) has three pools of different depths (lifeguard in July/Aug). Watersports and fishing in lake. Games room with table tennis, table football, pool, etc, large 'salle' with giant TV screen and library. Adventure style playground alongside a football/basketball pitch. Organised activities (late June-early Sept) include local visits, guided walks, riding, archery and climbing.

At a glance

Welcome & Ambience	✓✓✓✓✓	Location	✓✓✓✓
Quality of Pitches	✓✓✓✓	Range of Facilities	✓✓✓✓

Directions

Site is located on the D966, 3 km. west of Murol towards Le Mont Dore.

Charges 2003

Per pitch incl. 1 adult	€ 8.30 - € 13.00
child (1-5 yrs)	€ 2.30 - € 3.00
child (5-10 yrs)	€ 2.30 - € 4.50
electricity (6A)	€ 4.00
local tax	€ 0.30

Reservations

Essential for high season, made with € 39 p/week deposit. Tel: 04 73 88 63 04.
Email: prebas@lac-chambon.com

Open

1 May - 30 September.

FR63080 Camping Le Moulin de Serre

D73, vallée de la Burande, 63690 Singles (Puy-de-Dôme)

This very spacious family run site is set in beautiful wooded valley beside the River Burande where one can pan for gold. It offers a good base for those seeking a quiet relaxing holiday in this lesser known area of the Auvergne. The 90 good size pitches (55 for touring) are separated by a variety of trees and hedges giving good shade. Some pitches have a hardstanding and all have electricity. Although the roads leading to the site are twisting, access is easy. There are no problems here for large units.

Facilities

Two well appointed, very clean toilet blocks. One block is heated in spring, and has excellent facilities for disabled people and babies. Swimming pool with terrace (8/6-28/9). Takeaway and bar/restaurant (July/Aug). Bread (high season). Washing machine and dryer. Motorcaravan service point. Simple but very large play area. Football, table tennis. Canoe hire in high season. Daily programme of organised activities (July/Aug). Off site: Large play area on the adjacent banks of the river, ideal for paddling. Small lake for water sports (2 km). Château de Val (20 km). Spa town of la Bourboule (25 km). Barrage de Bort les Orgues offers water sports. Many marked walks and cycle tracks. Riding.

At a glance

Welcome & Ambience	✓✓✓✓	Location	✓✓✓
Quality of Pitches	✓✓✓✓✓	Range of Facilities	✓✓✓✓

Directions

Site is about 25 km. southwest of La Bourboule. Turn west off D922 near Tauves onto D29. Just before Singles turn left on D73 and follow signs, site is on right in just over 1 km.

Charges 2003

Per unit incl. 2 persons	€ 9.20 - € 12.95
extra adult	€ 2.40 - € 3.80
child (under 10 yrs)	€1.25 - € 2.45
electricity (3-10A)	€ 2.70 - € 4.50

Reservations

Advised in high season. Tel: 04 73 21 16 06.
Email: moulin-de-serre@wanadoo.fr

Open

5 April - 19 September.

Friendly atmosphere in a delightful setting in the heart of the upper Dordogne valley

Long heated swimming-pool !!
Camp site open from 10 of April to 19 of September 2004

LE MOULIN DE SERRE ★★★
63690 Singles (France)
Tel +33 (0)4 73 21 16 06
Fax +33 (0)4 73 21 12 56

www.moulindeserre.com

FR63060 Camping Le Clos Auroy

Rue de la Narse, 63670 Orcet (Puy-de-Dôme)

You are assured a friendly welcome at Le Clos Auroy. It is a very well maintained and popular site, 300 metres from Orcet, a typical Auvergne village just south of Clermont Ferrand. Being close (3 km) to the A75, and open all year, it makes an excellent stopping off point on the journey south. The 90 good size pitches (all with electricity and many fully serviced) are on level grass, separated by hedges, offering lots of privacy. In winter only 20 pitches are available. Access is easy for large units.

Facilities

Two high quality sanitary units include washbasins in cubicles. Dishwashing and laundry sinks. Washing machine and dryer. A smaller, heated unit at reception is used mainly for the winter season, when it is heated. Chemical disposal is at the motorcaravan service point, close to the site entrance (a long walk from some pitches). Small shop and takeaway (both 1/7-15/9). Bar (15/6-15/9). Heated pool with attractive terrace next to the bar (15/5-30/9). Playground. Coffee mornings. Tennis. Children's activities. Off site: Fishing and canoeing 500 m. Village with shops and three wine 'caves' 300 m. Large playground nearby and riverside walk just outside gate.

At a glance

Welcome & Ambience	✓✓✓✓✓	Location	✓✓✓✓
Quality of Pitches	✓✓✓✓	Range of Facilities	✓✓✓✓

Directions

From A75 take exit 4 or 5 towards Orcet and follow campsite signs. It is just before the village.

Charges 2003

Per unit incl. 2 persons	€ 14.00 - € 16.00
child (1-7 yrs)	€ 2.50
electricity (5/10A)	€ 2.60 - € 4.20
animal	€ 1.50
local tax	€ 0.14 - € 0.27

Less for longer stays in low season. No credit cards.

Reservations

Advised for July/August. Tel: 04 73 84 26 97.
Email: camping.Le.Clos.Auroy@wanadoo.fr

Open

All year.

the travel service
TO BOOK THIS SITE
0870 405 4055
Expert Advice & Special Offers

255

FR63090 Camping Les Domes

Les Quatre Routes de Nébouzat, 63210 Nébouzat (Puy-de-Dôme)

A friendly welcome awaits at this attractive, compact, well cared for site which is run by a family of enthusiastic caravanners. It is ideally situated for exploring the beautiful region around the Puy de Dôme. The site has 65 small to medium sized pitches, all with electricity, separated by trees and hedges and most are available for touring. Some pitches have a level, paved area ideal for caravans and motor-caravans. Rock pegs are advised. The attractive reception area comprising the office, a small shop for essentials (high season only) and a meeting room has lots of local information and interesting arte-facts. An added attraction is a heated, covered pool, which can be opened in good weather. There are many interesting old villages in the area (Orcival 8 km) and chateaux (Chateau de Corde 4 km).

Facilities

A well appointed central toilet block is kept very clean, but there are no special facilities for disabled visitors. Basic shop (baker calls). Breakfast, snacks and chips. Boules, Pool table, table football, table tennis, giant chess and drafts. Small play area. TV and games room. Off site: Fishing 100 m. Restaurant 200 m. Nebouzat 1.3 km (shops etc). Riding 6 km. Hang gliding and parascending 8 km (Puy de Dôme). Lac Adyat 9 km. Golf 10 km. Clermond Ferrand with its interesting old town and hypermarkets (18 km). Many marked walks and cycle routes.

At a glance

Welcome & Ambience	✓✓✓✓✓	Location	✓✓✓✓
Quality of Pitches	✓✓✓✓	Range of Facilities	✓✓✓✓

Directions

Site is 18 km. southwest of Clermont Ferrand and is well signed from the roundabout at the junction of the N89 and the D941A. It is a few hundred metres from the roundabout along the D216 towards Orcival.

Charges 2003

Per unit incl. 1 person	€ 8.50
extra person	€ 5.50
child (under 5 yrs)	€ 3.00
electricity (10A)	€ 3.00

Reservations

Advised in high season. Tel: 04 73 87 14 06. Email: camping.les-domes@wanadoo.fr

Open

15 May - 15 September.

FR87020 Camping du Château de Leychoisier

Domaine de Leychoisier, 87270 Bonnac-la-Côte (Haute-Vienne)

This well-established château site offers peace and quiet in superb surroundings and the large estate offers the opportunity to explore the grounds and to walk down to the four hectare lake. It is ideally situated only 2 km. from the A20/N20 and 10 km. north of Limoges. There are 90 large grass pitches, some partly sloping with a mixture of sun and shade, and 76 having electricity. The lake provides free fishing, boating, canoeing and a marked off area for swimming. Perhaps a little expensive for the facil-ities provided, this is, however, a quiet site where you have plenty of space and where there are no letting units and many people like it for these reasons.

Facilities

The partially refurbished sanitary block is in an old building. Very clean, but rather cramped it needs extending and updating to cope with demand at busy times. Some washbasins in private cabins and provision for disabled visitors. Washing machine. Basic food provisions sold from reception (order bread the night before). Restaurant (from 20/6), snack bar and bar housed in open-ended barn, partly protected by a canopy and attractive gazebo. Swimming pool (proper swimming trunks, no shorts). Lake. Play area. Bicycle hire, table tennis, tennis and boules courts (both in need of repair when we visited), volleyball and bar billiards. Torch useful. Winter caravan storage. Off site: Mini-market 2 km, supermarket 5 km. Golf 20 km, riding 7 km.

At a glance

Welcome & Ambience	✓✓✓✓	Location	✓✓✓✓✓
Quality of Pitches	✓✓✓✓	Range of Facilities	✓✓✓✓

Directions

From A20 take exit 27 (west) signed Bonnac-La-Côte. Site is well signed from the village.

Charges 2004

Per person	€ 5.50 - € 7.00
child (under 7 yrs)	€ 3.80 - € 4.50
pitch	€ 8.00 - € 9.00
motorcaravan plus	€ 2.60
electricity (10A)	€ 3.90
local tax	€ 0.60 - € 1.00

No credit cards.

Reservations

Made with deposit (€ 15,24) and fee (€ 12,20), although short reservations accepted without charge in low season. Tel: 05 55 39 93 43. Email: contact@leychoisier.com

Open

15 April - 20 September.

Map 13

With such a rich and varied landscape, the Rhône Valley offers a spectacular region of craggy gorges and scented hills, ideal for life at a leisurely pace - easy to do when there are so many stunning views to take in.

Départements: 01 Ain, 07 Ardèche, 26 Drôme, 42 Loire, 69 Rhône

Major city: Lyon

The region's 2,000 year history as a cultural crossroads has blessed the area with a rich blend of customs, architecture and sights of interest. The city of Lyon was developed by the Romans as a trading centre, and was once the capital. It is now the second largest city of France. The Place de la Terreur in the centre of the city is where the guillotine was placed during the French revolution – until it wore out through over-use. Not far from Lyon lies the Dombes, the land of a thousand lakes, and the medieval village of Pérouges and Roman ruins of Vienne.

The Rhône valley holds areas of great interest and natural beauty. From the sun-baked Drôme, with its ever-changing landscapes and the isolated mountains of the Vercors to the deep gorges and high plateaux of the Ardèche, studded with prehistoric caves and lush valleys filled with orchards; and encompassing the vineyards of the Beaujolais and the Rhône Valley. For the energetic there are cycling, horse riding and even white water rafting opportunities, while for the more leisurely inclined, the remote areas are a haven for bird watching and walking.

Cuisine of the region

The poultry, cheese, freshwater fish and mushrooms are superb. Local wines include Beaujolais, Côte Rotie, St Julien, Condrieu, Tain-Hermitage, Chiroubles and Julienas.

Bresse (Poulet, Poularde, Volaille de): the best French poultry, fed on corn and when killed bathed in milk; flesh is white and delicate

Gras-double: ox tripe, served with onions

Poulet au vinaigre: chicken, shallots, tomatoes, white wine, wine vinegar and a cream sauce

Poulet demi-deuil (half-mourning): called this because of thin slices of truffle placed under the chicken breast

Rosette: a large pork sausage

Sabodet: Lyonnais sausage of pig's head, pork and beef, served hot

Places of interest

Beaujolais: vineyards and golden-stone villages

Bourg-en-Bresse: church of Notre-Dame, craft shops, museum of Ain

Dombes: lakes, ornithological park

Lyon: Gallo-Roman artifacts, Renaissance quarter, historical Fabric Museum, silk museum.

Pérouges: medieval village, Galette de Pérouges

St Etienne: museum of Modern Art

Vallon-Pont d'Arc: base from which to visit Gorges de l'Ardèche; canoe and rafting centre

Vienne: Gothic style cathedral, 6th century church St Pierre

tip

IF YOU HAVE A SWEET TOOTH, TAKE A TRIP TO MONTÉLIMA, THE NOUGAT CAPITAL OF FRANCE. JOIN ONE OF THE FACTORY TOURS AND ENJOY A SAMPLE OR TWO!

FR01010 Camping La Plaine Tonique

Base de Plein Air, 01340 Montrevel-en-Bresse (Ain)

This site belongs to a syndicate of several local villages. It is a very well maintained, large site with 560 marked and numbered pitches, all with electricity. The majority are of a good size, hedged and on flat grass, with reasonable shade in most parts. Although large, the site is spacious and certainly does not feel so as it is broken up into smaller sections by trees and hedges. The site is on the edge of a large, 320-acre lake with its own beach and adjacent public beach. Sailing, windsurfing and canoeing are possible and, on other parts of the lake, waterskiing and fishing. Campers may bring their own boats, but not motor boats. A separate area of the site is used by Dutch tour operators (100 pitches).

Facilities

Sanitary facilities are in eleven blocks, with most now renovated to a very high standard. They include some washbasins in cabins, baby rooms and washing machines. Motorcaravan service point. Restaurant, bar (all season) and shop (July/Aug) are next to the site. 'Aquatonic' centre with five pools (reduced charge for campers). Watersports and fishing. Minigolf and several tennis courts. Adventure play area on beach. Games and TV rooms. Archery, bicycle hire and roller skating area. Off site: Riding 2 km. Montrevel town 300 m. walk.

At a glance			
Welcome & Ambience	✓✓✓	Location	✓✓✓✓
Quality of Pitches	✓✓✓✓	Range of Facilities	✓✓✓✓

Directions

Site is 20 km. north of Bourg-en-Bresse and 25 km. east of Macon. Montrevel is on the D975; site is signed in town centre towards Etrez on D28.

Charges 2003

Per unit incl. electricity (10A)	€ 6.90 - € 10.60
person	€ 2.60 - € 4.30
child (3-7 yrs)	€ 1.40 - € 2.10

Reservations

Write with 25% deposit. Tel: 04 74 30 80 52. Email: plaine.tonique@wanadoo.fr

Open

14 April - 28 September.

FR01020 Camping de L'Ile Chambod

01250 Hautecourt (Ain)

This small site has enthusiastic English-speaking owners. The 110 grassy pitches (about 100 sq m.) are separated by low hedges and most have some shade. They all have access to water points and electricity although some may need long leads. A lakeside beach is only 300 m. (charged for in high season), offering simple watersports and minigolf. There is plenty to see in the region and Bourg-en-Bresse offers a wealth of shops, restaurants, museums, etc.

Facilities

Two modern toilet blocks include some washbasins in cabins, dishwashing, laundry and vegetable preparation sinks. Washing machine and dryer. Both blocks have facilities suitable for disabled visitors and one has a baby room. Bread available to order. Small shop and takeaway (June, July and Aug). Small play area. Activities organised in high season for children up to 12 years.

At a glance			
Welcome & Ambience	✓✓✓✓	Location	✓✓✓✓
Quality of Pitches	✓✓✓	Range of Facilities	✓✓✓

Directions

Site is approx. 23 km. southeast of Bourg-en-Bresse via the D979. It is well signed from the crossroad in Hautecourt, and is a further 4 km. down the lane.

Charges 2003

Per person	€ 2.50 - € 3.50
pitch with electricity (5-10A)	€ 5.00 - € 6.00
No credit cards.	

Reservations

Advised for July/Aug. Tel: 04 74 37 25 41. Email: camping.chambod@free.fr

Open

1 May - 30 September.

FR07130 Camping Les Coudoulets

Pradons, 07120 Ruoms (Ardèche)

For those who prefer a more intimate, peaceful campsite, then this well cared for site is for you. Beside the river Ardèche, only a short distance away from the centre, it is run by an enthusiastic and friendly family who developed this site from their farm. They have a small vineyard and their wine is on sale in the bar. There are 125 grassy, level and shady pitches, separated by trees and shrubs. With 112 for touring, all have electricity. There is an area for bathing in the river and it is ideal spot for canoeists, etc.

Facilities

The very good, clean toilet block has all the necessary facilities including excellent facilities for disabled people. Motorcaravan service point. Small bar with TV and terrace, also selling bread, ices and drinks. Pizzas and chips in July/Aug. and B.Hs. Butcher calls three times a week in high season. Small heated swimming and paddling pools. Fishing, football, volleyball and table tennis. Organised events in July and Aug for all the family including the occasional evening event (no discos). Accompanied walks, canoe trips and visits to a wine cellar. Off site: Shop 300 m. Canyoning and rafting etc. Tennis 2 km, riding 2 km. Golf 7 km.

At a glance			
Welcome & Ambience	✓✓✓✓✓	Location	✓✓✓✓
Quality of Pitches	✓✓✓✓	Range of Facilities	✓✓✓✓

Directions

Leave Montélimar going west on N192 towards Aubenas. Shortly after Villeneuve de Berg turn left on D103 towards Vogüé for 5 km. Turn left on D579 (Ruoms) and site 10 km. in village of Pradons.

Latest charges

Per unit incl. 2 persons	€ 12.20 - € 15.40
child (under 7 yrs)	€ 2.44 - € 2.80
electricity (6A)	€ 3.10

Reservations

Made with deposit (€ 70) but no fee. Tel: 04 75 93 94 95. Email: camping@coudoulets.com

Open

1 May - 12 September.

FR07020 Camping Caravaning L'Ardéchois

Le Chambon, Gluiras, 07190 St Sauveur-de-Montagut (Ardèche)

This attractive site is quite a way off the beaten track and the approach road is winding and narrow in places. However, it is worth the effort, to find in such a spectacular setting, a hillside site offering a range of amenities. There are several different types of pitch, varying in size (85-140 sq.m) and with many separated by trees and plants. Some are alongside the small, fast-flowing river, while the rest (60%) are on higher, sloping ground nearer the restaurant/bar. All 83 touring pitches have electricity (10A). The main site access roads are tarmac but are quite steep and larger units may find access to some terraces difficult. The amenities have been created by the careful conversion of old buildings which provide modern facilities in an attractive style (all from Easter). The new friendly Dutch owners have developed an extensive excursion programme for exploring this attractive area on foot or by car. The site is popular with the Dutch. A 'Sites et Paysages' member.

Facilities

Two good sanitary blocks provide washbasins in private cabins, baths and showers for babies and facilities for people with disabilities. Maintenance can be variable. Dishwashing and laundry rooms. Motorcaravan service point. Shop. Bar/restaurant. TV room. Table tennis. Volleyball. Bicycle hire, archery and fishing. Swimming pool (heated in low season; no bermuda style shorts) with adjacent bar, snack bar and terrace, plus a paddling pool for children. Off site: Canyoning, climbing, and canoeing trips organised.

At a glance

Welcome & Ambience	✓✓✓✓	Location	✓✓✓✓
Quality of Pitches	✓✓✓✓	Range of Facilities	✓✓✓✓

Directions

From Valence take N86 south for 12 km, turn right onto D120 to St Sauveur de Montagut, then take D102 towards Mézilhac for 8 km. to site.

Charges 2004

Per unit incl. 2 persons	€ 19.00 - € 24.00
extra person	€ 4.00
animal	€ 3.00 - € 4.00

Low season price for over 55s.
Camping Cheques accepted.

Reservations

Write with deposit (€ 69) and fee (€ 23); min. 10 days 6/7-24/8. Tel: 04 75 66 61 87. Email: ardechois.camping@wanadoo.fr

Open

Easter - 31 October.

L'ARDECHOIS Camping Caravaning **** 07190 St Sauveur de Montagut

A peaceful 4-star family campsite in the heart of the beautiful Ardeche region. All amenities of a first class resort. Beautiful pitches and modern self-catering accommodation.

FR07050 Sunêlia Le Ranc Davaine

St Alban-Auriolles, 07120 Ruoms (Ardèche)

Le Ranc Davine is a quite large, busy, family oriented site set in two areas separated by a reasonably quiet road. The larger area provides all the entertainment facilities and most of the 430 pitches. The 113 touring pitches are mostly scattered between static caravan and tour operator pitches and are on fairly flat, rather stony ground under a variety of trees giving much needed shade. All are supplied with electricity, some needing very long leads which may cross tarmac roads. The lower part is beside the river (unfenced). Sunbathing areas surround the pool complex, overlooked by the terrace of the restaurant, providing very pleasant surroundings, especially attractive with evening floodlighting. A lively entertainment programme (July/Aug) is aimed at young children and teenagers. The site is popular with tour operators (113 pitches) and there are 162 mobile homes. It can get very busy for much of the season.

Facilities

Five toilet blocks are fully equipped with many washbasins in cabins. Not all blocks are opened outside the main season, in high season they get very busy. The lower area has a new, unisex block. Full facilities for disabled visitors. Dishwashing and laundry sinks, washing machines, dryers and irons. Large shop catering for most needs. Cash point. Internet point in reception. Bar/restaurant serving good range of meals. Pizzeria and takeaway. Attractive large, irregularly shaped swimming pool (no bermuda-style shorts or shirts) heated in cool weather, supplemented by two small square pools. Play area. Tennis, table tennis, basketball, football, archery and minigolf. Fishing. Extensive programme of sports in the pools, clubs for youngsters and teenagers, many other organised activities including discos (until 3 am four times a week in high season). Off site: Canoe hire nearby for excursions down the River Ardèche. Riding 2 km. Karting.

Directions

From Ruoms go south on the D111. Just before Grospierres turn right onto D246, cross the river bridge (2.5 m. width restriction) and then left on D208 towards Chandolas and site.

Charges 2003

Per unit incl. 2 persons	€ 20.00 - € 34.00
with electricity (6/10A)	€ 24.00 - € 38.00
extra person	€ 6.00 - € 9.00
child (2-13 yrs)	€ 3.50 - € 9.00
animal	free - € 4.00
local tax	€ 0.46

Camping Cheques accepted.

Reservations

Made with deposit (€ 100) and fee (€ 30).
Tel: 04 75 39 60 55.
Email: camping.ranc.davaine@wanadoo.fr

Open

23 March - 14 September.

At a glance

Welcome & Ambience	✓✓✓✓	Location	✓✓✓✓
Quality of Pitches	✓✓✓	Range of Facilities	✓✓✓✓✓

FR07080 Castel Camping Domaine de la Bastide

RD111, route de Gros-Pierres, Sampzon, 07120 Ruoms (Ardèche)

The Cargnelutti family are very keen to maintain high standards on their site near Vallon-Pont-d'Arc and this is evident as soon as arrive, with its neat and tidy appearance and flowers everywhere. On driving down to your pitch, it seems that there are lots of mobile homes. Actually there are only 46 mobile homes, 25 small chalets plus another 16 pitches used by a tour operator, which out of 300 pitches is really not many. Once past these, the site opens up to reveal pleasant, good sized pitches, all with some shade and bordered by flowering trees and bushes. All have electricity and 86 are fully serviced. Canoe trips are arranged down the Gorge d'Ardèche and in mid-June each year a large section of the river bank next to the site is cleared of boulders and sand put down – just the job for children.

Facilities

Two toilet blocks, the newest with very high quality fittings including washbasins in cubicles, a baby room and facilities for disabled people. The older block is only open in high season and has mainly Turkish style WCs, plus showers, etc. Shop. Attractive restaurant, pizzeria and bar (mid June to end Aug). Heated swimming pool with pleasant sunbathing area. Free sauna and gym with a resident instructor. Play area. Table tennis, boules, volleyball, football, basketball and tennis courts. Fishing. Games and competitions are organised in July/Aug. plus discos in a soundproof cellar. Security patrols ensure quiet nights. Doctor calls daily (July/Aug) and hairdresser weekly (July/Aug). Only gas barbecues are permitted. Off site: Riding and bicycle hire 3 km. Golf 6 km. The small town of Ruoms is 4 km, Vallon-Pont-d'Arc 7 km.

Directions

Going south from Ruoms on the D579, bear right on D111 signed Ales. Cross Chassezac river bridge and site is 200 m. on the left.

Charges 2003

Per unit incl. 2 persons	
with electricity (3/5A)	€ 20.00 - € 30.00
with water and drainage	€ 24.00 - € 33.00
extra person over 3 yrs	€ 4.50 - € 6.00
dog	free - € 4.00
local tax (over 10 yrs)	€ 0.32

No credit cards.

Reservations

Made with deposit (€ 100) and booking fee (€ 30).
Tel: 04 75 39 64 72.
Email: camping.bastide@wanadoo.fr

Open

1 April - 30 September.

At a glance

Welcome & Ambience	✓✓✓✓✓	Location	✓✓✓✓
Quality of Pitches	✓✓✓✓	Range of Facilities	✓✓✓✓✓

FR07030 Yelloh! Village Soleil Vivarais

Sampzon, 07120 Ruoms (Ardèche)

A large, quality site bordering the River Ardèche, complete with beach, Soleil Vivarais offers much to visitors, particularly families with children. A popular feature is the 'barrage' with its canoe ramp, used by children with rubber boats more than canoeists, and providing an invigorating shower for bathers. Water is shallow in high season, but swimming is then best attempted in one of the pools. Of the 330 pitches, 63 generously sized, level pitches are for tourers, all with electricity. Many are shaded and 30 have full services. During the day the proximity of the swimming pools to the terraces of the bar and restaurant make it a pleasantly social area. In the evening the purpose built stage, with professional lighting and sound system, provides an ideal platform for a regular family entertainment programme, mostly mimed musical shows. A new section beyond the beach houses good quality chalets and a very attractive pool complex, which all may use. The site is used by tour operators (80 pitches). A 'Sites et Paysages' and 'Yelloh Village' member.

Facilities

Three fairly modern and one very modern toilet block are clean and cope adequately with demands placed upon them. Baby and child room and four units for people with disabilities. Ample areas for dishwashing. Washing machines and dryers. Small supermarket, well stocked and sensibly priced. Bright, modern bar/restaurant complex which in addition to takeaways and occasional pizzas (cooked in a wood burning oven), caters for a range of appetites and budgets. Sound-proof disco adjacent to the bar (capacity 100-120), popular with teenagers. Heated main pool and paddling pool (no bermuda style shorts). Water polo, aqua-aerobics, pool games. Tennis (charged). Basketball, volleyball and football. Fishing. Petanque, table tennis and archery. Bicycle hire. Extensive animation programme for all ages in June, July and August. Off site: Activities nearby, many with qualified instruction and supervision, include mountain biking, walking, canoeing, rafting, climbing and caving. Riding 2 km, golf 10 km.

At a glance

Welcome & Ambience	✓✓✓✓	Location	✓✓✓✓✓
Quality of Pitches	✓✓✓✓	Range of Facilities	✓✓✓✓✓

Directions

From Le Teil, just west of Montelimar, turn off the N86 and take the N102 westwards through Villeneuve-de-Berg. Disregard the first sign for Vallon-Pont-d'Arc and continue for about 5km on N102 before turning left on D103, toward Vogue, then left on D579 and through Ruoms. Still on the D579, follow Vallon Pont D'Arc signs towards Sampzon. Site is on right via a bridge across the river controlled by lights.

Charges 2003

Per unit incl. 2 persons and electricity (10A)	€ 20.00 - € 38.00
extra person	€ 4.00 - € 7.00
child (1-10 yrs)	free - € 6.50
pet	free - € 3.00
local tax (over 10s)	€ 0.30

Reservations

Made by fax and credit card or write to site with deposit (€ 92) and fee (€ 30). Tel: 04 75 39 67 56. Email: info@soleil-vivarais.com

Open

Week before Easter - 20 September.

A river all around... and all around the open air.

Cottages, Chalets and Mobiles homes to rent. 800 m beach bordering the Ardèche.
Open from 03/04 to 11/09/2004.
Your children (under 16 years old) are our guests From 03/04 to 31/05/04.

DDB nouveau monde LE TOURISME

INFORMATION RESERVATIONS
Tel. +33 475 39 67 56 - Fax: +33 475 39 64 69
07120 SAMPZON - FRANCE
www.soleil-vivarais.com
E-mail : info@soleil-vivarais.com
ADAC

Camping Club
★★★★
SOLEIL VIVARAIS
Ardèche du Sud

yelloh! VILLAGE

FR07070 Camping Les Ranchisses

Route de Valgorge, Chassiers, 07110 Largentière (Ardèche)

Combining farming, wine-making, running an Auberge and a friendly family campsite is no simple task, but the Chevalier family seem to manage it quite effortlessly. Well run and with the emphasis on personal attention, this is a highly recommended site. In a somewhat lesser known area of the Ardèche at Chassiers, in a peaceful location on the Route de Valgorge, the site has developed from an original 'camping à la ferme' into a very well equipped modern campsite. There are 165 good-sized, level, grassy pitches, 88 for tourists with electricity which include 42 multi-serviced pitches (electricity, water, waste water). The pitches are in two distinct areas – the original site which is well shaded, and the lower part which is more open with less shade, serviced by tarmac and gravel access roads. There is an unfenced frontage onto a small lake connected to the river, providing opportunities for bathing, fishing or canoeing (free life jackets) with one part of the bathing area quite safe for youngsters (supervision essential). The site's own Auberge is set in a room of the original 1824 building that once used to house silk worms. It serves meals and takeaway food at lunch-time and evenings (all season). You may dine either inside the cave-like restaurant or outside on the attractive, shaded terrace. The food, traditional to the region, is both reasonably priced and of extremely good quality.

Facilities

Two modern, comprehensively equipped toilet buildings include washbasins in cubicles, dishwashing and laundry sinks and facilities for babies and disabled persons. It is an excellent provision, kept immaculate. Laundry. Motorcaravan service point. Small shop, takeaway and bar with terrace (all 10/4-19/9). Excellent pool complex with two large pools (20 x 10 m. and 15 x 7.5 m, both heated and open all season) and paddling pool. Adventure style playground. Organised amusements for children in high season. Tennis court. Minigolf. Table tennis. Boules. Canoeing. Off site: Medieval village of Largentière (1.5 km.) with Tuesday market and medieval festival in July. Canoe and kayaking on the Ardèche arranged from the site each Monday and Wednesday (mid -June - end Aug).

At a glance

Welcome & Ambience	✓✓✓✓✓	Location	✓✓✓✓✓
Quality of Pitches	✓✓✓✓	Range of Facilities	✓✓✓✓✓

Directions

Largentière is southwest of Aubenas and is best approached using the D104. 16 km. south of Aubenas turn northwest on the D5 and, immediately, on leaving Largentière, fork left signed Valgorge. Site is first on left, in about 1.8 km.

Charges 2004

Per unit incl. 2 persons	€ 19.00 - € 25.00
serviced pitch	€ 25.50 - € 32.00
child (1-10 yrs)	€ 4.50 - € 6.00
electricity (10A)	€ 4.50
dog	€ 2.20

Camping Cheques accepted.

Reservations

Made with 30% deposit plus booking/insurance fee (€15). Tel: 04 75 88 31 97.
Email: reception@lesranchisses.fr

Open

10 April - 19 September.

CAMPING ★★★★ LES RANCHISSES

FR07090 **Domaine des Plantas**

07360 Les Ollières-sur-Eyrieux (Ardèche)

A good quality site in a spectacular setting on the steep banks of the Eyrieux river, Domaine des Plantas offers an attractive alternative to those in the more popular southern parts of the Ardèche. The Eyrieux valley is less well known, but arguably just as attractive as those further south and a good deal less crowded, particularly in the main season. Perhaps the only drawback to this site is the narrow twisting three kilometre approach road which, although by no means frightening, may present something of a challenge to those with large outfits – however, the helpful owners have an ingenious convoy system designed to assist campers on departure. There is a sandy beach beside the quite fast-flowing, but fairly shallow, river (used for bathing) and a swimming pool and paddling pool with tiled surrounds for sunbathing. Facilities are housed in an original building which is quite impressive with its Protestant history and visible from the main road across the river long before you reach it. The restaurant terrace provides a stunning viewpoint. The 162 pitches (with electricity, water and drain) are terraced and shaded, so some up and down walking is required. They have electricity connections (long leads may be needed) and water points are very accessible.

Facilities

One large, modern toilet block, centrally situated in courtyard style, is well equipped with washbasins in cubicles and good facilities for children with small toilets and baby baths. An additional smaller block serves the higher terraces. Dishwashing and laundry sinks. Washing machine. Motorcaravan service point. Small shop (bread to order). Bar, restaurant and disco. Heated kidney shaped swimming pool and paddling pool. Adventure play area beside river. Mountain biking, canoeing, canyoning, riding and 'randonnées pedestres' (sounds better in French!). In high season animation for children organised six days a week, and discos for 14-18 year olds held in cellar twice weekly (strictly no alcohol). Many activities are possible and are arranged according to the campers' motivations, including excursions. Only gas barbecues are allowed. Off site: Riding 15 km.

At a glance

Welcome & Ambience ✓✓✓✓✓	Location	✓✓✓✓
Quality of Pitches ✓✓✓✓	Range of Facilities	✓✓✓✓✓

Directions

From A7 take exit 15 (Valence Sud). Immediately after the péage turn right to Valence centre, then follow signs to Montélimar via the N7 for 7km. Turn right towards Charmes sur Rhône, thence to Beauchastel. On leaving Beauchastel follow signs to Ollieres sur Eyrieux.

Latest charges

Per unit incl. 2 persons and electricity (10A)	€ 18.00 - € 26.00
extra person over 4 yrs	€ 4.00 - € 6.00
animal	€ 2.00
local tax	€ 0.31

Camping Cheques accepted.

Reservations

Made with deposit (€ 110) and fee (€ 20). Tel: 04 75 66 21 53. Email: plantas.ardeche@wanadoo.fr

Open

15 June - 15 September.

FR07120 Camping Nature Parc L'Ardéchois

Route touristique des Gorges, 07150 Vallon-Pont-d'Arc (Ardèche)

This very high quality, family run site is within walking distance of Vallon Pont d'Arc. It borders the Ardèche river and canoe trips are professionally run, direct from the site. This site is ideal for families with younger children seeking an active holiday. The facilities are comprehensive and of an extremely high standard. Of the 244 pitches, there are 225 medium to large grass pitches for tourers, separated by trees and individual shrubs. All have electricity and about half have full services. The focal point of the site is the bar and restaurant (good menus), with terrace and stage overlooking the attractive pool and sunbathing terrace. Activities are organised all season; these are family based – no discos.

Facilities

Two well equipped toilet blocks, one superb with 'everything' working automatically. Facilities are of the highest standard, very clean and include good facilities for babies, those with disabilities, washing up and laundry. Four private bathrooms to hire. Washing machines. Well stocked shop. Swimming pool (no Bermuda shorts). Football, tennis and table tennis. Play area. Internet point. Organised activities, canoe trips. Off site: Walking, riding, mountain biking.

At a glance

Welcome & Ambience	✓✓✓✓✓	Location	✓✓✓✓
Quality of Pitches	✓✓✓✓	Range of Facilities	✓✓✓✓

Directions

From Vallon Pont d'Arc (western end of the Gorge) go east on the D290. Site entrance is shortly on the right.

Latest charges

Per pitch incl. 2 persons electricity	€ 21.50 - € 34.00
	€ 4.00

Reservations

Made with deposit (€ 94) and fee (€ 31).
Tel: 04 75 88 06 63. Email: ardecamp@aol.com

Open

15 April - 22 September.

FR07140 Camping Les Lavandes

Le Village, 07170 Darbres (Ardèche)

Although slightly less sophisticated than some others in the region, this site should appeal to those seeking the real France for a pleasant family holiday. Situated to the northeast of Aubenas, in a quieter part of this region, Les Lavandes is surrounded by pretty countryside, vineyards and orchards. The enthusiastic French owners, who speak good English, run a site that appeals to all nationalities. The 70 pitches are arranged on low terraces separated by trees and shrubs that give welcome shade in summer. Most pitches have electricity but water taps are not so abundant. Traditional buildings house the reception, restaurant and cosy bar offering views over the pool to the village (just a stroll away).

Facilities

The recently refurbished facilities are comprehensive and well maintained. Excellent room with facilities for disabled people and a baby room. Washing machine. Two small play areas suited for younger children. Swimming pool and paddling pool surrounded by paved sunbathing area with larger grass area adjacent. Off site: Tennis 5 km. Canoeing, walking, cycling, riding and carting nearby.

At a glance

Welcome & Ambience	✓✓✓✓✓	Location	✓✓✓✓
Quality of Pitches	✓✓✓✓	Range of Facilities	✓✓✓✓✓

Directions

From Montélimar take N102 towards Aubenas. Pass through Villeneuve and, at Lavilledieu, turn right on D224 to Darbre (10 km). In the village turn sharp left by the post office and follow signs to site.

Charges 2003

Per unit incl. 2 persons	€ 11.00 - € 15.20
electricity (6/10A)	€ 3.50

Reservations

Made with deposit (€ 85) and fee (€ 15).
Tel: 04 75 94 20 65. Email: sarl.leslavandes@online.fr

Open

Easter - 15 September.

FR07150 Camping Domaine de Gil

Route de Vals-les-Bains, Ucel, 07200 Aubenas (Ardèche)

This very attractive, smaller site in a less busy part of the Ardèche should appeal to couples and families with smaller children. The 80 good sized, level pitches are surrounded by a variety of trees which offer plenty of shade. All have electricity. The focal point of the site is formed by the pool and sunbathing area, with the bar, restaurant and well appointed play areas all adjacent. A sports area and shady picnic/play area are alongside the river Ardèche – an ideal spot to cool off on a hot day.

Facilities

All facilities are in a single, cheerful, modern block adjacent to the pool. Most washbasins are in cabins. Washing machine and iron. Motorcaravan service point. Swimming pool and paddling pool, heated all season (proper swimming trunks only). Bar/restaurant and takeaway (mid June - mid Sept). Small shop for basics. Two play areas. Volleyball, boules, minigolf, football, tennis court. Canoeing. River fishing. Some organised activities in high season. Off site: Shops, bicycle hire and riding, 2 km.

At a glance

Welcome & Ambience	✓✓✓✓✓	Location	✓✓✓✓
Quality of Pitches	✓✓✓✓	Range of Facilities	✓✓✓✓

Directions

From the southeast on the N102, just after a tunnel, turn right at roundabout and cross the Ardèche into Pont d'Ucel. Shortly, at a roundabout, take last exit (D578B signed Ucel). Site is about 2 km on the left.

Charges 2003

Per unit incl. 2 persons	€ 11.40 - € 19.82
extra person	€ 2.70 - € 4.85
electricity (10A)	€ 3.35

Reservations

Made wiith 25% deposit and fee (€ 12.19).
Tel: 04 75 94 63 63. Email: raf.garcia@wanadoo.fr.

Open

15 April - 15 September.

FR07110 Domaine Le Pommier

RN102, 07170 Villeneuve-de-Berg (Ardèche)

Domaine Le Pommier is an extremely spacious Dutch owned site of 10 hectares in 32 hectares of wooded grounds. It has first class facilities, including the most up-to-date toilet blocks, a very good bar/restaurant and one of the best swimming pool complexes we have seen – ideal for all the family. The site is steeply terraced (a tractor is available for assistance) and has wonderful views over the Ardèche mountains and beyond. There are 400 pitches with 275 for tourists. They are grassy/stony, of good size and well spaced. Separated by young trees and hedges, some have little or no shade. All have access to electricity and water is close by.

Facilities

Four new toilet blocks, one with under floor heating, provide all the necessary facilities. Comprehensive shop. Bar/restaurant. Heated pool complex with water slides, a flowing 'river', several good, unusual paddling pools and a conventional pool for serious swimming. Large fitness room. Everything opens from the end of April. Boules, football, minigolf, badminton, games in the woods, table tennis, archery, water polo, tug of war, volleyball, tennis etc. Sound proof disco. Very extensive programme of events on and off site. Off season excursions to vineyards, wine tasting, museums, nougat factory and old villages. Also bridge classes and water colour classes. Off site: Villeneuve de Berg 1.5 km. River Ardèche 12 km. Potholing, rock climbing, canoeing, canyoning, mountain biking, walking or horse riding. Touring the many old villages and the Ardèche Gorge.

At a glance

Welcome & Ambience	✓✓✓✓✓	Location	✓✓✓✓
Quality of Pitches	✓✓✓✓	Range of Facilities	✓✓✓✓

Directions

Site is west of Montélimar on the N102. The entrance is adjacent to the roundabout at the eastern end of the Villeneuve de Berg bypass.

Charges 2003

Per unit incl. 2 persons	€ 14.00 - € 29.00
extra person over 4 yrs	€ 4.00 - € 6.50
electricity	€ 4.00
dog	free - € 4.00
local tax	€ 0.50

Special offers for longer stays in low season.

Reservations

Made with booking fee (€ 20) and cancellation insurance (4.5%). Tel: 04 75 94 82 81. Email: info@campinglepommier.com

Open

1 April - 15 October (all services from end of April).

CampingDomaine ★ ★ ★ ★
"Le Pommier"

- Pleasant 7 ha family campsite on a 10 ha domain
- 275 spacious shady and sunny pitches
- hire of caravans and chalets
- grill restaurant/pizzeria, cafeteria / take-away meals
- bar with terrace, discotheque, campsite store
- aqua park, slides, paddling pool, children's shallow pool, whirlpool
- river, mini golf 18 holes, fitness, Internet corner
- playground, volleyball, bicycle hire, football, table tennis
- extensive entertainment programme with children's club, day and evening programmes organised by our CIOS and ALO qualified team
- special senior programme: jeu de boules matches, bridge drives, water colour classes

SPECIAL OFFERS: IN THE LOW SEASON

Camping Domaine "Le Pommier" ★★★★ - 07170 Villeneuve-de-Berg, France
Tel. (+) 33 4 75 94 82 81 - Fax (+) 33 4 75 94 83 90
www.campinglepommier.com - email: info@campinglepommier.com

heated sanitary building
heated swimming pool

FR26020 Castel Camping du Château de Senaud

26140 Albon (Drôme)

Château du Sénaud, near the N7 south of Vienne, makes a useful stopover on the way south, but one could enjoy a longer stay to explore the surrounding villages and mountains. It is one of the original sites in the Castel chain and is still run with character and hands-on attention by Mme. Comtesse d'Armagnac. There are a fair number of permanent caravans used at weekends, but it also has some 85 pitches in tourist areas. Some have shade, some have views across the Rhône valley, and electricity and water connections are available on all pitches. There may be some noise from the autoroute.

Facilities

Four toilet blocks include British and one Turkish style toilets, washbasins in cabins, some en-suite with shower in one block. Facilities for babies. Washing machines. Motorcaravan service point. Shop (15/5-15/9). Bar, takeaway and good value small restaurant with simple menu (all 15/6-15/9). Swimming pool with water toboggan (1/5-15/9, depending on the weather) and new jacuzzi. Tennis court. Fishing. Bicycle hire. Table tennis, bowling alley and minigolf. Off site: Riding 10 km. Golf course and walks adjacent.

At a glance

Welcome & Ambience	✓✓✓✓✓	Location	✓✓✓✓
Quality of Pitches	✓✓✓✓	Range of Facilities	✓✓✓✓

Directions

Leave autoroute at Chanas exit, proceed south on N7 for 8 km. then east on D301 from Le Creux de la Thine to site. From south, exit autoroute for Tain-Tournon and proceed north, approaching the site on D122 through St Vallier then D132 towards Anneyron to site.

Charges 2003

Pitch	€ 6.05 - € 7.15
electricity (10A)	€ 3.50 - € 4.05
dog	€ 1.65 - € 1.83

No credit cards. Camping Cheques accepted.

Reservations

Made with deposit for min. 3 nights.
Tel: 04 75 03 11 31.
Email: camping.de.senaud@libertysurf.fr

Open

15 March - 31 October.

★★★★

Le Château de Senaud

26140 ALBON
Tel: 0033 475 03 11 31
Fax: 0033 475 03 08 06
www.chateau.de.senaud.com
camping.de.senaud@libertysurf.fr

LES CASTELS
★★★★

At the gateway to the Drome, the "Château de Senaud" offers you a rare treasure in a beautiful green country setting: a XVIIth century castle with its numerous annexes and outbuildings.
It contains a small water leisure complexae with toboggan, swimming pool and paddling pool.
Its geographic location offers a variety of walks and visits: Parc du Vercors, Palais du Facteur Cheval.
18 holes golfcourses.

Camping Cheque

FR26030 **Sunêlia Le Grand Lierne**

B.P. 8, 26120 Chabeuil (Drôme)

In addition to its obvious attraction as an overnight stop, fairly convenient for the A7 autoroute, this site provides a pleasant base to explore this little known area between the Ardèche and the Vercors mountains and the Côte du Rhône wine area. It has 140 marked pitches, 76 for touring units, mainly separated by developing hedges or oak trees. They have good shade, some are on flat ground and all have electricity. A more open area exists for those who prefer less shade and a view of the mountains. A varied entertainment programme has a particular emphasis on activities for children, with a range of activities and excursions. The owners wish to keep a balance between nationalities and are also keen to encourage rallies and will arrange visit programmes. Used by tour operators (30%).

Facilities

Two sanitary blocks include washbasins in cabins, facilities for disabled people and a small WC for children. Dishwashing under cover. Washing machines (powder provided), dryers and outdoor lines by the blocks. Motorcaravan services. Shop. Bar/snack bar with terrace for eating in and takeaway (all season). Fridge rental. Three swimming pools, one covered and heated in low season (no bermuda shorts), paddling pool and 50 m. water slide. Playgrounds and trampoline. Mini-tennis, minigolf, table tennis, volleyball, archery and football field. Bicycle hire. Library. Barbecues are permitted in special areas. Dogs and other pets are not accepted in high season (3/7-21/8). Caravan storage. Off site: Fishing 3 km, riding 7 km, golf 3 km, canoe/kayak near.

At a glance

Welcome & Ambience	✓✓✓✓✓	Location	✓✓✓✓
Quality of Pitches	✓✓✓	Range of Facilities	✓✓✓✓✓

Directions

Site signed in Chabeuil about 11 km. east of Valence (18 km. from autoroute). It is best to approach Chabeuil from the south side of Valence via the Valence ring road, thence onto the D68 to Chabeuil itself. Site is off the D125 to Charpey, 5 km. from Chabeuil, but well signed.

Charges 2004

Per unit incl. 2 adults	€ 16.00 - € 27.80
extra person	€ 6.60 - € 7.80
child (2-7 yrs)	€ 3.40 - € 5.60
electricity (6/10A)	€ 4.00 - € 5.50
animal	€ 4.00
local tax	€ 0.20

Camping Cheques accepted.

Reservations

Accepted with deposit (€ 92) and fee (€ 30). Tel: 04 75 59 83 14. Email: contact@grandlierne.com

Open

23 April - 12 September.

FR26040 **Camping Le Couspeau**

26460 Le Poet Célard (Drôme)

The approach to this site is via a steep road, and with several hairpin bends to negotiate, care is required – underpowered units should not attempt this hill. However, for others the views are reward enough as a magnificent landscape of mountains and valleys unfolds. The overall impression of beauty and tranquillity is reflected in the amiable attitude of the owners, who maintain a helpful, yet low profile, relaxed presence. Access to the 67 touring pitches (all with electricity) on the older section of the site is reasonably easy; levelling blocks may be handy as some of the terraced pitches are slightly sloping. Mature trees provide shade and there are adequate water points around the site. The 20 pitches on the new lower section of the site are very large (150 sq.m) and all have electricity, water and a drain. They are separated by small hedges and some small trees but have little shade. Access is via a steep road but tractor assistance is available. The site has a good restaurant/bar and a terrace with panoramic views. In July and August on one evening each week there is live music, on another a themed meal. Those seeking to unwind and relax should appreciate the delightful scenery and setting of this medium sized site.

Facilities

Three sanitary blocks, two in the old section and one in the new, are kept very clean. Laundry and dishwashing sinks, washing machines and dryer. Facilities for disabled campers (on the older section), but the site is not ideal due steep roads and steps. Well stocked shop (15/6-30/9). Restaurant/bar and takeaway (15/6-30/9). Main pool (1/6-30/9) and smaller, covered one (1/5-30/9 and heated in low seasons) plus a toddlers' pool. Children's play area and organised activities in high season. Tennis, table tennis and volleyball. Guided hill walks and cycle trips. Rafting, canoe trips (on the River Drôme), riding and paragliding arranged. Off site: Riding and fishing 5 km. Canoeing, rafting and paragliding. Ideal area for the serious cyclists, mountain bikers and hikers.

At a glance

Welcome & Ambience	✓✓✓✓	Location	✓✓✓✓
Quality of Pitches	✓✓✓✓	Range of Facilities	✓✓✓✓

Directions

From A7 autoroute exit 16 take D104 to Crest. At traffic lights, on the Crest bypass, turn hard right on D538 south towards Bourdeaux. Shortly before Bourdeaux turn right over small river bridge onto D328B, signed Le Poët Célard. After climbing for about 1.5 km, at T-junction, turn right on D328 and just before Le Poët Célard turn left onto D328A. Site is up the hill on the left, well signed.

Charges 2003

Per unit incl. 2 persons	€ 12.00 - € 20.00
extra large pitch	€ 32.00
child (under 7 yrs)	free - € 4.00
electricity (6A)	€ 3.00

Camping Cheques accepted.

Reservations

Advised for July/Aug. and made with deposit (€ 75) and fee (€ 23). Tel: 04 75 53 30 14. Email: info@couspeau.com

Open

1 May - 26 September.

FR26080 Camping Le Gallo Romain

Route du Col de Tourniol, 26300 Barbières (Drôme)

Surrounded by wooded hills and mountains, this small simple site makes a good base from which to explore the spectacular Vercors plateau. It is quiet and peaceful, in an attractive location with pitches set on terraces that descend to a small stream. There are 80 pitches, some with a little grass, most with electricity and some shade at some part of the day. The area is ideal for walking or mountain biking with many special cycle tracks in the hills, or for wild flower or butterfly enthusiasts. A small bar/restaurant offers well cooked local dishes at extremely reasonable prices (booking essential).

Facilities

Two sanitary blocks including washbasins in cubicles, are kept reasonably clean but could be stretched in peak season. Small shop high season only but fresh bread available all season. Bar/restaurant (1/6-10/9). Swimming pool (17 x 8 m) and paddling pool. Games room, pool table, table tennis and volleyball. Small play area. Off site: Riding or golf 6 km. Shops at Barbières 1 km.

At a glance

Welcome & Ambience	✓✓✓	Location	✓✓✓✓
Quality of Pitches	✓✓	Range of Facilities	✓✓✓✓

Directions

Leave A49/E713 autoroute at exit 7 (Romans-sur-Isère) and turn south on D149 (Col de Tourniol). Barbières is 12 km. along this road. Drive carefully through narrow village streets; the site is a little way on the right.

Charges 2003

Per person	€ 3.00 - € 3.70
pitch with electricity (6A)	€ 12.15 - € 15.15

No credit cards.

Reservations

Made with deposit and fee. Tel: 04 75 47 44 07. Email: info@legalloromain.net

Open

1 May - 15 September.

FR26090 Camping Les Truffières

Lieu-dit Nachony, 26230 Grignan (Drôme)

This is a delightful small site in a rural setting within walking distance of the picturesque ancient village of Grignan with wonderful views and providing peace and tranquility. The 85 good sized pitches are level and fairly stony with 79 for touring units. Shaded by oak trees and separated by rosemary or laurel hedging, each pitch has electricity. The Croze family are most welcoming and achieve high standards of cleanliness and order while maintaining a friendly and relaxed atmosphere. The Drôme is one of the most beautiful regions of France, vineyards, olive orchards, lavender, sunflowers, wild flowers and fruit orchards abound. Many old towns and villages, reading like a wine list, with their restaurants, shops and local markets are close at hand.

Facilities

The good, main toilet block provides all the necessary facilities. Extra facilities by the pool are opened when needed. Dishwashing and laundry facilities under cover. Washing machine and ironing model. Snack bar and takeaway with limited menu at mid-day and evening in congenial atmosphere (June - Sept). Swimming pool and smaller pool for children (no Bermuda shorts). Volleyball, table tennis and boules. Little in the way of on site entertainment but many off site activities can be booked. Dogs are not accepted.

At a glance

Welcome & Ambience	✓✓✓✓✓	Location	✓✓✓✓
Quality of Pitches	✓✓✓✓	Range of Facilities	✓✓✓✓

Directions

From N7 (or A7 autoroute exit 18) south of Montélimar, take D133 (changes to D541) signed Grignan. After 9 km, just before Grignan, take D71 towards Charamet and site is shortly on the left.

Charges 2003

Per unit incl. 2 persons	€ 13.00 - € 15.50
electricity (10A)	€ 4.00

Reservations

Contact site. Tel: 04 75 46 93 62. Email: info@lestruffieres.com

Open

20 April - 1 October.

FR26110 Les 4 Saisons Camping de Grâne

Route de Roche-sur-Grâne, 26400 Grâne (Drôme)

Opened just a few years ago, this small, terraced site nestles in the hillsides of the lower Drôme valley. With its 80 pitches, it provides mainly overnight accommodation but it is worth a longer stay. The modern main building houses the facilities and provides commanding views across the valley towards Crest and the Vercors. The pitches are level, cut out of the hillside and reached by a one-way system on tarmac roads. All have electricity, water and drain. This is an excellent base for exploring the Drôme.

Facilities

A short flight of steps to a lower level leads to very adequate sanitary facilities that include roomy showers, washbasins in cabins, dishwashing and laundry facilities, two washing machines and a baby-room. There are en-suite facilities for disabled visitors but the site is very sloping and not suitable for wheelchairs. Bicycle hire. Bar and snacks. Off site: The village is nearby. Riding 3 km.

At a glance

Welcome & Ambience	✓✓✓✓	Location	✓✓✓✓
Quality of Pitches	✓✓✓✓	Range of Facilities	✓✓✓

Directions

From A7 take exit 17, or N7 Loriol, on D104 (Crest). After 8 km. take D113 south from Grâne. Go through village for 600 m. to site on left.

Charges 2003

Per unit incl. 2 persons	€ 12.00 - € 14.00
electricity (6/16A)	€ 4.00

Reservations

Contact site. Tel: 04 75 62 64 17. Email: camping.4saisons@wanadoo.fr

Open

All year.

FR26120 Gervanne Camping

Bellevue, 26400 Mirabel et Blacons (Drôme)

This spacious, riverside family run site with 177 pitches, 167 for touring, is divided into two sections. The newer section is adjacent to the bar, restaurant, superb pool and large sunbathing terrace from which there are mountain views. The newer pitches are of average size with some shade and are separated by a few small shrubs and trees. The older section is close to the river and on the other side of the road, but is connected to the newer section by an underpass. It is less formally laid out and mature trees offer plenty of shade. All pitches have electricity. This interesting area on the edge of the Vercors National Park offers opportunities for outdoor activities.

Facilities

Each section has a well appointed, very clean toilet block with the majority of washbasins in cabins, and a baby room in each with bath, shower and changing facilities. Washing machine, dryer. Large en-suite unit for disabled people. Bar/restaurant (1/6-15/9) with takeaway and internet terminal. Swimming pool. Small play area, table tennis and boules. Bicycle hire. Charcoal barbecues not allowed. Off site: Supermarket next door. Fishing, canoeing and bathing in river Drome adjacent. Riding 5 km. Golf 13 km.

Directions

Site is 22 km. east of exit 16 (D104 to Crest) on the A7. After Crest follow signs to Die for 6 km. then turn left (D164A) and cross river into Mirabel et Blacons, turn left at roundabout and follow signs to campsite.

Charges 2003

Per unit incl. 2 adults	€ 11.90 - € 14.90
electricity (4/6A)	€ 2.50 - € 3.10

Reservations

Contact site. Tel: 04 75 40 00 20.
Email: info@gervanne-camping.com

Open

1 April - 31 October.

At a glance

Welcome & Ambience	✓✓✓✓	Location	✓✓✓✓
Quality of Pitches	✓✓✓✓	Range of Facilities	✓✓✓✓

FR26130 Camping L'Hirondelle

Bois de St Ferreol, 26410 Menglon (Drôme)

This natural, spacious and peaceful site is run by a very friendly family. It lies in a beautiful valley, south of the Vercors mountains and the Vercors National Park, beside the River Bez, a tributary of the River Drôme. It is close to the interesting and ancient town of Die. In natural woodland openings, the 100 large pitches (all with electricity) are stony and slightly bumpy (rock pegs advised). There are 80 for touring units. If you are lucky you may see red squirrels and beavers and, in June there is a wide variety of flowers including orchids. Although this site is not manicured, the pitches, separated from others by a wide variety of trees, the river bank on one side and the large open field on the other give privacy and space. It is a very good site for couples and young families. Member 'Sites et Paysages'.

Facilities

Two large and one small toilet block offer all the necessary facilities at a high standard. Very good bar/restaurant with good menus and takeaway (19/4-7/9). Small range of supplies, including bread, on sale from the bar. New pool complex with small slide, paddling pool, jacuzzi and a section that flows like a river (19/4-7/9). Ample room to play and paddle in the river. Playground. Club/TV room. Internet access. Fishing. Football, boules, volleyball, archery. Organised events for young children and adults. Occasional evening events. Off site: Riding and bicycle hire 3 km. Canoeing, kayaking, climbing, rambling, mountain biking.

Directions

From Die follow D93 south and after 5 km, at Pont de Quart, turn left on D539 (Chatillon). After 4 km. turn right on D140, signed Menglon. Site is on the right.

Charges 2004

Per pitch incl. 2 persons	€ 15.70 - € 22.60
electricity (3-6A)	€ 3.00 - € 4.00
Camping Cheques accepted.	

Reservations

Made with 30% deposit and fee (€ 18.50). Tel: 04 75 21 82 08. Email: contact@campinghirondelle.com

Open

3 April - 11 September with all services.

At a glance

Welcome & Ambience	✓✓✓✓✓	Location	✓✓✓✓✓
Quality of Pitches	✓✓✓✓	Range of Facilities	✓✓✓✓

FR42010M Camping Municipal de Charlieu

Rue Riottier, 42190 Charlieu (Loire)

Charlieu is a very attractive little town, and the well cared for municipal site here would make a good base for exploring the area. The 100 pitches (30 seasonal units), all have electricity, are reasonably large and well spaced, on level grass. Most are separated by trim hedges but with little shade. There are few facilities on the site as the small, historic town is within about five minutes walk.

Facilities

The clean toilet block should be adequate, except perhaps in high season. It has British and Turkish style WCs, facilities for disabled visitors. Dishwashing. Laundry facilities. Simple snacks and takeaways. Bicycle hire. Volleyball, boules. Playground. Fishing. Off site: Swimming pool adjacent.

Directions

From Pouilly, on the D482, take D487 to Charlieu (5.5 km). Site is southeast of town, signed from the centre.

Charges 2003

Per unit incl. 2 persons, electricity	€ 8.70 - € 11.70

Reservations

Made without fee; contact site. Tel: 04 77 69 01 70. Email: camp-charlieu@voila.fr.

Open

1 May - 30 September.

At a glance

Welcome & Ambience	✓✓✓✓	Location	✓✓✓
Quality of Pitches	✓✓✓	Range of Facilities	✓✓✓

FR69010M Camping International Porte de Lyon

Porte de Lyon, 69570 Dardilly (Rhône)

Camping International is a modern overnight site just off the A6 autoroute. Kept busy with overnight trade, reception and the café (in main season) open until quite late. There are 175 separate numbered plots with electricity (10A). Those for caravans are mostly on hardstandings on a slight slope, with another small grassy part, while those for tents are on a flatter area of grass. A very large commercial centre has been developed just outside the site, with eight hotels, restaurants, a supermarket, petrol station, etc. There is some road noise. A bus service for Lyon is nearby (timetables in reception).

Facilities

Three heated sanitary blocks have free hot water (solar heated) and washbasins in cabins. Dishwashing and laundry sinks. Baby changing facilities and washing machines. Bar/snacks and takeaway (15/6-15/9). Unheated swimming and paddling pools (charged for). Playground. TV room. Table tennis.

At a glance

Welcome & Ambience	✓✓✓✓	Location	✓✓✓✓
Quality of Pitches	✓✓✓	Range of Facilities	✓✓✓✓

Directions

Travelling south, do not take new A46 motorway around Lyon, but continue on A6 autoroute and take exit marked 'Limonest, Dardilly, Porte de Lyon' about 8 km. north of the Lyon tunnel; at once turn left for Porte de Lyon. Porte de Lyon is well signed from most directions.

Charges 2003

Per person	€ 2.90
child (7-15 yrs)	€ 2.20
motorcaravan or 1 axle caravan	€ 7.60
caravan, 2 axle	€ 15.30
electricity (higher in winter)	€ 3.00 - € 4.60

Reservations

Made if you write, but there is usually space.
Tel: 04 78 35 64 55.
Email: camping.lyon@mairie-lyon.fr

Open

All year.

FR69020M Camping Municipal La Grappe Fleurie

La Lie, 69820 Fleurie (Rhône)

With easy access from both the A6 autoroute and the N6, this site is ideally situated for night stops or indeed for longer stays to explore the vineyards and historic attractions of the Beaujolais region. Virtually surrounded by vineyards, but within walking distance (less than 1 km) of the pretty village of Fleurie, this is an immaculate small site, with 96 separated touring pitches. All are grassed and fairly level with the benefit of individual access to water, drainage and electrical connections. Restaurant and shopping facilities are available in the village.

Facilities

Sanitary facilities in two blocks have British and Turkish style toilets and very satisfactory shower and washing facilities (showers closed 22.00-07.00 hrs). Two cold showers are provided for those wishing to cool down in summer. Small playground. Table tennis, tennis and volleyball. Off site: Swimming pool 8 km.

At a glance

Welcome & Ambience	✓✓✓✓	Location	✓✓✓✓
Quality of Pitches	✓✓✓✓	Range of Facilities	✓✓✓✓

Directions

From N6 at Le Maison Blanche/Romanech-Thorins, take D32 to village of Fleurie from where site is signed.

Charges 2003

Per unit incl. 1 or 2 adults and electricity (10A)	€ 11.00 - € 12.00
extra adult	€ 3.50
child (5-10 yrs)	€ 2.50
tent (1 or 2 persons)	€ 10.00

Reservations

Advised in high season. Tel: 04 74 04 10 44.
Email: info@fleurie.org

Open

15 March - 26 October.

Map 14

This is a corner of France that evokes dreamy images of lazy afternoons amongst sleepy village squares, sunny vineyards and beautiful lavender fields basking under the dazzling blue of the sky.

Only the départements from the mountainous region of Provence have been included in this section:
04 Alpes-de-Haute-Provence, 05 Hautes-Alpes, 84 Vaucluse

Provence is a region of magical light, bleached landscapes, olive groves, herb-scented garrique, vineyards and Roman and medieval antiquities. The river valleys provide natural routes through the mountain barrier. Roman monuments can be seen at Orange, and Vaison-la-Romaine, where a 2,000 year old bridge is still in use. Avignon was the site of the papal court and the Palais des Papes at Avignon is a spectacular construction.

The Hautes-Alpes will reward with stunning vistas, peace and quiet. Briançon is the highest town in Europe and many of the high passes are not for the faint-hearted. The Vaucluse, where in the late spring the southern slopes of the Montagne du Luberon are a mass of colour with glades of wild flowers. The extinct volcanic cone of Mont Ventoux, of Tour de France fame provides dramatic views. The scents, the colours and an amazing intensity of light have encouraged artists and writers to settle amidst the sleepy villages, with narrow streets and ancient dwellings topped with sun-baked terracotta tiles, where the air is fragrant with the smell of wild herbs and lavender.

Cuisine of the region

Influenced by the Savoie area to the north and the Côte d'Azur to the south, with emphasis on herbs and garlic, and fish. The wine region is mainly known for its dry, fruity rosé wines: Bandol, Bellet, Palette, Cassis. Red wines include Côtes du Rhône and Châteauneuf-du-Pape.

Aigo Bouido: garlic and sage soup with bread (or eggs and cheese)

Farcement (Farçon Savoyard): potatoes baked with cream, eggs, bacon, dried pears and prunes

Pissaladière: Provencal bread dough with onions, anchovies, olives

Ratatouille: aubergines, courgettes, onions, garlic, red peppers and tomatoes in olive oil

Tartiflette: potato, bacon, onions and Reblochon cheese

Places of interest

Avignon: ramparts, old city, Papal Palace, old palace, Calvet museum

Mont Ventoux: near Carpentras, one of the best known stages of the classic Tour de France annual cycle race

Orange: Roman city, gateway to the Midi, Colline St Europe

St Vaison la Romaine: Roman city, the French Pompei

tip

VISIT THE HAUTE-PROVENCE GEOLOGICAL RESERVE, THE LARGEST IN EUROPE, WHICH HAS FOSSILS DATING BACK 300 MILLION YEARS. GUIDED DAY-TRIPS ARE AVAILABLE.

FR04020 **Camp du Verdon**

Domaine de la Salaou, 04120 Castellane (Alpes-de Haute-Provence)

Close to 'Route des Alpes' and the Gorges du Verdon, this is a very popular holiday area, the gorge, canoeing and rafting being the main attractions, ideal for active families. Two heated swimming pools and numerous on-site activities help to keep non-canoeists here. Du Verdon is a large level site, part meadow, part wooded, with 500 partly shaded, rather stony pitches (350 for tourists). Numbered and separated by newly planted bushes, they vary in size (but mostly over the average), have electricity and 120 also have water and waste water. They are mostly separate from the mobile homes (45) and pitches used by tour operators (110). Some overlook the unfenced river Verdon, so watch the children. One can walk to Castellane without using the main road. Dances and discos in July and August suit all age groups – the latest finishing time is around 11 pm. (after that time patrols make sure that the site is quiet). With the facilities open all season, the site is popular and very busy in July and August.

Facilities

The toilet blocks are being refurbished, the finished ones having British style WCs and all the latest equipment. As other blocks are upgraded, Turkish style toilets will be replaced. One block has facilities for disabled visitors. Washing machines and irons. Motorcaravan service and car wash points. Popular restaurant with terrace and bar including room with log fire for cooler evenings. Large well stocked shop. Pizzeria/crêperie. Takeaway (open twice daily). Two heated swimming pools and new paddling pool with 'mushroom' style fountain (all open all season). Entertainers provide games and competitions for all (July and August). Playgrounds. Minigolf, table tennis, archery, basketball and volleyball. Organised walks. Bicycle hire. Riding. Small fishing lake. Off site: Castellane (1 km) and the Ardèche Gorge. Riding 2 km, boat launching 4.5 km, golf 20 km. River Ardèche and many water sports.

Directions

From Castellane take D952 westwards towards Gorges du Verdon and Moustiers. Site is 1 km. on left.

Charges 2004

Per unit with up to 4 persons	€ 15.00 - € 26.00
with 6A electricity	€ 19.00 - € 30.00
dog	€ 2.50
local tax	€ 0.15 - € 0.30

Camping Cheques accepted.

Reservations

Made for any length with deposit (€ 80-110 depending on pitch) and fee (€ 20).
Tel: 04 92 83 61 29.
Email: contact@camp-du-verdon.com

Open

15 May - 15 September.

At a glance

Welcome & Ambience	✓✓✓✓	Location	✓✓✓✓
Quality of Pitches	✓✓✓✓	Range of Facilities	✓✓✓✓✓

FR04100 **Camping International**

Route Napoleon, 04120 Castellane (Alpes-de Haute-Provence)

Camping International has very friendly, English speaking owners and is a reasonably priced, less commercialised site situated in some of the most dramatic scenery in France with good views. The 250 pitches, 130 good sized ones for touring, are clearly marked, separated by trees and small hedges, and all have electricity and water. The bar/restaurant overlooks the swimming pool with its sunbathing area set in a sunny location, and all have fantastic views. In high season English speaking young people entertain children (3-8 years) and teenagers. On some evenings the teenagers are taken to the woods for campfire 'sing-alongs' which can go on till the early hours without disturbing the rest of the site. There are twice weekly guided walks into the surrounding hills in the nearby Gorges du Verdon – a very popular excursion. The weather in the hills here is very pleasant without the excessive heat of the coast. Access is good for larger units.

Facilities

Several small toilet blocks are of an older design with small cubicles and, although they are quite basic, the showers are fully controllable. One newer block has modern facilities, including those for disabled visitors, but this is not open early and late in the season. Washing machines, dryer and irons and a baby room. Chemical disposal at motorcaravan service point. Fridge hire. Shop. Restaurant/takeaway. Swimming pool (all 1/5-30/9). Club/TV room. Children's animation and occasional evening entertainment in July/Aug. Play area. Volleyball, football and boules pitches. Internet access. Off site: Castellane (1.5 km) is a very attractive little town with a superb river, canyon and rapids, good for canoeing, rafting and canyoning etc. Ideal area for walking and biking. Riding 800 m. Boat launching 5 km.

Directions

Site is 1 km. north of Castellane on the N85 'Route Napoleon'.

Charges 2003

Per unit incl. 2 persons	€ 12.00 - € 19.00
extra person	€ 3.00 - € 4.00
electricity (6A)	€ 3.00 - € 4.00
dog	€ 2.00
local tax	€ 0.30 - € 0.30

Camping Cheques accepted.

Reservations

Necessary for July/Aug. and made with deposit (€ 45), no booking fee. Tel: 04 92 83 66 67.
Email: info@campinginternational.fr

Open

1 April - 30 September.

At a glance

Welcome & Ambience	✓✓✓✓✓	Location	✓✓✓✓
Quality of Pitches	✓✓✓✓	Range of Facilities	✓✓✓✓

Camping International
Route Napoléon
04120 Castellane
Tél : +33 492 836 667
Fax : +33 492 837 767
www.campinginternational.fr

Castel Camping Caravaning
Domaine du Verdon
04120 Castellane
Tél : +33 492 836 129
Fax : +33 492 836 937
www.camp-du-verdon.com

LES CASTELS
N°209

Provence
Castellane
Canyon du Verdon

3 SEASONS ELITE

Camping Cheque

FR04030 Camping Lac du Moulin de Ventre

Niozelles, 04300 Forcalquier (Alpes-de Haute-Provence)

This is a friendly, English speaking, family run site in the heart of Haute-Provence, near Forcalquier, a bustling small French market town. Attractively located beside a small lake and 28 acres of wooded, hilly land, which is available for walking. Herbs of Provence can be found growing wild and flowers, birds and butterflies abound – a nature lovers delight. The 124 level, grassy pitches for tourists are separated by a variety of trees and small shrubs, 114 of them having electricity (long leads may be needed). Some pitches are particularly attractive, bordering a small stream. The site is well situated to visit Mont Ventoux, the Luberon National Park, the Gorges du Verdon and a wide range of ancient hill villages with their markets and museums etc.

Facilities

The toilet block, recently refurbished, provides very good, clean facilities including washbasins in cabins and facilities for disabled people. Baby bath. Washing machines. Fridge hire. Bread and a few essentials on sale. Bar/restaurant with waiter service, takeaway meals (all season) and themed evenings (high season). Pizzeria. Large and small swimming pools with large shallow area (15/5-15/9). Playground. Fishing and boules. Library. Some activities organised in high season. No discos. Only electric or gas barbecues are permitted. Off site: Shops, local market, doctor, tennis (2 km). Supermarket, chemist, riding, bicycle hire (5 km). Golf (20 km). Walking, cycling.

At a glance

Welcome & Ambience	✓✓✓✓	Location	✓✓✓✓
Quality of Pitches	✓✓✓✓	Range of Facilities	✓✓✓✓

Directions

From A51 motorway take exit 19 (Brillanne). Turn right on N96 then turn left on N100 (westwards signed Forcalquier) for about 3 km. Site is signed on left, just after a bridge 3 km. southeast of Niozelles.

Charges 2004

Per unit incl. 2 persons	€ 20.00
incl. electricity (6A)	€ 25.00
extra person	€ 5.50
child (0-4 yrs)	€ 3.00
dog	€ 3.00

Camping Cheques accepted.

Reservations

Advisable for July/Aug with 30% deposit and fee (€ 23). Tel: 04 92 78 63 31.
Email: moulindeventre@free.fr

Open

1 April - 30 September.

Haute-Provence
Camping Lac du Moulin de Ventre
04300 Niozelles
Tel: 0033 492 78 63 31
     0033 492 79 82 52
Fax: 0033 492 79 86 92
www.moulindeventre.com

FR04010 Sunêlia Hippocampe

Route de Napoléon, 04290 Volonne (Alpes-de Haute-Provence)

Hippocampe is a friendly, lakeside site situated in a beautiful area of France. The perfumes of thyme, lavender and wild herbs are everywhere and the higher hills of Haute Provence are not too far away. There are 447 level, numbered pitches (243 for touring units), medium to very large (130 sq.m) in size. All have electricity and 220 have water and a drain, most are separated by bushes and cherry trees (June is the time for the cherries and you may help yourself). Some of the best pitches border the lake. This is a family run site with families in mind, with games, aerobics, competitions, entertainment and shows, plus a daily club for younger family members in July/August. A soundproof underground disco is set well away from the pitches and is very popular with teenage customers. Staff tour the site at night ensuring a good night's sleep. The site is, however, much quieter in low season and, with its good discounts, is the time for those who do not want or need entertaining. The Gorges du Verdon is a sight not to be missed and rafting, paragliding or canoe trips can be booked from the site's own tourist information office. Being on the lower slopes of the hills of Haute-Provence, the surrounding area is good for both walking and mountain biking. All in all, this is a very good site for an active or restful holiday and is suitable for outfits of all sizes. Used by tour operators (20 pitches). English is spoken.

Facilities

Toilet blocks vary from old to modern, all with good facilities that include washbasins in cabins. They were very clean when we visited in June. Washing machines. Motorcaravan service point. Fridge rental. Bread available from reception (from 28/4), small shop (26/6-3/9). Bar (1/5-12/9). Restaurant, pizzeria and barbecue chicken shop (all 15/5-12/9). Large, attractive pool complex (from 1/5-30/9) with various pools of differing sizes and depths, heated in early and late seasons. Tennis (free outside 3/7- 21/8). Fishing, canoeing, boules. Bicycle and pedalo hire (high season). Large selection of sports facilities to choose from, some with free instruction. Charcoal barbecues are not permitted. Off site: Village of Volonne 600 m. Riding 500 m. Monuments, ancient churches, museums, markets, festivals and vineyards. Rafting, canyoning, torrent walking, mountain biking, paragliding and hang gliding.

At a glance

Welcome & Ambience	✓✓✓✓✓	Location	✓✓✓✓
Quality of Pitches	✓✓✓✓✓	Range of Facilities	✓✓✓✓✓

Directions

Approaching from the north turn off N85 across river bridge to Volonne, then right to site. From the south right on D4, 1 km. before Château Arnoux.

Charges 2004

Per unit with 2 persons and electricity (10A)	€ 15.00 - € 31.00
with water/drainage 100 sq.m.	€ 15.00 - € 33.00
with water/drainage 140 sq.m.	€ 19.00 - € 38.00
extra person (over 4 yrs)	€ 2.50 - € 6.00

Special low season offers.
Camping Cheques accepted.

Reservations

Made with deposit (varies with size of pitch from € 50 - € 95) and booking fee (€ 25).
Tel: 04 92 33 50 00.
Email: camping@l-hippocampe.com

Open

1 April - 30 September.

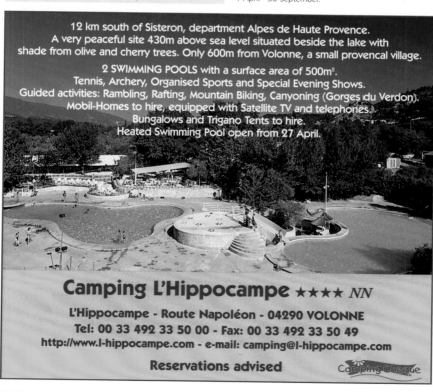

FR04060 Camping Caravaning Le Haut-Verdon

RD 908, 04370 Villars-Colmars (Alpes-de Haute-Provence)

On the banks of the Verdon, a good trout river, which then flows through the spectacular gorge, Camping Le Haut-Verdon is a family site. Surrounded by the majestic peaks of the Alpes-de-Haute-Provence, it is on the doorstep of the Mercantour National Park. It is however only open for a short season. Set amongst the pines, the 87 pitches are mostly on the large size but are rather stony. With 93 for touring units, all have electricity (but some will require long leads). There is a small village near, and the town of St André is 23 km. English is spoken. A 'Sites et Paysages' member.

Facilities
The main toilet block, recently refurbished, is heated and includes bidets and washbasins in cabins. Most WCs are British style. Washing machines and irons, dishwashing and laundry sinks. Freezer for ice packs and room for tenters when inclement weather strikes. Motorcaravan service point. Small shop has fresh food. Bar/restaurant and takeaway. Barbecue areas (portable ones banned). Swimming and paddling pools. Small play area. Volleyball, basketball, giant chess, bowling alley, table tennis, tennis and TV. Entertainers organise games and competitions. Fishing. Off site: Bicycle hire and riding 10 km.

At a glance
Welcome & Ambience	✓✓✓✓	Location	✓✓✓✓
Quality of Pitches	✓✓✓✓	Range of Facilities	✓✓✓✓

Directions
Follow D955 north from St André les Alpes towards Colmar. After about 11 km. the road number changes to D908. Site is on right at southern edge of Villars-Colmars. Caravans are not advised to use the D908 from Annot or the Col d'Allos from Barcelonnette.

Charges 2003
Per person over 6 yrs	€ 3.00 - € 4.00
pitch with electricity (6/10A)	€ 8.50 - € 13.00

Camping Cheques accepted.

Reservations
Made with deposit (30%) and fee (€ 15,24).
Tel: 04 92 83 40 09.
E-mail: campinglehautverdon@wanadoo.fr

Open
1 May - 30 September.

FR04080 Camping Caravaning L'Etoile des Neiges

04140 Montclar (Alpes-de Haute-Provence)

This attractive, family run site near the mountain village and ski resort of St Jean Montclar is open most of the year so is suitable for both summer and winter holidays. This beautiful alpine region offers all the usual alpine activities. Being at an altitude of 1300 m. the nights can get quite cold even in summer. The 121 shady pitches, with 80 for touring, are laid out in terraces and separated by small shrubs and alpine trees. All pitches are close to electricity and water points. An attractive bar and restaurant overlooks the two swimming pools, with the shallow pool having a water slide ideal for children. The site has no shop as the local shops are only a few minutes walk away. Although situated in the southern high Alps, the site can be reached without climbing any stiff gradients. A 'Sites et Paysages' member.

Facilities
The central toilet block, heated in winter, includes washbasins in cabins. Separate room containing facilities for disabled visitors. Two washing machines. Motorcaravan service point. Bar/restaurant (mid June - Sept). Swimming pool (from 1 June). Tennis, table tennis and boules. Two play areas. Rafting and walking organised in July/Aug. Off site: Shops in village a few minutes walk. Bicycle hire and riding in village. Fishing 1.5 km. Watersports and beach at Lac Serre Ponçon 7 km.

At a glance
Welcome & Ambience	✓✓✓✓✓	Location	✓✓✓✓
Quality of Pitches	✓✓✓✓	Range of Facilities	✓✓✓✓

Directions
Head south from Gap on the D900B. Beyond Serre Ponçon, turn right onto D900 signed Selonnet and St Jean Montclar. Immediately after entering St Jean Montclar turn left, go past the chalets and shops and then fork right to the campsite which is on the left.

Charges 2004
Per unit incl. 2 persons	€ 12.50 - € 21.00
electricity (6A)	€ 3.00 - € 4.00

Camping Cheques accepted.

Reservations
Deposit of 30% plus € 15 fee. Tel: 04 92 35 01 29.
Email: contact@etoile-des-neiges.com

Open
1 January - 30 September, and 22-31 December.

FR05000 Camping des Princes d'Orange

05700 Orpierre (Hautes-Alpes)

This attractive, terraced site, set on a hillside above the village, has been gradually and thoughtfully developed by its owners over 20 years. Their genuine, friendly welcome means many families return year upon year, bringing in turn new generations. Divided into five terraces, all its 120 generously sized pitches (96 for tourists) enjoy good shade from trees and wicker canopies and have electricity connections. Renowned as a serious rock climbing venue, Orpierre also has an enchanting maze of medieval streets and houses – almost like a trip back through the centuries. Whether you choose to drive, climb, walk or cycle there is plenty of wonderful scenery to discover in the immediate vicinity, whilst not far away, some exhilarating hang gliding and parascending can be enjoyed. Whilst the steepness of the terrain and its somewhat remote location may not suit all, there can be no doubt that you will be made most welcome and will enjoy the quiet splendours the region has to offer.

Facilities

Six toilet blocks with mostly British style WCs and washbasins in cubicles are extremely clean and accessible from all levels. Baby bath. Dishwashing and laundry sinks. Laundry facilities near reception. Bread available from bar each morning (other basics from village). Reasonably priced takeaway service from the bar in high season. Swimming pool (20 x 10 m), paddling pool (15/6-15/9). Play area. Table tennis, boules and games room. Fridge hire. Only gas barbecues are permitted. Off site: Orpierre with a few shops and bicycle hire 500 m. Nearest shopping centre Laragne, 12 km. Fishing 7 km. Riding 19 km. Hang gliding, parascending. Gorges de Guil.

Directions

Turn off N75 road at Eyguians onto D30 - site is signed on left at crossroads in centre Orpierre village.

Charges 2003

Per unit incl. 2 persons and 4A electricity	€ 21.00
incl. 3 persons	€ 22.50
child (under 7 yrs)	€ 3.00
dog	€ 1.50

Less 25% in low season. No credit cards.

Reservations

Made with deposit (€ 84) and fee (€ 9).
Tel: 04 92 66 22 53.
Email: campingorpierre@wanadoo.fr

Open

1 April - 25 October.

At a glance

Welcome & Ambience	✓✓✓✓	Location	✓✓✓✓
Quality of Pitches	✓✓✓✓	Range of Facilities	✓✓✓✓

LES **PRINCES D'ORANGE** ★★★★

Located in the heart of Haute-Provence, amongst the lavender fields, at 700m altitude, 30km from Sisteron and 50km from Gap

Tél. : 04 92 66 22 53 • Fax : 04 92 66 31 08
www.campingorpierre.com
e-mail : campingorpierre@wanadoo.fr

Reservation recommended.
Chalets, Mobile homes ans BTM to rent.

• 100 terraced pitches overlooking the charming mediaeval village of Orpierre
• Swimming and paddling pools (heated from 15 / 06 to 15 / 09), water slide
• Entertainment for children and teenagers, bivouacs...
• Bar, restaurant service, disco evenings...
• Mountain biking, walking trips, rock climbing
• Nearby : lakes, canyoning, via ferrata

Holidays with a family Œambience beneath the sun of Haute-Provence

FR05030 Camping Les Six Stations

Pont du Fossé, 05260 St Jean-St Nicolas (Hautes-Alpes)

This is a small, rural, unsophisticated site, run by a very friendly family, lying in the beautiful Drac Noir valley in the Parc National d'Ecrins. Level, grassy pitches are set in wooded glades with views of the surrounding mountains but with good shade. The 70 pitches, 48 for touring, all have access to electricity but very long leads may be necessary. Although the roads to the site offer no problems, the trees and narrow roads around the site makes access to some pitches difficult for large outfits. Some activities are organised in July and August for all the family and walks are arranged to see the marmots and mountain goats. The family pets, a donkey, pony and goat, share the woodland with campers. The area is fine for walking, cycling and canoeing and, in winter, for skiing (ski du fond direct from site).

Facilities

One modern toilet block, heated in winter, with all the usual facilities. Bar (June - Aug). Takeaway food (June - Aug). Small new swimming pool (June - Aug). Table tennis. Volleyball. Badminton. Walks and children's activities. Off site: Bicycle hire 1 km. Ski du fond 3 km. Riding 5 km. Golf 20 km. Restaurant outside gate. Paragliding. Climbing. Village of Fossé, only a 15 minute walk, with a few shops, restaurant and a bank.

Directions

Site is northeast of Gap. From N85, Route Napoleon, take D944 east and continue to village of Pont du Fossé. Site is on right 1 km. beyond the village.

Charges 2003

Per pitch incl. 2 persons	€ 12.50
electricity (2/4A)	€ 2.50

Reservations

Made with 25% deposit.Tel: 04 92 55 91 95.
Email: les.6.stations@wanadoo.fr

Open

All year.

At a glance

Welcome & Ambience	✓✓✓✓	Location	✓✓✓✓
Quality of Pitches	✓✓✓	Range of Facilities	✓✓✓✓

Provence

(277)

FR84020N **Domaine Naturiste de Bélézy**

84410 Bédoin (Vaucluse)

At the foot of Mt Ventoux, Bélézy is an excellent naturist site with many amenities and activities and the ambience is essentially relaxed and comfortable. The site has two areas joined by a short pedestrian tunnel and the 238 marked and numbered pitches are set amongst many varieties of trees and shrubs. Electricity points are plentiful but you may need a long cable in places. The emphasis is on informality and concern for the environment and during high season cars are banned from the camping area to the supervised parking areas nearby. So far as naturism is concerned, the emphasis is on personal choice (and weather conditions!), the only stipulation being the requirement for complete nudity in the pools and pool area. The leisure park side of the site is an area of natural parkland with an orchard, fishpond and woodland (complete with red squirrels), with a good range of sports facilities including tennis courts and swimming pools. The largest pool is for swimming and relaxation (you may enjoy a musical serenade), the smaller pool (heated 25/3-30/9) is also used for watersports and aquarobics. Near the pool area is the smart restaurant, with terrace, and the mellow old Mas Provencal farmhouse) that houses many of the activities and amenities. Unusually there is a hydrotherapy centre to tone up and revitalise with qualified diagnosis. Member 'France 4 Naturisme'.

Facilities

Sanitary blocks are a little different. The newer ones are of a standard type and excellent quality, with free hot showers in cubicles with separators, and washbasins in cabins. One block, refurbished in 2003, has heating in low season. Another has an attractive children's section. In the same area the adult block has hot showers in the open air, separated by natural stone dividers and washing up areas again mostly in the open. Shop (1/4-30/9). Restaurant provides excellent food, waiter service, and takeaway meals at affordable prices. Three swimming pools. Sauna. Tennis courts. Boules and table tennis. Adventure play area. Activities include painting and pottery courses, language lessons, archery, music (bring your own instrument) and guided walks. Children's clubs in holiday periods. Library and information centre. Disco. Hydrotherapy centre (1/4-30/9) - treatments include steam baths, massage and seaweed packs, osteopathy, Chinese medicine (including acupuncture) and Bach therapies. Barbecues are restricted to a central area. Dogs and pets are not accepted. Off site: It is possible to walk into Bédoin (excellent street market - Monday mornings), Mount Ventoux (Tour de France), Carpentras, Avignon, Orange, Gordes.

At a glance

Welcome & Ambience	✓✓✓✓	Location	✓✓✓✓
Quality of Pitches	✓✓✓✓	Range of Facilities	✓✓✓✓✓

Directions

From A7 autoroute or RN7 at Orange, take D950 southeast to Carpentras, then northeast via D974 to Bédoin. Site is signed in Bédoin, being about 1.5 km. northeast of the village

Charges 2003

Per unit incl. 1 adult	€ 13.00 - € 22.50
incl. 2 adults	€ 18.30 - € 28.50
incl. 3 adults	€ 25.50 - € 35.70
extra adult	€ 5.50 - € 8.50
child (3-8 yrs)	€ 4.00 - € 6.50
electricity (12A)	€ 3.50
large pitch	€ 4.00
pitch with water, drainage and sink	€ 5.00

Various offers and reductions outside high season. Camping Cheques accepted.

Reservations

Write with deposit (25%) and fee (€ 30).
Tel: 04 90 65 60 18. Email: info@belezy.com

Open

15 March - 4 October.

FR84110 **Camping Les Verguettes**

Route de Carpentras, 84570 Villes sur Auzon (Vaucluse)

Friendly and family run, this small campsite is surrounded by fields and vineyards and should appeal to those seeking a more relaxed holiday. It is probably not the ideal site for active youngsters. It lies on the outskirts of the village of Villes sur Auzon and at the foot of Mont Ventoux and the Nesque Gorge (1 km). Of the 89 pitches 81 are for touring. They are on the small side and are arranged in groups of six either side of the campsite road and are attractively laid out, separated by a variety of trees and shrubs. They all have electrical connections (5A but a few with 10A) but long leads may be necessary. Close to the attractive swimming pool are the bar and small outside restaurant which offers a simple menu – a pleasant place to relax after a day sightseeing.

Facilities

There are two toilet blocks, one near the entrance and other at the far end of the site. The buildings are old but have been refurbished to a high standard. Motorcaravan service point. Bar (all season). Small outside restaurant (20 May - end Aug) with simple menu and takeaway. Small swimming pool. Tennis. Minigolf. Boules. Table tennis, table football and small games/TV room. Internet point. Off site: Wine tasting, walking, cycling. Carpentras 10 km. Mont Ventoux, Nesque Gorge 1 km.

At a glance

Welcome & Ambience	✓✓✓✓	Location	✓✓✓✓
Quality of Pitches	✓✓✓✓	Range of Facilities	✓✓✓✓

Directions

Leave A7 at exit 22 just south of Orange and take D950 to Carpentras. Then D942 east, signed Sault and Mazan. Site is about 10 km. on the right just after a rounabout as you enter the village of Villes sur Auzon.

Charges 2004

Per person	€ 4.50 - € 5.00
pitch with electricity (5A)	€ 9.00 - € 9.90
water and drainage	€ 2.30 - € 2.50

Camping Cheques accepted.

Reservations

Made with deposit (€ 16) and booking fee (€ 23).
Tel: 04 90 61 88 18.
Email: info@provence-camping.com

Open

1 April - 15 October.

FR84050 Camping Caravaning La Sorguette

Route d'Apt, 84800 L'Isle sur la Sorgue (Vaucluse)

You are assured of a warm welcome by the English speaking staff. Arranged in fours, the 164 level pitches, 124 for touring, are of a good size, all with electricity. Each group of four is separated by tall hedges and most pitches have a little shade at some part of the day. In high season a few competitions are organised (boule or volleyball), plus some children's entertainment, but this is quite low key. Running alongside a part of the site (fenced with a gate), the river Sorgue is only 6 km. from its source in the mountains at Fontaine de Vaucluse (a big tourist attraction). It is still very clear and used for canoeing, swimming or fishing. Isle sur la Sorgue (1.5 km) is a very attractive small town, where the river forms small canals and waterways, interspersed with a few water wheels. There are many bars and restaurants, some with seating overlooking the water which has a cooling effect in the height of summer. The markets on Thursday's and Sunday's (free shuttle bus) virtually fill the old streets of the town, and brightly coloured pottery, table covers, fruit and vegetable make it a photographer's paradise.

Facilities

Three strategically placed, clean and well maintained toilet blocks include some washbasins in cubicles for ladies, mainly British style WCs and dishwashing and laundry sinks. Two blocks have washing machines, dryer, ironing boards and clothes lines. Units for disabled people at all three. Baby room. Motorcaravan service point. Fridge hire. Shop and bar with snacks (1/7-25/8) set well away from the pitches, outside the entrance which ensures that the occasional entertainment in July/Aug does not disturb campers. Play area, volleyball, half-court tennis and basketball. Canoe and bicycle hire. Internet access. Off site: Indoor/outdoor swimming pools (preferential rates, 2 km). Fishing and riding 5 km. Walking and cycling circuits.

At a glance

Welcome & Ambience	✓✓✓✓	Location	✓✓✓✓
Quality of Pitches	✓✓✓	Range of Facilities	✓✓✓

Directions

Site is 1.5 km. east of L'Isle sur la Sorgue on the N100 towards Apt. It is well signed from the town.

Charges 2003

Per unit incl. 2 persons	€ 14.50 - € 18.00
extra person (over 7 yrs)	€ 4.80 - € 6.20
child (1-6 yrs)	€ 2.50 - € 3.00
electricity (4/10A)	€ 3.50 - € 6.00
animal	€ 2.00 - € 2.50
local tax (over 12 yrs)	€ 0.35

Reservations

Made with deposit (€ 61) and fee (€ 12,20). Tel: 04 90 38 05 71. Email: sorguette@wanadoo.fr

Open

15 March - 15 October.

FR84070 Camping Club International Carpe Diem

Route de St Marcellin, BP 68, 84110 Vaison-la-Romaine (Vaucluse)

Perhaps Carpe Diem is a shade pretentious with its Greek statues and amphitheatre surround to its main pool. A developing site, it is only a few years old and will no doubt mellow as the trees and shrubs grow and old and new blend together. It is a good site for active families seeking all day entertainment and the situation is quite impressive with magnificent views over one of the most beautiful parts of France, yet only 800 m. from the village of Vaison la Romaine. There are 232 pitches with 100 small to medium sized, grass touring pitches all with electricity and many with some degree of shade. A new terraced area has mobile homes, chalets and unshaded touring pitches. The main pool is impressive with its tiered seating, plants, etc. It is used as a theatre for evening entertainment. A simpler square pool is near the play area with grass surrounds.

Facilities

The central toilet block - with fountain - provides mainly British and a few Turkish style toilets, washbasins in cabins and showers with an unusual cupboard for your clothes. Dishwashing and laundry sinks. Small editions of everything are provided for children. Washing machine. Extra facilities are behind the main pool. Motorcaravan service point. Reception provides a small shop (30/3-3/11). Bar near the main pool and pizzeria (both 1/5-30/9). TV room. Swimming pools (30/3-3/11). Play area. Minigolf, archery (cross-bow type), volleyball, football and basketball. Mountain bike hire. Mini-club. Extensive entertainment programme, incl Roman extravagansas (which can be noisy) and off site activities in high season. There is a charge for participation in sports and entertainment. Off site: Fishing 1 km. Riding 2 km. Golf 20 km. Organised canoeing, riding, climbing, walking, mountain biking. Vaison la Romaine (800 m) with its magnificent Roman ruins, shops, restaurants, market and excellent wine.

At a glance

Welcome & Ambience	✓✓✓✓	Location	✓✓✓✓
Quality of Pitches	✓✓✓✓	Range of Facilities	✓✓✓✓✓

Directions

Leave Vaison la Romaine on D938 heading south towards Carpentras. 1 km. beyond the Super U roundabout turn left on D151, signed St Marcellin. Site entrance is on the left immediately after the junction.

Charges 2003

Per pitch incl. 1-3 persons	€ 23.00 - € 26.00
extra person	€ 4.00 - € 5.00
child (2-10 yrs)	€ 2.50 - € 4.00
electricity (6A)	€ 3.20 - € 3.70
dog	€ 2.00 - € 2.50

Camping Cheques accepted.

Reservations

Made with deposit and fee (€ 77). Tel: 04 90 36 02 02. Email: contact@camping-carpe-diem.com

Open

1 April - 3 November.

FR84090 Camping du Pont d'Avignon

Ile de la Barthelasse, 84000 Avignon (Vaucluse)

This is a city site, yet it is in a quiet location and only a short walk or ferry ride from the town. With its island situation, some of the pitches are only yards away from the famous bridge, only the mighty Rhône separating them. A few pitches have views of the 'Pont' and also of the Pope's palace which is floodlit at night. There are 300 level pitches, some on grass and some with hardstanding. 118 with electricity. All have some shade but those with electricity are well shaded. A small play area, tennis courts and volleyball pitch are in the centre of the site separating the tent pitches on one side and the electric pitches on the other. Many pitches are separated by hedges. The amenities are grouped around the new pool. The site, although close to the historic centre of Avignon, has a very rural feel, due no doubt to the many flowering trees and shrubs and the fact it is on an island. English is spoken.

Facilities

Toilet blocks are placed around the periphery of the site and kept very clean and well maintained. Mainly British style toilets, roomy showers and all washbasins in cubicles. Dishwashing and laundry sinks. Three washing machines and a dryer. One block has full facilities for disabled visitors. Motorcaravan service point. Well stocked shop (1 April - end Sept). Bar/restaurant and takeaway (1 Jun-end Sept). Swimming pool and paddling pool (1 June - end Sept). Play area. Tennis (free). Volleyball. Bicycle hire (July/Aug). Internet access.

At a glance

Welcome & Ambience	✓✓✓✓✓	Location	✓✓✓✓✓
Quality of Pitches	✓✓✓✓	Range of Facilities	✓✓✓✓

Directions

Site is on the Ile de la Barthelasse in the middle of the river Rhône, to the west of the city, almost opposite the famous bridge. It is well signed from the many roads into Avignon and accessed from Pont Daladier towards Villeneuve les Avignon on the west bank of the river.

Charges 2003

Per unit incl. 2 persons	€ 9.60 - € 32.00
extra person	€ 2.80 - € 4.05
child (3-12 yrs)	free - € 4.05
electricity (6/10A)	€ 2.40 - € 2.80
dog	€ 0.85 - € 2.05
local tax	€ 0.34

Camping Cheques accepted.

Reservations

Necessary for July/Aug. Tel: 04 90 80 63 50.
Email: info@camping-avignon.com

Open

24 March - 26 October.

In an outstanding environment, an outstanding campsite!

Ile de la Barthelasse
84000 AVIGNON

Tél : 33 (0)4 90 80 63 50
info@camping-avignon.com
www.camping-avignon.com

Camping Qualité

Provence

FR84120 Camping des Sources

Route de Murs, 84220 Gordes (Vaucluse)

This family run campsite is only 2 km. from the stunning ancient hill village of Gordes. Also close by are many other equally magnificent villages. The views from the campsite over the valley, with its vineyards, lavender fields and olive trees and over the Luberon mountains (the real Provence) are fantastic. This site is ideal for 'lovers of the great outdoors'. The roads around the hillside campsite are stony and some slope significantly. The 100 terraced pitches (rock pegs essential) are placed naturally amongst a variety of ancient trees (mainly olives and oaks) and are irregular in shape and size. All pitches have access to electricity though some may need long leads and a few leads may cross the roads. There are plenty of water taps and some pitches have their own tap and drain. Access to some pitches is not easy and this site is not recommended for large or underpowered outfits.

Facilities

Two toilet blocks, one recently refurbished, have all the usual amenities - all of a high standard and clean. Facilities are provided for disabled people but the hilly terrain and uneven roads are not really suitable for the physically disabled. Motorcaravan service point. Bar (all season). Restaurant with simple menu and takeaway (open most of the season for breakfast and evening meals, in high season also lunchtime). Bread available but no shop. Excellent play room and simple playground. Volleyball, boules, mini football pitch. Activities arranged for adults and children in high season, walking, cycling, archery, donkey cart rides. Evening soirées etc (finishing around 11pm) but no discos. Bicycle hire. Card operated security barrier. Central barbecue point (individual barbecues forbidden). Off site: Gordes with all the usual shops, bank, etc. is 2 km. At 10 - 20 km, supermarket, local markets, canoeing, riding and golf.

At a glance

| Welcome & Ambience | ✓✓✓✓ | Location | ✓✓✓✓✓ |
| Quality of Pitches | ✓✓✓ | Range of Facilities | ✓✓✓ |

Directions

Leave A7 autoroute at exit 25 (Cavaillon) and take D2 northeast. Cross the N100 and continue to Gordes. In the centre turn left on D15, signed Murs (also signs for campsite). Continue up hill for 2 km and turn left at campsite sign. The entrance is a further 400 m. up a narrow lane.

Charges 2003

Per person	€ 3.30 - € 4.30
child (under 8 yrs)	€ 2.70 - € 3.20
caravan or motorcaravan	€ 5.00 - € 6.30
tent	€ 4.00 - € 5.50
electricity (5A)	€ 2.90
animal	free - € 1.10
local tax	€ 0.17

Reservations

Contact site. Tel: 04 90 72 12 48.
Email: info@campingdessources.com

Open

15 March - 15 October.

FR84100 Camping Le Soleil de Provence

Route de Nyons, 84110 St Romain en Viennois (Vaucluse)

The views from this spacious, family run site must take some beating. The 360 degree panorama includes Mont Ventoux, the surrounding hills and the vineyards of northern Provence. It offers an excellent base from which to explore this very interesting area. Within a few kilometres one can find old towns such as Nyons, the olive capital of France, Orange and Avignon. The countryside is full of vineyards, lavender and sunflowers and the mountains offer a challenge to walkers and cyclists. The site has been developed to a high standard. The 140 pitches are of average size, most having only a little shade. They are all supplied with electricity and there are a good number of water points. The excellent pool, surrounded by a sunbathing terrace, and overlooked by the bar, is an unusual shape with an island in the centre. Although there is no paddling pool one end of the pool is very shallow. This is a good family site with some organised entertainment in July and Aug.

Facilities

Two toilet blocks, heated early and late season, are very well appointed and include washbasins in cabins, facilities for disabled visitors and a baby changing room. Dishwashing and laundry sinks, washing machine, dryer and facilities for ironing. Motorcaravan service point. Small shop for bread, etc, open on demand. Bar and snack bar open all season. Swimming pool. Small play area. Off site: Tennis 1 km. Bicycle hire 5 km. Riding 5 km. Fishing 15 km. Vaison la Romaine 4 km.

At a glance

| Welcome & Ambience | ✓✓✓✓✓ | Location | ✓✓✓✓✓ |
| Quality of Pitches | ✓✓✓✓ | Range of Facilities | ✓✓✓✓ |

Directions

Site is 4 km. north of Vaison la Romaine on the D938 road to Nyon. Entrance is on the right.

Charges 2004

Per person	€ 3.50 - € 5.50
child (0-10 yrs)	€ 2.50 - € 3.00
pitch	€ 2.50 - € 3.00
electricity (10A)	€ 2.50

No credit cards.

Reservations

Advised for July/Aug. Tel: 04 90 46 46 00.
Email: info@camping-soleil-de-provence.fr

Open

15 March - 31 October.

Midi-Pyrénées

Rolling fields of yellow sunflowers, the Armagnac vineyards and crumbling, ancient stone buildings amidst the sleepy villages make this colourful region popular with those who enjoy good food, good wine and a taste of the good life.

Départements: 09 Ariège, 31 Haute-Garonne, 32 Gers, 65 Hautes-Pyrénées, 81 Tarn, 82 Tarn-et Garonne. We have left out the départements of Aveyron (12) and Lot (46), which are in our Dordogne/Aveyron region

Still a relatively unknown region, the Midi-Pyrénées is the largest region of France, extending from the Dordogne in the north to the Spanish border. It is blessed by radiant sunshine and a fascinating range of scenery. High chalk plateaux, majestic peaks, tiny hidden valleys and small fortified sleepy villages, which seem to have changed little since the Middle Ages, contrast with the high-tech, industrial and vibrant university city of Toulouse.

Lourdes is one of the most visited pilgrimage sites in the world. Toulouse-Lautrec, the artist, was born at Albi the capital of the département of Tarn. Much of the town is built of pink brick which seems to glow when seen from the distance. In the east, the little town of Foix, with its maze of steep, winding streets, is a convenient centre from which to explore the prehistoric caves at Niaux and the Aladdin's Cave of duty-free gift shops in the independent state of Andorra. The Canal du Midi that links Bordeaux to the Mediterranean was commissioned by Louis XIV in 1666 and is still in working order today.

Cuisine of the region

Food is rich and strongly seasoned, making generous use of garlic and goose fat, and there are some excellent regional wines. Seafood such as oysters, salt-water fish, or piballes from the Adour river are popular

Cassoulet: stew of duck, sausages and beans

Confit de Canard (d'oie): preserved duck meat

Grattons (Graisserons): a mélange of small pieces of rendered down duck, goose and pork fat

Magret de canard: duck breast fillets

Poule au pot: chicken simmered with vegetables

Ouillat (Ouliat): Pyrénées soup: onions, tomatoes, goose fat and garlic

Tourtière Landaise: a sweet of Agen prunes, apples and Armagnac

Places of interest

Albi: birthplace and Museum of Toulouse-Lautrec, imposing Ste Cécile cathedral with 15th century fresco of 'The Last Judgement'

Auch: capital of ancient Gascony, boasts a fine statue of d'Artágnan

Collonges-la-Rouge: picturesque village of Medieval and Renaissance style mansions and manors

Conques: 11th century Ste Foy Romanesque church

Cordes: medieval walled hilltop village

Foix: 11th/12th century towers on rocky peak above town; 14th century cathedral.

Lourdes: famous pilgrimage site where Ste Bernadette is said to have spoken to the Virgin Mary in a grotto and known for the miracles said to have been performed there

Alan Rogers tip

IF YOU LIKE JAZZ MUSIC, HEAD TO MARCIAC FOR THE ANNUAL JAZZ FESTIVAL HELD IN EARLY AUGUST.

Map 1

FR09020 Camping L'Arize

Lieu-dit Bourtol, 09240 La Bastide-de-Sérou (Ariège)

You will receive a warm welcome from Dominique and Brigitte at this friendly little family site and Brigitte speaks excellent English. The site sits in a delightful, tranquil valley among the foothills of the Pyrénées and is just east of the interesting village of La Bastide de Sérou beside the River Arize (good trout fishing). The river is fenced for the safety of children on the site, but may be accessed just outside the gate. Deer and wild boar are common in this area and may be sighted in quieter periods. The owners have built this site from ground level over the last few years and have put much love and care into its development. The 70 large pitches are neatly laid out on level grass within the spacious site. All have electricity (French type sockets) and are separated into bays by hedges and young trees. Discounts have been negotiated for several of the local attractions (details are provided in the comprehensive pack provided on arrival – in your own language). This is a comfortable and relaxing base for touring this beautiful part of the Pyrénées with easy access to the medieval town of Foix and even Andorra for duty-free shopping.

Facilities

The central sanitary block (unheated) includes washbasins in cabins and good facilities for babies and disabled people. Laundry room with dryer. Dishwashing under cover. Chemical disposal (into a large holding tank - the organic sewage system is incompatible with chemicals). Small swimming pool with paved sunbathing area. Entertainment in high season, weekly barbecues and welcome drinks on Sundays. Fishing, riding and bicycle hire on site. Off site: Golf 5 km. Several restaurants and shops are within a few minute's drive and the nearest restaurant, which is located at the national stud for the famous Merens horses just 200 m. away, will deliver takeaway meals to your pitch.

At a glance

Welcome & Ambience	✓✓✓✓✓	Location	✓✓✓✓✓
Quality of Pitches	✓✓✓✓	Range of Facilities	✓✓✓✓

Directions

Site is southeast of the village La Bastide-de-Sérou. Take the D15 towards Nescus and site is on right after approx. 1 km.

Charges 2003

Per pitch incl. 2 persons and electricity (3/6A)	€ 13.00 - € 19.70
extra adult	€ 4.00 - € 5.00
child (0-7 yrs)	€ 3.00 - € 3.50
dog	€ 1.00

Discounts for longer stays in mid and low season.

Reservations

Made with 25% deposit and fee (€ 10).
Tel: 05 61 65 81 51. Email: camparize@aol.com

Open

28 March - 4 November.

FR09030 Camping Le Montagnou

Route de Guzet, 09140 Le Trein d'Ustou (Ariège)

The road going south out of St Girons appears to lead to nowhere other than Guzet, but it is well worth the short detour over easy roads to the little village of Le Trein d'Ustou, which is no more than 10 or 15 minutes short of the up and coming winter sports resort of Guzet. Just before Le Trein d'Ustou you will find Le Montagnou, a delightful small campsite nestling among the lush lower slopes of the mountains. Robert and Daniele created this charming site from the forest and opened for the first time in 1996. It is an attractive proposition either as a base for winter sports or for touring this lovely area, with 60 level pitches on grass, 30 with electricity. The site has been developed on modern lines with good quality installations. At a lower level there is an area of the river running alongside the site which the locals use for swimming, but really the attraction here is the surrounding mountains which offer excellent winter sports facilities which include a ski-lift (10 minutes drive) and no less than 24 pistes! There are also many places of interest which Robert, who doubles as the local Director of Tourism, will be pleased to tell you about and brief you on the local wildlife. The walks in this area are renowned – watch out for marmots and, yes, even bears!

Facilities

Two toilet blocks (one open in low season) can be heated and are kept clean. They include washbasins in cabins, covered dishwashing and laundry sinks, washing machine and dryers, and good facilities for disabled visitors. Snack bar with takeaway. Gas supplies. Library (some English books) and TV. Fishing. Off site: Riding 15 km. Restaurant 50 m. in the village.

At a glance

Welcome & Ambience	✓✓✓✓	Location	✓✓✓✓✓
Quality of Pitches	✓✓✓	Range of Facilities	✓✓✓

Directions

Approaching from the A64 from St Girons follow signs for Guzet; take first right at roundabout (Guzet), second right at next roundabout (Guzet, Seix) and second right at third roundabout to Seix. From Foix take third right at first roundabout and follow good signs for Guzet and Seix. Go through Seix (the river is on your right) and at Pont de la Taule turn left towards Trein d'Ustou. Site is on left before village.

Charges 2004

Per unit incl. 2 persons and electricity (6-16A)	€ 14.50 - € 15.50
extra person	€ 4.00
child (2-7 yrs)	€ 2.50
dog	€ 1.10

No credit cards.

Reservations

Contact site by letter. Tel: 05 61 66 94 97.
Email: campinglemontagnou@wanadoo.fr

Open

All year.

FR09080 Camping du Lac

RN 20, 09000 Foix (Ariège)

Du Lac is a new, large and sprawling lakeside site with many facilities. It is just 3 km. north of the very pretty town of Foix. There is some road noise as the site is alongside the old N20 but there is lots of room to manoeuvre at the entrance and a smart, air conditioned reception building. The site is informally divided into four areas, one for parking vehicles. The other areas are generally flat and some shade can be found under mature trees. There are 135 pitches, most with electricity, but the site is so big there appear to be more – there is lots of room. Access to the lake is through a gate which is locked at night and the fence is secure. Children will need supervision in this area. The lake is owned by a separate company but campers have free use of the attractive area. Here you will find canoeing and pedaloes, along with fishing, or just picnics and barbecues with a small bar operating. The lake is not for swimming as there is a fair amount of forbidding green weed but there is a clear area for canoes. The site is ideal for visiting Foix and exploring the local area.

Facilities

Four unisex sanitary blocks of different designs are all new, some of brick and others resembling pretty 'wendy houses' made of wood. The facilities are modern, clean and well equipped. One of the little blocks contains a washing machine, excellent facilities for disabled campers and a well equipped baby room. Reception sells basic goods but no fresh food. Pizza hut and bar/drinks stall close to the pool (a restaurant is planned). Swimming pool and separate paddling pool. Play areas around the site and another by the lake. Watersports, fishing and canoe instruction (hire charges apply). TV room, electronic games. Tennis court and boules pitch. Some animation in high season. Torches are necessary. Off site: Cycling and walking tours, riding, golf or even white water rafting.

Directions

From Foix stay on the old N20 north for 3 km. (avoid the new bypass and tunnel). Site is well signed on the left.

Charges 2003

Per unit incl. 2 persons and 4A electricity	€ 10.00 - € 15.00
incl. 13A electricity	€ 20.00 - € 35.00
extra person	€ 1.50 - € 4.00
dog	€ 0.50 - € 1.50

Reservations

Advised for July/Aug. Tel: 05 61 65 11 58.
Email: camping-du-lac@wanadoo.fr

Open

All year.

At a glance

Welcome & Ambience	✓✓✓✓✓	Location	✓✓✓✓
Quality of Pitches	✓✓✓✓	Range of Facilities	✓✓✓✓

FR09090N Naturist Camping Millfleurs

Le Tuilier Gudas, 09120 Varilhes (Ariège)

Millfleurs is peaceful naturist site in superb location for mature naturists. Owned by a Dutch couple, Gert and Annie Kos who provide a warm welcome and speak excellent English, it really is camping at a relaxed and sublime level. It is so peaceful with some 70 acres of woods and meadows to explore providing guided naturist walks in total privacy. Annie has found 16 different types of orchids and keeps a picture record in the 'salle de reunion'. The long drive leads to a traditional farmhouse which houses the campsite office. The site has 40 large flat pitches (26 with electricity) on well spaced terraces, but there are also very secluded pitches in wooded areas with shade, or you can pitch a tent in the meadows if you prefer. Long leads are required if you decide to pitch off the terraces. There are few of the normal camping leisure facilities here and the site is definitely aimed at the more mature naturist camper. Transport is required as there is no bus service. Explore the nearby mediaeval town of Foix with its stunning castle towering over the busy centre, and investigate the history of the Cathares and the region with its underground rivers and caves. With its temperate climate, the Foix valley is a prime area for growing the grapes for the white wine used in the production of the famous Cava, and the vineyards are worth a visit.

Facilities

The excellent central unisex toilet block, well thought out, includes great facilities for disabled campers, inside and outside showers and cheerful flowers and potted plants. Bread available to order in high season. Guests dine together in the 'salle de reunion' within the farmhouse two nights a week (Sat/Wed) or you just relax and meet friends for a drink. Refrigerator with drinks operated on an honesty system. Petanque court and guide book for walks and cycle rides in local area. Torches essential at night. Pick ups from airports and stations can be arranged. Off site: The coast is about 1.5 hours

Directions

One can find the site very easily from the village of Varilhes which is 8 km. south of Pamiers on D624 (parallel to N20). Take D13 for Dalou and Gudas cross railway and N20. The site is 2 km. past Gudas, pass small road to left and site drive is further on right.

Charges 2003

Per person (all ages)	€ 4.00 - € 5.10
pitch	€ 4.00 - € 4.80
child (2-6 yrs)	€ 2.60 - € 2.80
dog	€ 1.60
electricity (4/6A)	€ 3.10 - € 3.20

No credit cards.

Reservations

Not necessary. Tel: 05 61 60 77 56.
Email: ag.kos@wanadoo.fr

Open

1 April - 15 October.

At a glance

Welcome & Ambience	✓✓✓✓✓	Location	✓✓✓✓✓
Quality of Pitches	✓✓✓✓✓	Range of Facilities	✓✓✓

FR09060 **Camping Le Pré Lombard**

09400 Tarascon sur Ariege (Ariège)

Didier Mioni, the manager here follows the town motto 'S'y passos, y demoros' – 'if you wish to come here, you will stay here' in his aim to ensure your satisfaction on his site. This busy, good value site is located beside the attractive river Ariége on the outskirts of the town. There are around 180 level, grassy, numbered pitches with shade provided by a variety of trees. At the rear of the site are 60 site-owned chalets and mobile homes. Electricity is available to all. A gate in the fence provides access to the river bank for fishing (licences required). Open all year, it is an excellent choice for early or late breaks, or as a stop-over en-route to the winter sun destinations in Spain. This region of Ariège is in the foothills of the Pyrénées and 45 km. from Andorra. At Tarascon itself you can go underground at the Parc Pyrénéen de l'Art Préhistorique to view prehistoric rock paintings, or the really adventurous can take to the air for paragliding, hangliding, or microlighting.

Facilities

Five sanitary units of varying age, design and size (not all open in low season). Mostly British WCs, open and cubicled washbasins. Facilities for disabled people. Dishwashing and laundry sinks. Laundry. Excellent motorcaravan service point. Bar and takeaway (open according to demand). Bread, gas, papers and daily requirements sold in the bar. Good restaurant (1/5-30/9). Fenced, unsupervised swimming pool (15/5-30/9). Separate playgrounds for toddlers and older children. Video games, Table tennis, table football. Boules. Volleyball. Fishing. Full programme of entertainment for families in main season. Off site: Supermarket 300 m. Town 800 m. Archery, kayaking and fishing nearby.

At a glance

Welcome & Ambience	✓✓✓✓	Location	✓✓✓✓
Quality of Pitches	✓✓✓✓	Range of Facilities	✓✓✓✓

Directions

Site is 800 m. south of the town centre next to the river. From north, turn off main N20 into town centre and there are prominent signs. From south (Andorra) site signed at roundabout on town approach.

Charges 2003

Per unit incl. 2 adults and 6A electricity	€ 14.00 - € 22.00

Camping Cheques accepted.

Reservations

Advised for high season and made with 25% deposit and € 15.24 booking fee. Tel: 05 61 05 61 94. Email: info@prelombard.com

Open

All year.

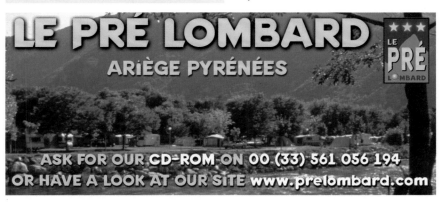

FR09050M **Camping Municipal La Prade**

09110 Sorgeat (Ariège)

Superbly situated high up on the mountainside overlooking the valley, this site has magnificent views, with the river 300 m distant and a lake at 2 km. A small site, it provides just 40 pitches on terraces. About two-thirds are occupied by long stay units. Well supervised, with the warden present at varying times, the site is kept very clean. Electrical connections are available. A small stream tinkles through the edge of the site and the attractive hills towering above it reverberate with the pleasant sounds of goat bells. A most reasonably priced campsite.

Facilities

The rather small sanitary block has only two showers and two WCs in each half. However, standards are very high and a further block is under construction. Hot water is provided for dishwashing. Facilities for the disabled are also very good with special washbasin and a very large shower suite. Chemical disposal and waste water point under construction. Small play area. Communal BBQ area. Off site: Fishing 0.5 km. Riding and bicycle hire 5 km.

At a glance

Welcome & Ambience	✓✓✓	Location	✓✓✓✓
Quality of Pitches	✓✓✓	Range of Facilities	✓✓✓

Directions

From N20 (Foix - Andorra) to Ax-les-Thermes. In centre of village take D613 left, signed Quillan (hairpin bends) for 5 km. Site is signed on right. The last kilometre is a very narrow two way winding road (twin axle and large units may find difficulty). There are several other sites so a sharp eye is needed to pick this one out.

Charges 2004

Per adult	€ 2.90
pitch with electricity (5/10A)	€ 4.30 - € 7.00

Reservations

Advised for high season. Tel: 05 61 64 36 34.

Open

All year.

FR32080 Camping Le Talouch

32810 Roquelaure (Gers)

Although enjoying an 'away-from-it-all' location Auch, the region's capital, is within a 10 km. drive from this family run site, which takes its name from the small Talouch river. The entrance, off the D148 road, is fronted by a parking area with reception to the right and the bar and restaurant facing. Beyond this point lies the top half of the touring area with generous pitches of at least 120 sq.m. located between mature trees and divided by hedges, some with chalets. There are 118 pitches, with electricity. The rear half of the site has unshaded pitches in a more open aspect, and chalets have been built on the hillside to one side of the site.

Facilities

There are two immaculate toilet blocks, the larger refurbished building offering modern units with a clean appearance. The smaller block is of a more modern and unusual style, situated to rear of site. Baby bathroom/shower which can be used by people with disabilities. Small shop selling basic foodstuffs and snacks (1/5-30/9). Two swimming pools and new pool with 'jetstream'. Bicycle hire. Two play areas, volleyball, tennis, basketball and 9 hole swin golf course. Organised entertainment in high season.

At a glance

Welcome & Ambience	✓✓✓✓	Location	✓✓✓✓
Quality of Pitches	✓✓✓✓	Range of Facilities	✓✓✓✓

Directions

From Auch take N21 for 8.5 km. north and turn west onto D272 to village of Roquelaure. Then follow signs to site 2 km. south of village on D148.

Charges 2003

Per unit incl. 2 adults	€ 18.87
with electricity (4A)	€ 22.22
extra person	€ 5.89
child (3-7 yrs)	€ 4.73
animal	€ 1.54

Discounts for longer stays.
Camping Cheques accepted.

Reservations

Advisable for July/Aug. Tel: 05 62 65 52 43.
Email: info@camping-talouch.com

Open

1 April - 30 September.

FR65010N Domaine Naturiste L'Eglantière

Aries-Espenan, 65230 Castelnau-Magnoac (Hautes-Pyrénées)

This pretty site is situated in the valley between the Pyrénées and the plain, within easy reach of Lourdes and the mountains. Alongside a small, fast flowing river, in wooded surroundings it comprises 12 ha. for camping and caravanning, with a further 32 for walking and relaxing in the woods and fields. The river is said to be suitable for swimming and canoeing, with fishing nearby. There are 83 traditional pitches of mixed size on fairly level grass, the older ones secluded and separated by a variety of tall trees and bushes, the newer ones more open, with a natural tenting area across the river (28+ pitches). The traditional pitches have 10A electrical connections (long lead for some). The site has is an attractive, central, medium sized swimming pool with sunbathing areas both on paving and grass, and a children's pool, overlooked by the attractive style clubhouse and terrace. A small health centre (massage, sauna) is being developed in the old farmhouse. A range of studios, mobile homes, chalets and tents is on site. Used by a tour operator (six pitches). Member of France 4 Naturisme.

Facilities

Two main sanitary blocks at each end of the site are in typically naturist style, providing under cover, open plan, controllable hot showers, and sinks for washing up. A small centrally located sanitary block has individual cubicles. Shop (July-Aug). Clubhouse with bar (all season), small restaurant (June-Sept), pizzeria and takeaway (July-Aug), internet access and indoor soundproofed activities/disco area, play room for younger children and table tennis for older ones. Swimming pool (all season). Play area and children's animation in season. Volleyball, badminton, table tennis, petanque and archery. Activities on the river. Canoe and mountain bike hire. Trekking and cross country cycling. Barbecues are officially forbidden. Torches useful. Off site: Restaurants in the nearby village.

At a glance

Welcome & Ambience	✓✓✓✓	Location	✓✓✓✓
Quality of Pitches	✓✓✓✓	Range of Facilities	✓✓✓✓

Directions

From Auch take D929 south towards Lannemezan. Just after Castelnau-Magnoac watch for signs to hamlet of Ariès-Espénan on left and follow site signs.

Latest charges

Per pitch incl. 2 persons	€ 11.89 - € 21.19
`wild` pitch (July/Aug. only)	€ 15.09
extra person	€ 3.09 - € 4.42
child (3-8 yrs)	€ 1.52 - € 2.74
electricity (10A)	€ 3.81
animal	€ 1.22 - € 1.98
leisure card (obligatory)	€ 0.38 - € 0.76

Plus local tax. Camping Cheques accepted.

Reservations

Made with deposit (25%) and fee (€ 27.44).
Tel: 05 62 39 88 00. Email: info@leglantiere.com

Open

Easter - October.

FR32010 Le Camp de Florence

Route Astaffort, 32480 La Romieu (Gers)

Camp de Florence is an attractive site on the edge of an historic village in pleasantly undulating Gers countryside. It is run by the Mynsbergen family who are Dutch (although Susan is English) and they have sympathetically converted the old farmhouse buildings to provide facilities for the site. The 201 pitches (95 for tourers) are all over 100 sq.m. plus, all with electricity, 10 with hardstanding and terraced where necessary. They are arranged around a large field (full of sunflowers when we visited) with rural views, giving a feeling of spaciousness. The older pitches near the main buildings have good shade but it gets progressively less the newer the pitch. However, 25 of these are fully serviced and shade will develop. The 13th century village of La Romieu is on the Santiago de Compostela pilgrim route and the collegiate church, visible from the site, is well worth a visit (the views are magnificent from the top of the tower), as is the local arboretum, the biggest collection of trees in the Midi-Pyrénées. The Pyrénées are a two hour drive, the Atlantic coast a similar distance. There are 20 tour operator pitches.

Facilities

Two unisex toilet blocks include some washbasins in cabins. These facilities may be under pressure at peak times and are a long walk from certain corners of the site. Washing machine and dryer. Motorcaravan services. Water points are limited. A good upstairs, air-conditioned restaurant, open to the public as well as campers, serves a range of food, including local specialities and an à la carte menu (15/5-30/9, closed Weds, with a barbecue instead). Takeaway. Bread on site in season. Swimming pool area (rebuilt by experts and an attractive feature) with jacuzzi, central island and protected children's pool (all open to the public in the afternoons). Adventure play area, games area and pets area. Games room, tennis, table tennis, volleyball and petanque. Bicycle hire. Video shows, discos, picnics, animation and musical evenings and excursions organised. Off site: Shop 500 m. in village. Fishing 5 km, riding 10 km. Walking tours, excursions and wine tasting arranged.

At a glance

Welcome & Ambience	✓✓✓✓✓	Location	✓✓✓✓
Quality of Pitches	✓✓✓✓	Range of Facilities	✓✓✓✓✓

Directions

Site is signed from D931 Agen - Condom road. Small units can turn left at Ligardes (signed) and follow D36 for 1 km. and take right turn for La Romieu (signed). Otherwise continue to outskirts of Condom and take D41 left to La Romieu and pass through village to site.

Charges 2003

Per unit incl. 2 persons	
and electricity	€ 13.50 - € 26.00
extra person	€ 3.50 - € 6.00
child (4-9 yrs)	€ 2.60 - € 4.30
dog (max 2)	€ 1.50 - € 2.00

Special prices for groups, rallies, etc.
Camping Cheques accepted.

Reservations

Write or phone for information (English spoken).
Tel: 05 62 28 15 58.
Email: info@campdeflorence.com

Open

1 April - 31 October.

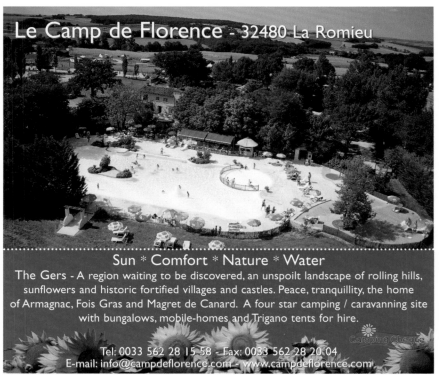

Le Camp de Florence - 32480 La Romieu

Sun * Comfort * Nature * Water

The Gers - A region waiting to be discovered, an unspoilt landscape of rolling hills, sunflowers and historic fortified villages and castles. Peace, tranquillity, the home of Armagnac, Fois Gras and Magret de Canard. A four star camping / caravanning site with bungalows, mobile-homes and Trigano tents for hire.

Tel: 0033 562 28 15 58 - Fax: 0033 562 28 20 04
E-mail: info@campdeflorence.com - www.campdeflorence.com

Great on-line holiday deals alanrogersdirect.com

FR65020 Sunêlia Les Trois Vallées

Ave des Pyrenees, 65400 Argelès-Gazost (Hautes-Pyrénées)

This is a large and ever-expanding site on the valley road from Lourdes into the Pyrénées. It has a rather unprepossessing entrance and pitches near the road suffer from noise (this should reduce a little with the opening of a new by-pass) but at the back, open fields allow views of surrounding mountains on all sides. Recent additions include an indoor pool, two jacuzzis and an enormous play area that seems to have everything! The site now has 500 flat, grassy pitches of which 200 are for tourers; they are marked out and of reasonable size, all with electricity. The proximity to the road is at least advantageous for touring the area, being by a roundabout with Lourdes one way, Luz-St-Sauveur and mountains another way, and the dramatic Pyrénées Corniche Col d'Aubisque going off to the west. Argelès-Gazost is an attractive town with excellent restaurants and cultural interests. The site is popular with young people and could be quite lively at times.

Facilities

The two unisex toilet blocks are fairly modern and include facilities for disabled people and a laundry room. Cleaning can be variable and facilities could be under pressure at peak times. Bread available on site. Bar/disco. Café and takeaway. Swimming pool complex (from 1/6) with paddling pool and two water slides. TV room. Good playground. Volleyball, football, boules and archery. Off site: Supermarket across the road. Fishing 500 m, bicycle hire 50 m, riding 3 km.

At a glance

Welcome & Ambience	✓✓✓✓	Location	✓✓✓
Quality of Pitches	✓✓✓✓	Range of Facilities	✓✓✓✓

Directions

Take N21 from Lourdes to Argelès-Gazost. Approachong Argelès, pass a Champion supermarket on your right, and then a roundabout - take the furthest left exit and the site entrance is 100 m. or so on the left. A new express way is planned.

Charges 2004

Per pitch incl. 2 persons	€ 10.50 - € 21.50
incl. 3/6A electricity	€ 13.50 - € 27.00
extra person	€ 3.80 - € 7.00
child (under 7 yrs)	€ 2.00 - € 6.00

Reservations

Advised for July/Aug. and made with deposit (€ 70) and fee (€ 30). Tel: 05 62 90 35 47. Email: info@camping-les-3-vallees.fr

Open

1 April - 30 September.

FR65030 Airotel Pyrénées

65120 Esquieze-Sere (Hautes-Pyrénées)

Airotel Pyrénées is a small site in the heart of the Pyrénées. It is located on the main road into the mountains, south from Argelès-Gazost and surrounded by the high peaks (some pitches will have daytime road noise). There are 163 level pitches, with 85 available for touring units, all with electricity and 45 fully serviced. They are on terraced ground and separated by bushes. In the high season a programme of activities and tournaments is arranged, from walking and mountain bike trips to rafting. There are tour operator pitches.

Facilities

Two toilet blocks, both fairly modern and well appointed, include washbasins in cubicles, mixed British and Turkish style WCs and can be heated. The block adjoining the indoor pool and sauna has full facilities for disabled people, also doubling as a baby room. Indoor dishwashing and laundry sinks. Bottled water is advised for drinking and cooking. Motorcaravan service point. Small, quite limited shop (1/7-31/8) but bread available 15/5-15/9. Outdoor pool (15/6-15/9). Indoor pool, sauna and fitness room (1/12-30/9). A third pool has water slides. Practice climbing wall, half court tennis, boule and table tennis. Off site: Skiing 10 km.

At a glance

Welcome & Ambience	✓✓✓	Location	✓✓✓✓
Quality of Pitches	✓✓✓	Range of Facilities	✓✓✓✓

Directions

Take N21 from Lourdes through Argelès-Gazost towards Luz-St-Sauveur. The site is on left at Esquièze-Sere, just before Luz-St-Sauveur. Site is on left immediately after Camping International.

Charges 2003

Per unit incl. 2 persons	€ 14.50 - € 16.50
extra person	€ 4.20
child (up to 2 yrs)	€ 1.50
electricity (3/10A)	€ 3.00 - € 6.20
dog	€ 1.50
local tax	€ 0.34

Reservations

Advised for most periods and made with deposit (€ 50) and fee (€ 25). Tel: 05 62 92 89 18. Email: airotel.pyrenees@wanadoo.fr

Open

All year, except 1 Oct - 30 Nov.

FR65070 Camping Caravaning Le Rioumajou

Bousrisp, 65170 St Lary Soulan (Hautes-Pyrénées)

Located in the heart of the Aure valley, next to a fast flowing unfenced river, and with views to the surrounding mountains and countryside, Le Rioumajou is a good base from which to explore this part of the Hautes-Pyrénées. There are 240 pitches, with 48 mobile homes, leaving around 190 pitches for tourists. They are generally separated, varying in size, some shady and some more open, and all with electricity, and ten are all weather pitches. A good cycle track runs alongside the main road in both directions from the site. Nearby is the Réserve Naturel du Néouvielle National Park, and the Spanish border via the Aragnouet - Bielsa tunnel, and the tourist village of Saint-Lary Soulan is 2 km.

Facilities

Three attractive, modern toilet blocks (one open and heated in winter) have some washbasins in cabins, controllable hot showers including some spacious twin units. Laundry with large drying room. One block (not open in winter) has a dedicated room with children's toilets, baby bath and shower, changing surfaces and basins. Facilities for disabled (access by key). Small shop for essentials (July/Aug). Well fenced, outdoor heated swimming pool (10 x 25m; June-Sept). Sauna and jacuzzi. Good adventure style playground.

At a glance

Welcome & Ambience	✓✓✓	Location	✓✓✓✓✓
Quality of Pitches	✓✓✓✓	Range of Facilities	✓✓✓✓

Directions

From Lannemezan take the D929 south, pass through Arreau, and continue for about 10 km. After passing through Guchen and Guchan, site is on right before Bourisp.

Charges 2003

Per person	€ 4.50 - € 6.50
child (4-10 yrs)	€ 2.60 - € 3.00
electricity (2-10A)	€ 3.00 - € 6.00
local tax	€ 0.34

Reservations

Advisable for high season. Tel: 05 62 39 48 32.

Open

All year.

Le RIOUMAJOU ★★★★
Camping Caravaning Caravaneige

Open all year.
Swimming pool, tennis courts,
jacuzzi and sauna, playground.
Entertainments, snack in season

Mobile homes and caravans to rent.

2 km from St Lary Soulan.

Bourisp 65170 St-Lary - Tel: 0033 562 39 48 32
E-mail: lerioumajou@wanadoo.fr - Website: www.camping-le-rioumajou.com

FR65080 Camping Le Lavedan

Lau-Balagnas, 65400 Argelès-Gazost (Hautes-Pyrénées)

Reasonably priced, Camping du Lavedan is an old established and very French site set in the Argelès Gazost valley south of the Lourdes. It is beside the road so there is some daytime road noise. The 105 touring pitches are set on grass with some shade. All have electricity, water and waste water point. The area is fine for walking, biking, rafting and of course in winter skiing. There is a swimming pool which can be covered in inclement weather.

Facilities

The toilet block, though quite old with some Turkish style toilets and also bidets, has recently been refurbished. Showers are quite small, but some washbasins are in cabins. Baby shower and bath. Facilities for disabled customers. Dishwashing sinks are under cover with hot tap to draw from. Washing machines and dryer in separate small block which is heated in winter. Restaurant and takeaway (1/5-15/9). Bar (all year). No shop but bread delivery daily (1/5-15/9). Swimming pool (can be covered), paddling pool and sunbeds. Good play area. A twice weekly event is organised in July/Aug and weekly in June. Off site: Supermarket 2 km. Fishing 1 km. Rafting 2 km. Riding 5 km. Bicycle hire 1 km. Golf 15 km.

At a glance

Welcome & Ambience	✓✓✓✓	Location	✓✓✓
Quality of Pitches	✓✓✓	Range of Facilities	✓✓✓✓

Directions

Site is on the right side of the N21 (Lourdes - Cauterets), south of Argelès and just past the village of Lau Balagnas, which is 15 km. south of Lourdes.

Charges 2003

Per unit incl. 2 persons	€ 12.20 - € 16.00
incl. 3 persons	€ 16.00 - € 19.00
extra person	€ 4.00 - € 5.00
child (under 7 yrs)	€ 3.00 - € 3.50
electricity (2-6A)	€ 2.00 - € 6.00
dog	€ 2.00

Camping Cheques accepted.

Reservations

Contact site. Tel: 05 62 97 18 84.
Email: contact@lavedan.com

Open

All year.

289

FR65060 Castel Camping Pyrénées Natura

Route du Lac, 65400 Estaing (Hautes-Pyrénées)

Pyrénées Natura, at an altitude of 1,000 metres, on the edge of the National Park. is the perfect site for lovers of nature. Eagles and vultures soar above the site and a small open air observatory with seats and binoculars is provided. The Ruysschaert family's aim is that you go home from your holiday feeling at peace with the world, having hopefully learned something about the flora and fauna of the High Pyrénées. Groups are taken walking in the mountains to see the varied flora and fauna (there are even a few bears but they are seen very rarely). The 60 pitches, all with electricity, are in a large, level, open and sunny field. Around 75 varieties of trees and shrubs have been planted – not too many to spoil the view though, which can only be described as fantastic. The reception and bar are in a traditional style stone building with an open staircase. The small shop in the old water mill is quite unique. Stocking a variety of produce, including wine, it is left unmanned and open all day and you pay at reception – very trusting, but they have not been let down yet. The last weekend in May is when the local shepherds take their flocks up to the high pastures. Campers help by walking up with them and then helping to separate the different flocks. Returning to the site by bus, with a good old sing-song with the shepherds, the site provides food for everyone. That sounds like a trip worth making.

Facilities

First class toilet facilities with high quality fittings include a cubicle for children, full facilities for disabled visitors and, in the same large room, baby bath, shower and changing mat. Dishwashing and laundry sinks. Washing machine and airers (no lines allowed). Motorcaravan service point. Small shop. Small takeaway (15/5-15/9). Small bar (15/5-15/9) and lounge area. Lounge, library and TV (mainly used for videos of the National Park). Play area for the very young. Table tennis, boule and giant chess. Weekly evening meal in May, June and Sept. Off site: Village has two restaurants.

At a glance

Welcome & Ambience	✓✓✓✓✓	Location	✓✓✓✓✓
Quality of Pitches	✓✓✓✓✓	Range of Facilities	✓✓✓✓

Directions

From Lourdes take N21 to Argelès-Gazost. At roundabout at Argelès, take D918 signed Aucun, turning left after 8 km. on D13 to Bun. After Bun cross the river and right on D103 to site (5.5 km). Some parts are narrow but with passing places.

Charges 2003

Per unit incl. 2 persons and electricity (3A)	€ 19.50
extra person	€ 3.50
child (under 8 yrs)	€ 2.00
electricity (6/10A)	€ 1.50 - € 3.00
animal	€ 1.50
local tax	€ 0.45
Less in low season.	

Reservations

Made with deposit (€ 55). Tel: 05 62 97 45 44.
Email: info@camping-pyrenees-natura.com

Open

1 May - 20 September.

FR65090 Camping Soleil du Pibeste

16 Avenue du Lavedan, 65400 Agos Vidalos (Hautes-Pyrénées)

Soleil du Pibeste is a quiet rural site with well tended grass and flower beds. It has 23 mobile homes to rent and 67 pitches for tourers. All pitches have electricity and there is some shade. The Dusserm family welcomes all arrivals with a drink and are clearly determined to ensure you have a good stay. They are particularly keen on developing eco-toursim in the Pyrenees. At times some domestic matters could perhaps have a little more attention. It is a perfect site for the active as many activities are organised from the site – from gentle ones like painting and Chinese dancing to walking, rafting, parasailing, climbing, riding and of course in the winter skiing. There is no shop but the supermarket is only 5 km. and ordered bread is delivered to your door daily. The swimming pool is on a terrace above the pitches with sunbeds, a paddling pool and waterfall and the most magnificent view of the mountains. The same wonderful view can be enjoyed whilst doing the washing up. A new by-pass should eliminate most of the road noise.

Facilities

Two heated toilet blocks have washbasins in cabins and large showers. Cleaning can be variable. Baby room. Facilities for disabled visitors (key). Washing machine and dryer. Motorcaravan service point. Bar with piano and internet access, which also servers snacks. Adjoining room for playing cards or reading. Swimming and paddling pools. Small play area. Boule, archery, basketball and volleyball. Table tennis. Bicycle hire. Off site: Fishing 800 m. Golf 10 km. Rafting 2 km. Skiing 2 km.

At a glance

Welcome & Ambience	✓✓✓✓✓	Location	✓✓✓✓
Quality of Pitches	✓✓✓	Range of Facilities	✓✓✓✓

Directions

Agos Vidalos is on the N21, 5 km. south of Lourdes. Leave express-way at second exit, signed Agos Vidalos and continue to site on the right in a short distance.

Charges 2003

Per unit incl. 2 persons and 3A electricity	€ 15.00 - € 18.00
extra person	€ 3.00 - € 4.00
6A electricity	€ 3.00
animal	€ 2.00

Reservations

Made with 25% deposit and € 26 fee.
Tel: 05 62 97 53 23.
Email: info@campingpibeste.com

Open

All year.

FR81020 Camping Le Moulin de Julien

81170 Cordes-sur-Ciel (Tarn)

Close to picturesque fortified old town in a secluded valley location in the heart of the Tarn region, this traditional style site has 130 spacious pitches. The pitches are mostly on grass, with good shade in parts, and are arranged around a fishing lake. All have electricity hook-ups (5A). The area has magnificent scenery to enjoy and picturesque fortified towns to discover, including medieval Cordes (1 km). This site is very quiet outside the main season and no English is spoken.

Facilities

Two rather elegant, well maintained sanitary buildings provide open and curtained washbasins, dishwashing and laundry sinks, a washing machine, plus facilities for disabled people. Well fenced swimming pool (June - Sept) and splash pool with water slide (July/Aug). Minigolf, table tennis, TV room and boules. Fishing. Gates locked 22.00-08.00 hrs.

At a glance

Welcome & Ambience	✓✓✓✓	Location	✓✓✓✓✓
Quality of Pitches	✓✓✓✓	Range of Facilities	✓✓✓✓

Directions

Cordes is 25 km. northwest of Albi. From D600 just east of Cordes take D922 south, and within 0.5 km. the site is signed at a minor road junction to your left.

Charges 2003

Per unit incl. 2 persons	€ 15.00

Reservations

Contact site for details. Tel: 05 63 56 11 10.

Open

1 April - 30 September.

FR81030M Camping Municipal de Gourjade

Route de Roquecourbe, 81100 Castres (Tarn)

Camping de Gourjade is set in a country park belonging to the town of Castres. It has the river running along one side and the country park on the other. There are 100 level pitches, all with electricity and separated by well trimmed hedges, and some with shade. There is a barrier at the entrance and a night watchman for security. A small play area caters for children of 3-12 yrs but the adjoining country park has everything – large indoor and outdoor swimming pools with slides etc, minigolf, table tennis, a miniature railway and a 9-hole golf course. In July/Aug competitions are organised. A boat makes regular trips for the 2 km. journey into the centre of Castres for markets and museums.

Facilities

The unisex toilet blocks are very clean with good adjustable showers, facilities for disabled visitors and baby changing. Washing machine and dryer. Drive over motorcaravan emptying point. Very limited shop, with shaded area daily. Attractive restaurant (all season). Bicycles kept at reception (in good condition) for the free use of campers. Country park with reduced charges for campers. Off site: Supermarket 1 km.

At a glance

Welcome & Ambience	✓✓✓✓	Location	✓✓✓✓
Quality of Pitches	✓✓✓✓	Range of Facilities	✓✓✓✓

Directions

From Castres follow signs to Roquecourbe until roundabout with supermarket, then signs to 'Rive droite', Castres and camping. Site is 1 km. on left.

Latest charges

Per person	€ 1.60
pitch and vehicle	€ 6.79
electricity (6A)	€ 2.21

Reservations

Made with 20% deposit. Tel: 05 63 59 72 30.
Email: gourjade@ville-castres.fr

Open

1 April - 30 September.

FR81040M Camp Municipal des Auzerals

81800 Rabastens (Tarn)

Camping Municipal des Auzerals is a small, reasonably priced site. The 44 pitches are near the lake where fishing is possible and there are walks from the site (leaflets from the tourist information office in the town). This is a perfect site for couples seeking peace and quiet, especially in May, June and Sept. All the pitches are on grass, hedged with neat bushes and all with water, drainage and electricity. The local swimming pool is adjacent and the village is only 2.5 km. away. There is no shop (ices from the reception) but a baker calls in July/Aug. All provisions can be found in the village – gas, food and restaurants. This is an unspoilt region of the Tarn within easy reach of Albi and Montauben.

Facilities

The sanitary block is basic but very clean, with mainly Turkish style WCs, good adjustable showers and some washbasins in cubicles. The dishwashing and laundry sinks have hot water and there is a washing machine and a freezer available in the telephone room. Baker calls. Off site: Village 2.5 km.

At a glance

Welcome & Ambience	✓✓✓✓	Location	✓✓✓✓
Quality of Pitches	✓✓✓✓	Range of Facilities	✓✓✓

Directions

Site is northeast of Toulouse. Heading south leave A20 at exit 66 and take D930 south. This road changes to the D630 in 23 km. Follow until sign for Albi on D988. Rabastens is 8 km. and site is signed to left on entry to village.

Latest charges

Per person	€ 2.13
pitch	€ 1.52
electricity (10/12A)	€ 1.37

Reservations

Contact site. Tel: 05 63 33 70 36.

Open

1 May - 15 September.

FR81060 Camping Les Clots

81190 Mirandol-Bourgnounac (Tarn)

Les Clots is a very rural, simple site in the heart of the countryside taking 48 units. The 2.5 km. road from the nearest village of Mirandol is quite narrow but if you arrive after 1 pm there should be no problem. Set around an old farmhouse, the outbuildings have been sympathetically converted, all giving the site lots of character. The site has been carved out of a steep hillside giving variously sized terraces taking from one to ten units. Nearly all pitches have electricity. A few pitches, mainly for tents, are set well away the others giving lots of seclusion. Being amongst the trees there is some sunshine in places. A quiet site with no entertainment at all - the noisiest things we heard were the owls.

Facilities

The toilet blocks are quite basic but have everything needed and are kept very clean. Baby bath and facilities for disabled visitors. Washing machines. Bar in the barn with lots of character (July/Aug). as Shop with basic provisions incl. bread (July/Aug). Simple swimming pool and paddling pool (1/7-30/9). Table tennis. Minigolf. In July/Aug a local comes twice weekly to prepare an evening meal (to order). Leaflets for walks in the area.

At a glance

| Welcome & Ambience | ✓✓✓✓ | Location | ✓✓✓✓ |
| Quality of Pitches | ✓✓✓✓ | Range of Facilities | ✓✓✓ |

Directions

On N88 south of Rodez, take D911 at Baraqueville towards Villefranche. In 19 km. at Rieupeyrove take D905 south to La Salvetat, then to Mirandol (22 km). On outskirts of Mirandol, site is signed to the right.

Charges 2003

| Per unit incl. 3 persons | € 16.40 - € 18.40 |
| electricity (6A) | € 2.80 |

Reservations

Contact site.Tel: 0563769278.
Email: campclots@wanadoo.fr.

Open

1 May - 1 October .

FR81070 Camping Indigo Rieu Montagné

81320 Nages (Tarn)

Rieu Montagné is a delightful site in the heart of the Haut Languedoc Regional park, and at the corner of the départements of the Tarn, Aveyron and Hérault. The site is a member of the Indigo group and lies close to the Lac du Laouzas where a wide range of sporting activities can be enjoyed. There are 147 touring pitches, mostly on broad terraces with reasonable shade, and all with electricity. A heated swimming pool overlooks the lake. In high season there is a varied entertainment programme and guided walks. Many leisure facilities are at the lakeside complex, a five minute walk from the site.

Facilities

The two toilet blocks operate on a unisex basis, and are kept clean although both are quite old. Toilets are mainly Turkish style, but with a reasonable number of British style. Washing and drying machines. Site shop with basic provisions. Bar and snack bar with takeaway. Swimming pool. Entertainment programme (high season). Chalets and mobile homes to let. Off site: Lakeside leisure complex.

At a glance

| Welcome & Ambience | ✓✓✓ | Location | ✓✓✓✓ |
| Quality of Pitches | ✓✓✓ | Range of Facilities | ✓✓✓✓ |

Directions

Site is on north side of the Lac de Laouzas on D162, well signed from village of Nages, which is roughly halfway between Lacaune and Murat-sur-Vebre.

Charges 2003

| Per unit incl. 2 persons and 6A electricity | € 23.00 |
| extra person | € 2.30 - € 4.50 |

Reduced prices in low season.

Reservations

Made with deposit. Tel: 05 63 37 24 71.
Email: rieumontagne@camping-indigo.com

Open

5 April - 31 October.

FR82010 Camping Les Trois Cantons

82140 St Antonin-Noble-Val (Tarn-et-Garonne)

With only 100 pitches, Les Trois Cantons is a very friendly site with level pitches, some set among trees, others open and sunny. All have electricity connections. The swimming pool is covered and heated in early and late season, with activities organised there in July and August. There are also walks, archery and boules, plus wine tastings and a weekly dance. It is though, primarily a site for nature lovers with peaceful evenings and nights. There are walks and mountain bike rides from the site.

Facilities

There are two toilet blocks, one quite basic but the other one refurbished. Both British and Turkish style WCs, quite large showers, and facilities for the disabled. Very limited shop (bread daily). Bar serving snacks and takeaways (all season). Games room. Play area. Tennis court. Volleyball. Boules. English spoken. Off site: Riding 4 km, fishing 7 km. The area has many pretty medieval villages to visit.

At a glance

| Welcome & Ambience | ✓✓✓✓ | Location | ✓✓✓ |
| Quality of Pitches | ✓✓✓ | Range of Facilities | ✓✓✓✓ |

Directions

From N20 at Caussade, take D296 signed Caylus and Septfonds. In 13 km. site is signed right (7 km. after Septfonds). Don't take the D5 towards St Antonin.

Charges 2004

Per person	€ 2.50 - € 5.35
pitch	€ 4.80 - € 6.70
electricity (2/5A)	€ 2.00 - € 3.65

Plus local tax. Camping Cheques accepted.

Reservations

Contact site. Tel: 05 63 31 98 57.
Email: info@3cantons.fr

Open

15 April - 30 September.

Languedoc and Roussillon form part of the Massif Central. With its huge sandy beaches the mountainous Languedoc region is renowned for its long sunshine records, and the pretty coastal villages of Roussillon are at their most beautiful at sunset erupting in a riot of colour.

This section covers the south west coastal region of the Mediterranean, départements:
11 Aude, 30 Gard, 34 Hérault,
66 Pyrénées-Orientales.

Once an independent duchy, the ancient land of Languedoc combines two distinct regions: the vineyards of the Corbières and Minervois and the coastal plain stretching from the Rhône to the Spanish border. Much of the region is rugged and unspoilt, offering opportunities for walking and climbing.

There is ample evidence of the dramatic past. Ruins of the former Cathar castles can be seen throughout the region. The walled city of Carcassonne with its towers, dungeons, moats and drawbridges is one of the most impressive examples of medieval France.

Today, Languedoc and Roussillon are wine and agricultural regions. Languedoc, with considerable success, is now a producer of much of the nation's better value wines. But above all, vast hot sandy beaches and long hours of sunshine make this a paradise for sun worshippers and beach enthusiasts. La Grande Motte, Cap d'Agde and Canet, are all being promoted as an alternative to the more famous Mediterranean stretches of the Côte d'Azur.

Cuisine of the region

Cooking is Provençal, characterised by garlic and olive oil with sausages and smoked hams. Fish is popular along the coast. Wines include Corbières, Minervois, Banyuls and Muscat

Aïgo Bouido: garlic soup

Boles de picoulat: small balls of chopped-up beef and pork, garlic and eggs

Bouillinade: a type of *bouillabaisse* with potatoes, oil, garlic and onions

Boutifare: a sausage-shaped pudding of bacon and herbs

Cargolade: snails, stewed in wine

Ouillade: heavy soup of *boutifare* leeks, carrots, and potatoes

Touron: a pastry of almonds, pistachio nuts and fruit

Places of interest

Aigues-Mortes: medieval city

Béziers: wine capital of the region, St Nazaire cathedral, Canal du Midi

Carcassonne: largest medieval walled city in Europe

Limoux: medieval town, Notre Dame de Marseilla Basilica, St Martin church

Montpellier: universities, Roman sites; Gothic cathedral

Nîmes: Roman remains, Pont du Gard

Perpignan: Kings Palace; Catalan characteristics, old fortress

Pézenas: Molière's home

Villeneuve-lès-Avignon: Royal City and residence of popes in 14th century

Alan Rogers **tip**

TO ESCAPE THE HEAT OF THE DAY, TAKE A TRIP UP INTO THE PYRÉNÉES AND VIST THE NATIONAL PARKS WHERE YOU'LL FIND BIRDS OF PREY AND BEARS.

FR11060 Yelloh! Village Domaine d'Arnauteille

11250 Montclar (Aude)

Enjoying some beautiful and varied views, this rather unusual site is ideally situated for exploring, by foot or car, the little known Aude Département, the area of the Cathars and for visiting the walled city of Carcassonne (10 minutes drive). However, access could be difficult for large, twin axle vans. The site itself is set in 115 hectares of farmland and is on hilly ground with the original pitches on gently sloping, lightly wooded land and newer ones of good size with water, drainage and electricity, semi-terraced and partly hedged. The facilities are quite spread out with the swimming pool set in a hollow basin surrounded by green fields and some newly developed pitches. The reception building is vast; originally a farm building, with a newer top floor being converted to apartments. This is a developing site with enthusiastic owners. Some up and down walking between the pitches and the facilities is unavoidable. A 'Sites et Paysages' member.

Facilities

The main, heated sanitary block is now a distinctive feature, rebuilt to a very high specification with a Roman theme. Three other smaller blocks (one rebuilt) are located at various points. They include washbasins in cabins, dishwashing under cover (hot water), laundry, facilities for disabled people and a baby bath. Motorcaravan service point. Gas. Small shop (15/5-30/9 - the site is a little out of the way). Restaurant in converted stable block offers plat du jour, grills, takeaway (15/5-30/9). Swimming pool (25 x 10 m.) with children's pool. Games court. Boules. Play area. Table tennis and volleyball. Riding (1/7-31/8). Day trips organised. Off site: Bicycle hire 8 km, fishing 3 km, golf 10 km, rafting and canoeing near, plus many marked walks.

At a glance

Welcome & Ambience	✓✓✓✓✓	Location	✓✓✓✓
Quality of Pitches	✓✓✓✓	Range of Facilities	✓✓✓✓✓

Directions

On D118 from Carcassonne, bypass small village of Rouffiac d'Aude, to small section of dual carriageway. Before the end of this, turn right to Montclar up a rather narrow road (passing places) for 2.5 km. Site is signed very sharp left and up hill before the village.

Charges 2003

Per pitch incl. 2 persons	€ 13.50 - € 20.00
with 5A electricity	€ 17.00 - € 23.50
with water and drainage	€ 20.00 - € 27.50
child (under 7 yrs)	€ 2.50 - € 3.60
Camping Cheques accepted.	

Reservations

Made with deposit (25%) and fee (€ 23).
Tel: 04 68 26 84 53. Email: Arnauteille@mnet.fr

Open

1 April - 30 September.

Domaine d'Arnauteille ★★★★
11250 Montclar
Tel: 0033 468 26 84 53 - Fax: 0033 468 26 91 10
Arnauteille@mnet.fr - www.arnauteille.com

New 2004: waterpark with 4 pools in a Greek-Roman style.

FR11030M Camping Municipal La Pinède

Avenue Gaston Bonheur, 11200 Lézignan-Corbières (Aude)

Within walking distance of the little town and only 35 km. from Narbonne Plage, La Pinède is laid out in terraces on a hillside, with good internal access on made-up roads. The 90 individual, level pitches vary in size and are divided up mainly by various trees and shrubs with 6A electricity (about 20 for mobile homes and chalets). The guardian sometimes organises local wine tasting and he also has a vegetable patch in one corner of the site where you can sample really fresh vegetable (charged). Outside the gates are a municipal swimming pool (July/Aug), a disco, restaurant and tennis courts.

Facilities

Three sanitary blocks of good quality are fully equipped and recently refurbished. Not all blocks are opened outside high season. Washing machine. Small shop with gas. Pleasant bar also providing decently priced hot food that can be eaten on the terrace (all July/Aug). A barbecue functions here in season (private barbecues are not permitted). Torches are necessary. Caravan storage. Off site: Fishing 4 km, bicycle hire or riding 2 km.

At a glance

Welcome & Ambience	✓✓✓✓	Location	✓✓✓✓
Quality of Pitches	✓✓✓✓	Range of Facilities	✓✓✓

Directions

Access is off main N113 on west side of Lézignan-Corbières. From A61 (to avoid low bridge) exit at Carcassonne or Narbonne on N113 and follow to site.

Charges 2003

Per person	€ 3.00 - € 4.20
pitch	€ 5.50 - € 7.30
No credit cards.	

Reservations

Advisable in season. Tel: 04 68 27 05 08.

Open

1 March - 30 October.

FR11110 **Camping Val d'Aleth**

11580 Alet les Bains (Aude)

In the gateway to the upper Aude valley and open all year round, this popular small site is run by Christopher and Christine Cranmer who offer a warm welcome and personal service. The mellow medieval walls of Alet les Bains form one boundary of the site, while on the other and popular with anglers, is the River Aude (fenced for safety). Beyond this is the D118 and a railway which produces noise at times. The 37 mainly small, numbered pitches with electricity hook-ups are separated by hedges and mature trees which give shade. Recent works include improvements to the pitches and some hardstandings for winter use. Medieval Alet is a spa town with a thermal pool where the French take 'the cure'. The past life of the old city can be traced through its narrow streets, interesting buildings and the remains of an abbey and cathedral. The town has all services, including three restaurants and a Casino (a remnant of old aristocratic days). The site owners are keen to assist, with books, guides and walking maps available on loan along with brochures (in English) of attractions in the area. Bed and breakfast is also available.

Facilities

There are plans (in 2005) to replace the unsophisticated toilet block which is just adequate, with mostly British type WCs and high pressure hot showers. Laundry sinks and washing machine under cover, very basic dishwashing in the open. Reception has small stocks of essential goods, drinks, wine and beer, and the use of a freezer. Small play area. Mountain bike hire. Off site: White water sports nearby. The area is a Mecca for walkers and mountain-bikers. Bus and train services to Carcassonne and Quillan. Some shops and restaurants in town, full range at Limoux (10 km. north).

At a glance			
Welcome & Ambience	✓✓✓	Location	✓✓✓✓
Quality of Pitches	✓✓✓	Range of Facilities	✓✓

Directions

From Carcassonne take D118 south for 32 km. Ignore first sign to Alet (to avoid narrow stone bridge) and after crossing the river, turn into town. Site is 800 m. on the left (signed).

Charges 2003

Per unit incl. 2 persons	€ 9.50
extra person	€ 2.60
child (under 8 yrs)	€ 1.50
dog	€ 1.00
electricity (4A)	€ 2.50

No credit cards.

Reservations

Contact site. Tel: 04 68 69 90 40.
Email: camping.valdaleth@wanadoo.fr

Open

All year.

FR11040 **Camping Le Martinet Rouge**

11390 Brousses et Villaret (Aude)

Le Martinet Rouge provides a peaceful retreat in the Aude countryside to the north of Carcassonne. It is a small site where the owners have been working hard to improve the facilities. The most striking features are the massive granite boulders (outcrops of smooth rock from the last ice age). The site offers 55 pitches, all with electricity, in two contrasting areas – one is well secluded with irregularly shaped, fairly level, large pitches amongst a variety of trees and shrubs, while the other is on a landscaped gentle sloping hill with mature trees. The pool is attractively landscaped using the original boulders. This is a useful situation from which to visit Carcassonne, the Canal du Midi or to follow the Cathare trail.

Facilities

Four sanitary blocks, including an excellent new one, have washbasins and showers in cabins, facilities for disabled visitors, baby bathroom, dishwashing and laundry facilities. Swimming pool (1/7-15/9, no bermuda style shorts). Small shop (no others locally). Small 'pub' bar with terrace serving snacks (both 15/6-15/9). Barbecue area. Fitness room. Croquet, volleyball, half court tennis, table tennis and small play area. Off site: Tennis, riding and fishing quite close.

At a glance			
Welcome & Ambience	✓✓✓✓	Location	✓✓✓✓
Quality of Pitches	✓✓✓	Range of Facilities	✓✓✓✓

Directions

Site is just south of Brousses-et-Villaret, approx. 20 km. northwest of Carcassonne. It is best approached from the D118 Carcassonne - Mazamet road. Turn onto D103 15 km. north of Carcassonne to Brousses-et-Villaret. On western outskirts of village turn south to site (signed) in 50 m.

Charges 2003

Per standard pitch incl. 2 persons	€ 11.50
with electricity (6A)	€ 14.00
extra person	€ 3.50
child (under 7 yrs)	€ 2.00
animal	€ 1.00

No credit cards.

Reservations

Made with deposit of € 30. Tel: 04 68 26 51 98.

Open

1 April - 31 October.

FR11070 Camping Les Mimosas

Chaussée de Mandirac, 11100 Narbonne (Aude)

Being some six kilometres inland from the beaches of Narbonne and Gruissan, this site benefits from a somewhat less hectic situation than others in the popular seaside environs of Narbonne. The site itself is, however, quite lively with plenty to amuse and entertain the younger generation while, at the same time, offering facilities for the whole family. A purchase of a club card is required in July/Aug. to use the children's club, gym, sauna, tennis, minigolf, billiards etc. (€ 26 per family for your entire stay). A very large, purpose built entertainment centre is under construction. The 150 pitches are mainly of good size, most with electricity, including a few 'grand confort', and they benefit from a reasonable amount of shade, mostly from 2 m. high hedges. This could be a very useful site offering many possibilities to meet a variety of needs, on-site entertainment (including an evening on Cathare history), and easy access to popular beaches, interesting towns such as Narbonne itself, Béziers or the 'Cité de Carcassonne', the Canal du Midi and Cathare castles.

Facilities

Four sanitary buildings, all refurbished to high standards, include washbasins in cabins, some British WCs, baby baths, laundry and dishwashing sinks, and washing machines. Shop (1/4-31/10). Bar. Small lounge, amusements. Auberge with takeaway (1/4-30/9). Heated pool complex including new, landscaped pool with slides and islands, the original pool and a children's pool (open 1/5-31/8 when weather is suitable). Adventure play area. Minigolf. Mountain bike hire. Off site: Riding near. Windsurfing/sailing school 300 m. Gruissan's beach 10 minutes by car. Lagoon for boating and fishing can be reached via footpath (about 200 m).

At a glance

Welcome & Ambience	✓✓✓✓	Location	✓✓✓✓
Quality of Pitches	✓✓✓✓	Range of Facilities	✓✓✓✓✓

Directions

From A9 take exit 38 (Narbonne Sud) and go round roundabout to last exit taking you back over the autoroute (site signed from here). Follow signs to La Nautique and then Mandirac and site (total 6 km. from autoroute). Also signed from Narbonne centre.

Charges 2003

Per pitch incl. 1 or 2 persons	€ 12.30 - € 18.00
pitch with electricity (6A)	€ 15.00 - € 22.30
with electricity, water and waste water	€ 19.60 - € 26.80
extra person	€ 3.60 - € 4.90
child (2-7 yrs)	€ 2.10 - € 3.20
local tax	€ 0.30

Camping Cheques accepted.

Reservations

Made with deposit (€ 100) and fee (€ 22). Tel: 04 68 49 03 72. Email: info@lesmimosas.com

Open

24 March - 31 October.

Camping Club ★★★
Les Mimosa's
1 heated swimming-pool

• Tennis • Sauna
• Mini golf
• Restaurant - Bar
• Shop
• Riding 50 m
• Windsurfing and fishing 300 m
• 6 km to beach at Gruissan

Camping Club LES MIMOSAS
Chaussée de Mandirac · 11100 NARBONNE
℡ + 33 4 68 49 03 72 · Fax +33 4 68 49 39 45
www.lesmimosas.com
e-mail : info@lesmimosas.com

CHALETS AND MOBILE HOMES TO RENT

THE REGION OF CATHAR CASTELS AND PINK FLAMINGOS

FR11080 Camping La Nautique

La Nautique, 11100 Narbonne (Aude)

This extremely spacious site is situated on the Etang de Bages, where flat water combined with strong winds make it one of the best windsurfing areas in France and is owned and run by a very welcoming Dutch family. The site is fenced off from the water for the protection of children and windsurfers can have a key for the gate (with deposit) that leads to launching points on the lake. La Nautique has 390 huge, level pitches (a small one is 130 sq.m), including a good number used for site owned mobile homes and chalets and 30 tour operator pitches. There are also six or seven overnight pitches with electricity in a separate area. The wide range of evergreens, flowering shrubs and trees on site give a pleasant feel and each pitch is separated by hedges making some quite private and providing shade. All have electricity (10A) and water. The difference between this and other sites is that each pitch has an individual toilet cabin. Various entertainment is organised for adults and children in July/Aug, plus a sports club for supervised surfing, sailing, rafting, walking and canoeing (some activities are charged for). The unspoilt surrounding countryside is excellent for walking or cycling and locally there is horse riding and fishing. English is spoken in reception by the very welcoming Schutjes family. This site caters for families with children including teenagers (in fact they say 8 months to 86 years!)

Facilities

Each individual cabin has a toilet, shower and washbasin (key deposit) and as each pitch empties, the facilities are cleaned in readiness for the next. Special pitches for disabled people with facilities are fitted out to cater for their needs. Two fully equipped laundry areas. Dishwashing sinks. Shop (1/6-15/9) with reasonable stock. Bar/restaurant (evenings only May and Sept) plus large TV. Snack bar 1/7-31/8. Takeaway. Swimming pools (solar heated), water slide and paddling pool with fountain and slide, poolside bar (1/7-31/8). Play areas and children's club. Tennis, table tennis, basketball, volleyball, football, minigolf and boules. Teenagers' disco organised in high season. Internet point. Only electric barbecues are permitted. Torch useful. Off site: Large sandy beaches at Gruissan (10 km) and Narbonne Plage (15 km). Narbonne is only 4 km. Walking and cycling. Canoeing, sailing and windsurfing on the Etang.

At a glance

Welcome & Ambience ✓✓✓✓✓ Location ✓✓✓✓
Quality of Pitches ✓✓✓✓ Range of Facilities ✓✓✓✓✓

Directions

From A9 take exit 38 (Narbonne Sud). Go round roundabout to last exit and follow signs for La Nautique and site, then further site signs to site on right in 3 km.

Charges 2004

Per unit incl. 1 or 2 persons, electricity, water and sanitary unit	€ 7.40 - € 17.50
extra person	€ 4.00 - € 5.20
child (1-7 yrs)	€ 2.00 - € 3.60
dog or cat	€ 1.35 - € 2.35
local tax	€ 0.30

Reservations

Made with deposit (€ 104) and fee (€ 16).
Tel: 04 68 90 48 19.
Email: info@campinglanautique.com

Open

1 February - 21 November.

FR30000 Camping Domaine de Gaujac

Boisset et Gaujac, 30140 Anduze/ Boisset et Eaujac (Gard)

This large, woodland holiday site is enthusiastically run by the energetic and friendly Holley family (English is spoken). The 303 level pitches, include 175 for touring and 70 for tour operators, they all have electricity and they are well shaded. Access to some areas can be difficult for larger units due to narrow winding access roads, trees and hedges. Larger units should ask for lower numbered pitches (1-148) where access is a little easier. In high season this region is dry and hot, thus grass quickly wears off many pitches leaving just a sandy base. There are 12 special hardstanding pitches for motorcaravans. The site has a new covered animation area and courtyard terrace. The extensive and lively programme of activities in the main season includes a children's club, plus cabaret, karaoke, disco, buffet parties and even cinema shows. Just across the lane is the river with a small beach where one can swim, boat or fish.

Facilities

Four sanitary units of varying ages and design are opened one by one as the season progresses. They include some washbasins in cubicles and a children's unit with special low level equipment. Dishwashing and laundry sinks, washing machines, dryer and ironing facilities. Units for disabled visitors. Clean and practical rather than luxurious, one small block can be heated in cool weather. Motorcaravan service point. Well stocked shop (15/6-30/8), newsagent. Takeaway/crêperie (7/5-15/9). Bar and restaurant (7/5-15/9, on demand at other times). Fenced swimming pool and children's pool complex (1/5-15/9 with lifeguard 5/7-15/8). Playground plus sports field for football, volleyball etc. Two tennis courts (free off season). Minigolf. Off site: Riding 6 km. Bicycle hire 5 km. Golf 6 km. Mining museum at Alès, steam trains run between Anduze and St Jean-du-Gard, a music museum at Anduze, and a number of spectacular caverns and grottoes.

At a glance

Welcome & Ambience	✓✓✓✓	Location	✓✓✓
Quality of Pitches	✓✓✓	Range of Facilities	✓✓✓✓

Directions

From Alès take N110 towards Montpellier. At St Christol-les-Alès fork right on D910 towards Anduze and in Bagard turn left on D246 to Boisset et Gaujac. Site is signed from village.

Charges 2003

Per unit incl. 2 adults	€ 13.00 - € 16.50
extra person	€ 3.00 - € 3.80
child (2-7 yrs)	€ 2.00 - € 2.90
dog	free - € 2.30
electricity (4/6A)	€ 2.50 - € 4.10
Camping Cheques accepted.	

Reservations

Necessary in high season and made with deposit (€ 107) and fee (€ 12,20). Tel: 04 66 61 80 65. Email: gravieres@club-internet.fr

Open

1 April - 30 September.

FR30060 Camping Domaine des Fumades

Les Fumades, 30500 Allègre (Gard)

Domaine des Fumades is a pleasant, busy site with a friendly atmosphere near the thermal springs at Allègre. Reception at the site is a joy to behold. Set in an attractive courtyard, within the farmhouse, it has a central fountain and masses of tubs and baskets of colourful flowers. The entrance as a whole has a very tropical feel with its banana plants and palm trees. The 230 pitches are large and level, all with 4A electricity. A variety of trees add privacy and welcome shade. Three pleasantly landscaped swimming pools have ample sunbathing space, bridges and jacuzzis. This is a good area for walking, cycling, riding, climbing and fishing. Used by tour operators (80 pitches). A 'Sites et Paysages' member.

Facilities

Two well appointed sanitary blocks and one new one seem to cope well in high season. Some washbasins in cabins, baby baths and facilities for disabled people. Laundry and dishwashing sinks. These facilities are both clean and well maintained. Well stocked shop. Bar, enlarged restaurant, snack bar and takeaway (all with reasonable prices). Two designated barbecue areas. Swimming pools with ample sunbathing space. Large, well equipped and fenced playground. Games room, tennis, volleyball, table tennis and boules. Well planned animation and entertainment programme, designed to appeal to families. Barbecues are not permitted. Off site: Riding 2 km.

At a glance

Welcome & Ambience	✓✓✓✓	Location	✓✓✓✓
Quality of Pitches	✓✓✓	Range of Facilities	✓✓✓✓✓

Directions

From Alès take D16 through Salindres, continue towards Allègre, until signs for Fumades (and thermal springs) on the right.

Charges 2003

Per pitch incl. 2 persons	€ 13.50 - € 24.00
with electricity (4A)	€ 16.00 - € 30.00
extra person	€ 2.70 - € 7.00
child (2-7 yrs)	€ 1.60 - € 3.50
pet	€ 2.00
local tax	€ 0.20

Reservations

Made with deposit (€ 121) and fee € 22,87). Tel: 04 66 24 80 78. Email: domaine.des.fumades@wanadoo.fr

Open

15 May - 5 September (with all services)

FR30030 Camping Abri de Camargue

320 rte du Phare de l'Espiguette, Port Camargue, 30240 Le Grau-du-Roi (Gard)

This pleasant site has an attractive pool area overlooked by the bar and its outdoor tables on a pleasant sheltered terrace. The larger outdoor pool has surrounds for sunbathing and the smaller indoor one is heated. With 470 level pitches, there are 139 for touring units, mainly of 100 sq.m (there are also smaller ones). Electricity and water are available on most, and the pitches are well maintained and shaded, with trees and flowering shrubs quite luxuriant in parts. A summer fair is within walking distance which can be noisy until quite late. English is spoken.

Facilities

Two well appointed toilet blocks, include washbasins in cubicles, dishwashing and laundry sinks. Facilities for handicapped. Convenient motorcaravan service point. Shop. Bar with TV, restaurant and takeaway with reasonably priced food (all open when site is open). Heated indoor pool and outdoor pool. New cinema room. Play area of the highest quality (one of few with a rubber EU standard safety base). Petanque. Off site: Tennis 800 m. Fishing, riding, golf and bicycle hire within 2 km. The nearest beach at Port Camargue is 900 m. and the one at L'Espiguette is 4 km. (in high season a free bus passes the gate to L'Espiguette).

At a glance

Welcome & Ambience	✓✓✓✓	Location	✓✓✓✓
Quality of Pitches	✓✓✓✓✓	Range of Facilities	✓✓✓✓✓

Directions

A road now bypasses Le Grau-du-Roi from the west as well as the approach from Aigues-Mortes. Follow signs 'Port Camargue' and 'Campings' just northeast of Grau-du-Roi then 'Rive gauche' signs towards Phare l'Espiguette over roundabout and site is on right opposite the 'Jumbo jet' Tobbogan Park.

Latest charges

Per unit incl. 1 or 2 persons and electricity	€ 21.00 - € 43.00
incl. 3-5 persons	€ 25.00 - € 45.00
extra person or extra car	€ 5.00 - € 9.00
pet	€ 5.00

Reservations

Advised for high season (1/7-31/8) when made for min. 1 week with € 33 fee. Tel: 04 66 51 54 83. Email: abridecamargue@hotmail.com

Open

1 April - 30 September.

FR30100N Camping Naturiste de la Sablière

Domaine de la Sablière, St Privat de Champclos, 30430 Barjac (Gard)

Spectacularly situated in the Cèze Gorges, this naturist site with a surprising 604 pitches tucked away within its wild terrain offers a wide variety of facilities, all within a really peaceful, wooded and dramatic setting. Pitches are grouped in areas – 'Mesange' (mainly for tents with cars parked 200 m. away) and 'Fauvette' at the bottom of the gorge alongside the river at some points close to the main access road, which is well surfaced but steep and winding. A newer area, 'Pinson', is near the top of the hill. The pitches themselves are mainly on flat terraces, attractively situated among a variety of trees and shrubs (some with low overhang). Many are of a good size and have electricity. A pool complex (dynamited out of the hill and built in local style) provides a children's pool area and two large pools, one of which can be covered, sunbathing terraces, saunas and a bar. This is a family run and orientated site and the owner, Gaby Cespedes, provides a personal touch that is unusual in a large site. This no doubt contributes to the relaxed, informal atmosphere and first time naturists would find this a gentle introduction to naturism. You must expect some fairly steep walking between pitches and facilities, although there is a minibus shuttle service in high season. Member 'France 4 Naturisme'.

Facilities

Six good unisex sanitary blocks (most refurbished 2003) have excellent free hot showers in typical open plan, naturist style, washbasins (cold water), baby baths and facilities for people with disabilities. Dishwashing and laundry sinks. Laundry. Supermarket. Open air, covered restaurant (all season) with good value waiter service meals and a takeaway. Swimming pool complex. Bar with TV room and disco. Small café/crêperie. Varied activities include walking, climbing, swimming, canoeing, fitness trail, fishing (permit required), archery, tennis, minigolf and volleyball, book binding, pottery, yoga etc. Entertainment for adults and children (mid June - end Aug). Mobile homes, caravans, chalet and tents to rent. Torch useful. Off site: Barjac with its Antiques Fair at Easter and mid-August. Alès, Chemin de Fer des Cevennes.

At a glance

Welcome & Ambience	✓✓✓✓	Location	✓✓✓✓
Quality of Pitches	✓✓✓	Range of Facilities	✓✓✓✓✓

Directions

From Barjac take D901 east for 3 km. Site is signed just before St Privat-de-Champclos and is approx. 3 km. on narrow roads following camp signs.

Charges 2003

Per pitch incl. 2 persons	€ 11.00 - € 28.00
extra person	€ 3.00 - € 6.10
child (under 8 yrs)	free - € 5.60
electricity (6/10A)	€ 3.60
dog	€ 1.00 - € 2.50

Plus local tax. Camping Cheques accepted.

Reservations

Made with deposit (25%) and fee (€ 30) - contact site. Tel: 04 66 24 51 16. Email: sabliere@club-internet.fr

Open

Easter - end September.

FR30070 Camping Château de Boisson

Boisson, 30500 Allegre-Les Fumades (Gard)

Château de Boisson is a quiet family site within easy reach of the Cévennes, Ardèche or Provence. It is set in the grounds of the château, beside the small medieval village of Boisson. Reception at the entrance is light and cool, built from the local stone in the local style so it blends beautifully with the rest of the buildings. The site is hilly so the pitches are on three levels, but they are level and have electricity. A few have cabins that provide a WC, washbasin and shower. Trees provide some shade. The large pool with a slide is at the castle in a sunny location and there is also an indoor pool (all season) of excellent quality. The restaurant in the castle is cool and elegant with tables also available outside.

Facilities

The two toilet blocks are quite old, but very clean and well maintained with washbasins in cabins. Washing machines at both blocks, baby bath and shower, facilities for disabled visitors. Small shop. Restaurant, bar and snacks. Internet point. Play area. Indoor pool (all season). Outdoor pool (1/4-30/9). Bridge tournaments in low season. Painting classes. Tennis, boule, volleyball and basketball. Animation in July and Aug for 4-12 yr olds and outdoor competitions for adults. Dogs are not accepted. Barbecues are not allowed. Apartments to rent in the castle.

At a glance

Welcome & Ambience	✓✓✓✓	Location	✓✓✓✓
Quality of Pitches	✓✓✓✓	Range of Facilities	✓✓✓✓✓

Directions

From Alès take D16 northeast towards Salindres and Auzon. Just after Auzon turn right on D37 signed Boisson and site is signed from there.

Latest charges

Per unit incl. 2 persons and electricity (5A)	€ 16.50 - € 30.00
with water and drainage	€ 18.00 - € 33.00

Reservations

Made with deposit and €15 fee; contact site. Tel: 04 66 24 82 21. Email: reception@chateau-boisson.com

Open

30 March - 3 November.

FR30080 Camping Le Mas de Reilhe

Crespian, 30260 Quissac (Gard)

This spacious family site has only 90 pitches (70 for tourers). All but the highest pitches have electricity and some of the upper ones may require long leads. The large lower pitches are separated by tall poplar trees and hedges, close to the main facilities and may experience some road noise. The large terraced pitches in the upper section are scattered under mature pine trees, some with good views, and are more suited to tents and trailer tents. Mas de Reilhe will probably appeal to couples and young families. The entertainment in July and August is for the children with just the occasional competition for adults. The pool is in a sunny position with sunbeds and a paddling pool. There are no shops in the village, the nearest being at the medieval city of Sommières 10 km. away (and well worth a visit).

Facilities

The toilet blocks, one new, are clean and functional, with washbasins in cabins and pre-set showers. Dishwashing and laundry sinks. Washing machine. Reception doubles as a bar. Limited shop (from 1/6). Takeaway and restaurant (21/6-31/8). Swimming pool. Small play area on grass. Table tennis. Off site: Riding 5 km. Fishing 3 km. Tennis 1 km. Bicycle hire 25 km. The sea, the gorges and Nimes are all approx 40 km.

At a glance

Welcome & Ambience	✓✓✓✓	Location	✓✓✓
Quality of Pitches	✓✓✓✓	Range of Facilities	✓✓✓✓

Directions

Site is on N110 road (Ales - Montpellier) at southern end of the small village of Crespian, just north of the junction with the D999 road (Nimes - Quissac).

Charges 2003

Per unit incl. 2 persons	€ 12.50 - € 19.00
child (2-7 yrs)	€ 1.50 - € 2.50
electricity (6/10A)	€ 3.30 - € 4.00

Camping Cheques accepted.

Reservations

Made with deposit (€ 45,73 per week booked) and booking fee (€ 12,20). Tel: 04 66 77 82 12. Email: info@camping-mas-de-reilhe.fr

Open

1 May - 24 September.

FR30120 Camping Campeole–TCS Ile des Papes

Barrage de Villeneuve, 30400 Villeneuve les Avignon (Gard)

Ile des Papes, new in '94, is a large, open and very well equipped site near Avignon with an extensive swimming pool area and a fishing lake. The railway is quite near but noise is not too intrusive. The 342 pitches are of a good size on level grass and all have electricity, some taken by mobile homes or chalets. Avignon and its Palace and museums is 8 km. away.

Facilities

Toilet blocks of very good quality include baby rooms. Dishwashing and laundry sinks. Washing machines. Motorcaravan service point. Well stocked shop (limited hours in low seasons). Bar and restaurant. Two large swimming pools and one for children. Play area. Lake for fishing. Archery, tennis, table tennis, volleyball, minigolf and basketball (all free). Bicycle hire. Games and competitions for all ages in high season. Off site: Riding 3 km.

At a glance

| Welcome & Ambience | ✓✓✓ | Location | ✓✓✓ |
| Quality of Pitches | ✓✓✓ | Range of Facilities | ✓✓✓✓ |

Directions

Take N100 Nîmes road out of Avignon towards Bagnoles-sur-Cèze and turn right after crossing the Rhône. Turn left along the river bank and follow signs for Roquemaure (D980). After 6 km. turn right on D228 signed Barrage de Villeneuve and site is 1 km.

Charges 2003

Per unit incl. 2 persons	€ 16.00 - € 25.00
extra person	€ 4.00 - € 6.00
child (2-6 yrs)	€ 2.60 - € 3.00
dog	€ 1.60 - € 3.00
electricity (6A)	€ 3.10 - € 3.20
local tax	€ 0.60

Various special offers.

Reservations

Made with deposit (25%) and fee (€ 15,21). Tel: 04 90 15 15 90. Email: ile.papes@wanadoo.fr

Open

25 March - 20 October.

FR30140 Camping La Soubeyranne

Route de Beaucaire, 30210 Remoulins (Gard)

This site is well positioned for visiting the Pont du Gard, Nîmes and Uzès, famed for their Roman connections. It is approached by a short tree-lined avenue which leads to reception. The 200 pitches offer extremely generous amounts of shade and keeping the 4.5 hectares watered involves over 5 km. of hose pipe. Pitches are large, level, numbered and separated, with 170 having electricity connections. An animation programme (July/August) is mainly for young children (teenagers may find the site rather quiet). Whilst quiet in some respects, train noise both by day and night can be an irritant.

Facilities

Two well appointed, unisex toilet blocks are basic but clean give more than adequate facilities and include washbasins in cubicles. Provision for dishwashing, laundry, water and refuse points is equally generous. Motorcaravan service point. Fridges for hire. Small shop selling basics. Restaurant, bar and takeaway (all from 5/5) - menu not extensive but adequate and moderately priced. Swimming pool complex with 20 x 10 m. pool and smaller toddlers' pool (unsupervised), and partly shaded. Play area, including trampoline, table tennis, boules, tennis and volleyball. Bicycle hire. Off site: Fishing 1 km. Remoulins 1.5 km.

At a glance

| Welcome & Ambience | ✓✓✓ | Location | ✓✓✓ |
| Quality of Pitches | ✓✓✓ | Range of Facilities | ✓✓✓✓✓ |

Directions

From Uzès take D981 to Remoulins, turn right at lights over river bridge, left at roundabout, then left (signed D986 Beaucaire). Site is 1.5 km. further on left.

Charges 2004

Per unit incl. 2 persons	€ 12.00 - € 16.00
with electricity (6A)	€ 14.00 - € 19.00
extra person	€ 3.00 - € 4.20
animal	€ 1.07
local tax	€ 0.30

Reservations

Contact site for details. Tel: 04 66 37 03 21. Email: soubeyranne@wanadoo.fr

Open

3 April - 13 September.

FR30160 Camping Caravaning Le Boucanet

B.P. 206, 30240 Le Grau du Roi (Gard)

On the beach between Grande Motte and Le Grau-du-Roi, this is a sunny site with only a little shade. Many trees have been planted but as yet most are not tall enough to give much shade. As to be expected, the 458 pitches are sandy and level. The 343 for touring units are separated by small bushes, (most with electricity). The pleasant restaurant overlooks the large pool and is open lunchtimes and evenings. An excellent shopping arcade provides groceries, fruit, newspapers, a butcher and cooked meats, rotisserie and pizzas. In July and August organised activities include games, competitions, gymnastics, water polo, jogging and volleyball for adults. Horse riding on the white horses of the Camargue is to be found within a few kilometres.

Facilities

The toilet blocks are convenient for the pitches providing washbasins in cubicles and some British style toilets in two blocks, the remainder Turkish style (about 70%). Facilities for disabled people at two blocks. Baby rooms. Dishwashing and laundry sinks have warm water. Washing machines, dryers, irons and fridge hire. Motorcaravan service point. Range of shops. Restaurant. Bar with snacks. Large swimming pool and paddling pool. Play area on sand and miniclub in July/Aug. Table tennis, tennis. Bicycle hire. Dogs are not accepted. Off site: Golf 1.5 km. Riding 500 m.

At a glance

Welcome & Ambience	✓✓✓	Location	✓✓✓✓
Quality of Pitches	✓✓✓	Range of Facilities	✓✓✓✓✓

Directions

Site is between La Grand Motte and Le Grau-du-Roi on the D255 coastal road, on the seaward side of the road.

Charges 2004

Per unit incl. 2 persons	€ 19.00 - € 30.00
with electricity (6A)	€ 22.50 - € 33.50
pitch on first row of beach, plus	€ 5.00
extra adult	€ 6.80 - € 8.50
child (under 7 yrs)	€ 5.40 - € 7.00
local tax	€ 0.20 - € 0.30

Camping Cheques accepted.

Reservations

Necessary for July/Aug. and made with 25% deposit and booking fee (€ 23); by money order or credit card only. Tel: 04 66 51 41 48.
Email: campingboucanet@wanadoo.fr

Open

3 May - 24 September, with all facilities.

Camping **Le Boucanet** ★★★★
Route de Carnon - 30240 Le Grau du Roi

Tel : 33 (0) 466 514 148 - Fax : 33 (0) 466 514 187
contact@campingboucanet.fr - www.campingboucanet.fr

FR30190 Camping International des Gorges du Gardon

Chemin de la Barque Vieille, 30210 Vers-Pont-du-Gard (Gard)

Probably the main attraction in the Gardon area of France is the Pont du Gard, an amazing Roman aqueduct built around 50AD. There are, however, other attractions worthy of a visit, such as the medieval village of Castillon-du-Gard perched on a rocky peak with narrow cobbled streets, and Collias at the bottom of the gorge from where you can hire canoes. Camping International is within easy (walking or cycling) distance of these attractions. It provides 200 level, good-sized pitches with electricity; some are open while others are shaded. There is direct access to the river where swimming is permitted, although in summer the water level may be a little low. Unsupervised heated pools provide an alternative. The owners, Joseph and Sylvie Gonzales speak a little English, and visitors will always receive a warm and friendly welcome from them. Tourist information is in the reception (open all day) and Sylvie will share her local knowledge if you need any additional help.

Facilities

Two toilet blocks provide unisex facilities: showers, washbasins (some in cabins), and toilets. Facilities for disabled visitors in building nearest reception. Baby room. Washing machine, dishwashing and laundry sinks. Bar and restaurant (table service and takeaway). Swimming and paddling pools (unsupervised). Play areas. Table tennis. Games room and TV. Organised family entertainment during July/Aug. Off site: Pont du Gard approx 4 km. Collias 5 km. Canoeing arranged from site. Good area for walking and cycling.

At a glance

Welcome & Ambience	✓✓✓✓✓	Location	✓✓✓✓✓
Quality of Pitches	✓✓✓✓	Range of Facilities	✓✓✓✓

Directions

Exit A9 at Remoulins, then take D981 towards Uzès. Follow campsite signs from this road - about 2 miles from the town.

Charges 2003

Per unit incl. 2 persons	€ 11.50 - € 15.00
extra adult	€ 3.50 - € 5.00
child (7-14 yrs)	€ 2.50 - € 3.00
electricity (6-16A)	€ 3.00
dog	€ 2.00

Reservations

Advisable during July and August. Tel: 04 66 22 81 81.

Open

15 March - 30 October.

Camping International Les Gorges du Gardon

30210 vers pont du gard / tel. 33 466 228 181 - fax. 33 466 229 012
www.le-camping-international.com   camping.international@wanadoo.fr

FR30180 Camping Mas de la Cam

Route de St Andre de Valborgne, 30270 St Jean-du-Gard (Gard)

Camping Mas de la Cam is rather an unusual site for France in that all the pitches are used for touring units (no mobile home for rent). It is a very pleasant site with well trimmed grass anmd hedges and a profusion of flowers at the entrance. Lying alongside the Gardon river, the banks have been left free of pitches giving neat grass for sunbathing and some trees for shade, whilst children can amuse themselves in the water (no good for canoes). Slightly sloping, the pitches are on level teraces, some with shade and all with electricity. A quiet, family site, there is no evening entertainment and just a few, low key daytime competitions in July and August.

Facilities

Good quality toilet blocks provide washbasins on cabins, adjustable showers in quite large cubicles, a baby bath and facilities for disabled visitors. Washing machines. Bar/restaurant and terrrace. Small shop with bread daily (to order). Attractive swimming and paddling pools. Play area. Club room used in low season for bridge, in high season as a games room. Fishing. Off site: Riding 5 km. St Jean-de-Gard (3 km.) is a very attractive village.

At a glance

Welcome & Ambience	✓✓✓✓	Location	✓✓✓✓
Quality of Pitches	✓✓✓✓	Range of Facilities	✓✓✓✓

Directions

Site is 3 km. northwest of St Jean-du-Gard in the direction of St André de Valborgne on the D9.

Charges 2003

Per unit incl. 2 persons	€ 12.00 - € 17.00
with electricity (6A)	€ 15.00 - € 20.00
child (under 7 yrs)	€ 2.10 - € 3.00

Reservations

Made with deposit (€ 100) and fee (€ 15). Tel: 04 66 85 12 02. Email: camping@masdelacam.fr

Open

20 April - 22 September.

FR30170 Camping La Sousta

Avenue duy Pont du Gard, 30210 Remoulins (Gard)

With a long season, La Sousta is a former municipal site set under tall trees and with a ten minute walk of the famous Pont du Gard, a World Heritage site. The 374 pitches (including 41 mobile homes to rent) are mainly level and numbered, but are not very clearly defined. The reception office provides plenty of tourist information and coach trips are organised in high season to various places of interest. A large swimming pool set in a sunny location has surrounding grassy areas for sunbathing. A footpath leads to a private beach on the river.

Facilities

The four toilet blocks are quite basic but give clean facilities with mainly British style WCs, baby bath and showers, and facilities for disabled people. Washing machines and dryer. Bar. Snack bar and takeaway. Swimming and paddling pools. Various play area. Volleyball, tennis and football field. Bicycle hire. Weekly disco in July/Aug. Entertainment and canoes trips organised. Communal barbecue areas.

At a glance

Welcome & Ambience	✓✓✓✓	Location	✓✓✓✓
Quality of Pitches	✓✓✓	Range of Facilities	✓✓✓✓

Directions

Site is signed from the centre of Remoulins. From the N100 follow signs for Beaucaire and Nimes, then site signs. Site is beside the D981, just before Pont du Gard.

Charges 2003

Per unit incl. 2 persons	€ 11.00 - € 17.00
dog	free - € 2.00
electricity	€ 3.00 - € 4.00

Reservations

Contact site. Tel: 04 66 37 12 80. Email: info@lasousta.com.

Open

1 March - 31 October

FR34020 Camping Le Garden

44, Place des Tamaris, 34280 La Grande Motte (Hérault)

Le Garden is a mature site, situated 300 m. back from a fine sandy beach and with all the choice of sports, entertainment and other facilities of the popular holiday resort of La Grand Motte. With space for 108 caravans and 101 mobile homes, the 100 sq.m. pitches are hedged with good shade on sandy/grass base. All have electricity, water and waste water drains. The fine sandy beach and port are only 300 m. away, with a shopping complex, bar and restaurant next to site.

Facilities

Three well situated toilet blocks, 2 smartly refurbished in Mediterranean colours, include washbasins in cabins and baby bath. Dishwashing and laundry sinks. Washing machines. Unit for disabled people. Shop to one side of the site with groceries, cigarettes, newspapers, boutique, etc., restaurant, bar and takeaway service (from 15/5). Swimming pool and paddling pool (from 15/5). Off site: Tennis courts, a riding club, a casino and a nightclub nearby.

At a glance

Welcome & Ambience	✓✓✓✓	Location	✓✓✓✓
Quality of Pitches	✓✓✓✓	Range of Facilities	✓✓✓✓

Directions

Entering La Grand Motte from D62 dual-carriageway, keep right following signs for 'campings'. Turn right at traffic lights by the Office de Tourism and right again by the Bar Le Garden and site immediately on right.

Charges 2003

Per unit incl. 1-3 persons	€ 24.00
4 persons	€ 31.00
with 6A electricity, water and drainage	€ 32.00
extra person	€ 7.00

Reservations

Not made. Tel: 04 67 56 50 09.

Open

1 March - 31 October.

FR34190 Camping Caravaning Les Champs Blancs

Route de Rochelongue, 34300 Agde (Hérault)

Les Champs Blancs is set in high trees, two km. from Agde and two km. from the sea. The 169 touring pitches, on level, sandy grass, are bordered with bushes with plenty of shade and greenery. All have 10A electricity and 58 have private sanitary cabins. Separate area for mobile homes. The pool area has now been augmented by a super new irregular pool, with toboggans, cascade, jacuzzi, bridges and palms with plenty of space for sunbeds but retaining the original pool and paddling pool. Games, shows and competitions are arranged in July and August. There are tennis courts and other leisure facilities in the area nearest the road, bordered by trees to deaden possible road noise.

Facilities

Two toilet blocks have been refurbished to provide showers and washbasins together, plus British style WCs. Unit for disabled visitors. Dishwashing and laundry sinks. Washing machines and dryers. Also 58 en-suite private cabins containing WC, shower and washbasin with an outside sink for dishes. Well stocked shop in high season; only bread available in low season. Bar (all season). Restaurant and bakery at busy times. Swimming complex. Good play area, minigolf, table tennis, tennis, basketball and volleyball. Bicycle hire. Off site: Golf 1.5 km. Riding 1 km.

At a glance

Welcome & Ambience	✓✓✓✓	Location	✓✓✓
Quality of Pitches	✓✓✓✓✓	Range of Facilities	✓✓✓✓✓

Directions

From A9 autoroute exit 34, follow N312 for Adge which joins the N112 Beziers - Sete road, after crossing high river bridge take first turning signed Rochelongue and turn right, next left and next left (signed Adge) i.e. round 3 sides of a square. Site on left before you cross the bridge back over the N112.

Charges 2003

Per pitch incl. 2 persons	€ 16.00 - € 34.00
with individual sanitary facilities	€ 18.00 - € 40.00
incl. 4 persons	€ 22.00 - € 42.00
with individual sanitary facilities	€ 23.00 - € 48.00
extra person	€ 5.00 - € 9.00
dog	€ 2.00

Camping Cheques accepted.

Reservations

Necessary for July and August. Tel: 04 67 94 23 42. Email: champs.blacs@wanadoo.fr

Open

1 April - 30 September.

FR34130 Camping Le Neptune

Route du Grau, 34300 Agde (Hérault)

Camping Neptune is a rare find in this area of 'all singing, all dancing' campsites. This small, family run site with only 165 pitches makes a delightful change. There are also a few mobile homes. The Fray family are very welcoming and, even though it is in a busy area, it is a little oasis of calm, very suited to couples and young families. Placed along the D32 to Grau d'Agde which is beside the river Herault, there will be a little daytime road noise. The pitches are mostly separated by flowering bushes, with some shade and most have electricity. The swimming pool is in a sunny position with sunbeds and over-looked by the bar. The only entertainment is in high season and is a twice weekly mini-club for children. The beach and the small resort of Grau d'Agde are 1.5 km. and Aqualand 5 km.

Facilities

The large toilet block provides roomy pre-set showers, washbasins in cabins and mainly British style WCs, plus three cold showers for really hot weather. An extra new small block is at the top of the site. Laundry and dishwashing sinks. Two washing machines and dryer. Small shop. Bar (both 15/5-30/9). Fridge hire. Swimming pool heated in cool weather, bracelets required (€ 8 deposit). Table tennis and field for sports. Bicycle hire. Boat mooring facility on the River Herault across the road. Not all breeds of dog are accepted and only one is allowed.

At a glance

Welcome & Ambience	✓✓✓✓	Location	✓✓✓✓✓
Quality of Pitches	✓✓✓✓✓	Range of Facilities	✓✓✓✓

Directions

From A9 autoroute exit 34, follow N312 for Agde which joins the N112. After crossing bridge follow signs for Grau d'Agde then at triangle turn left at Grau d'Agde and turn left almost immediately at roundabout towards the river and left again at next roundabout signed Grau d'Agde/Les Berges de l'Herault on D32 which runs parallel to the River Herault. Site signed on left.

Charges 2003

Per unit incl. 2 persons	€ 15.00 - € 22.00
with electricity (6A)	€ 16.00 - € 24.50
with water	€ 17.00 - € 26.00
extra person	€ 4.00 - € 5.00
child (under 7 yrs)	€ 2.00 - € 2.50

Camping Cheques accepted.

Reservations

Necessary for July and August. Tel: 04 67 94 23 94. Email: info@campingleneptune.com

Open

1 April - 30 September.

FR34170 Camping Caravaning Les Mimosas

Port Cassafières, 34420 Portiragnes Plage (Hérault)

Les Mimosas is quite a large site with 400 pitches – 200 for touring units, the remainder for mobile homes – in a rural situation. The level, grassy pitches are of average size, separated and numbered, all with 6A electricity (long leads may be required). Some are in the shade, the choice is yours. The pool area, a real feature of the site, includes an impressive wave pool, various toboggans, a large swimming pool and a paddling pool (six pools in all) with lots of free sun beds. Many day trips and excursions are arranged all season, from canoeing to visiting castles. Portiragnes Plage is about 1 km. and it can be reached by cycle tracks. The Canal du Midi runs along the edge of the site (no access), providing another easy cycle ride. This is a friendly, family run site with families in mind.

Facilities

One large new toilet block has family sized, en-suite facilities, washbasins both open and in cabins, baby rooms, children's toilets and very good facilities for disabled people (the whole site is wheelchair friendly). The other two older blocks, with some Turkish style toilets, are to be refurbished. Dishwashing and laundry sinks. Washing machines and dryers. Fridge hire. Large well-stocked shop (bread baked daily all season). Bar with snacks all season, restaurant (from 1/6). Pool complex (early June) with lifeguards in July/Aug. Play area. Boules. Gym and sauna (charged). Off site: Portiragnes Plage with beach bars and restaurants 2 km.

At a glance			
Welcome & Ambience	✓✓✓✓	Location	✓✓✓✓
Quality of Pitches	✓✓✓✓	Range of Facilities	✓✓✓✓✓

Directions

From A9 exit 35 (Bezieres Est) take N112 south towards Serignan (1 km). At large roundabout follow signs for Cap d'Agde but watch for D37 Portiragnes (1-2 km) and follow signs for Portiragnes Plage. Site is well signed before Portiragnes Plage (5 km).

Charges 2003

Per unit incl. 2 persons	€ 20.00 - € 27.00
with electricity	€ 23.00 - € 31.00
private sanitary unit	€ 7.00 - € 8.00

Reservations

Necessary for July/Aug. Tel: 04 67 90 92 92.
Email: les.mimosas.portiragnes@wanadoo.fr

Open

1 May - 15 September.

Port Cassafières   34420 Portiragnes Plage - FRANCE   Tél : +33 4 67 90 92 92   Fax : +33 4 67 90 85 39
www.mimosas.com   www.mimosas.fr   E-mail : les.mimosas.portiragnes@wanadoo.fr

FR34210 Camping Les Berges du Canal

Promenade les Vernets, 34420 Villeneuve-les-Béziers (Hérault)

Although most campers or caravanners will be aware of the Canal du Midi, there are surprisingly few campsites which provide an opportunity to enjoy the rather special ambience for which this famous waterway is renowned, so we were really pleased to discover this delightful campsite right alongside the canal at Villeneuve-les-Beziers. It is also within a few minutes drive of the beaches at Serignan Plage, Vias or Valras, the old city of Beziers and the famous resort of Cap d'Agde. The campsite has 75 level pitches on sandy grass of average size, mostly with electricty (some occupied by mobile homes) in a peaceful and shady situation, separated from the canal only by an access road. There is a pleasant swimming pool complex, one of the two pools being fitted with a jacuzzi-style facility, but there are no big slides or toboggans thereby ensuring that it is relatively peaceful.

Facilities

A fully equipped toilet block has mainly British-style WCs and some Turkish style, and some washbasins in cabins. Facilities for disabled visitors (with key). Washing machine, laundry and dishwashing sinks, etc. Motorcaravan service point. Two swimming pools. Bar/snack-bar (serving breakfast too). Evening entertainment during high season.

At a glance			
Welcome & Ambience	✓✓✓✓✓	Location	✓✓✓✓✓
Quality of Pitches	✓✓✓✓	Range of Facilities	✓✓✓✓

Directions

From A9 take exit 35, follow signs for Agde and at first roundabout take N112 (Beziers). Take first left on D37 signed (Villeneve-les-Beziers). Pass lights, then left at roundabout and follow site signs.

Latest charges

Per unit incl. 2 persons	€ 13.00 - € 18.00
with electricity (6A)	€ 15.00 - € 21.00

Reservations

Contact site. Tel: 04 67 39 36 09.
Email: contact@lesbergesducanal.com

Open

15 April - 15 September.

FR34150 Yelloh! Village Nouvelle Floride

34340 Marseillan Plage (Hérault)

Marseillan Plage is a small, busy resort just east of Cap d'Adge and La Nouvelle Floride enjoys a super position immediately beside a long gently shelving sandy beach. It is a good quality site, very traditional in style and set under tall trees with neat hedges to separate the 520 pitches (370 for tourers). These are on sandy soil and all have water and electricity. Some of the pitches in the newer area (across a small lane) and the hardstanding pitches near the beach have little shade as yet. There are a number of mobile homes but the site is mainly for tourers. Amenities and facilities are generally of excellent quality and include a strikingly attractive bar area overlooking the beach with a raised stage for entertainment. Alongside the play area is a multi-purpose ball court and fitness centre, also on sand with robust machines with the idea of keeping Mum and Dad fit whilst still keeping an eye on the children. Essentially a 'holiday site', there is an extensive programme of entertainment and activities catering for all ages, and a good pool complex. However, the main attraction for most will almost certainly be the direct access to a fine beach. The gates on the beach entrance are locked at 9 pm. for security. This is a well run, family run site aimed at families.

Facilities

The four toilet blocks are impressive, including two with a number of en-suite showers and washbasins, otherwise washbasins all in cabins. Baby rooms, excellent facilities for disabled visitors and even a dog shower. The showers and washing up areas are closed between 23.00-07.00 hrs. Motorcaravan service point. Bar and restaurant. Shop all season, plus a range of shops at Charlemagne across the road. Pool complex with slides, jacuzzi, paddling pools, etc (all season). Play area, fitness centre and multi-purpose ball court. Table tennis. Weekly films (DVD) and variety of organised games, competitions, dances and discos. Mini-club in school holidays. Bicycle hire. Off site: Riding and bicycle hire 500 m. Golf 5 km.

At a glance

Welcome & Ambience	✓✓✓✓	Location	✓✓✓✓✓
Quality of Pitches	✓✓✓✓	Range of Facilities	✓✓✓✓✓

Directions

From A9 autoroute exit 34, follow N312 to Agde then take N112 towards Sete. Watch for signs to Marseillan Plage from where site is well signed.

Charges 2003

Per unit incl. 1 or 2 persons, water and electricity (6A)	€ 19.00 - € 38.00
extra person (over 1 yr)	€ 5.00 - € 8.00
pet	€ 3.00 - € 3.50
local tax	€ 0.30

Reservations

Contact site. Tel: 04 67 21 94 49. Email: info@nouvelle-floride.com

Open

12 April - 28 September.

At "Les Mediterranées", your holiday will literally revolve around and breathe the sea. In the Nouvelle Floride area, time rhymes with fun as you swim, engage in sports and take out a pedal boat. And why not enjoy lazy moments in the shade of the palm trees, tantalized by the blue motion of the swimming pool. In the Charlemagne area, life moves to a sweet, peaceful pace.
Choose whatever you like. That is what "Les Méditerranées" is all about.

Charlemagne - Nouvelle Floride
CAMPING VILLAGE ★★★★
Les Méditerranées

34340 Marseillan-Plage - France
Tel. + 00 33 825 08 08 19 / +00 33 467 21 94 49 / Fax +00 33 467 21 81 05
www.lesmediterranees.com

yelloh! VILLAGE

FR34160 Yelloh! Village Charlemagne

34340 Marseillan Plage (Hérault)

Charlemagne is under the same family ownership as Nouvelle Floride and situated across the road from it, 200 metres from the beach. It boasts a large range of amenities, consisting of a large supermarket, bakery, takeaway/fast food, bar, restaurant and disco. Facing the main street, these facilities are open to the public and are consequently well stocked, well equipped and open for the whole season. The site is traditionally laid out under the shade of tall trees providing 480 level pitches. Of these 270 are available for touring units, neatly hedged and all with electricity and water. Access to the beach is by a footpath past Nouvelle Floride but the site also has a super new pool complex complete with 'Niagara Falls'. This is a site which caters for all ages with a wide range of activities.

Facilities

Four toilet blocks, two of the same modern design and quality as at Nouvelle Floride, with washbasins in cabins, dishwashing under cover, laundry sinks and washing machine. The two more traditional blocks have some Turkish style toilets. Motorcaravan service point. Fridge hire. Full range of shops, bar/cafe, restaurant, takeaway and disco, all open all season. Pool complex (all season). Good fenced play area. Mini-club (May-Sept). Range of evening entertainment covering concerts, cabarets, dances and discos. Off site: Nearby tennis, golf, karting, riding, bicycle hire and range of water sports.

At a glance

Welcome & Ambience	✓✓✓✓	Location	✓✓✓✓✓
Quality of Pitches	✓✓✓✓	Range of Facilities	✓✓✓✓✓

Directions

From A9 exit 34, follow N314 to Agde then take the N112 towards Sete and watch for signs to Marseillan Plage from where site is well signed.

Charges 2003

Per unit incl. up to 2 persons,	
water and electricity (6A)	€ 15.00 - € 38.00
extra person (over 1 yr)	€ 5.00 - € 8.00
Camping Cheques accepted.	

Reservations

Necessary for July and August. Tel: 04 67 21 92 49. Email: info@charlemagne-camping.com

Open

5 April - 27 September.

FR34110 Yelloh! Village Le Club Farret

34450 Vias-Plage (Hérault)

This superb site of excellent quality has been developed by the Giner family with love and care over the last 40 years. Well maintained and with welcoming, helpful staff (English spoken), everywhere is neat and tidy – quite outstanding and impressive. It is a large site but even though it was very busy when we visited, the atmosphere seemed very relaxed and not too frantic. There are 756 pitches, with 370 for touring units and only 14% for tour operators, which do not overwhelm at all. The good-sized, level pitches are on grass and sand, with 6A electricity. There is some shade and many trees and shrubs provide a green environment. The mobile home areas are very smart, and some have been attractively landscaped, with an African theme. The large heated pool has lots of sunbathing room. The safe beach is alongside the site so some pitches have sea views. There is a wide range of evening entertainment and the extensive list of activities includes an unusual art programme offering pottery, silk painting, mosaics and water colours. The restaurant is high above the pool with views of the sea. Everything is open all season, so a visit in the quiet months of May, June or September doesn't mean less facilities (especially the heated pool). There is a policy of no advance booking for the touring pitches – they say that they rarely turn anyone away and will accept a phone call the day before arrival to give details of availability. A 'Yelloh Village' member.

Facilities

Seven very clean toilet blocks provide excellent facilities, especially the new blocks, with British style toilets (one or two Turkish in the older blocks). Large showers, many with washbasin. Children's toilets, baby rooms and showers in the guise of a clown. Full facilities in large rooms for disabled customers. Washing machines. Dog shower at the block nearest the beach. The toilets are open all night but the showers are closed. Well stocked supermarket. Hairdresser. Bars with pizzas and snacks to takeaway. Restaurant. Swimming pool complex with lifeguard all season. Play areas. Mini-club (5-10 yrs). Teenagers' club (11-15 yrs). Tennis, table tennis, archery, volleyball, football and a full programme of games. Bicycle hire. Off site: Golf 5 km. Riding 1 km. Windsurfing on beach.

At a glance

Welcome & Ambience	✓✓✓✓	Location	✓✓✓✓✓
Quality of Pitches	✓✓✓✓	Range of Facilities	✓✓✓✓✓

Directions

Site is south of Vias at Vias Plage. From N112 (Beziers - Agde) take D137 signed Vias Plage. Site signed on left.

Charges 2004

Per unit incl. 1 or 2 persons	€ 15.00 - € 38.00
extra person	€ 6.00
pet	€ 3.00
local tax	€ 0.40

Reservations

Not accepted. Tel: 04 67 21 64 45. Email: farret@wanadoo.fr.

Open

Easter - end September.

FR34030 Camping International Le Napoléon

Avenue de la Méditérranée, 34450 Vias-Plage (Hérault)

Le Napoléon is a smaller, family run site in the village of Vias Plage bordering the Mediterranean. The town of Vias itself is set further back from the sea, in the wine-growing area of the Midi, an area which includes the Camargue, Béziers and popular modern resorts such as Cap d'Agde. The single street that leads to Vias Plage is hectic to say the least in season, but once through the security barrier and entrance to Le Napoléon, the contrast is marked – tranquillity, yet still only a few yards from the beach and other attractions. Not that the site itself lacks vibrancy, with its Californian style pool, amphithe-atre for entertainment and other new facilities, but thoughtful planning and design ensure that the camping area is quiet. With good shade from many tall trees, the 250 mainly hedged pitches (105 with hire units) vary in size from 80-100 sq.m. and most have electricity. No British tour operators.

Facilities

Three sanitary blocks are of a reasonable standard and were well maintained. They include washbasins in cabins, laundry and facilities for disabled people and babies. Motorcaravan services. Fridges for hire. Well stocked supermarket. Bar. Restaurant/pizzeria. Heated swimming pool with lively piped music. Gym/fitness room. Sauna (on payment) and sun room. Bicycle hire. Tennis, archery, volleyball, basketball, boules. New TV and young people rooms. Children's club. New amphitheatre and wide range of free entertainment until midnight. Site-owned disco outside campsite (Easter-Sept). Off site: Shops, restaurants, and laundry etc. immedi-ately adjacent. Fishing nearby. Golf 5 km. Riding 1 km.

At a glance

Welcome & Ambience	✓✓✓✓	Location	✓✓✓✓
Quality of Pitches	✓✓✓✓	Range of Facilities	✓✓✓✓✓

Directions

From autoroute take exit for Vias. From town, take D137 towards Vias Plage. Site is on right near the beach; watch for turn between restaurant and shops.

Charges 2003

Per unit incl. 1 or	
2 persons and electricity	€ 18.00 - € 40.00
extra person	€ 3.50 - € 5.00

Reservations

Taken from 1 Jan. with 30% deposit and fee incl. cancellation insurance. Tel: 04 67 01 07 80. Email: reception@camping-napoleon.fr

Open

2 April - 30 September.

FR34200 Camping Club Californie Plage

Côte Ouest, 34450 Vias-Plage (Hérault)

With the benefit of direct access to a sandy cove, with a few, much sought-after pitches overlooking the sea, this is a fairly typical holiday-style campsite with a range of good quality facilities. These include a covered pool on the site and a swimming pool complex with the inevitable toboggans, etc., and even a naturist swimming pool across the road from the Californie Plage site in the grounds of its sister site. Both sites are located away from Vias Plage, on the Côte Ouest and thereby enjoy a degree of tranquillity in this bustling resort area. The site is traditionally laid out, with mobile homes to one side of the central road and touring pitches to the other. Pitches are mostly of 100 sq.m, although those close to the beach are slightly smaller, and mainly on level sandy ground, separated by low hedging. Nearly all have electricity and in most parts there is a fair amount of shade from tall poplars.

Facilities

Sanitary facilities are of a generally good standard, in three traditional blocks which have been fully refurbished in recent years. Washbasins in cabins, baby rooms, facilities for disabled visitors. Laundry. Shop. Comfortable restaurant. Bars. Covered pool on site (1/4-30/10). Range of pools on sister site across the road (1/7-31/8; code supplied). Tennis court. Bicycle hire. Games room. Extensive entertainment programme and children's activities in July/Aug.

At a glance

Welcome & Ambience	✓✓✓	Location	✓✓✓
Quality of Pitches	✓✓✓	Range of Facilities	✓✓✓

Directions

From N112 (Beziers-Agde) take D137 Vias Plage turn. Watch for signs to 'Cote Ouest' then campsite signs.

Latest charges

Per unit incl. 1 or 2 persons	
and 6A electricity	€ 15.25 - € 29.00
extra person (4 yrs and over)	€ 2.80 - € 4.60

Reservations

Made with deposit (€ 102) and fee (€ 23). Tel: 04 67 21 64 69.

Open

Easter - 15 October.

FR34220 Camping La Creole

74 avenue des Campings, 34340 Marseillan-Plage (Hérault)

This is a surprisingly tranquil, well cared for small campsite almost in the middle of this bustling resort that will appeal especially to those seeking a rather less frenetic ambience than that which typifies many sites in this area. Essentially a family orientated site, it offers around 100 good-sized, level grass pitches, all with electricity connections, and mostly with shade from tall poplars and other trees and shrubs. It also benefits from direct access to an extensive sandy beach and the fact that there is no swimming pool or bar actually contributes to the tranquillity and may even be seen as an advantage for families with younger children. The beach will be the main attraction here no doubt, and the town's extensive range of bars, restaurants and shops are all within a couple of minutes walk.

Facilities

Toilet facilities are housed in a traditional building, modernised inside to provide perfectly adequate, if not particularly luxurious, facilities including some washbasins in private cabins, a baby room and dog shower. Small play area. Table tennis. In high season beach games, dances, sangria evenings etc, are organised, all aimed particularly towards families. Barbecue area. Bicycle hire. Off site: Local market day Tuesday. Riding 1 km.

At a glance

Welcome & Ambience	✓✓✓✓	Location	✓✓✓✓✓
Quality of Pitches	✓✓✓✓✓	Range of Facilities	✓✓✓

Directions

From A9 take exit 34 on N312 towards Agde, then N112 towards Sete looking out for signs to Marseillan Plage off this road. Site is signed in Marseillan Plage.

Latest charges

Per unit incl. 2 persons	€ 12.00 - € 18.00
electricity (6A)	€ 2.50

Reservations

Contact site. Tel: 04.67.21.92.69.
Email: campinglacreole@wanadoo.fr

Open

6 April - 8 October.

FR34140 Haven Camping La Carabasse

Vias-Plage, 34450 Vias-sur-Mer (Hérault)

La Carabasse, a Haven Europe holiday park, is on the outskirts of Vias Plage, a popular place with lots of shops and restaurants. The site has everything you could need with two good pools, and its own bars and a restaurant 'L'Atoll'. The bars and restaurant provide live music in the evenings and entertainment. There are 950 pitches in total, 400 for touring, with many mobile homes and a good number of tour operator pitches. The touring pitches are set amongst tall poplar and birch trees. Level and spacious, all have electricity and partial shade. Some have private sanitary facilities. The wonderful Mediterranean beaches are close and La Carabasse has its own beach club. It is a lively busy site in high season, and Vias Plage itself can also be quite hectic. Haven Europe are continuing to develop and improve the site with a wide range of facilities for children and teenagers. Football coaching from U.F.A. qualified staff, for two hours a day, five days a week, can be booked from € 40 or you can learn snorkelling, life saving or body-boarding and become a 'wave rider'!

Facilities

Two of the toilet blocks are modern and fully equipped. With an older block used in high season. Some pitches have their own private sanitary cabin providing a WC and shower (extra charge). Bars, restaurant and swimming pools. Beach club for windsurfing and pedaloes. Wealth of daytime activities (some charged for) from golf lessons to aqua-aerobics and tennis tournaments. Children's clubs and multi-sports unit. Evening entertainment in the Haven Europe style. Off site: Trips on the Canal du Midi. Vias town with twice weekly market. Modern resort of Cap d'Adge nearby with Aqualand and golf course (18 holes).

At a glance

Welcome & Ambience	✓✓✓	Location	✓✓✓✓
Quality of Pitches	✓✓✓	Range of Facilities	✓✓✓✓✓

Directions

Site is south of Vias. From N112 (Agde - Beziers) road turn right at signs for Vias-Plage (D137) and site.

Charges 2003

Per pitch incl. up to 6 persons and electricity	€ 11.00 - € 37.00
with private sanitary cabin	€ 12.00 - € 43.00

Reservations

Accepted at any time for min. 4 days; no booking fee.
Tel: 04 67 21 64 01.
Email: carabasse@haven.fr.

Open

30 April - 19 September.

FR34070 Yelloh! Village Le Sérignan Plage

Le Sérignan Plage, 34410 Sérignan (Hérault)

A large, friendly, family-orientated site with direct access to superb sandy beaches, including a naturist beach, Serignan Plage exudes a strongly individualistic style which we find very attractive. However, those who look for 'manicured' sites may be less impressed, as its situation on 'the littoral' and proximity to the beach makes it difficult to keep things neat and tidy. With some 450 mainly good sized, level touring pitches, including some (with little shade) actually alongside the beach, coupled with perhaps the most comprehensive range of amenities we've come across, the hugely enthusiastic owners, Jean-Guy and Katy Amat continually surprise us with new ideas and developments. They are even planning an 'aqua-village' for 2004, with more new pools, fitness centre, jacuzzi etc! The amenities are just too extensive to describe in detail, but they include a superb pool complex, with slides, etc., surrounded by large grassy sunbathing areas with sun-loungers, and another indoor pool too. Perhaps the most remarkable aspect is the cluster of attractive buildings which form the 'heart' of this site with courtyards housing attractive bars, a smart restaurant, shops, takeaway, a stage for entertainment, disco, etc. – all very attractive and with a very special ambience.

Facilities

Nine unisex toilet blocks. The older ones with a mixture of British and Turkish style WCs are nearest the sea and central 'village' area and thus take the brunt of the wear and tear. The touring area, furthest from the sea has three modern blocks of individual design. Well planned with good facilities, including a number of large controllable hot showers with washbasin (non-slip floor) and WC en-suite, well equipped baby rooms and facilities for disabled people. Dishwashing and laundry facilities in all blocks. At peak times maintenance can be a little variable. Well stocked supermarket, bakery, newsagent/tabac, ATM and range of market stalls. Poissonnerie and boucherie (7/6-8/9). Launderette. Hairdresser. Bars, restaurant and takeaway all (7/4-10/9). Animation for children and evening entertainment. Secluded roof-top bar (9 pm - 1 am). Soundproof disco. Heated indoor pool and outdoor pool complex (also heated) with lifeguards in the main season and an ID card system (April - Sept). Sporting activities organised. Bicycle hire. Off site: Riding 2 km, golf 10 km. Bicycle hire. Sailing and windsurfing school on beach (lifeguard in high season).

Directions

From A9 exit 35 (Béziers Est) follow signs for Sérignan on D64 (9 km). Don't go into Sérignan, but take sign for Sérignan Plage for 4 km. At small multi sign (blue) turn right on single carriageway. At T-junction turn left over small road bridge and after left hand bend, site is 100 m. after Sérignan Plage Nature.

Charges 2003

Per unit incl. 1 or 2 persons and 5A electricity	€ 17.00 - € 33.00
extra person	€ 5.50 - € 6.00

Plus local tax. Low season offers. Discounts in low season for children under 7 yrs. Camping Cheques accepted.

Reservations

Made from 1 Feb. with deposit (25%) and fee (€ 30). Tel: 04 67 32 35 33. Email: info@leserignanplage.com

Open

10 April - 22 September.

At a glance

Welcome & Ambience	✓✓✓✓	Location	✓✓✓✓✓
Quality of Pitches	✓✓✓✓	Range of Facilities	✓✓✓✓✓

FR34080N Camping Le Sérignan Plage Nature

34410 Sérignan (Hérault)

Benefiting from many improvements over the past few years, Serigan Plage Nature is a distinctly characterful family-orientated site right beside a superb sandy naturist beach. At present it has some 260 good sized touring pitches, on level grass and with plenty of shade except on those right beside the beach. A friendly bar and restaurant are housed in the Romanesque style buildings which form the 'heart' of the site, including the setting for evening entertainment. In recent years the site has been developed by Jean-Guy and Katy Amat, but was originally owned by Jean-Guy's father, who retains an interest and who has been the mastermind behind the award-winning environmentally friendly irrigation system which serves both this site and Camping Serignan Plage, the adjoining 'textile' site whose extensive range of facilities are available to visitors here. At the time of going to press (autumn 2003) Jean-Guy and Katy have some very ambitious plans for both their sites, which may involve significant developments on Serignan Plage Nature in particular, including a new 'aqua-village' with pools, fitness centre, jacuzzi, etc. These developments will take a couple of years to complete, so it may be worth checking out the latest state of play before you book or visit. Member 'France 4 Naturisme'.

Facilities

The toilet blocks of differing design have all been refurbished, and offer modern facilities with some washbasins in cabins and both British and Turkish style WCs. All is clean and well maintained. Dishwashing. Washing machines. Large supermarket, market for fresh fruit and vegetables, newsagent/souvenir shop and ice cream kiosk. Bar, reasonably priced restaurant. Evening entertainment. Children's disco. Off site: Riding 2 km.

Directions

Follow as for site 34070, Site is not the first, but the second naturist site.

Charges 2003

Per unit incl. 1 or 2 persons	€ 13.00 - € 27.00
electricity (5A)	€ 4.00

Camping Cheques accepted.

Reservations

Made from 1 Feb. with deposit (€ 61), fee (€ 15,24) and cancellation insurance (€ 70). Tel: 04 67 32 09 61. Email: info@serignannaturisme.com

Open

1 April - 30 September.

At a glance

Welcome & Ambience	✓✓✓✓	Location	✓✓✓✓✓
Quality of Pitches	✓✓✓✓	Range of Facilities	✓✓✓✓

YOUR HOLIDAYS BY THE SEA

Sérignan-Plage can be likened to an open-air auberge with the Mediterranean on your doorstep

FROM APRIL TO SEPTEMBER: 850m² heated lagoon pool • heated indoor pool • activities and shows • mini-club • restaurant • bar • shops...

NEW WATER SPA FITNESS CENTER of 1.800 m².

SUNSHINE GUARANTEE in April, May or September (see conditions).

Le Sérignan Plage
34410 Sérignan
Languedoc-Roussillon
tél. 00 33 467 32 35 33
fax. 00 33 467 32 26 36
info@leserignanplage.com
www.leserignanplage.com

BORD DE MER

Le sérignan plage

CAMPING AUBERGE
MÉDITERRANÉE

DDB nouveau monde LE TOURISME

CAMPING VILLAGES
yelloh!
VILLAGE

FR34100 Camping Le Mas du Padre

4 chemin du Mas du Padre, 34540 Balaruc les Bains (Hérault)

The Durant family took over this site a few years ago and since then have made many alterations and improvements. Madame Durant speaks excellent English. It is a small site, just 2.5 km. from Balaruc-Les-Bains, near the Lake of Thau and unusually is part of an estate that has obviously been built around it over the years. Its 116 secluded pitches of varying sizes are enclosed by hedges and mature trees, some on a very gentle slope and 98 have electricity. The site is peaceful and popular with the French who love its simplicity, although a large commercial centre is just 500 m. Beaches and many local attractions are close, but if you decide to stay here it would be advisable to have transport. The road from the site to Sete passes some rather unsightly factory works – don't be put off.

Facilities

Two neat, fully equipped toilet blocks include baby changing area, facilities for disabled campers, dishwashing and laundry sinks, and washing machines. Reception sells basic provisions, gas and bread (to order in low season). Two small circular pools including one for children (20/5-16/9). Tennis half-court, table tennis, boules courts, mini-adventure playground. Sports programme including tournaments, aqua-aerobics, animation for children, along with a weekly dance when a temporary bar is organised (all in high season). Torch useful. Off site: Fishing or riding 2 km, golf 20 km. Bus service to the historic city of Balaruc-Les-Bains from just outside the site.

At a glance

Welcome & Ambience	✓✓✓✓	Location	✓✓✓
Quality of Pitches	✓✓✓✓	Range of Facilities	✓✓✓✓

Directions

From A9 take exit for Sete and follow N800 to Balaruc le Vieux, at the first roundabout follow Sete/Balaruc les Bains. Pass the centre commercial (Carrefour on the left). At second roundabout again follow Balaruc les Bains/Sete. After 50 m take left for Balaruc les Bains and immediately right across the road you have just left and back down it (50 m) to go immediately right, and follow Chemin du Mas du Padre site on left well hidden.

Charges 2003

Per unit incl. 2 persons and electricity (6/10A)	€ 13.05 - € 31.00
1 person, 60 sq.m. pitch	€ 7.40 - € 15.35
extra person	€ 2.60 - € 3.90
child	€ 1.00 - € 3.20
dog	€ 0.85 - € 1.85

Reservations

Advised for high season only. Tel: 04 67 48 53 41.
Email: mas-du-padre@wanadoo.fr

Open

29 March - 12 October.

FR34040 Camping Lou Village

B.P. 30, chemin des Montilles, 34350 Valras-Plage (Hérault)

Valras is perhaps smarter and is certainly larger than nearby Vias and it has a good number of campsites. Lou Village is a well kept, family owned site with direct access to a sandy beach. A busy site with lots of facilities and quite competitive prices, it does becomes crowded in high season as this is a popular area. The central 'village' area is a veritable hive of holiday activity, with several attractively designed pools and water slides, bars, pizzeria, restaurant and a purpose built stage for the site's extensive entertainment programme. With straw parasols and palm trees, it is an attractive, clean area with a pleasant ambience. There are 600 pitches (200 used for mobile homes), all with electricity and 100 with water and waste water facilities. Pitches further inland are of grass, partly separated by tall trees that provide good shade; nearer the beach the pitches are smaller, sandy and separated by bushes and bamboo hedges. There is lots to do off the site and the history of the Languedoc to discover. English is spoken.

Facilities

Four modern, well sited toilet blocks, all recently refurbished, have reasonable facilities. Mixture of Turkish and British style WCs, showers with no separator and half the washbasins in cabins. Facilities for disabled visitors and babies. Dishwashing and laundry sinks at each block. For a beach site, maintenance seems quite satisfactory. Supermarket, bakery, bazaar and, in high season, a boutique for gifts. Bar and restaurant with ample seating. Takeaway. Swimming pools (some heated), water slides and paddling pool. Playground, children's club and football field. Tennis. Volleyball. Minigolf. Bicycle hire. Sailing and windsurfing. Off site: Riding 500 m. Canoe kayaking, river fishing 1 km. Golf 12 km.

At a glance

Welcome & Ambience	✓✓✓✓	Location	✓✓✓✓✓
Quality of Pitches	✓✓✓✓	Range of Facilities	✓✓✓✓✓

Directions

Site is south of Béziers. From autoroute, take Béziers-Ouest exit for Valras Plage and continue for about 14 km. Follow 'Casino' signs and site is 1 km. south of centre of Valras Plage in the direction of Vendres. Site is signed to the left at the end of Valras Plage and the start of Vendres Plage.

Charges 2003

Per unit incl. 2 persons and electricity (10A)	€ 18.00 - € 30.00
extra person	€ 4.00 - € 5.50
child (under 7 yrs)	free - € 3.00
dog	€ 3.00 - € 4.00
local tax	€ 0.40
Pool complex bracelet € 5.50 (once only payment).	

Reservations

Made with deposit (€ 183) and fee (€ 30).
Tel: 04 67 37 33 79. Email: info@louvillage.com

Open

End April - mid September.

FR34060 Hotel de Plein Air L'Oliveraie

Chemin de Bedarieux, 34480 Laurens (Hérault)

Situated at the foot of the Cevennes, L'Oliveraie has many attractive features and is open all year. Don't assume that the extensive range of sport and recreation available here means that it is all hectic activity – in fact it is surprisingly peaceful. Most of the 116 pitches are large (up to 150 sq.m. in some parts) and all have electrical connections. Arranged in rows on two levels, those on the higher level are older and have more shade from mature trees (mainly olives). The ground is stony. The large leisure area is slightly apart from the pitches on the lower area, overlooked by the bar. The old village of Laurens is well worth visiting and is walkable through the vineyards. A 'Sites et Paysages' member.

Facilities

The main modern toilet block on the higher terrace includes washbasins in cabins, baby bathroom, and covered dishwashing and washing machine. The second block on lower level is open for high season. All perfectly adequate and clean when seen in high season. Small, well stocked shop (1/7-31/8). Bar/restaurant. Indoor bar, also used for films and activities for younger children. Good sized pool (1/6-30/9). Tennis court and tennis practice wall. Volleyball, basketball, minigolf. Bicycle hire. Play area. Barbecue area. Adjoining riding stables (1/7-30/8). Good facilities for archery. Off site: Local shops at Laurens, 1 km.

At a glance

Welcome & Ambience	✓✓✓✓	Location	✓✓✓✓
Quality of Pitches	✓✓✓✓	Range of Facilities	✓✓✓✓

Directions

Site is signed 2 km. north of Laurens off the D909 (Béziers-Bédarieux) road.

Charges 2003

Per unit incl. 1 or 2 persons	€ 15.75 - € 22.50
extra person	€ 4.60
electricity (6/10A)	€ 3.05 - € 4.60
Special rates for longer stays.	

Reservations

Contact site. Tel: 04 67 90 24 36. Email: oliveraie@free.fr

Open

All year.

L'OLIVERAIE

★ ★ ★

CAMPINGS SITES PAYSAGES FRANCE

Over towards the bluish outline of the Cévennes foothills, the beauty of the sky is only equalled by the purity of the air. Comfort, tranquility and cultural interests, as well as tennis, volleyball, archery, boules, various other games, cycling, walks and horse-riding, will play a large part in making your stay enjoyable.

We extend a warm welcome to you.

Camping-Caravaning L'OLIVERAIE
34480 Laurens
Tel: 0033 467.90.24.36
Fax: 0033 467.90.11.20
E-mail: oliveraie@free.fr

FR34180 Camping La Borio de Roque

34220 St Pons de Thonières (Hérault)

A small peaceful site, La Borio de Roque is set in a very rural location on a quiet hillside 4 km. from St Pons. It lies at the end of a 1.5 km. track (rough in places) but it is well worth the effort and is set around a typical farmhouse with the outbuildings made into four very attractive gites. The 25 large, level terraced pitches have electricity and some shade. Some are very private which Ted the owner will escort you to. Children are encouraged to help with feeding and grooming the goats, sheep, donkeys and horses. Riding is possible on a daily, half daily or lessons basis and the rides into the forest with a picnic are very popular. There are numerous walks and tracks for mountain bikes from the site. Marit and Ted, your Dutch hosts, are only too happy to advise on routes. St Pons (4 km.) is an attractive small town with bars, restaurants and a museum. La Borio is especially suited to couples and young families – not a site for teenagers who like lots of entertainment.

Facilities

The modernised toilet blocks provide adjustable, roomy showers and washbasins en-suite. Baby bath. Dishwashing and laundry sinks. Free use of large freezer. Bread is available all season and ices. Local wine and home produced goat's cheese, honey and cherry jam are for sale. A set menu is cooked four times weekly (to order) and eaten with the family in the bar/barn. This is a very popular event and well subscribed. Swimming pool (from 1/6) and small lake for fishing. Small play area on grass. Barbecue areas. The site is not suitable for American motorhomes.

At a glance

Welcome & Ambience	✓✓✓✓✓	Location	✓✓✓✓
Quality of Pitches	✓✓✓✓✓	Range of Facilities	✓✓✓✓

Directions

St Pons is on the N112 northwest of Beziers. Site is 4.5 km. north of the town on D907 (Salvatat), on the right on a bend; then 1.5 km. on a rough track.

Latest charges

Per adult	€ 3.00
child (under 7 yrs)	€ 2.00
pitch incl. electricity (10A)	€ 8.00 - € 12.00
No credit cards.	

Reservations

Contact site. Tel: 04 67 97 10 97. Email: info@borioderoque.com

Open

15 May - 1 September.

FR34090 Camping Caravaning Domaine de la Yole

B.P. 23, 34350 Valras-Plage (Hérault)

We were pleasantly surprised when we visited de la Yole - the thought of over 1,100 pitches was a little daunting and we expected things to be very hectic when we arrived on a busy day in mid-August. However, the multi-lingual reception was calm and people were enjoying themselves. There are 590 pitches for touring units, the remainder taken by mobile homes and a few tour operator pitches. Most pitches are of a good size, all are level and have electricity, water and waste water points and, very importantly for this area, they all have shade. The extensive pool area is attractive with lots of sunbathing areas and the impressive activities are located in a central area. A shopping area provides a supermarket, outdoor vegetable stall, butchers, wine shop (take your own bottles for really good wines on draught), boutique and a takeaway, all set under low trees very much like a village market. The beach, a long stretch of beautiful sand, is 500 m. and here is trampolining, paragliding and jet-skis. This is a busy site with something for all the family. English is spoken.

Facilities

Well maintained toilet blocks include some showers and washbasins en-suite, mostly British style WCs and many washbasins in cubicles. Extra large cubicles with everything including a baby bath can be used by families or disabled visitors. Seven blocks have been recently refurbished and the eighth one is new. All have dishwashing and laundry sinks. Central laundry with washing machines and dryers. Motorcaravan service point (the only chemical disposal point is here, a long walk from many pitches). Refrigerators for hire. Shops. Good restaurant with huge terrace and amphitheatre for daily entertainment (in season). Two large pools and paddling pool, all supervised by lifeguard in July/Aug. Two half size tennis courts (free) and two full size (charged July/Aug), large play areas with amusements such as moto-track and daily children's club, minigolf, table tennis, boules, volleyball and basketball. Doctor calls daily in high season. Off site: Fishing or riding 1 km.

Directions

From A9 autoroute take Beziers Ouest exit for Valras Plage (13-14 km) and follow Casino signs. Site is on left, just after sign for Vendres Plage.

Charges 2004

Per unit incl. 2 adults	€ 16.35 - € 31.80
extra adult	€ 5.20
child under 7 yrs	free - € 1.65
child 7-16 yrs	free - € 3.20
dog	free - € 3.00

Reservations

Made with deposit (€ 90 or € 130) and, in high season, a fee (€ 25); contact site for form.
Tel: 04 67 37 33 87. Email: layole34@aol.com

Open

1 May - 18 September.

At a glance

Welcome & Ambience	✓✓✓✓	Location	✓✓✓✓
Quality of Pitches	✓✓✓	Range of Facilities	✓✓✓✓✓

FR34230 Sunêlia Le Plein Air des Chênes

Route de Castelnau, RD 112, 34830 Clapiers (Hérault)

Situated just outside the village of Clapiers, just 3 km. from the exciting and interesting city of Montpellier, yet only 15 km. from the beach, this is one of those few campsites which really does seem to provide something for everyone, even for those who prefer to spend their holidays without ever leaving the campsite! Here there are large touring pitches (some with their own individual toilet cabin), plus chalets, bungalows and mobile homes to rent – all in a nicely shaded terraced setting – in fact you name it and Des Chênes seems to have it. The site boasts an amazing landscaped swimming pool complex, with multi-lane toboggan, four pools and surrounding facilities such as bars, restaurants, etc., which is very impressive. It is also open to the public and obviously very popular.

Facilities

Three well equipped modern toilet blocks of circular design provide washbasins in cabins and facilities for disabled people. Laundry and dishwashing sinks. Three washing machines. Shop. Restaurant open to the public, bar and pool side bar and café. Swimming pools (1/6-30/8). 4 tennis courts. Multi-sports court. Play area. Mini club and range of evening entertainment in main season. Off site: Golf 10 km.

Directions

Site is north of Montpellier, 8 km. from A9 autoroute. Take exit 28 on N113 toward Montpellier passing village of Vendargues, leaving N113 and crossing the N110 (which joins the N 113) to follow the D65 for Clapiers circling north of Montpellier. Follow signs for village then for site.

Charges 2004

Per unit incl. 2 persons and electricity	€ 22.00 - € 35.00
with water and drainage	€ 17.00 - € 43.00
extra person	€ 3.00 - € 6.00
child (3-10 yrs)	€ 2.00 - € 3.00
Camping Cheques accepted.	

Reservations

Made with booking fee (€ 28); contact site.
Tel: 04 67 02 02 53. Email: pleinairdeschenes@free.fr

Open

All year.

At a glance

Welcome & Ambience	✓✓✓✓	Location	✓✓✓✓
Quality of Pitches	✓✓✓✓	Range of Facilities	✓✓✓✓✓

FR34050N Camping Naturiste Le Mas de Lignières

Cesseras-en-Minervois, 34210 Olonzac (Hérault)

A naturist site hidden in the hills of the Minervois, this is a delightful find, only 3 km. from the medieval town of Minerve with its Cathar connections. Parts of this site enjoy some marvellous views to the Pyrénées, the Corbières and the coast at Narbonne. We recommend that you watch at least one wonderful sunrise over the Pyrénées. The owners Jeanne and Gilles, offer a warm welcome and promote a most enjoyable family atmosphere. The site provides 50 large (200 sq.m.) pitches, all with electricity, and 25 with water and waste water connections. Mainly level grass, they are separated by mature hedges that give considerable privacy. Some smaller pitches (100 sq.m.) are available for tents, with cars parked elsewhere. There is natural shade and a variety of fauna and flora including four types of orchid. Within the confines of the seven hectare site there are some good walks with superb views and, although the camping area is actually quite small, the very large pitches create a very relaxing ambience and a nice introduction to naturist camping. If you ask nicely, Gilles may take you out in his Landrover (he's a bit of an expert on all things natural) to places you would never find otherwise. The owners are proud that the site has recently been awarded the coveted 'Clef Vert' award for environmental awareness (similar to the Blue Flag award for beaches).

Facilities

The pleasant, clean toilet block has open washbasins and semi-open showers. Dishwashing and laundry sinks. En-suite facilities for disabled people. Washing machine. Simple shop for essentials and local specialities. Bread can be ordered (15/06 -15/09). Bar and snack bar (15/7-15/8). Swimming pool with sliding cover for use in early and late season. Paddling pool. Comfortable room for general use with TV, library and tourist information and separate provision for young people. Playground. Tennis, volleyball and boules (all free). Torch useful. Only gas barbecues are permitted. Off site: Sailing, riding and canoeing nearby at Lac de Jouarres. Canal du Midi.

At a glance

Welcome & Ambience	✓✓✓✓✓	Location	✓✓✓✓✓
Quality of Pitches	✓✓✓✓	Range of Facilities	✓✓✓✓

Directions

From A61 autoroute take Lézignan-Corbières exit, through town via the D611 to Homps, then on D910 to Olonzac. Go through village following the signs to Minerve (D10). Follow road for approx. 4 km. taking left hand turn to Cesseras (D168). At Cesseras follow signs to Fauzan for approx 4 km. Site is signed to the right where there is a climb up a winding road, which is a little narrow in places.

Charges 2003

Per pitch incl. 2 persons and electricity (6A), water and drainage	€ 23.00
smaller pitch excl. electricity	€ 16.50
extra person	€ 3.80
child (2-7 yrs)	€ 2.60
dog	€ 1.50
electricity 10A, plus	€ 1.50
Less for longer booked stays.	

Reservations

Made until 25/6 with deposit (25%) and fee (€ 10). Tel: 04 68 91 24 86. Email: lemas1@tiscali.fr

Open

1 April - 31 October.

FR66190 Sunêlia Les Tropiques

Bvd de la Méditerranée, 66440 Torreilles-Plage (Pyrénées-Orientales)

Les Tropiques makes a pleasant holiday venue, only 400 metres from a sandy beach and also boasting two pools. There are 450 pitches with 200 given over to mobile homes and chalets. Pleasant pine and palm trees with other Mediterranean vegetation give shade and provides an attractive environment. Activities are provided for all including a large range of sports, caberets and shows but an identity bracelet for entry to the site is obligatory in high season (small payment required).

Facilities

Modern, fully equipped sanitary facilities include provision for disabled visitors. Launderette. Bar, restaurant with takeaway meals and pizzeria (all 14/6 -15/9). Shop. Two outdoor swimming pools (1/6 - 30/9) Tennis, table tennis, football, volleyball and pétanque. Archery (1/7-31/8). TV and billards room. Play area. Disco (every evening and club for 6-12 yr old children in July/Aug. Off site: Minigolf 300 m, Windsurf board hire and sea fishing 400 m. Riding 400 m. Bicycle hire 5 km. Golf 15 km.

At a glance

Welcome & Ambience	✓✓✓✓	Location	✓✓✓✓
Quality of Pitches	✓✓✓✓	Range of Facilities	✓✓✓✓✓

Directions

From autroute A9 take exit for Perpignan Nord and follow D83 towards Le Barcarès for 9 km. Take D81 suth towards Canet for 3 km. before turning left at roundabout for Torreilles Plage. Site is the last but one on the left.

Charges 2003

Per unit incl. 2 persons	€ 14.40 - € 24.00
with electricity (6A)	€ 16.80 - € 28.00
extra person	€ 3.60 - € 6.00
child (0-13 yrs)	€ 2.70 - € 4.50
animal	€ 4.00
Camping Cheques accepted.	

Reservations

Contact site. Tel: 04 68 28 05 09. Email: camping.tropiques@wanadoo.fr

Open

1 April - 30 September.

Great on-line holiday deals *danrogersdirect*.com

FR66210 Chadotel Camping Le Roussillon

Chemin de la Mer, 66750 St Cyprien (Pyrénées-Orientales)

This a comfortable site, although perhaps somewhat lacking in character. It is part of the Chadotel Group and is quietly situated on the edge of St Cyprien village, 2 km. from the beach. A bus service runs in the main season. The site benefits from having a good sized, traditionally shaped pool, with the added attraction of a water slide for children, and plenty of sunbathing areas for adults. Many pitches are occupied by mobile homes but there are 36 well-kept, grassy and level touring pitches. Of a good size, they all have electricity.

Facilities

Two toilet blocks (one older but refurbished, one more modern) provide modern facilities including a baby bath, laundry and facilities for disabled visitors. Bar/snack-bar with entertainment in season. Play area on grass.

At a glance

Welcome & Ambience	✓✓✓	Location	✓✓✓✓
Quality of Pitches	✓✓✓✓	Range of Facilities	✓✓✓✓

Directions

Via D81 southwards, do not go into St Cyprien Plage, but follow signs towards Argelès. At roundabout ('Aqualand' signed to the left) turn right towards St Cyprien village. Bear right and site is signed.

Charges 2004

Per pitch incl. 2 adults	€ 14.00 - € 22.50
incl. electricity (16A)	€ 18.00 - € 26.50

Reservations

Contact Chadotel Central Reservations, BP 12 85520 Jard-sur-Mer. Tel: 02 51 33 05 05.
Tel: 04 68 21 06 45. Email: info@chardotel.com

Open

30 March - 30 September.

FR66220 Camping du Stade

Avenue du 8 Mai 1945, 66702 Argelès-sur-Mer (Pyrénées-Orientales)

Quieter and more peaceful family orientated sites are about as rare as hens' teeth in this immediate area, so we were pleasantly surprised to discover one in a pleasant shady setting midway between the village and the beach resort – less than a kilometre from both. The 180 good sized pitches, (most with electricity) are in green surroundings with plenty of shade. This traditionally French campsite, could be a quiet haven for those who want to relax at the end of the day without the distraction of a noisy pool and bar, but who want to be close to all the various attractions offered at this resort.

Facilities

With so much within easy walking distance the site itself has few facilities, but it does have two good quality, part modern, part traditional, well-maintained toilet blocks with good sized showers, washbasins in cabins, etc. Unit for disabled people, facilities for babies, covered dishwashing area and washing machine. Snack-bar and takeaway (high season only). Adventure-style play area. Table tennis. Off site: Beach within walking distance.

At a glance

Welcome & Ambience	✓✓✓✓	Location	✓✓✓✓
Quality of Pitches	✓✓✓✓	Range of Facilities	✓✓✓

Directions

From A9 exit 42 (Perpignan Sud) take N114 towards Argelès. Take exit 10 for Pujols, and follow signs towards Centre Plage. At first roundabout go straight on, at next (small) roundabout turn left to site.

Latest charges

Per unit incl. 2 persons	€ 11.45 - € 16.35
electricity (6A)	€ 2.20 - € 3.15

Reservations

Contact site. Tel: 04 68 81 04 40.
Email: info@campingdustade.com

Open

1 April - 30 September.

FR66240 Chadotel Camping Le Trivoly

Route des Plages, 66440 Torreilles Plage (Pyrénées-Orientales)

The popularity of Torreilles derives mainly from its huge sandy beach and for off-site nightlife, shopping, etc. but for smarter resorts one really needs to visit Le Barcares or Canet a few kilometres distance in either direction. Le Trivoly (a member of the French Chadotel Group) is about 500 m. gentle stroll from the beach, in a fairly tranquil setting. It has 250 good size, well shaded and hedged pitches with electricity. It perhaps offers a rather more peaceful situation than do the other sites here.

Facilities

Four toilet blocks, although not new, provide modern facilities, including washbasins in (rather small) cabins, and were all clean and well cared for when we visited. Small shop (June- mid Sept). Snack-restaurant and takeaway (June-mid Sept). Reasonably sized pool with water slide and paddling pool. Play area. Bicycle hire. Table tennis. Basketball. Entertainment programme in high season. Off site: Centre Commercial 300 m.

At a glance

Welcome & Ambience	✓✓✓✓	Location	✓✓✓✓
Quality of Pitches	✓✓✓✓	Range of Facilities	✓✓✓✓

Directions

From A9 take exit 42 (Perpignan Nord) towards Le Barcarès for 9 km., then south on the D81 towards Canet. After 3 km. turn left at roundabout, signed Torreilles Plage. Site is on left, after about 500 m.

Charges 2004

Per unit incl. 2 persons	€ 15.00 - € 22.50
with electricity (6A)	€ 18.00 - € 26.50

Reservations

Contact Chadotel Central Reservations, BP 12, 85520 Jard-sur-Mer. Tel: 02 51 33 05 05.
Tel: 04.68.28.20.28. Email: info@chadotel.com

Open

1 April - 30 September.

FR66170 **Camping Mar i Sol**

Route de la Plage, 66440 Torreilles (Pyrénées-Orientales)

Good quality sites with direct access to the beach are hard to find and Mar i Sol is a useful addition. It is a fairly large site with 377 pitches with a significant number of mobile homes but with 170 available for touring units. These are sandy grass pitches of good size with some shade and connected by hardcore roads. All have electricity. The new owners have renovated the pool area and continue with other improvements. This is essentially a 'holiday' site with all the popular facilities and an extensive entertainment programme and children's club throughout the main season.

Facilities

Three fully equipped toilet blocks of the same design include mixed British and Turkish toilets, some washbasins in cabins and covered dishwashing and laundry sinks. Washing machine in each block. Small supermarket. Bar (1/6-15/9) TV. Restaurant and takeaway. Swimming pool, water slide and children's pool. All facilities are open in the main season. Play area. Tennis court (charged). Table tennis. Archery. Fitness room. Football and volleyball. Side gate with access to path across semi-sand dunes to sandy beach (lifeguards in main season). Watersport activities possible.

At a glance

Welcome & Ambience	✓✓✓✓✓	Location	✓✓✓✓✓
Quality of Pitches	✓✓✓✓	Range of Facilities	✓✓✓✓✓

Directions

From A9 take exit 41 (Perpignan Nord) towards Le Barcarès for 9 km then south on D81 towards Canet for 3 km. before turning to Torreilles Plage. Site is signed.

Charges 2003

Per unit incl. 2 persons	€ 16.40 - € 26.40
extra person (over 6 yrs)	€ 3.60 - € 5.90
child (under 6 yrs)	free - € 2.90
electricity (10A)	€ 4.20
dog	€ 5.00

Reservations

Necessary for July/Aug. and made with deposit (€ 150,45) and booking fee (€ 22,87).
Tel: 04 68 28 04 07.
Email: marisol@camping-marisol.com

Open

1 April - 30 September.

FR66030 Camping Cala Gogo

La Vigie, 66750 St Cyprien-Plage (Pyrénées-Orientales)

This is an excellent large and well organised site (sister site to 66040, Le Soleil) and it is agreeably situated by a superb sandy beach where there is a beach bar and boats can be launched. The 450 pitches for touring units are on flat ground and around 100 sq.m. They are fully marked out on level grass with easy access, electrical connections everywhere and some shade. The site has a most impressive pool complex carefully laid out with palm trees in ample sunbathing areas. The large bar complex becomes very busy in season and dancing or entertainment is arranged on some evenings on a large stage recently built alongside the bar. A large Aquapark, reputed to be amongst the best in southern France, is nearby. Used by tour operators (148 pitches).

Facilities

All four toilet blocks have been refurbished to a high standard, including British and Turkish style toilets and washbasins in cabins. Good supermarket, small shopping mall and wine boutique. Sophisticated restaurant with excellent cuisine and service, plus a self-service restaurant with simple menu and takeaway. Bar and small bar by the beach in high season. Disco. TV. Three adult pools plus one for children, water-jets, jacuzzi and waterfall. Tennis, table tennis and a playground. Programme of events and sports organised in season. Torches useful. Off site: Fishing, riding, bicycle hire and golf within 5 km. Boat excursions and courses in skin-diving, windsurfing or sailing nearby

At a glance

Welcome & Ambience	✓✓✓✓	Location	✓✓✓✓✓
Quality of Pitches	✓✓✓✓✓	Range of Facilities	✓✓✓✓

Directions

Using D81 (southward) avoid St Cyprien Plage and continue towards Argeles. Turn right at roundabout signed Le Port and Aquapark and pick up site signs. Site is just past the Aquapark.

Charges 2004

Per person (over 5 yrs)	€ 7.50
pitch	€ 10.50
electricity (6A)	€ 3.00
dog	€ 3.50
local tax	€ 0.30

Reservations

Made for Sat. to Sat. and necessary for Jul/Aug, with deposit (€ 81,70) and fee (€ 18,30). Tel: 04 68 21 07 12. Email: calagogo@campmed.com

Open

15 May - 25 September, with all services.

FR66040 Camping Le Soleil

Route du Littoral, 66702 Argelès-sur-Mer (Pyrénées-Orientales)

Le Soleil (sister site to Cala Go-Go, no. 66030), with direct access to the beach, is a busy, popular, family owned site which has grown in the last few years. A large site, more like a small village, it has over 800 individual numbered pitches of ample size, with over 200 used by tour operators, over 70 occupied by mobile homes and around 550 used for touring units. On sandy/grassy ground and with a mixture of trees and shrubs providing some shade, electricity connections are provided in all areas. Access for caravans sometimes needs care on the narrow access roads. The site has a wide range of amenities, including an impressive pool complex. Spain and the Pyrénées are near enough for excursions. English is spoken and there is a comprehensive reservation system (advised for most of July/Aug).

Facilities

Seven toilet blocks of the type with external access to individual units should give good coverage with showers in four of them. Two of the others have undergone major refurbishment and now offer family cabins with washbasins and showers with unusually two additional pressure water outlets at waist level in each. Washing machines. Supermarket, general shop, press, tabac and restaurant for sit down or takeaway food is centrally situated. ATM machine. Internet connection. Bar with disco (July/Aug) and beach bar. California type swimming pool complex and entertainment area. Adventure playground. TV room. Tennis. Riding in high season (charge). Dogs are not accepted. Off site: Fishing and mooring boats on the adjacent river. Golf 5 km.

At a glance

Welcome & Ambience	✓✓✓✓	Location	✓✓✓✓✓
Quality of Pitches	✓✓✓✓	Range of Facilities	✓✓✓✓

Directions

Site is at north end of the beach about 1 km. from Argelès-Plage village.

Charges 2004

Per person (over 5 yrs)	€ 7.50
pitch	€ 11.50
electricity (6A)	€ 3.00
local tax	€ 0.45

Less 20% outside July/Aug.
Swimming pool deposit € 15,24 per pitch.

Reservations

Made from Sat or Wed (min. 1 week) with deposit (30%) and booking fee (€ 18.30). Tel: 04 68 81 14 48. Email: camping.lesoleil@wanadoo.fr

Open

15 May - 30 September.

FR66020 Camping Caravaning Ma Prairie

Route de St Nazaire, 66140 Canet-en-Roussillon (Pyrénées-Orientales)

The Gil family provide a warm welcome immediately as you arrive at the very pretty ivy covered reception area, which boasts an impressive international collection of hats/helmets and uniform caps. Ma Prairie is an excellent site set 3 km. back from the sandy Canet beaches. It has an excellent pool complex over looked by large air conditioned bar situated across a small road from the camping area. There are 260 pitches of around 100 sq.m. on flat grassy ground, separated by various trees and bushes which provide shade (possible road noise). Most have electricity, with water and drainage on 35. The Gils have produced another superb touch in their restaurant which is very much a family affair down to mother's cushion designs and grandfather's paintings on the wall. The area of the old restaurant is now used for children's entertainment. Organised wine tastings are held once a week in high season. Used by tour operators (40 pitches). There is a lively family atmosphere. A 'Sites et Paysages' member.

Facilities

Three toilet blocks, two excellent new ones and one more mature, include washbasins in cabins with dividers. Baby bath. Washing machines and dryers. Dishwashing and laundry sinks. Extra provision near reception. Shop for basics only, covered snack bar and takeaway. Large air-conditioned bar and quality restaurant. Large adult pool (10 x 22 m), splendid children's pool. Play area. Tennis. Bicycle hire. Volleyball. Satellite TV, table tennis, billiards and amusement machines. Dancing about three times weekly and busy daily animation programme in season. Caravan storage. Off site: Riding 600 m, golf 6 km. Canet Village within walking distance with all amenities. Bus/tram services to the busy modern resort of Canet Plage.

Directions

Leave autoroute A9 at Perpignan North towards Barcares. Site access is from the D11 Perpignan road close to the junction with D617 in Canet-Village.

Charges 2003

Per unit with 2 persons	€ 15.00 - € 26.00
extra person	€ 3.00 - € 5.50
child under 4 yrs	free - € 2.70
child 4-10 yrs	€ 2.30 - € 4.00
electricity (10A)	€ 3.80
water and drainage	€ 4.60

Plus local tax. Camping Cheques accepted.

Reservations

Made for any length with deposit (€ 61) and fee (€ 12,20). Tel: 04 68 73 26 17. Email: ma.prairie@wanadoo.fr

Open

5 May - 25 September.

At a glance

Welcome & Ambience	✓✓✓✓✓	Location	✓✓✓✓
Quality of Pitches	✓✓✓✓✓	Range of Facilities	✓✓✓✓✓

FR66050 Camping Le Haras

Domaine Sant Galdric, 66690 Palau del Vidre (Pyrénées-Orientales)

A distinctly 'French' site, Le Haras is situated midway between the coast (about 8 km) and the Pyrénées on the edge of a village, in quiet countryside removed from the bustle of the coastal resorts. Under the same family management as Ma Prairie at Canet Village (66020), they are dedicated to many improvements. Le Haras has some 75 individual pitches all with electricity and drainage, arranged informally in bays of four, in the grounds of an old hunting lodge (designed by Gustave Violet on the lines of a small Italianate palace). A marvellous mixture of trees, shrubs and flowers provides colour and shade. There is an attractive pool complex and courtyard area beside the restaurant (developed in the old stables, with an excellent chef) and large function room, often used for weddings, with a distinctly Italian feel. Rail noise is possible from the line that runs beside the site, although this is screened by large trees.

Facilities

The unusually designed toilet block, fully equipped with mixed British and Turkish toilets, has been supplemented by a smart new block decorated in greens and terracotta in keeping with the site. It is planned that the smaller block near the pool will be renovated and heated. Covered dishwashing and laundry sinks. Washing machines. Bar. Restaurant, also open to the public (all year, but not every day). Takeaway. Swimming pool and paddling pool.(May - Sept). Play area. Off site: Three bakers in the village, two butchers and a general stores. Beaches 10 minutes drive. Golf 7 km. Riding 2 km. Bicycle hire 6 km. Fishing 500 m.

Directions

To avoid possible heavy traffic around Perpignan leave autoroute at exit 43 (Le Boulou) and follow D618 in the direction of Argelés for approx. 13 km. Take left turn for Palau-del-Vidre (D11) as you bypass St André. Bear right through village still on D11 in direction of Elne. As you leave village, site is on right, entrance just before railway bridge.

Charges 2003

Per pitch incl. two persons	€ 13.00 - € 22.00
extra person	€ 2.70 - € 4.80
child (under 7 yrs)	free - € 3.40
electricity (5A)	€ 3.50
dog	€ 2.70

Camping Cheques accepted.

Reservations

Necessary for July and August. Made with € 100 deposit and €16 booking fee. Tel: 04 68 22 14 50.

Open

20 March - 20 October.

At a glance

Welcome & Ambience	✓✓✓✓	Location	✓✓✓✓
Quality of Pitches	✓✓✓✓	Range of Facilities	✓✓✓✓✓

FR66070 Yelloh! Village Le Brasilia

B.P. 204, 66140 Canet-en-Roussillon (Pyrénées-Orientales)

We continue to be very impressed with La Brasilia – it is pretty, neat and well kept with an amazingly wide range of facilities and activities. It is a large site, but does not seem so, with 807 neatly hedged pitches all with electricity. Some long pitches are suitable for two families together. With a range of shade from mature pines and flowering shrubs, less on pitches near the beach, there are neat access roads (sometimes narrow for large units) and many flowers. The sandy beach here is busy, with a beach club (you can hire windsurfing boards) and a naturist section is on the beach to the west of the site. There is also a large California type pool, with sunbathing areas bounded by an attractive mosaic wall and bar. The village area of the site provides bars, a busy restaurant, entertainment (including a night club) and a range of shops. In fact you do not need to stir from the site which is almost a resort in itself also providing a cash dispenser, exchange facilities, telephone, post office, gas supplies and even weather forecasts. It does have a nice, lively atmosphere but is orderly and well run – very good for a site with beach access. They seem to have thought of everything, including an escort to your pitch and advice on the best way to site your unit. A 'Yelloh Village' member.

Facilities

Nine modern sanitary blocks are very well equipped and maintained, with British style WCs (some Turkish) and washbasins in cabins. One is very modern and impressive with good facilities for children (as has one other block). Facilities for disabled people. All have dishwashing and laundry sinks. Laundry room with washing machines and dryers. Special refuse areas. Hairdressing salon. Bars and restaurant. Swimming pool (heated and free). Sports field and a smaller games pitch (with 'Astroturf'). Tennis courts. Sporting activities such as aqua gym, aerobics, football, etc. Library, games and video room. Internet café planned. Bicycle hire. Fishing. Special dog walking area, cleaned daily. Torches useful (lighting is at knee level and sometimes lacking). No barbecues are allowed. English is spoken. Off site: Riding 5 km, golf 12 km.

At a glance

Welcome & Ambience	✓✓✓✓	Location	✓✓✓✓✓
Quality of Pitches	✓✓✓✓	Range of Facilities	✓✓✓✓✓

Directions

From A9 motorway take exit 41 (Perpignan Centre/Rivesalts) follow signs for Le Barcarès/Canet on D83 for 10 km, then signs for Canet (D81). Arriving at first Canet roundabout, make a full turn back on yourself (direction Sainte-Marie) and watch for Brasila sign almost immediately on right and follow.

Charges 2004

Per unit incl. 2 persons and electricity (6A)	€ 15.00 - € 38.00
extra electricity (10A)	€ 1.50
child (1-4 yrs)	free - € 4.00
dog	€ 2.00 - € 3.50

Reservations

Advised for July/Aug. Tel: 04 68 80 23 82.
Email: camping-le-brasilia@wanadoo.fr

Open

30 April - 25 September.

FR66000 Camping Caravaning Le Pujol

Route du Tamariguer, 66700 Argelès-sur-Mer (Pyrénées-Orientales)

Argelès is a busy tourist area and in high season it doesn't matter which of the 50 or so sites you are on, there are various loud open air discos and activities which may impinge on the wrong side of midnight for a while. However, it is possible to avoid the standard hectic seaside sites in otherwise attractive Argelès, and Pujol may represent the best chance of doing so. It is a very attractive, pretty and well cared for site which has been thoughtfully designed. There are 310 numbered pitches, all larger than 100 sq.m. on flat grass, nearly all with electricity. They include some 100 privately owned British mobile homes. The number of pitches has been increased (by 50) and these will be taken by mobile homes over the next few years, but in the meantime they are useful large pitches with electricity for tourers. Care is taken to ensure that the bar is a family bar rather than one overrun by youngsters, who are catered for in an attractively covered meeting area opposite which also houses animation and dances. The site's pride and joy is a delightful pool complex with semi-tropical shrubs and fountains. The site is very close to an interesting fortress and only 2 km. from the fast N114, via which the pretty ports of Collioure and Port-Vendres are but a short distance to the south. There is some road noise near the entrance to the site.

Facilities

Well kept fully equipped toilet blocks include a very smart shower block. Baby bath. Washing machines in each block with free ironing. Small supermarket (1/6-15/9). Good terraced restaurant and friendly family bar (1/6-15/9). Fairly large L-shaped swimming pool, children's pool, and spa pool (1/6-15/9). Table tennis, small multi-gym, volleyball, boules and minigolf. Playground. Games room. Only gas or electric barbecues are permitted. Off site: Fishing, bicycle hire 1 km, riding 500 m. Argelès Plage and quiet resort of Racou short distance if you want to exchange the pool for a Mediterranean beach.

At a glance

Welcome & Ambience	✓✓✓✓	Location	✓✓✓✓
Quality of Pitches	✓✓✓✓✓	Range of Facilities	✓✓✓✓

Directions

Perpignan-Nord exit from autoroute, follow N114 from Perpignan and use exit 10 for Argelès. Cross first roundabout onto Chemin de Negeubous (avoiding town). Turn left at second roundabout and site is 200 m. on right opposite Tour de Pujol.

Latest charges

Per pitch incl. 2 adults	€ 20.00
with electricity (6A)	€ 23.00
extra person	€ 5.00
child (under 3 yrs)	€ 2.50

Less 20% in June and Sept. No credit cards.

Reservations

Made with € 100 deposit. Tel: 04 68 81 00 25.

Open

1 June - 30 September.

FR66110 Camping Le Dauphin

Route de Taxo-d'Avall, 66701 Argelès-sur-Mer (Pyrénées-Orientales)

Near Taxo in the quieter, northern part of Argelès (a somewhat frenzied resort in season), this site on flat, grassy parkland enjoys good views of the Pyrénées, particularly from the terrace area surrounding its excellent complex of swimming pools. There are 310 level, grassy well shaded pitches, all with electricity and some with individual sanitary units. Although located some 1.5 km. from the town and beach, there is a regular connecting 'road train' service to and fro throughout the day and evening up to midnight. Used by tour operators (70 pitches).

Facilities

A central sanitary block, although mature, provides modern facilities including a number of showers and washbasins en-suite. One third of the pitches have their own fully equipped individual sanitary unit. Shops, bar/restaurant, pizzeria with takeaway (all 1/6-15/9). Pool complex (small charge). Small children's play area. Tennis courts, minigolf, table tennis, multi-sport court, sports ground and games room. Entertainment programme in high season. Torches useful in some areas. Off site: Fishing 2 km, riding 1 km.

At a glance

Welcome & Ambience	✓✓✓✓	Location	✓✓✓✓
Quality of Pitches	✓✓✓✓✓	Range of Facilities	✓✓✓✓✓

Directions

Site is on north side of Argelès. From autoroute take exit Perpignan-Nord for Argelès and follow signs for Plage-Nord and Taxo d'Avall (similarly from the N114).

Charges 2004

Per unit incl. 2 adults	€ 19.00 - € 24.50
with electricity (10A)	€ 21.50 - € 28.50
extra person	€ 4.00 - € 6.00
child (under 5 yrs)	€ 2.50 - € 3.50
water and drainage	€ 2.50 - € 4.00
Individual sanitation	€ 6.00 - € 8.00
local tax (over 10 yrs)	€ 0.42

Reservations

Made with deposit (€ 77) and booking fee (€ 16).
Tel: 04 68 81 17 54.
Email: camping.ledauphin66@wanadoo.fr

Open

1 June - 30 September.

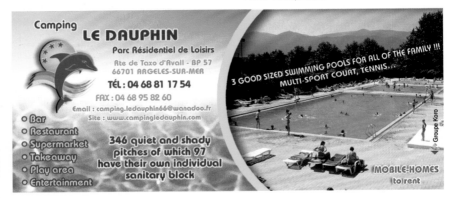

Camping LE DAUPHIN
Parc Résidentiel de Loisirs
Rte de Taxo d'Avall - BP 57
66701 ARGELES-SUR-MER
TÉL : 04 68 81 17 54
FAX : 04 68 95 82 60
Email : camping.ledauphin66@wanadoo.fr
Site : www.campingledauphin.com

○ Bar
○ Restaurant
○ Supermarket
○ Takeaway
○ Play area
○ Entertainment

346 quiet and shady pitches of which 97 have their own individual sanitary block

3 GOOD SIZED SWIMMING POOLS FOR ALL OF THE FAMILY !!!
MULTI-SPORT COURT, TENNIS...

MOBILE HOMES to rent

Groupe Karo

FR66200 Camping Les Marsouins

Avenue de la Retirada, 66702 Argelès-sur-Mer (Pyrénées-Orientales)

Les Marsouins is a large site situated on the beach road out of Argelès. About 103 of the 587 pitches are taken by mobile homes, those for tourers of a good size on level, mown grass divided by hedging. There is a degree of shade from some tall trees and electricity is available to all. An outdoor entertainment area is located at the entrance beside the bar and restaurant (for high season entertainment) but the lagoon style heated pool and paddling pool (no water slides) are tucked away to one side of the site with ample space for sunbathing on the lawns surrounding it. The site is well situated for easy access to the good sandy beach, with activities like windsurfing possible. English is spoken.

Facilities

Four fully equipped toilet blocks provide facilities for the handicapped and there are dishwashing and laundry sinks, washing machine and iron. Motorcaravan service point. Shop (26/5-8/9). Bar (7/6-5/9) and self-service restaurant (16/6-5/9) near entrance. Takeaway (1/4-30/9). Mini-market (8/6-7/9). Heated swimming pool (identity bracelet required; 15/04 - 29/9). Large play area. Children's club with free organised activities (24/6-1/9). Tennis, volleyball, table tennis. Range of evening entertainment (30/5-30/8). Off site: Beach 800 m. Riding next door. Boat launching 2 km. Golf 7 km.

At a glance

Welcome & Ambience	✓✓✓✓✓	Location	✓✓✓✓
Quality of Pitches	✓✓✓✓	Range of Facilities	✓✓✓✓✓

Directions

Take Perpignan sud exit from A9 . Follow signs for Argelès (RN114). Take exit 10 for Pujols at roundabout then Plage Nord at next. Site is 1.5 km. on left.

Charges 2003

Per unit incl. 2 persons and 5A electricity	€ 11.50 - € 22.00
with water and drainage	€ 13.00 - € 23.50
extra person (over 5 yrs)	€ 3.20 - € 5.00
local tax	€ 0.33

Reservations

Made with booking fee (€ 15). Tel: 04 68 81 14 81.
Email: marsouin@campmed.com

Open

1 April - 30 September.

FR66230 Camping Caravaning Le Romarin

Route de Sorède, Chemin des Vignes, 66702 Argelès-sur-Mer (Pyrénées-Orientales)

In an area dominated by 'all-singing, all-dancing' holiday sites, we were pleased to discover almost by accident this charming little site tucked away some 2 km. behind the busy resort of Argelès. Essentially a site for families with younger children, or for adults seeking peace and quiet, it provides 110 good sized touring pitches, all with electricity set among pine, eucalyptus, oak and mimosas. Ideal for exploring this area, especially the Albères range of Pyreneen mountains and the ancient city of Perpignan, it is nevertheless within easy reach of shops and all the attractions of Argelès, both village and Plage.

Facilities

One good large toilet block (half traditional style, half modern) provides a mix of British and Turkish WCs, showers, washbasins in cabins, dishwashing and laundry sinks and washing machine. Snack bar (mid June - end Sept). Swimming pool (mid June - end Sept). Play area. Table tennis. Some traditional (local) family entertainment in high season. Off site: Supermarket 2 km. Riding and bicycle hire 2 km. Fishing 4 km. Golf 8 km.

At a glance

Welcome & Ambience	✓✓✓✓✓	Location		✓✓✓✓
Quality of Pitches	✓✓✓✓✓	Range of Facilities		✓✓✓✓

Directions

From A9 take exit 42 (Perpignan Sud) on N114 towards Argelès for 25 km. to exit 11a. At roundabout follow to St Andre for 300 m. then turn left to pick up the Route de Sorède. Site is 2 km. along this road.

Charges 2004

Per unit incl. 2 persons	€ 11.00 - € 22.00
electricity (6/10A)	€ 2.00 - € 3.50

Reservations

Made with 25% deposit. Tel: 04.68.81.02.63. Email: camping.romarin@libertysurf.fr

Open

15 May - 30 September.

FR66180 Mas Llinas Camping

66160 Le Boulou (Pyrénées-Orientales)

The highest terraces on this campsite have commanding views over the valley and to the surrounding mountains. The roads up to the level, terraced, hillside pitches (100) are paved to make access easy, with good places to choose from. Some are larger, some grassy and a few hedged for privacy, many with outstanding views and lovely trees (electricity is available). The ground is stony and may be difficult for tents. This is a simple, peaceful and well maintained site with a relaxed feel and helpful, friendly owners. Explore the region of the Roussillon wine or just enjoy the peace and quiet.

Facilities

Two unisex toilet blocks, one clean and modern, the other rather small, basic and cramped. Full range of facilities for disabled campers. Washing machine. Motorcaravan services. Limited bar/café. Bread and croissants (July/Aug). Small swimming pool (mid-May - Oct. depending on weather). Volleyball. Table tennis. Games room. Electronic games. Torches necessary. Riding. Bicycle hire. Only gas barbecues are permitted. Off site: VTT with guide. Fishing 5 km.

At a glance

Welcome & Ambience	✓✓✓✓✓	Location		✓✓✓✓
Quality of Pitches	✓✓✓✓	Range of Facilities		✓✓✓✓

Directions

Travel south from Perpignan on A9/E15 or N9 to Le Boulou (30 km). Site is well signed from town, through a light commercial area. Follow uphill for 2 km.

Charges 2003

Per person	€ 4.50
pitch with electricity (5/10A)	€ 8.50 - € 9.50

Less 10% for 7 days, 20% for 14 days, in low season.

Reservations

Contact site. Tel: 04 68 83 25 46. Email: info@camping-mas-llinas.com

Open

1 February - 30 November.

FR66130 Hotel de Plein Air L'Eau Vive

Chemin de St Saturnin, 66820 Vernet-les-Bains (Pyrénées-Orientales)

Enjoying dramatic views of the towering Pic du Canigou, this small site is 1.5 km. from the centre of the spa town of Vernet-les-Bains, approached via a twisting road. The 77 pitches, all with electricity and water, are on a slight slope, part hedged, some terraced. Most have some shade. The site has a very attractive, more or less natural pool (created by circulating running water from the nearby stream) that even provides a small beach with slide. Parents should keep an eye on children around the pool as there is no fence. Well situated for touring this area, the site has very comfortable amenities.

Facilities

First class toilet facilities in two modern blocks include washbasins in cabins and facilities for disabled people. Washing machine in each block. Bread can be ordered in main season. Bar/reception with pool table, amusement machine, library, etc. Attractive open air (but under cover) snack bar with takeaway (1/6-30/9). Natural pool for children. Sports field. Basketball. Bicycle hire. Off site: Fishing 200 m. Organised rafting and canoeing. The nearby medieval, walled town of Ville Franche de Conflent, the Grottes des Canalettes and Fort Libena are worth visiting.

At a glance

Welcome & Ambience	✓✓✓✓✓	Location		✓✓✓✓✓
Quality of Pitches	✓✓✓✓	Range of Facilities		✓✓✓✓

Directions

From N116 at Villefranche de Conflent turn for Vernet-les-Bains. Continue up hill for 5 km. and keep right avoiding town centre. Turn right (Sahorre) and, at one end of block of shops, turn right and follow for 1 km.

Charges 2003

Per unit incl. up to 3 persons and electricity (4A)	€ 11.00 - € 13.00

Camping Cheques accepted.

Reservations

Contact site. Tel: 04 68 05 54 14. Email: leauv@club-internet.fr

Open

All year except 12 Nov - 15 Dec.

Mediterranean East

Bathed in sunshine from early spring to late autumn, surrounded by stunning scenery, cosmopolitan towns and superb sandy beaches, no wonder this is one of France's most sought-after destinations.

This section covers the eastern coastal region of the Mediterranean. We include two départements from the official region of Provence and the region of Côte d'Azur: 13 Bouches-du-Rhône, 83 Var, 06 Alpes-Maritime

The glittering Côte d'Azur, perhaps better known as the French Riviera, is a beautiful stretch of coast studded with sophisticated towns such as the famous Monte Carlo, Nice, and Cannes, not forgetting the other famous and arguably the most glamourous resort of St Tropez. With its vast expanses of golden sandy beaches and long lazy hours of sunshine, this is a paradise for sun worshippers and beach enthusiasts. It's a spectacular coast of rugged coves, sweeping beaches and warm seas.

The quaint harbours and fishing villages have become chic destinations, now full of pleasure yachts, harbour-side cafes and crowded summertime beaches. Further up in the hills are quieter tiny medieval villages with winding streets and white-walled houses with terracotta roofs, which have attracted artists and visitors for many years. In St Paul-de-Vence visitors can browse through shops and galleries set on narrow winding cobblestone streets and inland Grasse is the perfume capital of the world, surrounded by the provencal lavender fields and shady olive groves which pervade the air with a magical scent at certain times of the year.

Cuisine of the region

Aigo Bouido: garlic and sage soup

Bouillabaisse: fish soup

Rouille: an orange coloured sauce with peppers, garlic and saffron

Bourride: a creamy fish soup

Pissaladière: Provençal bread dough with onions, anchovies and olives

Pistou (Soupe au): vegetable soup bound with *pommade*

Pommade: a thick paste of garlic, basil, cheese and olive oil

Ratatouille: aubergines, courgettes, onions, garlic, *red peppers and tomatoes in olive oil*

Salade Niçoise: tomatoes, beans, potatoes, black olives, anchovy, lettuce, olive oil and tuna fish

Places of interest

Aix-en-Provence: old town with 17th-18th century character, Paul Cézanne and Tapestry museums

Cannes: popular for conventions and festivals, Cannes Film Festival, la Croisette, old city

Monte Carlo: main city of Monaco, casinos, gardens, Napoleon Museum. motorsport circuit

tip

THE PHOENIX FLORAL PARK IN NICE, HAS BOTANICAL GARDENS, A BIRD AND INSECT ZOO PLUS A THEME PARK - A GREAT DAY OUT FOR THE WHOLE FAMILY

FR06080 Camping Caravaning Les Cigales

505 ave. de la Mer, 06210 Mandelieu la Napoule (Alpes-Maritimes)

It is hard to imagine that such a peaceful site could be in the middle of such a busy town and so near to Cannes – we were delighted with it. The entrance (easily missed) with reception and parking has large electronic gates that ensure that the site is secure. There are only 115 pitches (20 used for mobile homes) so this is really quite a small, personal site. There are three pitch sizes, from small ones for tents to pitches for larger units. All are level with much needed shade in summer, although the sun will get through in winter when it is needed, and all have electricity (6A), some with water and drain also. The site is alongside the Canal de Siagne and for a fee small boats can be launched at La Napoule, then moored outside the site's side gate. Les Cigales is open all year so it is useful for the Monte Carlo Rally, the Cannes Film Festival and the Mimosa Festival, all held out of the main season. English is spoken.

Facilities

Two well appointed unisex toilet blocks are kept very clean, one heated for the winter months. Washbasins in cabins and facilities for babies and disabled visitors. Dishwashing and laundry sinks. Washing machine. Motorcaravan service point. Restaurant at entrance also serves takeaways (April - 30 Sept). Swimming pool (heated mid-March - mid-Oct). Small play area. Table tennis and two games machines. Fishing possible in the canal (but not many fish!) Off site: The town is an easy walk. Centre commercial (supermarket and 40 shops) 2 km. Railway station 1 km. for trains to Cannes, Nice, Antibes and Monte Carlo. Riverside and canal walks. Two golf courses within 1 km. Beach 800 m.

At a glance

Welcome & Ambience	✓✓✓✓✓	Location	✓✓✓✓✓
Quality of Pitches	✓✓✓✓	Range of Facilities	✓✓✓✓

Directions

From A8 take exit 40 and bear right. Remain in right hand lane and continue right signed Plages-Ports and Creche-Campings. Casino supermarket is on the right. Continue under motorway to T-junction. Turn left and site is 60 m. on left opposite Chinese restaurant.

Charges 2003

Per unit incl. 2 persons	€ 26.50 - € 29.00
extra person	€ 5.00
child (under 5 yrs)	€ 2.50

Reservations

Made with deposit (€ 77). Tel: 04 93 49 23 53. Email: campingcigales@wanadoo.fr

Open

All year.

FR06010 Camping Domaine Saint Madeleine

Route de Moulinet, 06380 Sospel (Alpes-Maritimes)

Domaine Sainte Madeleine is an attractive, peaceful site, with swimming pool, in spectacular mountain scenery. It is about 28 kilometres miles inland from Menton, and very near the Italian border. The approach to this site is not for the faint-hearted although having said that, when we visited, the site was very busy with touring caravans so it can't be too bad. The site itself makes the effort worthwhile, situated on a terraced hillside with mountain views towards Italy. On a fairly steep hill, manoeuvring within the site presents no problem and the pitches are on level, well drained grass. The lower ones have shade but those higher up on the hill have none. Electricity is available to 70 of the 90 pitches. There are way-marked walks for serious walkers in the surrounding hills. English is spoken.

Facilities

The single toilet block is of good quality, including washbasins in cabins and showers on payment. Hot water (often only warm) for dishwashing and laundry sinks drawn from single tap. Washing machines. Motorcaravan services. Gas supplies. Bread can be ordered. Swimming pool (140 sq.m. and heated in spring and autumn). Off site: The attractive small town of Sospel is only 4 km. with many restaurants, bars, cafés and shops. Tennis, riding and a centre for mountain biking. Fishing 1 km.

At a glance

Welcome & Ambience	✓✓✓✓	Location	✓✓✓✓
Quality of Pitches	✓✓✓	Range of Facilities	✓✓✓

Directions

Site is on D2566, 4 km. north of Sospel. The D2566 is reached from either A8 Menton exit, or N7 at Menton.

Charges 2004

Per unit incl. 2 adults	€ 17.00
extra person	€ 2.10 - € 3.70
electricity (10A)	€ 2.90

Less 15% outside July/Aug. No credit cards.

Reservations

Made with € 50 deposit. Tel: 04 93 04 10 48. Email: camp@camping-sainte-madeleine.com

Open

1 April - 30 September.

FR06070N Domaine Naturiste Club Origan

06260 Puget-Theniers (Alpes-Maritimes)

Origan is a naturist site set in the mountains behind Nice. Despite its rather spectacular location, it is easily accessible from the coast and you only discover that you are at a height of 500 m. when you arrive! The access road is single track and winding with a few passing places for about a mile, so arrival is not recommended until late afternoon. The terrain within the extensive confines of the site is fairly wild and the roads distinctly stony. The site is not suitable for caravans longer than six metres due to the steep slopes, although the site will assist with a 4x4 vehicle if requested. The scenery is impressive and footpaths in and around the site offer good, if fairly strenuous, walks up to a height of 1,000 m. The 100 touring pitches, in three different areas with many wild flowers, are of irregular size and shape and all have good views. Electricity connection is possible on most pitches (by long cable). Reservation is necessary in high season. Member 'France 4 Naturisme'

Facilities

Sanitary facilities, exceptionally clean when we visited, are of a standard and type associated with most good naturist sites - mainly British type WCs, mostly open plan hot showers and ample washbasins with hot and cold water. Laundry facilities. Shop (1/5-21/8). Bar/restaurant (all season). Takeaway. Heated swimming pools, one for children (1/5-31/8). Jacuzzi and sauna. Disco in cellars. Tennis. Fishing. Bicycle hire. Organised activities for adults and children (high season). Only gas or electric barbecues are permitted. Torches advised. Off site: The nearby small town of Puget-Theniers is very pleasant and offers choice of bars, cafés, shops, etc. Steam train. Eco-museum of the Roudoule.

At a glance

Welcome & Ambience	✓✓✓✓	Location	✓✓✓✓
Quality of Pitches	✓✓✓✓	Range of Facilities	✓✓✓✓

Directions

Heading west on the N202, just past the town of Puget-Theniers, turn right at camp sign at level crossing; site is 1.5 km.

Charges 2003

Per unit incl. 2 persons	€ 15.00 - € 27.90
extra person	€ 5.00 - € 8.00
child (4-9 yrs)	free - € 5.00
electricity (5/6A)	€ 4.00
dog	€ 2.30

Plus local tax. Camping Cheques accepted.

Reservations

Made with 25% deposit and fee (€ 30) - contact site. Tel: 04 93 05 06 00. Email: info@club-origan.com

Open

12 April - 30 September.

FR06050 Camping La Vieille Ferme

296 boulevard des Groules, 06270 Villeneuve-Loubet-Plage (Alpes-Maritimes)

Open all year, in a popular resort area, La Vieille Ferme is a family owned site with good facilities. It provides 131 level gravel-based pitches, 106 with electricity, water and drain, and the majority separated by hedges. Some are only small, simple pitches for little tents. There is also a fully serviced pitch on tarmac for motorhomes. There are special winter rates for long stays with quite a few long stay units on site. The entrance to the site is very colourful with well tended flower beds. English is spoken at reception and the whole place has a very friendly feel to it. A one kilometre walk beside the road towards Antibes brings you to the railway station, giving access to all the towns along the coast and to the beach.

Facilities

Three modern, well kept toilet blocks (two heated in winter) provide washbasins all in cabins, children's toilets, baby room and two units for disabled people. Motorcaravan service point. Dishwashing and laundry sinks. Three washing machines and dryer. Shop (Easter - Sept). Drinks, sweets and ices machine in the TV room for all year use. Gas, bread and milk to order when shop closed. Refrigerator hire. Swimming pool (20 x 10 m.) and children's pool, heated and covered for winter use (closed mid Nov-mid Dec) with jacuzzi. Internet point. Table tennis, basketball and boule pitch. Games and competitions organised in July/Aug. Off site: Fishing 1 km, golf 2 km.

At a glance

Welcome & Ambience	✓✓✓✓✓	Location	✓✓✓✓
Quality of Pitches	✓✓✓✓	Range of Facilities	✓✓✓✓

Directions

From west take Antibes exit from Esterel autoroute and turn left towards Nice when joining the N7 outside Antibes. After 3.5 km. on N7 turn left for site. From east take N7 towards Antibes and turn right after Villeneuve Loubet Plage. The turning off the N7, though signed, is not easy to see particularly at busy times but, coming from Antibes, it is on the left, more or less between the Marine Land and the Parc de Vaugrenier. Site is 150 m. on right. Avoid N98 Route du Bord de Mer. Site has prepared its own small, yellow site signs.

Charges 2003

Per tent incl. 2 persons and car	€ 8.00 - € 35.00
caravan incl. 2 persons and car	€ 17.00 - € 26.00
extra person	€ 3.50 - € 4.50
child (under 5 yrs)	€ 2.30 - € 3.00
electricity (2-10A)	€ 2.30 - € 5.00
dog	€ 1.50
local tax	€ 0.38

Reservations

Advised over a long season and made with 25% deposit and € 20 fee; Sat.-Sat. only in July/Aug. and at Easter. Tel: 04 93 33 41 44. Email: vieilleferme@bigfoot.com

Open

All year.

FR06090 Camping Caravaning Les Gorges du Loup

965 chemin des Vergers, 06620 Le Bar sur Loup (Alpes-Maritimes)

In the hills above Grasse, Les Gorges du Loup is situated on a steep hillside. Many of the pitches are only suitable for tents and certainly not for large caravans, mainly due to the steepness of the site roads, but also because of the narrow one kilometre track which leads to the site. The 70 pitches are on level terrace areas and all have electricity connections. A quiet family site, there is no organised entertainment. Bar-de-Loup with its few shops and restaurants is only a 500 m. walk. Grasse (9 km.) is surrounded by fields of lavender, mimosa and jasmine and has been famous for the manufacture of perfume since the 16th century. The Musée International de la Perfume has a garden of fragrant plants and the cathedral in the old town has three paintings by Reubens. The very friendly and enthusiastic owners will site your caravan with their 4x4 free of charge if you find the steepness of the site a little daunting. They also speak a little English.

Facilities

Two tiled toilet blocks are kept very clean and include washbasins mostly in cubicles. Around half the WCs are British style. Dishwashing and laundry sinks have a single hot tap to draw from. Washing machine and iron. Reception has small shop with bread daily. Small bar/restaurant and takeaway (July/Aug). Swimming pool (no Bermuda style shorts), small slide and diving board, but no pool for small children. Boules pitches, table tennis, volleyball and skittles. TV room with tables and chairs for board games, plus a library useful in early and late season. Children's climbing frame. Charcoal barbecues are not allowed. Chalets and mobile homes for hire.

At a glance

| Welcome & Ambience | ✓✓✓✓ | Location | ✓✓✓✓ |
| Quality of Pitches | ✓✓✓ | Range of Facilities | ✓✓✓✓ |

Directions

From Grasse take D2085 Nice road. Take D3 briefly and then at Châteauneuf Pré du Lac take D2210 to Pont-de-Loup and Vence. Site is signed on right. Pass village of Bar-sur-Loup on left and then, after a very tight right turn, take 1 km. long, very narrow access road (a few passing places).

Charges 2003

Per unit incl. 2 persons	€ 13.00 - € 23.70
extra person	€ 3.80
child (under 5 yrs)	€ 3.10
dog	€ 2.00
electricity (4/10A)	€ 2.30 - € 4.00

No credit cards.

Reservations

Advised in high season. Tel: 04 93 42 45 06. Email: les-gorges-du-loup@wanadoo.fr

Open

1 April - 1 October.

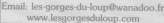

Les Gorges du Loup
Camping ★★★G
965 chemin des Vergers
06620 LE BAR DU LOUP
Pays de Grasse / Côte d'Azur
Tel / Fax: 0033 493 424 506
Email: les-gorges-du-loup@wanadoo.fr
www.lesgorgesduloup.com

CAMPING — CARAVANNING
★★★★
La Vieille Ferme
Tel. 0033 493.33.41.44
Riviéra
Côte d'azur
Heated Pools
Winter Facilities
VILLENEUVE LOUBET PLAGE (PAR RN 7)
www.vieilleferme.com

FR06030 Camping Caravaning Domaine de la Bergerie

Route de la Sine, 06140 Vence (Alpes-Maritimes)

La Bergerie is a quiet, family owned site, situated in the hills about 3 km. from Vence and 10 km. from the sea at Cagnes-sur-Mer. This extensive, lightly wooded site has been left very natural and is in a secluded position about 300 m. above sea level. Because of the trees most of the pitches are shaded and all are of a good size. It is a large site but because it is so extensive it does not give that impression. There are 450 pitches, 300 with electricity and 65 also with water and drainage. There are no organised activities and definitely no groups allowed.

Facilities

Both toilet blocks have been refurbished and include washbasins in cabins and excellent provision for disabled people (pitches near the block are reserved for disabled people). Shop, small bar/restaurant with takeaway (all 1/5-30/9). Large swimming pool, paddling pool and spacious sunbathing area (5/6-30/9). Playground. Bicycle hire. Table tennis, tennis courts and 10 shaded boules pitches (lit at night) with competitions in season. Barbecues are not permitted. Off site: Riding 6 km, fishing 10 km, golf 12 km. Hourly bus service (excl. Sundays) from site to Vence.

At a glance

Welcome & Ambience	✓✓✓✓	Location	✓✓✓✓
Quality of Pitches	✓✓✓✓	Range of Facilities	✓✓✓✓✓

Directions

From A8 exit 47 take Cagnes-sur-Mer road towards Vence. Site is west of Vence - follow 'toutes directions' signs around the town to join the D2210 Grasse road. Follow this to roundabout (2 km), turn left and follow site signs for 1 km. Site is on right in light woodland.

Charges 2003

Per unit incl. 2 persons with electricity (2A)	€ 13.00 - € 17.50 € 16.50 - € 21.00
with water, drainage, electricity (5A)	€ 21.00 - € 26.00

Camping Cheques accepted.

Reservations

Necessary only in July/Aug. for the special pitches and made with 25% deposit and € 12.96 fee. Tel: 04 93 58 09 36.

Open

25 March - 15 October.

Provence Alpes Côte d'Azur

DOMAINE LA BERGERIE

★★★

Route de la Sine, 06140 Vence
Tel: 0033 493 58 09 36
Fax: 0033 493 59 80 44
Two pools ~ Tennis ~ Chalets in 13h

FR06110 Camping Caravaning Panoramic

1,630 Ave de la République, 06550 La Roquette-sur-Siagne (Alpes-Maritimes)

You receive a friendly welcome at this site and, although virtually within sight of the resort of Cannes, it enjoys a quiet location facing mimosa covered hillsides. The grass pitches are on two levels, the upper level having a steep approach. All have electricity and some have water. There are 60 pitches, about half for touring units, the remainder for mobile homes and chalets. There is plenty of shade and as the name of the site suggests, it offers a fine view. Panoramic opens all year round and makes an ideal spot for a low season break, but becomes more lively in July/August when varying ages can enjoy dancing twice weekly. Within 100 m. is a sports complex with tennis courts, etc. The on site pool is one way of keeping cool, but the sandy beaches of Cannes and Mandelieu can be reached in a few minutes.

Facilities

Two toilet blocks are of a reasonable standard, only one fully opened in low season; walls and floors tiled, but not ultra modern. Washbasins in cabins and pre set showers with a divider; dishwashing facilities, laundry sinks and a washing machine. No dedicated chemical disposal (the toilets are used). Restaurant/takeaway (July/Aug). Bar (all season). Heated swimming pool, solarium and sunbathing patio, but no paddling pool. Children's play area on grass. TV. No shop.

At a glance

Welcome & Ambience	✓✓✓✓	Location	✓✓✓
Quality of Pitches	✓✓✓	Range of Facilities	✓✓✓✓

Directions

Leave A8 autoroute at exit 40 onto N7 and turn north onto D109 signed Pegomas. Continue on D109 for 5 km. and site is on right.

Latest charges

Per person	€ 3.50
child under 5 yrs	€ 2.50
pitch	€ 15.50
electricity (6A)	€ 3.00

Reservations

Contact site. Tel: 04.92.19.07.77. Email: campingpanoramic@wanadoo.fr

Open

All year.

FR06100 Camping Les Pinèdes

Route du Pont de Pierre, 06480 La Colle-sur-Loup (Alpes-Maritimes)

Les Pinèdes is seven kilometres inland from the busy coast, located at the centre of all the attractions of the Côte d'Azur, yet far enough away to be peaceful retreat at the end of a busy day sightseeing. In a terraced situation on a wooded hillside where olives and vines used to grow the site, has been in the hands of the welcoming Dugauguez family for the past 30 years. All the level pitches have electricity, most also with water and are separated by low bushes. Due to the nature of the terrain there are no facilities for wheelchair users. The owners are keen to attract wildlife to the site and there are many varieties of birds and the odd fox to be seen. For three weeks from the end of May into June, the evenings are alive with fireflies lighting up the site. The restaurant at the site entrance (also owned by the family) has an excellent reputation. The owner is very interested in all the local art galleries and will advise on where all the famous painters have paintings hung. There are many typical Provencal villages in close proximity not to mention the towns of Grasse, Menton, Monaco and Antibes, and all are well worth a visit – the family will be only too pleased to give advice. A 'Sites et Paysages' member.

Facilities

Two clean and well maintained toilet blocks have both British and Turkish style toilets and large shower cubicles. One block has been refurbished, the other is due to be soon. All the usual facilities for dishwashing and laundry etc and a baby room. Small shop. Bar, restaurant and takeaway. Swimming pool. Two small play areas. Field for volleyball, basketball and archery. Boule pitch. Entertainment is organised for young and old in July/Aug. Weekly walks in the surrounding hills June - Sept. Off site: Fishing in Loup river (50 m). Village 1 km with tennis court, riding school, leisure park with keep fit course and antiques quarter.

At a glance

| Welcome & Ambience | ✓✓✓✓ | Location | ✓✓✓✓ |
| Quality of Pitches | ✓✓✓✓ | Range of Facilities | ✓✓✓✓ |

Directions

From A8 take D2 towards Vence. At Colle sur Loup roundabout take D6 signed Grasse, site on right in approx. 3 km.

Charges 2004

Per tent incl. 2 persons	€ 13.50 - € 17.50
caravan or motorcaravan	€ 14.80 - € 22.50
extra person	€ 3.70 - € 4.60
child (under 5 yrs)	€ 1.90 - € 2.90
dog	€ 1.50 - € 2.00
electricity (3-10A)	€ 2.90 - € 4.20

Reservations

Necessary for July/Aug. and made with 25% deposit and fee (€ 18.29). Tel: 04 93 32 98 94. Email: camplespinedes06@aol.com

Open

15 March - 5 October.

FR13050M Camping Municipal du Mas de Nicolas

Avenue Plaisance du Touch, 13210 St Rémy-de-Provence (Bouches du Rhône)

St Rémy de Provence is a very popular town and this reflects on Mas de Nicolas, as this too is very popular and always reasonably busy. The site has a very spacious feel to it, due mainly to the central area of gently sloping grass, dotted with shrubs, that is kept clear of pitches and used for leisure and sunbathing. The 140 pitches are separated by hedges, 120 with electricity, water and drainage, and access roads are wide. Some pitches are an irregular shape and some are sloping, but many have views and they are mostly organised into groups of two and four.

Facilities

Two toilet blocks have been refurbished to give excellent facilities including British style toilets, washbasins in cabins, a baby bathroom and even a dog shower. The other blocks are of an older design with mainly Turkish style WCs. Dishwashing and laundry sinks, washing machines and drying lines. Swimming pool (15/5-15/9). Off site: Adjacent municipal gymnasium, tennis and volleyball courts. Fishing 2 km, bicycle hire or riding 1 km, golf 15 km. St Rémy has a wide selection of restaurants and a Wednesday market.

At a glance

| Welcome & Ambience | ✓✓✓✓ | Location | ✓✓✓✓ |
| Quality of Pitches | ✓✓✓✓ | Range of Facilities | ✓✓✓✓ |

Directions

St Rémy de Provence is located where the D571 from Avignon connects with the D99 Tarascon - Cavaillon road. Site is signed from the village centre on the north side. Leave autoroute A7 at Cavaillon or Avignon-Sud.

Latest charges

Per unit incl. 2 persons	€ 12.96 - € 14.18
extra adult	€ 4.27
child (under 10 yrs)	€ 1.98
animal	€ 1.52
electricity (6A)	€ 2.90
local tax	€ 0.46

Reservations

Necessary for main season and made with €16.77 fee (non returnable). Tel: 04 90 92 27 05. Email: camping-mas-de-nicolas@wanadoo.fr

Open

15 March - 15 October.

Mediterranean East

331

Great on-line holiday deals alanrogersdirect.com

FR83020 Camping Caravaning Esterel

Avenue des Golf, 83700 St Raphael (Var)

For caravans only, Esterel is a quality site east of St Raphaël, set among the hills at the back of Agay. Developed by the Laroche family over the last 27 years, the site has an attractive quiet situation with good views of the Esterel mountains. The site is 3.5 km. from the sandy beach at Agay where parking is perhaps a little easier than at most places on this coast. In addition to a section for permanent caravans, it has some 250 pitches for tourists, on which caravans of any type are taken but not tents. Pitches are on shallow terraces, attractively landscaped with good shade and a variety of flowering plants, giving a feeling of spaciousness. Each pitch has an electricity connection and tap, and 18 have their own individual en-suite washroom adjoining. A pleasant courtyard area contains the shop and bar, with a terrace overlooking the attractively landscaped pool complex, which has recently been extended. Wild boar come to the perimeter fence each evening to be fed by visitors. This is a very good site, well run and organised in a deservedly popular area. A member of 'Les Castels' group.

Facilities

Toilet facilities in three blocks have been refurbished and are excellent. They can be heated and include washbasins mostly in cabins. Individual toilet units on 18 pitches. Facilities for disabled people. Laundry room. Motorcaravan service point. Shop. Takeaway. Bar/restaurant. Five circular swimming pools (two heated), one large for adults, one smaller for children and three arranged as a waterfall (1/4-30/9). Disco. Archery, volleyball, minigolf, two tennis courts, pony rides, petanque and squash court. Playground. Bicycle hire. Events and entertainment are organised in season. Barbecues of any type are forbidden. Off site: Good golf courses very close. Trekking by foot, bicycle or by pony in the surrounding natural environment of L'Esterel forest park. Beach 3 km.

At a glance

Welcome & Ambience	✓✓✓✓	Location	✓✓✓✓✓
Quality of Pitches	✓✓✓✓	Range of Facilities	✓✓✓✓✓

Directions

You can approach from St Raphaël via Valescure but easiest way is to turn off the coast road at Agay where there are good signs. From Fréjus exit from autoroute A8, follow signs for Valescure throughout, then for Agay, and site is on left. (Reader's comment: If in doubt, follow golf complex signs, or Leclerc). The road from Agay is the easiest to follow.

Latest charges

Standard pitch incl. 2 persons	€ 25.92 - € 29.73
de-luxe pitch	€ 32.78 - € 36.59
extra person	€ 6.86
child (1-7 yrs)	€ 4.57
animal	€ 1.52
local tax	€ 0.30

Reservations

Necessary for high season and made for min. 1 week with deposit (€ 80) and fee (€ 30). CD brochure available from site. Tel: 04 94 82 03 28. Email: contact@esterel-caravaning.fr

Open

1 April - 30 September.

FR13010M Camping Municipal Les Romarins

13520 Maussane (Bouches du Rhône)

A well kept, neat municipal site, Les Romarins has been in the guide for several years and remains popular with readers. Tarmac access roads lead to 145 good sized grassy pitches separated by hedges and bushes, all with electrical connections. The municipal swimming pool (with discounts) is near and shops and restaurants are in the pleasant little town. Les Baux and St Remy-de-Provence are tourist attractions not to be missed, especially St Remy's Roman ruins. Les Romarins is popular and becomes very busy from 1 July - late August.

Facilities

There are three good toilet blocks, especially the newly refurbished one which provides British style toilets, adjustable, roomy showers and washbasins in cubicles. Baby room, washing machine, laundry and dishwashing sinks and facilities for disabled visitors. The two older blocks have some Turkish style WCs and are of an older design, but still kept very clean and well maintained. Children's play area. Free tennis courts. Pleasant reading room for cooler days. Off site: Bicycle hire or golf 1 km, fishing or riding 3 km.

At a glance

Welcome & Ambience	✓✓✓✓	Location	✓✓✓
Quality of Pitches	✓✓✓✓	Range of Facilities	✓✓✓

Directions

Site is within the little town of Maussane on the eastern edge.

Charges 2003

Per unit incl. 1 or 2 adults and 1 child	€ 13.20
extra person	€ 3.00
child	€ 1.70
dog	€ 2.00
electricity (4A)	€ 2.40 - € 3.00

Less 10-20% for longer stays.

Reservations

Made for any length with fee. Tel: 04 90 54 33 60.

Open

15 March - 15 October.

FR83230 Camping Caravaning Domaine du Colombier

Route de Bagnols en Forêt, 83600 Fréjus

Domaine du Colombier is a busy site alongside a main road, so a few of the pitches will have some road noise. The majority however are down a hillside and pine trees help to deaden the noise. The pitches (326 for touring units out of 470) vary in size from small ones to quite large, of which 40 are fully serviced. The hillside is terraced, with all pitches level and with electricity. The pool area with palm trees, a tiled surround and free sunbeds is in a sunny location. There are also three slides and water polo nets for competitions. A disco is underground to deaden the noise. Like the cabarets and competitions all these facilities operate in high season. This is a family site and no groups are accepted. The only downside is that the pool is at the bottom of the site, giving a long pull back up to the majority of pitches. The site was affected by fires in summer 2003, but after much hard work, are looking forward to an excellent 2004 season. We wish them well.

Facilities

Well maintained and positioned toilet blocks are fully equipped, including baby rooms. Three blocks have en-suite units for disabled people. Two can be heated on cooler days. Well equipped laundry. Well stocked shop. Bar/restaurant with takeaway. Snack bar (from 1/6). Disco. Large heated swimming pool (30 x 20 m) and paddling pool (all season). Communal barbecue areas for July/Aug. Internet terminal. Two play areas of excellent quality on rubber safety bases. Games room, mini-club room. Half court tennis, volleyball, basketball and boule. Tourist office with bookings to major attractions possible. Only gas or electric barbecues are permitted. Off site: Bus passes the gate.

At a glance

Welcome & Ambience	✓✓✓✓	Location	✓✓✓✓
Quality of Pitches	✓✓✓✓	Range of Facilities	✓✓✓✓✓

Directions

From A8 autoroute take 38 and follow D4 for Frejus. Site is on left, well signed.

Charges 2003

Per unit incl. 2 or 3 persons	
and electricity (10A)	€ 23.00 - € 38.50
extra person	€ 4.80 - € 6.50
child (under 10 yrs)	€ 2.00 - € 4.90
tent pitch incl. 2 persons	€ 14.00 - € 30.20

Plus local tax. Special low season offers.

Reservations

Made with 25% deposit plus booking fee (€ 25). Tel: 04 94 51 56 01.

Open

15 June - 30 September.

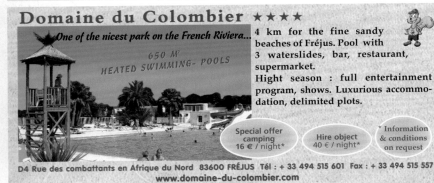

Domaine du Colombier ★★★★

One of the nicest park on the French Riviera...

650 M² HEATED SWIMMING- POOLS

4 km for the fine sandy beaches of Fréjus. Pool with 3 waterslides, bar, restaurant, supermarket.

Hight season : full entertainment program, shows. Luxurious accommodation, delimited plots.

Special offer camping 16 € / night*

Hire object 40 € / night*

* Information & conditions on request

D4 Rue des combattants en Afrique du Nord 83600 FRÉJUS Tél : + 33 494 515 601 Fax : + 33 494 515 557
www.domaine-du-colombier.com

FR83600 Holiday Green – Camping-Caravanning

Route de Bagnols, 83600 Fréjus

Holiday Green is seven kilometres inland from the busy resort of Fréjus. It is a large, modern campsite with a fantastic view of the red massif of Esterelle – very impressive as you arrive. The site has been developed on a hillside and by reception at the top of hill is a large Californian style heated swimming pool and a wide range of other facilities. This is where everything happens and it is said there are activities and entertainment from morning until closing. The rest of the site is terraced into the hillside and almost completely hidden in the 15 hectares of pine woods which absorbs about 500 large touring pitches and some 200 mobile homes. Sloping in parts, there is plenty of shade and electricity connections (6A) available. The site provides a free daily bus (16/6-14/9) to go to the beach.

Facilities

Modern toilet facilities include good hot showers. Dishwashing and laundry sinks. Laundry. Shopping centre. Bar, restaurant and fast food. Sound proof disco. Swimming pool. Three tennis courts. Archery. Petanque. Excursions are organised on foot, on horse-back and on mountain bikes (to hire) offering the chance to explore the countryside. Entertainment programme of dances, concerts and festivals. Playground. Children's club (July/Aug). Charcoal barbecues are not permitted. Off site: Beach 7 km. Golf 8 km.

At a glance

Welcome & Ambience	✓✓✓✓	Location	✓✓✓✓
Quality of Pitches	✓✓✓✓	Range of Facilities	✓✓✓✓✓

Directions

From A8 autoroute exit 38 follow signs for Bagnols-en-Forêt about 2 km. back over the autoroute, and the site is clearly signed at roundabout.

Charges 2003

Per unit incl. 2 persons	€ 36.00
child (under 6 yrs)	€ 5.50

Reservations

Advanced booking necessary for high season. Tel: 04 94 19 88 30. Email: info@holiday-green.com

Open

30 March – 30 September (with all facilities).

FR83060 Camping Caravaning de la Baume

Route de Bagnols, 83618 Fréjus (Var)

La Baume is large, busy site that has been well developed with much investment. It is about 5.5 km. from the long sandy beach of Fréjus-Plage, but it has such a fine and varied selection of swimming pools on site that many people do not bother to make the trip. The pools with their palm trees are a feature of this site and are remarkable for their size and variety (water slides, etc.) – the very large 'feature' pool a highlight. The site has nearly 500 pitches of varying but quite adequate size with electricity, water and drainage, with another 200 larger ones with mains sewerage to take mobile homes. Separators are being installed to divide the pitches and shade is available over most of the terrain. Although tents are accepted, the site concentrates mainly on caravanning. It is likely to become full in season, but one section with unmarked pitches is not reserved, and there is plenty of space off-peak. La Baume's convenient location has its 'downside' as there is some traffic noise from the nearby autoroute – somewhat obtrusive at first but we soon failed to notice it. A popular site with tour operators. Adjoining La Baume is its sister site La Palmeraie, containing self-catering accommodation, its own landscaped pool and providing some entertainment to supplement that at La Baume.

Facilities

The seven toilet blocks should be a satisfactory supply. Two have been enlarged recently, the others refurbished to provide mainly British style toilets with a few Turkish; washbasins in cabins and sinks for clothes and dishes with hot water. Supermarket and several other shops. Bar with external terrace overlooking pools and TV. Restaurant and takeaway. Five swimming pools. Fitness centre. Tennis courts. Archery (July/Aug). Oganised events - sports, competitions, etc. in daytime and some evening entertainment partly in English. Amphitheatre for shows. Discos daily in season. Off site: A bus to Fréjus passes the gate.

At a glance

Welcome & Ambience	✓✓✓	Location	✓✓✓✓
Quality of Pitches	✓✓✓✓	Range of Facilities	✓✓✓✓✓

Directions

Site is 3 km. up the D4 road, which leads north from N7 just west of Fréjus. From west on autoroute A8 take exit for Fréjus/St Raphaël (junction 37), turn towards them and after 4 km., turn left on D4. From east take exit for Fréjus/St Raphaël (junction 38); after exit turn right immediately on small road marked 'Musée' etc. which leads you to D4 where right again.

Charges 2003

Per unit incl. 2 persons, electricity (6A), water and drainage	€ 18.00	€ 35.00
extra person	€ 4.00 -	€ 7.70
child (under 7 yrs)	free -	€ 4.70
local tax		€ 5.00

Min. stay for motorhomes 3 nights.

Reservations

Essential for high season, and made for exact dates with substantial deposit and fee (€ 31.25), from 1 Jan. Tel: 04 94 15 88 88. Email: reception@labaume-lapalmeraie.com

Open

22 March - 30 September, with full services.

FR83250 Sunêlia Douce Quiétude

3435 boulevard Jacques Baudino, 83700 St Raphaël (Var)

Douce Quiétude is only seven kilometres from the beaches at Saint Raphaël and Agay but is quietly situated at the foot of the Estérel massif. There are 400 pitches, but only 70 of these are for touring units (around half are used for mobile homes) set in pleasant pine woodland or shaded, green areas. The pitches are of a comfortable size, separated by bushes and trees with electricity (6A), water, drainage and telephone/TV points provided. This mature site offers a wide range of services and facilities complete with a pool complex. It can be busy in the main season yet is relaxed and spacious. Security is good with the wearing of identity bracelets mandatory throughout your stay.

Facilities

Fully equipped modern toilet blocks have changing facilities for babies and provision for disabled visitors. Launderette. Bar and restaurant with takeaway and pizzeria (1/6 -3/9). Shop. Three outdoor swimming pools (two heated), water slide and jacuzzi. Play area. Children's club and activities for teenagers (all July/Aug). Sports area for volleyball, basketball and petanque. Games room (July/Aug). Tennis. Table tennis and billards. Minigolf. Archery. Fitness centre and sauna (July/Aug). Evening entertainment with shows, karaoke and discos. Mountain bike hire. Only gas barbecues are permitted. Off site: Golf and riding 5 km. Windsurf hire and sea fishing 7 km.

At a glance

Welcome & Ambience	✓✓✓✓	Location	✓✓✓✓
Quality of Pitches	✓✓✓✓	Range of Facilities	✓✓✓✓✓

Directions

Take exit 38 from A8 autoroute signed Fréjus/St Raphaël. Follow directions for Valescure then Agay on the D100, then site signs (takes you round the back of Fréjus/St Raphael). The site can also be reached from the N98 coast road turning north at Agay on D100; continue past Esterel Camping to pick up site signs.

Charges 2003

Per unit incl. 2 persons	€ 30.00 - € 40.00
extra person	€ 6.00 - € 7.50
child (3-12 yrs)	€ 5.00 - € 5.50
animal	€ 4.00

Camping Cheques accepted.

Reservations

Contact site. Tel: 04 94 44 30 00. Email: info@douce-quietude.com

Open

6 April - 30 September.

FR83070 Caravaning L'Etoile d'Argens

83370 St Aygulf (Var)

First impressions of L'Etoile d'Argens are of space, cleanliness and calm. Reception staff are very friendly and English is spoken (open 24 hrs). This is a site run with families in mind and many of the activities are free, making for a good value holiday. There are 493 level grass pitches (265 for touring units) laid out in typical French style, separated by hedges. There are five sizes of pitch, ranging from 50 sq.m. (for small tents) to 250 sq.m. These are exceptionally large and two families could easily fit two caravans and cars or one family could have a very spacious plot with a garden like atmosphere. All pitches are fully serviced with fresh and waste water and 10A electricity, with mainly good shade although the site is not overpowered by trees which leads to a spacious feeling. The pool and bar area is attractively landscaped with old olive and palm trees on beautifully kept grass. Two heated pools (one for adults, one for children) have been added recently – both very much with families in mind, not teenagers as there are no big slides. The river runs along one side of the site and a free boat service (15/6-15/9) runs every 40 minutes to the beach. It is also possible to moor a boat or fish. This is a good family site for the summer but also good in low season for a quiet stay in a superb location with excellent pitches. Tour operators take 85 pitches and there are 175 mobile homes but for a large site it is unusually calm and peaceful even in July.

Facilities

Two new toilet blocks were added in 2000, whilst all but 4 of the 20 original small unisex blocks have been renovated. All are well kept and include some washbasins in cubicles. Dishwashing sinks and laundry with outside clothes line. Supermarket and gas supplies. Bar, restaurant, pizzeria, takeaway. Two adult pools (one heated), paddling pool, jacuzzi and solarium. Tennis (two of the four courts are floodlit) with coaching and minigolf (both free in low season), aerobics, archery (July/Aug), football and swimming lessons. Volleyball, basketball, table tennis and boule. Play area with rubber safety base. Children's entertainer in July/Aug. Activity programme includes games, dances for adults and escorted walking trips to the surrounding hills. within 3 km. Off site: Golf 2 km. Riding 3 km. Bicycle hire 2.5 km. Beach 3.5 km.

At a glance

| Welcome & Ambience | ✓✓✓✓ | Location | ✓✓✓✓ |
| Quality of Pitches | ✓✓✓✓✓ | Range of Facilities | ✓✓✓✓✓ |

Directions

Leave A8 at exit 36 and take N7 to Le Muy and Fréjus. After about 8 km. at roundabout take D7 signed Roquebrune and St Aygulf. In 9.5 km. (after roundabout) turn left signed Fréjus. Watch for site sign and ignore width and height limit signs as site is 500 m. to right.

Charges 2003

Per tent pitch (100 sq.m.) with electricity and 2 persons	€ 20.00 - € 37.00
'comfort' pitch (100 sq.m.) incl. 3 persons, water and drainage	€ 26.00 - € 43.00
child (under 7 yrs)	€ 3.50 - € 5.50

Reservations

Made for any period with substantial deposit and fee. Tel: 04 94 81 01 41. Email: letoiledargens@wanadoo.fr

Open

Easter - 30 September, with all services.

FR83240 Camping Caravaning Moulin des Iscles

83520 Roquebrune-sur-Argens (Var)

A haven of peace and tranquillity, Moulin des Iscles is hidden down 0.5 km. of private, unmade road – an unusual find in this often quite hectic part of Provence. Based around a former mill, it is a small, pretty site beside the river Argens with access to the river in places for fishing, canoeing and swimming, with a concrete bank and fenced where deemed necessary (some sought after pitches overlook the river). The 90 grassy, level pitches with electricity and water to all, radiate out from M. Dumarcet's attractive, centrally situated home which is where the restaurant and shop are situated. A nice mixture of deciduous trees provide natural shade and colour and the old mill house rests comfortably near the entrance which has a security barrier closed at night. This is a quiet site with little on site entertainment, but with a nice little restaurant. A good effort has been made to welcome visitors wih disabilities. It is a real campsite not a 'camping village'.

Facilities

The toilet block is fully equipped, including ramped access for disabled visitors. Some Turkish style toilets. Washbasins have cold water, some in cubicles. Baby bath and changing facilities en-suite. Covered laundry and dishwashing sinks. Small separate unisex provision for pitches near the entrance. Washing machine. Restaurant with home cooked dish-of-the-day on a weekly rotation. Surprisingly well stocked shop. Library - some English books. TV room incl. satellite, Pool table, table tennis. Play area, minigolf and boules all outside the barrier for more peace and quiet on site. Internet terminal. Canoeing possible. Off site: Riding and golf 6 km. Bicycle hire 2 km. (new bicycle way to St Aygulf). Beach 7 km.

At a glance

| Welcome & Ambience | ✓✓✓✓ | Location | ✓✓✓✓ |
| Quality of Pitches | ✓✓✓✓ | Range of Facilities | ✓✓✓ |

Directions

Follow as for site no. 8320, Les Pecheurs, but continue past it through the village of Roquebrune towards St Aygulf for 1 km. Site signed on left. Follow private unmade road for approx. 500 m. to site entrance in front of you.

Charges 2003

Per unit incl. 2 or 3 persons	€ 18.00
extra person	€ 3.20
child (over 10 yrs)	€ 2.20
electricity (6A)	€ 2.70
local tax	€ 0.30

Prices are lower out of high season.

Reservations

Contact site. Tel: 04 94 45 70 74. Email: moulin.iscles@wanadoo.fr

Open

1 April - 30 September.

L'Étoile d'Argens

2004

" 35 years experience "

83370 St Aygulf - Tél. +33 4 94 81 01 41

www.provence-campings.com/frejus/etoile-argens

FR83010 Camping Caravaning Les Pins Parasols

Route de Bagnols, 83600 Fréjus (Var)

Not everyone likes very big sites, and Les Pins Parasols with its 189 pitches is of a size which is quite easy to walk around. It is family owned and run. Although on very slightly undulating ground, virtually all the pitches are levelled or terraced and separated by hedges or bushes with pine trees for shade. They are around 100 sq.m. and all have electricity. What is particularly interesting, as it is the most unusual feature, is that 48 of the pitches are equipped with their own fully enclosed, tiled sanitary unit, consisting of WC, washbasin, hot shower and washing up sink, all quite close together. These pitches naturally cost more but may well be of interest to those seeking extra comfort. The nearest beach is the once very long Fréjus-Plage (5.5 km) now reduced a little by the new marina, and adjoins St Raphaël. Used by tour operators (10%).

Facilities

Besides the individual units there are three toilet blocks of good average quality providing washbasins in cabins and facilities for disabled people. One block can be heated when necessary. Small shop with reasonable stocks and restaurant with takeaway (both 1/5-20/9). General room with TV. Swimming pool (200 sq.m) with attractive rock backdrop and separate long slide with landing pool and small children's pool (heated). Half-court tennis. Off site: Bicycle hire or riding 2 km, fishing 6 km, golf 10 km. Bus from the gate into Fréjus 5km.

At a glance

| Welcome & Ambience | ✓✓✓✓ | Location | ✓✓✓✓ |
| Quality of Pitches | ✓✓✓✓ | Range of Facilities | ✓✓✓✓✓ |

Directions

From autoroute A8 take exit 38 for Fréjus Est. Turn right immediately on leaving pay booths on a small road which leads across to D4, where right again and under 1 km. to site.

Charges 2004

Per normal pitch with electricity incl. 2 persons	€ 17.40 - € 24.90
with sanitary unit	€ 22.00 - € 31.00
child (under 7 yrs)	€ 2.90 - € 3.65

Reservations

Made for min. 10 days for exact dates with deposit (€ 92) but no fee. Tel: 04 94 40 88 43. Email: lespinsparasols@wanadoo.fr

Open

Easter - 30 September.

LES PINS PARASOLS

CAMPING CARAVANNING ★★★★NN
ROUTE DE BAGNOLS - F-83600 FRÉJUS
Telephone 0033 494.40.88.43
SWIMMING POOL
Supermarket - Snackbar - Individual washing cabins and hot water in all sanitary facilities - Separated pitches (80-100m2) all with electricity. Pitches with individual sanitary facilities (shower, washbasin, sink with hot water, WC) - Children's playground and solarium - Caravan pitches - Water points - Mini-tennis
SUN AND SHADE near the beaches
Fax : 0033 494.40.81.99
Email : lespinsparasols@wanadoo.fr
Internet : www.lespinsparasols.com

FR83030 Camping Caravaning Leï Suves

Quartier du Blavet, 83520 Roquebrune-sur-Argens (Var)

This quiet, pretty site is a few kilometres inland from the coast, 2 km. north of the N7. Close to the unusual Roquebrune rock, it is within easy reach of resorts such as St Tropez, Ste Maxime, St Raphaël and Cannes. The site entrance is appealing – wide and spacious, with a large bank of well tended flowers. Mainly on a gently sloping hillside, the 310 pitches are terraced with shade provided by the many cork trees which give the site its name. All pitches have electricity and access to water, with a good number taken by mobile homes. A pleasant pool area is beside the bar/restaurant and entertainment area. It is possible to walk in the surrounding woods as long as there is no fire alert.

Facilities

Two modern, well kept toilet blocks include washbasins in cabins, external dishwashing sinks, laundry room with washing machines. Facilities for disabled visitors. Shop. Good sized swimming pool and paddling pool. Bar and terrace, snack bar and takeaway (all 15/5-30/9). Outdoor stage near the bar for evening entertainment in high season. Excellent play area for all ages. Table tennis, tennis and sports area. Internet terminal. Only gas barbecues are permitted. Off site: Fishing 3 km, bicycle hire 5 km, riding 1 km, golf 7 km. Beach at St Aygulf 15 km.

At a glance

| Welcome & Ambience | ✓✓✓✓ | Location | ✓✓✓✓ |
| Quality of Pitches | ✓✓✓✓ | Range of Facilities | ✓✓✓✓✓ |

Directions

Leave autoroute at Le Muy and take N7 towards St Raphaël. Turn left at roundabout on D7 heading north signed La Boverie (site signed). Site on right in 2 km.

Charges 2003

Per unit incl. 2 persons	€ 19.00 - € 22.60
incl. 3 persons	€ 19.50 - € 23.10
child (under 7 yrs)	€ 2.70 - € 3.20
electricity	€ 2.90

Reservations

Contact site. Tel: 04 94 45 43 95. Email: camping.lei.suves@wanadoo.fr

Open

1 April - 15 October.

FR83200 Camping Caravaning Les Pêcheurs

83520 Roquebrune sur Argens (Var)

Developed over three generations by the Simoncini family, this peaceful, friendly site is set in more than four hectares of mature, well shaded countryside at the foot of the Roquebrune Rock. It will appeal to families who appreciate natural surroundings together with many activities, cultural and sporting. Interspersed with a number of mobile homes, the 130 touring pitches are all of a good size with electricity and separated by trees or flowering bushes (there are 24 mobile homes and 75 pitches used by tour operators). The Provencal style buildings are delightful, especially the bar, restaurant and games room, with its terrace down to the river and the site's own canoe station (locked gate). Adjacent to the site, across the road, is a lake used exclusively for water skiing with a sandy beach, a restaurant and minigolf. Activities include climbing the 'Rock' with a guide. We became more and more intrigued with stories about the Rock, as unfolded by Sabine Simoncini. The Holy Hole, the Three Crosses and the Hermit all call for further exploration which Sabine is happy to arrange, likewise trips to Monte Carlo, Ventiniglia (Italy) and the Gorges du Verdon, etc. The medieval village of Roquebrune is within walking distance.

Facilities

Modern, well designed toilet facilities are in three blocks, one new and attractively designed, the other two refurbished. Overall, it is a good provision, with washbasins in cabins (warm water only), baby baths and facilities for disabled visitors. Dishwashing and laundry sinks (H&C). Washing machines. Sheltered swimming pool (25 x 10 m) with separate paddling pool (child-proof gates, lifeguard in high season; closed lunch times in July/Aug.) with ice cream bar. Shop. Bar, restaurant and games room (all open all season). Play field with nets and play equipment. Fishing. Canoeing (free) and water skiing. Animation arranged in main season for children and adults, visits to local wine caves and sessions at rafting and diving schools. Only gas or electric barbecues are permitted. Only one dog per pitch is accepted. Off site: Riding 6 km. Golf 6 km (reduced fees). Bicycle hire 1 km.

At a glance

Welcome & Ambience	✓✓✓✓✓	Location	✓✓✓✓
Quality of Pitches	✓✓✓✓	Range of Facilities	✓✓✓✓✓

Directions

From A8 autoroute take Le Muy exit and follow N7 towards Frèjus for approx. 13 km. bypassing Le Muy. After crossing over the A8, turn right at roundabout towards Roquebrune sur Argens. Site is on left after 2 km. just before bridge over river (watch carefully for fairly narrow entrance).

Charges 2004

Per unit incl. 2 persons	€ 18.00 - € 31.00
incl. 3 persons	€ 20.00 - € 32.50
child (under 7 yrs)	€ 3.00 - € 5.00
electricity (6/10A)	€ 4.00 - € 5.00
dog (max 1)	€ 3.00

Camping Cheques accepted.

Reservations

Made for touring pitches with deposit and fee.
Tel: 04 94 45 71 25.
Email: info@camping-les-pecheurs.com

Open

1 April - 15 October.

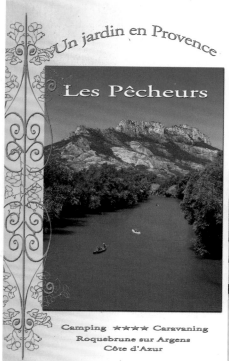

Un jardin en Provence

Les Pêcheurs

Camping ★★★★ Caravaning
Roquebrune sur Argens
Côte d'Azur

FR83170 Camping Domaine de la Bergerie

Vallée du Fournel, 83520 Roquebrune sur Argens (Var)

This is yet another site near the Côte d'Azur which will take you away from all the bustle of the Mediterranean to total relaxation amongst the cork, oak, pine and mimosa. The 60 hectare site is quite spread out. The terrain varies from natural, rocky, semi-landscaped areas for mobile homes to flat, grassy terrain with avenues of 200 separated pitches for touring caravans and tents. All pitches average over 80 sq.m. and have electrical connections, with those in one area also having water and drainage. The restaurant/bar, a converted farm building, is surrounded by shady patios, whilst inside it oozes character with high beams and archways leading to intimate corners. Tournaments and programmes are organised daily and, in the evening, shows, cabarets, discos, cinema, karaoke and dancing at the amphitheatre prove popular (possibly until midnight). This is a good site for families with children and teenagers.

Facilities

Four sanitary blocks are kept clean and include washbasins in cubicles, facilities for disabled people and babies, plus dishwashing and laundry areas with washing machines. Well stocked supermarket. Bar/restaurant. Takeaway. New pool complex (1/4-30/9) with indoor pool and fitness centre (body building, sauna, gym, etc). Five tennis courts and two half courts. Archery, roller skating and minigolf. Volleyball and mini football. Mini-farm for children. Fishing. Only gas barbecues are permitted. Off site: Riding or golf 4 km, bicycle hire 7 km. Water skiing and rock climbing nearby. St Aygulf or Ste Maxime are 7 km.

At a glance

Welcome & Ambience	✓✓✓✓	Location	✓✓✓✓
Quality of Pitches	✓✓✓✓	Range of Facilities	✓✓✓✓✓

Directions

Leave A8 at Le Muy exit on N7 towards Fréjus. Proceed for 9 km., then right onto D7 signed St Aygulf. Continue for 8 km. and then right at roundabout on D8; site is on the right.

Charges 2003

Per unit incl. 2 adults and electricity (5A)	€ 16.00 - € 26.50
3 persons and electricity	€ 20.00 - € 35.00
with water and drainage	€ 23.00 - € 38.00
extra person	€ 4.00 - € 6.80
child (under 7 yrs)	€ 3.00 - € 5.20
electricity (10A)	€ 1.80 - € 2.60
dog	free - € 2.50
local tax	€ 0.30

Reservations

Made with deposit (€ 200) and fee (€ 20). (Mobile homes available 15 February - 15 November). Tel: 04 98 11 45 45. Email: info@domainelabergerie.com

Open

1 June - 15 September.

FR83080 **Au Paradis des Campeurs**

La Gaillarde-Plage, 83380 Les Issambres (Var)

Having direct access to a sandy beach (via an underpass) and being so well maintained are just two of the reasons which make Au Paradis so popular. Family owned and run, it now has 180 pitches, all with electricity and 132 with water tap and drainaway. The original pitches vary in size and shape but all are satisfactory and most have some shade. The new pitches are all large but at present have little shade although trees and bushes have been planted and shade is developing. There is no entertainment which gives peaceful nights. The gates are surveyed by TV (especially the beach gate) and a security man patrols all day. The site has become popular and it is essential to book for June, July and August.

Facilities

Two toilet blocks, refurbished to an excellent standard with high quality fittings and well maintained, include the majority of washbasins in cabins. Facilities for children are very good with baby baths and a shower at suitable height. En-suite unit for disabled visitors. Dishwashing, laundry sinks, two washing machines and dryer. Motorcaravan service point. Shop and restaurant (with takeaway service) front onto main road and open all season. TV room. Two excellent play areas, catering for the under and over 5s, both with top quality safety bases. Boules. Off site: Bicycle hire 2.5 km, riding 3 km, golf 6 km.

At a glance

Welcome & Ambience	✓✓✓✓	Location	✓✓✓✓
Quality of Pitches	✓✓✓✓	Range of Facilities	✓✓✓

Directions

Site is signed from N98 coast road at La Gaillarde, 2 km. south of St Aygulf.

Charges 2003

Per unit incl. 2 persons	€ 12.60 - € 19.50
with water and drainage	€ 14.50 - € 23.50
extra person	€ 5.00
child (under 4 yrs)	€ 2.80
electricity (6A)	€ 3.40
local tax	€ 0.30

Reservations

Advised for main season. Tel: 04 94 96 93 55.

Open

20 March - 15 October.

THE LOW SEASON SPECIALIST - 30% off from 28/03 to 28/06 and from 1/09 to 04/10

DIRECT ACCESS TO THE BEACH

CAMPING AU PARADIS DES CAMPEURS ★★★★

LA GAILLARDE-PLAGE
F-83380 LES ISSAMBRES
TEL: 0033 494 96 93 55
www.paradis-des-campeurs.com

FR83100 **Camping de la Plage**

RN 98, 83310 Grimaud (Var)   *no mobile homes etc.*

A site actually on the beach is always in great demand, and Camping de la Plage is no exception and consequently it becomes very crowded. The site is divided into two parts by the N98 but a dangerous crossing is avoided by an underpass. All pitches are numbered and can be reserved – the pitches away from the beach will be the more peaceful. They are mostly of a decent size, with the ones over the road having more grass and more shade. All pitches have electricity but long leads may be required. Ste Maxime is 6 km. and it is not very far to all the familiar names of the south of France – St Tropez, Port Grimaud, Fréjus and St Aygulf.

Facilities

There are three toilet blocks on each side of the site. Of varying quality, but clean when we visited and, according to regulars, cleaned regularly. They are fully equipped, the majority of WCs of the British type. Baby bath. Large, well stocked supermarket (all season). Bar, restaurant and takeaway (from May). Beach volleyball. Tennis. Small play area. Off site: Bicycle hire 2 km, golf and riding 3 km. Boat hire nearby.

At a glance

Welcome & Ambience	✓✓✓	Location	✓✓✓✓✓
Quality of Pitches	✓✓✓	Range of Facilities	✓✓✓

Directions

Site is on N98 main coast road about 6 km. southwest of St Maxime. Take care - this road is very busy in main season.

Charges 2003

Per unit with 2 persons	€ 19.00
extra person	€ 5.00
child (under 7 yrs)	€ 2.50
electricity (2-10A)	€ 3.50 - € 6.50

Reservations

Bookings taken for exact dates with booking fee from Oct.- March only. Tel: 04 94 56 31 15.

Open

Two weeks before Easter - 21 October.

341

FR83160 Parc Camping Les Cigales

721, chemin du Jas de la Paro, 83490 Le Muy (Var)

Parc Les Cigales has been developed over the last 30 years by the same family to become a pleasant site benefiting from the shady environment of cork umbrella pines, further enhanced by olives, palm trees, sweet smelling mimosa and colourful shrubs. It has now undergone major rejuvenation. The entrance has been completely resited which, in fact, turns the site round utilising the top of the site around the pretty pool area more. The entrance is wide and smart with a new reception, shop and all facilities but the 'piece de resistance' is the new 'survival area' with courses for all ages and a wide range of equipment including arial runways. All the necessary safety equipment is in evidence and it is open to the public with costs varying according to the type of course used. A riding school, a vegetable garden and a small animal farm complete this unusual but environmentally thought out development. The terrain is typical of the area with rough, sloped and stony, dry ground but the pitches are of a good size, terraced where necessary and nestling amongst the trees. There are 163 pitches in total with 35 mobile homes to rent, nicely landscaped. The restaurant/bar area overlooks the attractive pool complex including a children's pool with sloping beach effect. Convenient for the autoroute, this is a spacious family site away from the hectic coast to be enjoyed.

Facilities

Six modern sanitary blocks of varying size more than serve the site and include washbasins in cabins and facilities for disabled people. Dishwashing sinks outside but under cover. Laundry area with washing machines and ironing boards. Shop (1/5-30/8). Restaurant/bar with patio. Heated pool complex and sunbathing area. Adventure play area. Survival courses. Multi-sport area (basketball, volleyball, etc). Trampoline. Riding. Canoeing and hang-gliding are organised. Entertainment organised each evening in season, with a disco twice weekly and daytime activities for children and senior citizens. Internet terminal. Charcoal barbecues are not permitted. Off site: Le Muy (2 km) has a Sunday market. Fishing 2 km, riding 7 km, golf 10 km. The N7 is on a bus route or take a train at Les Arcs (8 km).

At a glance

Welcome & Ambience	✓✓✓✓✓	Location	✓✓✓✓
Quality of Pitches	✓✓✓✓	Range of Facilities	✓✓✓✓✓

Directions

Site is signed off approach to autoroute péage on A8 at Le Muy exit and is 2 km. west of Le Muy on N7. It is necessary to cross the dual-carriageway as you approach the toll booth from Le Muy. Site entrance is well signed.

Charges 2003

Per unit incl. 2 persons	€ 11.00 - € 21.00
extra person	€ 3.00 - € 5.00
child (under 7 yrs)	free - € 3.00
electricity (6-10A)	€ 3.00 - € 5.00

Local tax included. Less 5% for stays over 3 weeks.

Reservations

Advised for July/Aug. Tel: 04 94 45 12 08. Email: contact@les-cigales.com

Open

28 March - 1 November.

FR83120 Camp du Domaine

La Favière, B.P. 207, 83230 Bormes-les-Mimosas (Var)

Camp du Domaine, 3 km. south of Le Lavandou, is a large, attractive beach-side site with 1,200 pitches set in 45 hectares of pine woods, although surprisingly it does not give the impression of being so big. Most pitches are reasonably level and 800 have electricity. The most popular pitches are at the beach, but the ones furthest away are, on the whole, larger and have more shade amongst the trees, although many of them are more suitable for tents. The beach is the attraction, however, and every-one tries to get as near to it as they can. Despite its size, the site does not give the feeling of being busy, except perhaps around the supermarket. This is mainly because many pitches are hidden in the trees, the access roads are quite wide and it all covers quite a large area (some of the beach pitches are 600 m. from the entrance). Its popularity makes early reservation necessary over a long season (about mid June to mid Sept.) as regular clients book from season to season. English is spoken.

Facilities

Ten modern toilet blocks are kept clean but, due to high usage because of the popularity of the site, parts soon begin to show wear and tear. WCs are mostly of the Turkish type (management policy). All facilities have pre-mixed hot water with many washbasins in cabins (some with showers). Facilities for disabled visitors (but steep steps). Block for children and baby room. Washing machines in most blocks. Fridges to hire. Well stocked supermarket. Bars and a pizzeria. Excellent play area. Boats and pedaloes for hire. Wide range of watersports. Games and competitions arranged in July/Aug. Children's club. Six tennis courts, table tennis and minigolf. Multi-sports courts. American motorhomes not accepted. Barbecues are strictly forbidden. Off site: Bicycle hire 500 m, riding or golf 15 km.

At a glance

Welcome & Ambience	✓✓✓✓✓	Location	✓✓✓✓✓
Quality of Pitches	✓✓✓✓	Range of Facilities	✓✓✓✓✓

Directions

Just outside and to west of Le Lavandou, at new roundabout, turn off D559 towards the sea on road signed Favière. After 2 km. turn left at camp signs.

Charges 2003

Per unit incl. 2 persons	€ 15.50 - € 21.50
with electricity (10A) and water	€ 23.00 - € 28.00
extra person	€ 4.60 - € 6.00
child (under 7 yrs)	€ 2.60 - € 3.00
local tax	€ 0.30

Reservations

Made with 30% deposit and fee (€ 22,87). Tel: 04 94 71 03 12. Email: mail@campdudomaine.com

Open

April - 31 October.

FR83220 Camping Caravaning Cros de Mouton

B.P.116, 83240 Cavalaire-sur-Mer (Var)

Cros de Mouton is a reasonably priced campsite in a popular area. High in the hills on a steep hillside, 1.5 km. from Cavalaire and its popular beaches, the site is a calm oasis away from the hectic coast. Unfortunately, due to the nature of the terrain, some of the site roads are very steep – the higher pitches with the best views are especially so. However, Olivier and Andre are happy to take your caravan up with their 4x4 Jeep if you are worried. There are 199 terraced pitches under cork trees which include 46 for mobile homes, 80 suitable only for tents with parking close by, and 80 for touring caravans. These have electricity, some also have water. The restaurant terrace and the pools have wonderful view of Cavalaire and the bay. English is spoken.

Facilities

Two clean and well maintained toilet blocks have all the usual facilities including washbasins in cubicles. Washing machine at each and a fully fitted facility for disabled customers (although site is perhaps a little steep in places for wheelchairs). Bar/restaurant serving reasonably priced meals, plus takeaways. Swimming and paddling pools with lots of sun-beds on the terrace and small bar serving snacks and cold drinks. Small play area and games room.

At a glance

Welcome & Ambience	✓✓✓✓	Location	✓✓✓✓
Quality of Pitches	✓✓✓	Range of Facilities	✓✓✓✓

Directions

Site is very well signed from the centre of Cavalaire.

Charges 2004

Per person	€ 5.80 - € 7.10
child (under 7 yrs)	€ 4.00
pitch	€ 5.80 - € 7.10
electricity (10A)	€ 4.00

Camping Cheques accepted.

Reservations

Made with deposit (€ 84) and fee (€ 16).
Tel: 04 94 64 10 87.
Email: campingcrosdemouton@wanadoo.fr

Open

15 March - 31 October.

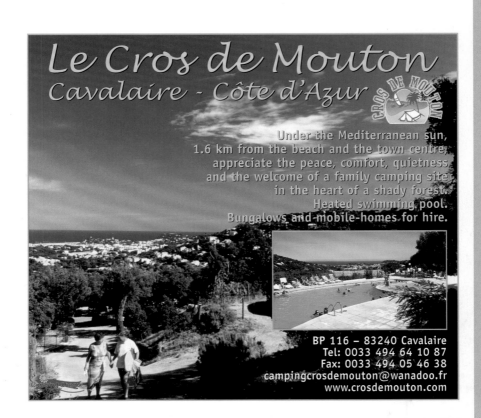

Le Cros de Mouton
Cavalaire - Côte d'Azur

Under the Mediterranean sun,
1.6 km from the beach and the town centre,
appreciate the peace, comfort, quietness
and the welcome of a family camping site
in the heart of a shady forest.
Heated swimming pool.
Bungalows and mobile-homes for hire.

BP 116 – 83240 Cavalaire
Tel: 0033 494 64 10 87
Fax: 0033 494 05 46 38
campingcrosdemouton@wanadoo.fr
www.crosdemouton.com

FR83210 Camping Les Tournels

Route de Camarat, 83350 Ramatuelle (Var)

Les Tournels is a large site set on a hillside and some of the pitches have wonderful panoramic views of the Gulf of St Tropez and Pampelonne beach. The whole hill is covered in parasol pines and old olive trees, so all pitches have some shade. Reasonably level, but varying in size, there is electricity on the majority (long electricity leads may be required). The rest are reserved for tents. Clean and well equipped sanitary blocks are within reasonable distance of the pitches, but the swimming pool, play area, shop and bar could turn out to be quite some distance away. The large swimming pool is of an unusual shape, the circular paddling pool has a mushroom shaped fountain, and both are surrounded by sunbathing areas with sun-beds. Competitions and shows are produced for adults and children in July/Aug. A shuttle bus runs the 500 m. to the local shopping centre and also to Pampelonne beach. Reception opens for long hours and English is spoken. The beaches are a big draw, but also who can resist a visit to St Tropez where perhaps you will see someone famous as they parade along the famous waterfront, and the floating 'gin palaces' are a sight to behold.

Facilities

Two of the toilet blocks are of older design, the other six being very good. These include some washbasins in cubicles, mainly British style WCs (paper required), baby baths, children's WCs and facilities for disabled visitors. Three blocks are heated in low season. Washing and drying machines at five blocks, with refrigerators to rent outside all of them. Dishwashing and laundry sinks. Bar/restaurant (1/4-15/10). Takeaway. Another bar with disco at the furthest end of the site, well away from most pitches. Large swimming pool (600 sq.m, open 1/4-20/10 and heated in low season). Large fenced play area with good quality equipment. Table tennis, volleyball, basketball and boules pitches. Archery. Mini-club for children over 5 years for sporting activities. Safety deposit boxes to rent. Only gas barbecues are permitted. Off site: Shopping centre 500 m. from the site entrance (owned by the family) contains supermarket, tobacconist, launderette, rotisserie and a snack bar. Beach 1.5 km.

Directions

From A8 exit 36 take D25 to Ste Maxime, then D98 towards St Tropez. On outskirts of St Tropez, take D93 to Ramatuelle. Site is signed on left in 9 km.

Charges 2003

Per unit incl. 2 persons	
with electricity and water	€ 21.50 - € 29.50
extra person	€ 5.20 - € 7.00
child (2-7 yrs)	€ 2.70 - € 3.50
animal	€ 2.70 - € 3.30
electricity (10A)	€ 3.60
local tax	€ 0.30

Reservations

Contact site for details. Tel: 04 94 55 90 90.
Email: info@tournels.com

Open

All year except 11 Jan - 25 February.

At a glance

Welcome & Ambience	✓✓✓	Location	✓✓✓
Quality of Pitches	✓✓✓	Range of Facilities	✓✓✓

FR83130 Camping Le Beau Vezé

Route de la Moutonne, 83320 Carqueiranne (Var)

Le Beau Vezé is a quiet site, some way inland from the busy resort of Hyères. The owner tries to keep it as a family site with its quiet position, although the superb beaches and hectic coastal areas are within easy reach. On a steep hillside it has terraced pitches and a plateau with more pitches on the top. The 150 pitches are well shaded but unfortunately some will be rather difficult to manoeuvre onto due to over-hanging trees and could be difficult for motorcaravans. There is some road noise on the lower pitches. The lovely old town of Hyères is only 8 km.

Facilities

Three sanitary blocks of a reasonable standard, two quite modern with heating, although maintenance may be variable in high season. All have hot showers and some cubicles have a washbasin also, making them more roomy. British and Turkish style WCs. Baby room. Laundry and dishwashing sinks. Two washing machines. Bar/restaurant and takeaway. Bread to order. Medium sized pool and paddling pool. Play area. Bicycle hire, minigolf, table tennis, volleyball, boule and tennis court. Off site: Riding and golf 2 km.

Directions

From D559 between Carqueiranne and Le Pradet, take D76 northwards signed La Moutonne and site is signed on right of D76.

Charges 2003

Per unit incl. 2 persons	€ 26.00
extra person	€ 6.20
child (under 10 yrs)	€ 4.57
electricity (6A)	€ 3.81
animal	€ 2.30
Camping Cheques accepted.	

Reservations

Made with deposit (€ 46) and fee (€ 15,24).
Tel: 04 94 57 65 30.

Open

1 May - 15 September.

At a glance

Welcome & Ambience	✓✓✓	Location	✓✓✓
Quality of Pitches	✓✓✓	Range of Facilities	✓✓✓

FR83140 Camping Les Lacs du Verdon

Domaine de Roquelande, 83630 Réguisse (Var)

In beautiful countryside and within easy reach of the Grand Canyon du Verdon and its nearby lakes, this site is only 90 minutes from Cannes. This bustling and possible noisy campsite is suitable for active families and teenagers. The 30 acre wooded park is divided in two by a minor road. The 480 very stony, but level pitches (rock pegs advised) are marked and separated by trees and lines of stones. There are 130 pitches for tourists which are scattered amongst the trees and often have an irregular shape, although all are of average to good size. There are plenty of electricity boxes but long leads may be necessary. Water taps are few. The part across the road is used mainly for mobile homes but has some pitches for tourers, mostly at the far end. There are toilet blocks close by but the pitches are a long way from all the other site facilities. The main site is much more pleasant and closer to all the activities. Tour operators and mobile homes, for hire and privately owned, take up nearly three quarters of the site.

Facilities

The toilet blocks are old and much of the equipment is looking very jaded, but they are just about acceptable. They mainly have British style WCs and some washbasins in cubicles with warm water only. The block we tried had fairly hot water but campers complained they were not so lucky. All blocks have sinks for laundry and dishes. Washing machines and dryers. At the end of May very little was open and the level of cleanliness was just about adequate. Motorcaravan service point (with charge). Shop. Bar. Restaurant (recently rebuilt) and pizzeria (all 18/5-13/9). TV and teenage games. Discos, dances and theme nights. Excellent swimming pool/paddling pool complex (all season) and new artificial grass tennis courts - the highlight of this campsite. Volleyball, table tennis, archery and boules. Bicycle hire. Playground. Daily entertainment for all the family in May and June, with a more extensive programme in high season. Only electric barbecues are permitted. Off site: Fishing, beach, sailing and windsurfing at the site's club at Saint Croix (15 km). The village of Regusse is about 2.5 km. and the small town of Aups is 7 km. Riding 10 km.

Directions

Leave the A8 motorway at St Maximin and take the D560 northeast to Barjols. At Barjols turn left on D71 to Montmeyan, turn right on D30 to Regusse and follow site signs.

Latest charges

Per pitch incl. 1 or 2 persons	€ 17.00 - € 20.00
extra person	€ 5.00 - € 6.00
child (3-7 yrs)	€ 4.00 - € 5.00
electricity (10A)	€ 4.00
dog	€ 2.00
local tax	€ 0.30

Camping Cheques accepted.

Reservations

Made with 25% deposit and fee (€ 20).
Tel: 04 94 70 17 95. Email: info@lacs-verdon.com

Open

27 April - 28 September.

At a glance

Welcome & Ambience	✓✓✓✓	Location	✓✓✓✓
Quality of Pitches	✓✓✓	Range of Facilities	✓✓✓✓✓

FR83260 Camping Château de L'Eouvière

Route de Tavernes, 83670 Montmeyan (Var)

This spacious new site is in the grounds of an 18th century château, close to the magnificent hill village of Montmeyan. There are 30 hectares of grounds to explore and the swimming pool, bar, restaurant which are in front of the château, have lovely views over the valley and hills beyond. The toilet block and children's play area are to one side. The 80 large pitches (all for tourers) are well marked and separated on terraces, mostly behind the château. Many have magnificent views. Newly laid out, the pitches are part grassy, part stony with varying amounts of shade. The majority have water and electricity points at the edge of the pitch. Some are a long way from the main facilities and your own sanitation would be an advantage. A 'portacabin' type toilet block is to be installed in the upper reaches for the high season. This is a quieter site for those seeking the 'real' France.

Facilities

The single toilet block has just been refurbished and includes all the necessary facilities. Disabled facilities are available though the steeply sloping roads and paths are not ideal. Laundry and dishwashing sinks, washing machine and iron. Bar, restaurant and small shop (June - Sept). Swimming pool with large grass sunbathing area. Small play area and paddling pool (some distance from the pool). Some entertainment and children's activities in high season. Off site: Montmeyan 1 km. Beach at Lake Quinson (7 km) and other lakes with watersports. Gorges du Verdon. Many interesting towns with their markets and museums.

Directions

Leave A8 autoroute at St Maximin and take D560 to Barjols and then D71 to Montmeyan. At roundabout on entering village, take D13 southeast signed Cotignac and site entrance is very shortly on the right.

Charges 2003

Per person	€ 4.50 - € 6.00
child (under 7 yrs)	€ 3.00 - € 3.50
pitch	€ 7.00 - € 10.00

Reservations

Contact site. Tel: 04 94 80 75 54.
Email: leouviere@wanadoo.fr

Open

15 April - 15 October.

At a glance

Welcome & Ambience	✓✓✓✓✓	Location	✓✓✓✓
Quality of Pitches	✓✓✓✓	Range of Facilities	✓✓✓✓

travel service
TO BOOK THIS SITE
0870 405 4055
Expert Advice & Special Offers

345

FR83270 Camping La Cigale

83350 Ramatuelle (Var)

One of those delightful 'little gems' in a pretty setting yet close (about ten minutes by car) to the trendy resort of St Tropez, this is a family-run site with 115 pitches. Of these 75 are for tourers, all with electrical connections. The pitches, with some terracing, vary in size but are mostly pretty level, with varying amounts of shade. Mainly on hard sandy earth, they are nothing to write home about, but are generally quite adequate. Although only around 800 m. from the well known, sandy Plage d'Escalet, the site nevertheless has its own quietly situated small swimming pool (no noisy toboggans or slides) and its own attractive restaurant.

Facilities

Sanitary facilities, in two blocks, include large showers, mainly British style WCs, washbasins in cabins and a washing machine - all clean and well cared for when we visited. Shop, Bar/restaurant. Takeaway. Swimming pool. Bicycle hire. Off site: Beach and boat launching 800 m. Golf 7 km. Riding 5 km.

At a glance

Welcome & Ambience	√√√√√	Location	√√√√√
Quality of Pitches	√√√	Range of Facilities	√√√√

Directions

From N98 coast road just east of St Tropez take D93 towards Ramatuelle. After around 10 km. fork left towards L'Escalet (site is signed).

Charges 2003

Per unit incl. 2 persons	€ 15.00 - € 30.00
extra person	€ 5.50 - € 6.50
child (under 7 yrs)	€ 2.50 - € 3.50
electricity (6A)	€ 5.00
animal	€ 3.00

Camping Cheques accepted.

Reservations

Contact site. Tel: 04 94 79 22 53.
Email: campinglacigale@wanadoo.fr

Open

1 April - 15 October.

FR83280 Campasun Mas de Pierredon

652 chemin Paoul Coletta, 83110 Sanary-sur-Mer (Var)

Situated on the outskirts of the pretty resort of Sanary, this small site is open from Easter through to October. Terraced under the traditional pines of the area, it provides 120 pitches of which a number are taken by mobile homes. The ground is fairly rocky but some sand and grass exists and trees and shrubs help to divide the pitches making it an attractive environment. All pitches have electricity connections. The bar and restaurant overlook the heated pool at the entrance to the site and provide a comfortable family environment, all are open all season. The site is situated close to a fairly busy main road and the access is quite sharp and uphill. English is spoken at reception.

Facilities

Two toilet blocks with modern facilities include washbasins in cabins, controllable showers with a further 16 en-suite individual units on pitches. En-suite unit for disabled visitors. Washing machine in each block, plenty of laundry sinks and dishwashing sinks (H&C). Motorcaravan service point. Bar/restaurant with pizza oven. Bread to order from reception. Oudoor heated pool and paddling pool. Play equipment. Table tennis, minigolf, boules and tennis court. Pool table. Entertainment provided in July/Aug. for all ages. Off site: Shop 800 m. Beach 3 km.

At a glance

Welcome & Ambience	√√√√√	Location	√√√√
Quality of Pitches	√√√√	Range of Facilities	√√√√√

Directions

From A50 take exit for Bandol and follow directions for 'Jardin Exotique'. After Mercedes garage take first right and follow straight on for 5 km. (narrow road with lots of roads off) until a T-junction with a stop sign. Turn right and site is almost immediately on left.

Charges 2003

Per person	€ 4.40 - € 5.80
child (under 7 yrs)	€ 3.00 - € 4.30
pitch	€ 5.85 - € 10.35
electricity (10A)	€ 4.50 - € 4.60
animal	€ 1.70 - € 3.90
local tax	€ 0.60

Camping Cheques accepted.

Reservations

Made with deposit (€ 80) and booking fee (€ 23). Tel: 04 94 74 25 02. Email: campasun@free.fr

Open

1 April - 15 October.

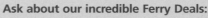
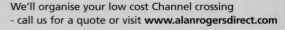

Map 16

Corsica

The island of Corsica is both dramatic and beautiful. The scenery is spectacular with bays of white sand lapped by the clear blue waters of the Mediterranean. At certain times of the year the entire island is ablaze with exotic flowers, aided by Corsica's excellent sunshine record.

Départements: 2A Corse-Sud; 2B Haute-Corse

Major Cities: Ajaccio and Bastia

Corsica is regarded by some as the jewel of the Mediterranean islands and is made up of two départements: Haute Corse (upper Corsica) and Corse du Sud (southern Corsica). The island has endured a bloody history, having being much disputed the Greeks, Romans and Lombards. Five hundred years of Italian rule has influenced the look of the island with Italian-style hilltop hamlets and villages developed alongside mountain springs. Many of the villages feature rustic, unadorned churches and also a few Romanesque examples too.

The variety of scenery is spectacular. Across much of the island one can discover dramatic gorges, glacial lakes, gushing mountain torrents and magnificent pine and chestnut forests.You'll also experience the celebrated perfume of the Corsican maquis: a tangled undergrowth of fragrant herbs, flowers and bushes that fills the warm spring and summer air. The highest mountains lie to the west, while the gentler ranges, weathered to strange and often bizarre shapes, lie to the south and a continuous barrier forms the island's backbone.

Cuisine of the region

Brocchui: sheeps' milk cheese is used much in cooking in both its soft form (savoury or sweet) or more mature and ripened.

Capone: local eels, cut up and grilled on a spit over a charcoal fire

Dziminu: fish soup, like bouillabaise but much hotter. Made with peppers and pimentos

Figatelli: a sausage made of dried and spiced pork with liver. Favourite between-meal snack

Pibronata: a highly spiced local sauce

Prizzutu: a peppered smoked ham; resembles the Italian prosciutto, but with chestnut flavour added

Places of interest

Ajaccio: a dazzling white city full of Napoleonic memorabilia

Bastia: historic citadel towering over the headland. The old town has preserved its streets in the form of steps connected by vaulted passages, converging on the Vieux port (the old port). The new port is the real commercial port of the island

Alan Rogers **tip**

TO ESCAPE THE CROWDS AND APPRECIATE THE SCENERY CLOSE-UP, HEAD INLAND AND TAKE ADVANTAGE OF THE NETWORK OF TRAILS AND FOREST TRACKS.

FR20010 Camping Arinella Bianca

Route de la Mer, 20240 Ghisonaccia (Haute-Corse)

Arinella is a lively, family oriented site situated on Corsica's east coast. It is a tribute to its owner's design and development skills as it appears to be in entirely natural glades where, in fact, these have been created from former marshland with a fresh water lake. The 429 marked pitches (182 for touring units) are on flat grass among a variety of trees and shrubs providing ample shade. They are irregularly arranged but are all of a good size with electricity (long leads may be necessary). The site is right beside a beach of soft sand that extends a long way either side of the attractive central complex which, together with the swimming pool, forms the hub of this site. A large range of sport and leisure facilities is available at or adjacent to the site. Evening entertainment starts at 10 pm. and continues until past midnight and unfortunately a local disco nearby can go on until the early hours. Used by tour operators (76 pitches). A 'Sites et Paysages' member.

Facilities

Four open plan sanitary blocks provide showers in larger than average cubicles (some with dressing area), washbasins in cabins and mainly British, some Turkish style WCs. Open air dishwashing areas. Laundry with washing machines and ironing boards. Motorcaravan service point. Shop, bar, terraced restaurant, amphitheatre and snack bar (all 10/5-15/9). Swimming pool (from 1/5)on payment. Windsurfing, canoeing, fishing, volleyball, bicycle hire, tennis, riding. Children's mini-club and play area. Disco. Entertainment programme in the main season.

At a glance

Welcome & Ambience	✓✓✓	Location	✓✓✓✓✓
Quality of Pitches	✓✓✓✓	Range of Facilities	✓✓✓✓✓

Directions

Site is 4 km. east of Ghisonaccia. From N198 after entering Ghisonaccia look for sign 'La Plage / Li Mare' (this road is easy to miss coming from south and difficullt for caravans to turn into, so go further through town and turn in garage forecourt to approach from north). Turn east on to D144 and continue for 3.5 km. to roundabout. Turn right and site is on left in approx. 500 m.

Charges 2004

Per unit incl. 2 adults	€ 19.00 - € 33.00
extra person	€ 6.50 - € 9.00
child (up to 7 yrs)	free - € 5.00
electricity (6A)	€ 3.50
animal	€ 2.50
local tax	€ 0.30 - € 0.80

Camping Cheques accepted.

Reservations

Contact site. Made with € 155 deposit and € 30.50 fee. Tel: 04 95 56 04 78.
Email: arinella@arinellabianca.com

Open

Easter - 30 September.

ARINELLA
Bianca

Camping Caravaning
20240 Ghisonaccia

Arinella Bianca is a family site with a lively atmosphere. Situated beside the sea, there is direct access to a magnificent 100 km beach. This shady site provides spacious and clearly marked pitches. The chalets can house 5 to 6 persons, they are close to the sea and the swimming pool. The mobil-homes are a bit more set back and are for 4 persons.
The sanitary blocks are kept impeccably clean, the facilities are open from the start of May until the end of September. We rent out bikes, we speak all languages and are always at your service. There are excursions to all of the beautiful sites on the island. We will give you all the advice you need. We stand for quality, decency and a good atmosphere.
New mobil-homes 6 persons.

For a splendid holiday, come and see us !

Tel: 0033 495 56 04 78 - Fax: 0033 495 56 12 54

FR20000 Camping Caravaning U Farniente

Pertamina Village, 20169 Bonifacio (Corse-du-Sud)

Irrespective of whether or not you are using the ferry to Sardinia, Bonifacio deserves a visit and it would be difficult to find a more attractive or convenient site than this one at which to pitch for a night stop or longer stay. The 120 pitches, many with electricity, are partially terraced and are hedged with trees and bushes, providing reasonable shade. They are reasonably flat and vary in size, many being well over 100 sq.m. A central feature of the site is the large attractive swimming pool, which is surrounded by terraces and a bar and a good pizzeria/grill.

Facilities

Two toilet blocks include washbasins in semi-private cubicles, British and Turkish style WCs, dishwashing and washing machines plus drying and ironing facilities. Shop. Takeaway. Pizzeria/grill serving set meals and à la carte at reasonable prices (shorter opening hours in May, June and Oct). Swimming pool. Tennis, table tennis. Play area. TV room. Off site: Bonifacio 4 km.

At a glance

Welcome & Ambience	✓✓✓✓	Location	✓✓✓✓
Quality of Pitches	✓✓✓✓	Range of Facilities	✓✓✓✓

Directions

Site is on RN198, 4 km. north of Bonifacio to the east. Watch for the sign - you come on it quite suddenly.

Latest charges

Per unit incl. 2 persons	
with electricity	€ 16.80 - € 20.75
extra person	€ 5.35 - € 6.40
child (under 8 yrs)	€ 2.75 - € 3.82
electricity (3A)	€ 3.51
local tax	€ 0.15

Camping Cheques accepted.

Reservations

Contact site. Made with €15.25 fee and 30% deposit. Tel: 04 95 73 05 47. Email: pertamina@wanadoo.fr

Open

Easter - 15 October.

FR20060 Camping La Vetta

Route de Bastia, La Trinité, 20137 Porto-Vecchio (Corse-du-Sud)

In a pleasing country park setting to the north of La Trinité village, La Vetta is only 3 km. from Porto-Vecchio and its magnificent sandy beaches. This 8.5 ha. campsite enjoys a tranquil setting and is a part sloping, part terraced site, that seems to stretch endlessly. It is well maintained and has an abundance of tree varieties including cork oaks. Giving the impression of being off the beaten track, many of the delights of Corsica are only a short drive away. If you want to do no more than relax there is much on offer – a pool for hot days, plenty of trees for shade and a patio area for cool drinks. The site has 100 pitches, most with electrical connections. The entrance is directly off the main road with security gates closed midnight - 7 am.

Facilities

Clean, modern, fully equipped toilet facilities are more than adequate and include dishwashing, laundry sinks and washing machine. Shop (July/Aug) with gas supplies. Patio bar (July/Aug). Swimming pool (all season), table tennis, table football, snooker table, a play area, TV and entertainment in high season. Barbecues are not permitted in certain weather conditions. Off site: Riding 4 km, fishing 3 km, bicycle hire 5 km, golf 7 km.

At a glance

Welcome & Ambience	✓✓✓✓✓	Location	✓✓✓✓
Quality of Pitches	✓✓✓	Range of Facilities	✓✓✓✓

Directions

Site is in La Trinité village, off the RN198 (east side), north of Porto-Vecchio.

Charges 2003

Per adult	€ 5.50 - € 6.50
child (under 7 yrs)	€ 3.00 - € 3.50
tent or caravan	€ 2.50 - € 3.00
motorcaravan	€ 4.50 - € 5.00
car	€ 2.00
electricity (16A)	€ 3.00
local tax	€ 0.30

No credit cards.

Reservations

Made with 30% deposit. Tel: 04 95 70 09 86. Email: info@campinglavetta.com

Open

15 May - 15 September.

FR20070 Camping Caravaning Santa Lucia

Lieudit Mulindinu, 20144 St Lucie-de Porto-Vecchio (Corse-du-Sud)

Camping Santa Lucia isa friendly, family run site in a delightful southern Corscian setting. It is a well appointed site set in a cork oak forest just off the main road, the entrance enhanced by a huge palm tree which characterises the approach to reception. At this point you also find the restaurant and bar which overlook the swimming pool – particularly pleasant in the evening when ornamental lamps light up the patio area. There are 160 pitches, 40 with electrical connections. Pitches are numbered and some are in little enclosed bays which offer privacy. Chalets and bungalow tents blend unobtrusively with the setting. Based at this site you are only minutes by car from Porto Vecchio which is surrounded by lovely beaches.

Facilities

Two toilet blocks include some washbasins in cubicles, dishwashing and laundry sinks, and a washing machine. Bread to order. Bar (15/6-15/9). Restaurant and takeaway (1/7-31/8). Play area. Table tennis, volleyball, and minigolf. Barbecues are only permitted in specific area. Off site: Fishing 5 km. Supermarket opposite site entrance and services such as a doctor, chemist, grocers and newsagent in village

At a glance

| Welcome & Ambience | ✓✓✓ | Location | ✓✓✓✓ |
| Quality of Pitches | ✓✓✓✓ | Range of Facilities | ✓✓✓✓ |

Directions

Site is at south end of Sainte-Lucie-de-Porto-Vecchio village, off N198 and well signed.

Latest charges

Per pitch	€ 1.80 - € 3.50
with electricity (6A)	€ 5.00 - € 6.00
per adult	€ 4.00 - € 6.00
child (2-10 yrs)	free - € 3.00
car	€ 1.50 - € 2.50
motorcycle	€ 0.80 - € 1.50

Reservations

Contact site. Made with deposit and €15 fee. Tel: 04 95 71 45 28. Email: santalucia@wanadoo.fr

Open

15 May - 10 October.

FR20050N Camping Naturiste Club La Chiappa

20137 Porto-Vecchio (Corse-du-Sud)

This holiday paradise stands in a magnificent setting on the Chiappa peninsula, which juts out into the bluest of seas. It is an extensive naturist site with 3 km. of private beach. There are 220 pitches for caravans and tents, plus 430 bungalows to rent. Even when full, there should be lots of space and something to suit all tastes – in fact, here you can be as private and relaxed or as convivial as you wish. There are three beaches where you are sure to find a quiet spot and where it is safe to swim, or alternatively enjoy the swimming pool. There are also extensive grounds and gardens. The pitches are large, part shaded and mainly level, and some have 6A electrical connections (long leads necessary).

Facilities

There are more than enough sanitary blocks and open plan facilities, which are clean and modern. Dishwashing sinks. Washing machines. Motorcaravan service point. Well stocked shop. Three bars, restaurant meals and snacks. Baby sitting service. Swimming pool. Play area and mini club for children. Riding, tennis, minigolf, fishing, diving, windsurfing, sailing, keep fit, sauna and much more (some at extra cost). Torches useful.

At a glance

| Welcome & Ambience | ✓✓✓✓ | Location | ✓✓✓✓✓ |
| Quality of Pitches | ✓✓✓✓ | Range of Facilities | ✓✓✓✓ |

Directions

From Bastia on N198 heading south, continue through Porto-Vecchio for 2 km. Turn left onto unclassified road signed 'Pointe de la Chiappa' and follow camp signs.

Charges 2004

Per pitch incl. electricity	€ 13.00
tent pitch	€ 8.50
per adult	€ 9.50
child (5-13 yrs)	€ 4.50

Less for longer stays in low season.

Reservations

Contact site. Tel: 04 95 70 00 31. Email: chiappa@wanadoo.fr

Open

15 May - 2 October.

FR20100 Camping Caravaning Santa Barbara

RN 200 route d'Aleria, Aerodrome de Corte, 20250 Corte (Haute-Corse)

Santa Barbara is a developing campsite in Corsica's mountainous interior. Corte, the historical capital of the island, stands at 396 m. altitude in the central mountains where you get a feel of the real Corsica and the site is 3 km. east of the town. Already established as a restaurant/bar, the campsite is an ongoing project with, at present, 50 level touring pitches and 10 mobile holiday homes. The pitches are separated by young shrubs and there are 32 electricity connections. An excellent swimming pool is an established focal point and very welcome in this hot, mountainous region. The patio area, which overlooks the pool, is popular and the restaurant is outside near the pool. The owners of the site are friendly and helpful. There could be some noise from the road or small local airport.

Facilities

The toilet facilities are modern and spotlessly clean units including facilities for the disabled, dishwashing, laundry sinks and washing machine. Restaurant/bar offers varied menu also pizza style hut. Swimming pool. Play area, table tennis and pool table. Off site: Corte has a full range of shops.

At a glance

| Welcome & Ambience | ✓✓✓✓✓ | Location | ✓✓✓ |
| Quality of Pitches | ✓✓✓✓ | Range of Facilities | ✓✓✓✓ |

Directions

Site is 3 km. southeast of Corte by the N200 Aléria road.

Latest charges

Per adult	€ 4.50
child (under 10 yrs)	€ 2.60
caravan	€ 3.70
car	€ 2.50
motorcaravan	€ 5.40
electricity (12A)	€ 3.70
local tax	€ 0.15

Reservations

Write to site. Tel: 04 95 46 20 22.

Open

April - 31 October.

FR20030 Camping Merendella

Moriani-Plage, 20230 San-Nicolao (Haute-Corse)

This attractive smaller, family run site has the advantage of direct access to a pleasant beach. The site is peacefully situated on level grass with many trees and shrubs providing shade and colour. There are 133 pitches of a min. 100 sq.m. with electricity available on practically all (although long cables may be needed). The site is about 800 m. from the village but also has its own well stocked shop.

Facilities

Modern toilet facilities are in two main blocks, apart from a couple of individual cabin units near beach. Washbasins in private cubicles and some British style WCs plus further Turkish style ones. Washing up and laundry areas. Two washing machines. Shop. Restaurant/Pizzeria. TV and games room. No dogs or cats are accepted. Off site: Tennis, riding and various watersports including a diving centre nearby.

At a glance

| Welcome & Ambience | ✓✓✓✓ | Location | ✓✓✓✓ |
| Quality of Pitches | ✓✓✓✓ | Range of Facilities | ✓✓✓✓ |

Directions

Site is to seaward side of the RN198, 800 m. south of Moriani Plage.

Charges 2003

Per person	€ 5.05 - € 5.85
child (2-12 yrs)	€ 3.15 - € 3.75
car	€ 2.30
caravan	€ 2.60 - € 3.50
tent	€ 2.20 - € 2.60
motorcaravan	€ 4.65 - € 5.35
electricity (2/5A)	€ 2.90 -€ 3.20
local tax (1/7-15/9)	€ 0.15

Reservations

Are advisable; write to site. Tel: 04 95 38 53 47.

Open

15 May - 15 October.

FR20130 **Camping San Damiano**

Lido de la Marana-Pineto, 20620 Biguglia-Bastia (Haute-Corse)

What we found pleasing about this site was the friendly reception we received and also its convenient situation only 9 km. from the port of Bastia. It makes an excellent night halt, or alternatively a suitable base for visiting Bastia, the northeast of the island or its mountainous interior. Despite being on the outskirts of a city, it enjoys an ideal location off the busy N193, situated between the Etang de Biguglia and the golden sands of Corsica's east coast. It is divided in two by a public access road to the beach and is a sprawling site with 280 pitches, all separated by shrubs and shaded by trees. There are 180 electricity connections. A security guard patrols in high season and quiet is enforced after 11 pm.

Facilities

Two basic toilet blocks, but clean when we visited, include washing cabins and good provision for disabled visitors. Motorcaravan service point. Well-stocked shop (1/6-20/9). Bar and restaurant (from 1/5). Launderette. TV room. Minigolf. Play area for children. Fishing. Riding. Jet-ski and quad-bike hire. Off site: Golf 15 km.

At a glance

Welcome & Ambience	✓✓✓✓	Location	✓✓✓✓
Quality of Pitches	✓✓✓✓	Range of Facilities	✓✓✓✓

Directions

From Bastia travel 5 km. on N193 then take D107 towards Lido de la Marana for 4 km. Site is on the left.

Charges 2003

Per pitch	€ 4.50 - € 6.50
person	€ 5.00 - € 6.00
child (under 8 yrs)	€ 3.00 - € 4.00
electricity (6A)	€ 3.00

Reservations

Possible by phone. Tel: 04 95 33 68 02. Email: san-damiano@lespiedsdansleau.co

Open

1 April - 15 October.

FR20120 **Camping Le Panoramic**

Route de Lavatoggio, Lumio, 20260 Calvi (Haute-Corse)

On the scenic route that winds inland and upwards from the coast between Calvi and L'Ile Rousse, Le Panoramic, as its name suggests, enjoys magnificent views across the Golfe d'Ambroggio. It is a simple family run site with 120 pitches laid out in named avenues (Rue Josephine, etc) and the marked places are shaded by many trees and vegetation, with quite a number having electricity connections. Whilst the ground is level, the site is terraced and hard going if climbing from the bottom towards reception. It is probably best suited for small motorcaravans or tents. A recommended scenic drive is the 5 km. climb to St Antonino, a mountain village piled upon a rock face.

Facilities

Four sanitary blocks are housed in typical rough-cast buildings with basic decor, but appear well maintained and fully equipped. Sinks for dishwashing and two washing machines. Chemical disposal can be arranged through reception. Small shop, takeaway and bar. Swimming pool. Table football, pool table. Children's play area. Caravan storage. Off site: Bicycle hire 4 km, riding 3 km, golf 5 km.

At a glance

Welcome & Ambience	✓✓✓	Location	✓✓✓✓
Quality of Pitches	✓✓✓✓	Range of Facilities	✓✓✓✓

Directions

From Calvi take N197 towards L'Ile Rousse. Proceed for 10 km. to village of Lumio, then east on D71 and site is 2 km. on the left.

Latest charges

Per pitch	€ 3.50 - € 5.20
person	€ 5.30
electricity (15A)	€ 2.90

No credit cards.

Reservations

Phone or write. Tel: 04 95 60 73 13.

Open

1 June - 15 September.

FR20220 **Camping Les Oliviers**

20150 Porto (Corse-du-Sud)

Because of its location on this difficult to access west coast of Corsica and the steepness of the site itself, Les Oliviers is best suited for tents and small motorhomes. An attractive, family run site on the edge of this busy coastal resort, it has direct access to the river. The 190 pitches are mainly small and terraced, with 64 having electricity connections. Whilst there are a number of shops and restaurants in the vicinity, the site itself has an attractive restaurant/pizzeria/bar.

Facilities

Toilet facilities are in four blocks spread throughout the site. Some washbasins in cubicles, British style WC's. Washing up and laundry areas. Four washing machines. Refrigerator hire. Bread supplies. Restaurant, pizzeria and bar. Play area. Off site: Supermarket 50 m. Corsican Trek organises a variety of active sports. Visits to Scandola nature reserve.

At a glance

Welcome & Ambience	✓✓✓✓	Location	✓✓✓✓
Quality of Pitches	✓✓✓✓	Range of Facilities	✓✓✓✓

Directions

On approaching Porto the road crosses a river bridge. Les Oliviers is on the right immediately after bridge.

Charges 2003

Per person	€ 5.00 - € 6.50
caravan with electricity (10A)	€ 7.00 - € 8.50

Reservations

Essential for caravans and motorcaravans at all times, advised for tents in July/Aug. Tel: 04 95 26 14 49. Email: guy@campinglesoliviers.com

Open

28 March - 30 October.

FR20230 Camping Le Sagone

Route de Vico, 20118 Sagone (Corse-du-Sud)

Situated just outside the bustling seaside resort of Sagone, this campsite is in a superb location for exploring Corsica's wild and rocky west coast or its mountainous interior. Next to a mixed farm with orchards, there are 300 pitches which are all marked out, the majority with electrical connections. The restaurant/bar and games room overlooking the pool are a focal point of this well managed site.

Facilities

Four clean, fully equipped toilet blocks include two with internal courtyard gardens. Washbasins in cubicles, washing up and laundry area. Facilities for disabled people. Washing machines, one dryer. Motorcaravan service point. Coccinelle supermarket at entrance. Restaurant, pizzeria, bar and games room. Swimming pool. Half court tennis, volleyball, table tennis, basketball. Play area. Off site: Riding 500 m. Diving, wind surfing, mountain biking and climbing nearby.

At a glance

Welcome & Ambience	✓✓✓✓	Location	✓✓✓✓
Quality of Pitches	✓✓✓✓	Range of Facilities	✓✓✓✓✓

Directions

From Ajaccio take the RD81 in direction of Cergése and Calvilby (by coast road). In Sagone take RD70 in direction of Vico, Sagone camping can be found on left after 1.5 km. next to Coccinelle supermarket.

Charges 2004

Per unit incl. 2 persons	€ 13.50 - € 21.70
child (under 12 yrs)	€ 2.10 - € 3.60
electricity (6A)	€ 3.00

Camping Cheques accepted.

Reservations

Made with 30% deposit and € 18,50 booking fee; write to site. Tel: 04 95 28 04 15. Email: sagone.camping@wanadoo.fr

Open

1 May - 30 September.

FR20040N Domaine Naturiste Riva Bella

B.P. 21, 20270 Alèria (Haute-Corse)

A relaxed, informal naturist site beside a glorious beach, Riva Bella is arguably camping and caravanning at its very best. Although offering a large number and variety of pitches, they are situated in such a huge area of varied and beautiful countryside and seaside that it is difficult to believe it could ever become overcrowded. The site is divided into several distinct areas - pitches and bungalows, alongside the sandy beach, in a wooded glade with ample shade, behind the beach, or beside the lake/lagoon which is a feature of this site. The ground is undulating, so getting an absolutely level pitch could be a problem in the main season. Although electric hook-ups are available in most parts, a long cable is probably a necessity. There is an interesting evening entertainment programme. A recent addition is a therapy centre with treatments and massages based on marine products. Noël Pasqual is fully proud of his site and the fairly unobtrusive rules are designed to ensure that everyone is able to relax, whilst preserving the natural beauty of the environment. There is, for example, a restriction on the movement of cars in certain areas (but ample free parking). Generally the ambience is relaxed and informal with nudity only obligatory on the beach itself. Member 'France 4 Naturisme'.

Facilities

Toilet facilities in several blocks have been completely refurbished. Whilst fairly typical in design for naturist sites, they are fitted and decorated to the highest standards facilities for disabled people and babies. Large well stocked shop (15/5-30/9). Fridge hire. Excellent restaurant (all season) with reasonable prices overlooks the lagoon. Snack bar beside the beach during the main season (1/6-30/9). Watersports including sailing school, fishing, sub-aqua etc. Therapy centre. Sauna. Volleyball, aerobics, table tennis, giant draughts and archery. Fishing. Mountain bike hire. Half-court tennis. Herd of llamas to watch. The police/fire service ban barbecues during the summer as a safety precaution. Off site: Riding 5 km

At a glance

Welcome & Ambience	✓✓✓✓	Location	✓✓✓✓
Quality of Pitches	✓✓✓✓	Range of Facilities	✓✓✓✓✓

Directions

Site is approx. 8 km. north of Aleria on N198 (Bastia) road. Watch for signs and unmade road to it and follow for 4 km

Charges 2003

Per unit incl. 2 persons	€ 17.00 - € 29.00
child (0-8 yrs)	€ 2.00 - € 4.50
electricity	€ 3.50

Special offers and half-board arrangements available. Camping Cheques accepted.

Reservations

Made with deposit and fee/cancellation insurance. Tel: 04 95 38 81 10. Email: riva-bella@wanadoo.fr

Open

12 April - 11 October.

Naturist Sites

We have had very favourable feedback from readers concerning our choice of naturist sites, which we first introduced in our 1992 edition. Over the last few years we have gradually added a few more, including two in Corsica.

Apart from the need to have a 'Naturist Licence' (see below), there is no need to be a practising naturist before visiting these sites. In fact, at least as far as British visitors are concerned, many are what might be described as 'holiday naturists' as distinct from the practice of naturism at other times. The emphasis in all the sites featured in this guide at least, is on naturism as 'life in harmony with nature', and respect for oneself and others and for the environment, rather than simply on nudity. In fact nudity is really only obligatory in the area of the swimming pools.

There are a number of rules, which amount to sensible and considerate guidelines designed to ensure that no-one invades someone else's privacy, creates any nuisance, or damages the environment. Whether as a result of these rules, the naturist philosophy generally, or the attitude of site owners and campers alike, we have been very impressed by all the naturist sites we have selected. Without exception they had a friendly and welcoming ambience, were all extremely clean and tidy and, in most cases, provided much larger than average pitches, with a wide range of activities.

The purpose of our including a number of naturist sites in our guide is to provide an introduction to naturist camping in France for British holidaymakers; we were actually surprised by the number of British campers we met on naturist sites, many of whom had 'stumbled across naturism almost by accident' but had found, like us, that these sites were amongst the nicest they had encountered. You may still be required to have a Naturist Licence. These can be obtained in advance from either the British or French national naturist associations, but are also available on arrival at any recognised naturist site (a passport sized photograph is required).

Vendée & Charente		
FR85330N	Cap Natur'	134

Atlantic Coast		
FR40120N	Arnaoutchot	204

Provence		
FR84020N	Bélézy	278

Midi-Pyrénées		
FR09090N	Millfleurs	284
FR65010N	Eglantière	286

Mediterranean		
FR30100N	La Sablière	300
FR34080N	Sérignan Plage Nature	312
FR34050N	Mas de Lignières	317
FR06070N	Origan	328

Corsica		
FR20050N	La Chiappa	351
FR20040N	Riva Bella	354

Reports by Readers

We always welcome reports from readers concerning sites which they have visited. Generally reports provide us with invaluable feedback on sites already included in the Guide or, in the case of those not featured, they provide information which we can follow up with a view to adding them in future editions. However, if you have a complaint about a site, this should be addressed to the campsite owner, preferably in person before you leave.

Please make your comments either on this form or on plain paper. It would be appreciated if you would indicate the approximate dates when you visited the site and, in the case of potential new sites, provide the correct name and address and, if possible, include a site brochure. Send your reports to:

Alan Rogers Guides, Manor Garden, Burton Bradstock, Bridport DT6 4QA

Name of Site and Ref. No. (or address for new recommendations):

....

....

Dates of visit: ....

Comments:

Open all year

The following sites are understood to accept caravanners and campers all year round, although **the list also includes some sites that are open for at least ten months.** For sites marked with a star (*) – please refer to the site's individual entry for dates and other restrictions. In any case, it is always wise to phone as the facilities available, for example, may be reduced.

Normandy
FR76100M Cany-Barville
FR76090M Etennemare

Northern France
FR02030   Croix du Vieux Pont
FR59050M Mauberge
FR80030   Port de Plaisance

Paris & Ile de France
FR75020   Bois de Boulogne
FR78010   International
FR78040M Etang d'Or *

Eastern France
FR88040   Lac de Bouzey
FR88090   Lac de la Moselotte

Vendée & Charente
FR85540   Eden

Loire Valley
FR36050M Vieux Chênes
FR28110M Bonneval
FR41060   De Dugny
FR86040   Le Futuriste

Burgundy
FR21060   Les Bouleaux

Savoy & Dauphiny Alps
FR38080   Au Joyeux Réveil *
FR73030   Les Lanchettes *
FR73020   Le Versoyen *
FR74010   Deux Glaciers
FR74130   La Plage *
FR74070   Escale *

Atlantic Coast
FR40090M Lou Broustaricq
FR64040   Les Gaves

Dordogne & Aveyron
FR24280   Barnabé
FR24150   Deux Vallées

Limousin & Auvergne
FR63060   Le Clos Auroy

Rhône Valley
FR26110   Les 4 Saisons
FR69010M Porte de Lyon

Provence
FR05030   Les Six Stations

Midi-Pyrénées
FR09030   Le Montagnou
FR09080   Du Lac
FR09060   Le Pré Lombard
FR09050M La Prade
FR65030   Pyrénées *
FR65070   Le Rioumajou
FR65080   Le Lavedan
FR65090   Soleil du Pibeste

Mediterranean West
FR11110   Val d'Aleth
FR34060   Oliveraie
FR34230   De Chênes
FR66180   Mas Llinas *
FR66130   Eau Vive *

Mediterranean East
FR06080   Les Cigales
FR06050   La Vieille Ferme
FR06110   Panoramic
FR83210   Les Tournels *

Dogs

Since the introduction in 2000 of the Passports for Pets scheme many British campers and caravanners have been encouraged to take their pets with them on holiday. However, Pet Travel conditions are understandbly strict, the procedure is quite lengthy and complicated so we would advise you to check the current situation before travelling. The Passports for Pets website is: http://www.freespace.virgin.net/passports.forpets

For the benefit of those who want to take their dogs to France, we list here the sites which have indicated to us that they do not accept dogs or have certain restrictions. If you are planning to take your dog we do advise you to phone the park first to check – there my be limits on numbers, breeds, or times of the year when they are excluded.

Brittany
FR22010   Les Capucines
FR29140   Kerlann

Normandy
FR14090   Brévedent

Northern France
FR02030   Croix du Vieux Pont

Vendée & Charente
FR17040   Bonne Anse Plage
FR17020   Puits de L'Auture
FR17010   Bois Soleil
FR17180   La Pignade
FR85420   Bel
FR85210   Les Ecureuils
FR85150   La Yole

Atlantic Coast
FR40040   La Paillotte
FR40170   La Réserve
FR64060   Pavillon Royal

Dordogne & Aveyron
FR16020   Gorges du Chambon
FR24040   Moulin du Roch
FR46040   Moulin de Laborde

Rhône Valley
FR26090   Les Truffières

Provence
FR84020N Bélézy

Mediterranean
FR30070   Boisson
FR30160   Le Boucanet

FR34140   La Carabasse
FR66040   Le Soleil
FR06080   Les Cigales

Corsica
FR20030   Merendella

Sites that accept dogs but with certain restrictions:
FR50030   Lez-Eaux
FR68080   Clair Vacances
FR40050   Le Col-Vert
FR40120N Arnaoutchot
FR24290   Moulin du Bleufond
FR23010   Poinsouze
FR26030   Grand Lierne
FR34130   Le Neptune
FR83200   Les Pêcheurs

Bicycle Hire

We understand that the following campsites have bicycles to hire **on site**. Where bicycle hire facilities are within an easy distance (and we have been given details) we include this information in the individual reports. However, we would recommend that you contact the site to check as the situation can change.

FR01010	La Plaine Tonique	FR24150	Deux Vallées	FR37060	Arada Parc
FR01020	Ile Chambod	FR24170	Port de Limeuil	FR37090	La Rolandière
FR02000	Vivier aux Carpes	FR24180	Saint Avit Loisirs	FR38010	Coin Tranquille
FR03010	La Filature	FR24220	Chênes Verts	FR39030	Chalain
FR03050	La Petite Valette	FR24230	Moulin de Paulhiac	FR40020	Les Chênes
FR03170M	Dompierre	FR24240	Les Bo-Bains	FR40030	Pins du Soleil
FR04010	Hippocampe	FR24310	La Bouquerie	FR40040	La Paillotte
FR04020	Verdon	FR24320	Les Peneyrals	FR40050	Le Col-Vert
FR06030	La Bergerie	FR24350	Moulin de la Pique	FR40060	Eurosol
FR07020	Ardéchois	FR24360	Le Mondou	FR40070	Lous Seurrots
FR07030	Soleil Vivarais	FR25000	Val de Bonnal	FR40090M	Lou Broustaricq
FR07090	Des Plantas	FR25030	Bois de Reveuge	FR40100	La Rive
FR07110	Le Pommier	FR26020	De Senaud	FR40110	Sen Yan
FR07130	Les Coudoulets	FR26040	Le Couspeau	FR40120N	Arnaoutchot
FR09020	Arize	FR26120	Gervanne	FR40140	Lou P'tit Poun
FR09060	Le Pré Lombard	FR28110M	Bonneval	FR40160	Les Vignes
FR11070	Les Mimosas	FR29010	Ty-Nadan	FR40170	La Réserve
FR11080	La Nautique	FR29050	Orangerie de Lanniron	FR40180	Le Vieux Port
FR11110	Val d'Aleth	FR29080	Le Panoramic	FR40200	Sylvamar
FR12070	Grange de Monteillac	FR29090	Raguénèz-Plage	FR41010	Val de Loire
FR12080	Les Genêts	FR29110	La Plage	FR41020	Grenouillière
FR12150	Marmotel	FR29120	Manoir de Kerlut	FR41030	Alicourts
FR12170	Le Caussanel	FR29130	Des Abers	FR41040	Des Marais
FR14030	Martragny	FR29140	Kerlann	FR41060	De Dugny
FR14060	Hautes Coutures	FR29160	Genets d'Or	FR41070	Grande Tortue
FR14070	La Vallée	FR29250	Bois des Ecureuils	FR41090	de la Varenne
FR14090	Brévedent	FR29290	Grand Large	FR42010M	Charlieu
FR14140	Pont Farcy	FR29310	Roche Percée	FR43030	Vaubarlet
FR15030	Le Val Saint Jean	FR30120	Ile des Papes	FR44040	Sainte-Brigitte
FR16020	Gorges du Chambon	FR30140	Soubeyranne	FR44090	Deffay
FR16030M	Le Champion	FR30160	Le Boucanet	FR44100	Le Patisseau
FR17010	Bois Soleil	FR30170	La Sousta	FR44130	Hermitage
FR17020	Puits de L'Auture	FR32010	Florence	FR44170	Ajoncs d'Or
FR17040	Bonne Anse Plage	FR32080	Le Talouch	FR45010	Bois du Bardelet
FR17050	Orée du Bois	FR33080	Barbanne	FR46040	Moulin de Laborde
FR17110	Monplaisir	FR33110	Côte d'Argent	FR46050	Le Rêve
FR17140	Sequoia Parc	FR33130	Les Grands Pins	FR46080	Lacomté
FR17170	Les Charmilles	FR33210	Pointe du Medoc	FR46110	Du Port
FR17190	Logis du Breuil	FR33220	Petit Nice	FR47010	Moulin du Périé
FR17210	Interlude	FR33230	Le Truc Vert	FR47030	Fonrives
FR17220	La Brande	FR33240	L'Océan	FR48060	Les Terraces
FR19050	La Rivière	FR33320	Talaris	FR49000	Lac de Maine
FR19060	Le Mialaret	FR34030	Le Napoléon	FR49010	Etang de la Brèche
FR19070	Chateau de Gibanel	FR34040	Lou Village	FR49020	Chantepie
FR20040N	Riva Bella	FR34060	Oliveraie	FR49040	Etang
FR21000	Lac de Panthier	FR34070	Sérignan Plage	FR49060	Montsabert
FR21050	Grappe d'Or	FR34080N	Sérignan Plage Nature	FR49080	Ile d'Offard
FR22050	Le Vieux Moulin	FR34090	La Yole	FR49090	Isle Verte
FR22130	Port l'Epine	FR34110	Le Club Farret	FR50000	Etang des Haizes
FR22160	Le Neptune	FR34130	Le Neptune	FR50030	Lez-Eaux
FR22200	Le Bocage	FR34170	Les Mimosas	FR50050	Le Cormoran
FR23010	Poinsouze	FR34200	Californie Plage	FR50070	Anse du Brick
FR24010	Le Verdoyer	FR34210	Berges du Canal	FR52020	Forge de Ste Marie
FR24060	Le Paradis	FR35020	Des Ormes	FR56010	Grande Métairie
FR24080	Moulin de David	FR37010	Mignardière	FR56020	La Plage
FR24100	Le Moulinal	FR37030	Moulin Fort	FR56120	Les Iles
FR24110	Aqua Viva	FR37050	La Citadelle	FR56130	Mané Guernehué

FR62010	La Bien-Assise	FR80060	Val de Trie	FR85320	Val de Vie
FR63040	La Grange Fort	FR80090	Val d'Authie	FR85330N	Cap Natur'
FR63060	Le Clos Auroy	FR81030M	Gourjade	FR85360	La Forêt
FR63080	Le Moulin de Serre	FR83020	Esterel	FR85400	Bois Soleil
FR64070	Le Ruisseau	FR83060	La Baume	FR85430	Bolée D'Air
FR64110	Col d'Ibardin	FR83130	Le Beau Vezé	FR85440	Les Brunelles
FR64140	Bérrua	FR83140	Lacs du Verdon	FR85450	Les Roses
FR65010N	Eglantière	FR83160	Les Cigales	FR85460	Dune des Sables
FR65090	Soleil du Pibeste	FR83170	La Bergerie	FR85470	Les Pirons
FR66020	Ma Prairie	FR83210	Les Tournels	FR85490	Beaulieu
FR66070	Le Brasilia	FR83250	Douce Quiétude	FR85500	Bahamas Beach
FR66130	Eau Vive	FR83270	La Cigale	FR85510	Le Bois Joli
FR66180	Mas Llinas	FR83600	Holiday Green	FR85530	Parée Préneau
FR66200	Les Marsouins	FR84050	La Sorguette	FR85550	Port de Moricq
FR66210	Le Roussillon	FR84070	Carpe Diem	FR85560	Le Curtys
FR66240	Le Trivoly	FR84090	Pont d'Avignon	FR85570	Le Pomme de Pin
FR68070	Les Sources	FR84120	Des Sources	FR85580	Les Blancs Chenes
FR71050	Moulin de Collonge	FR85020	Du Jard	FR85590	Plein Sud
FR71060	Montrouant	FR85040	La Garangeoire	FR85610	Calypso
FR71070	Epervière	FR85070	Les Biches	FR85630	Maison Blanche
FR71090	Lac de St-Point	FR85080	Puerta del Sol	FR85640	Les Chouans
FR71110	Du Lac	FR85090	Abri des Pins	FR86010	Petit Trianon
FR72030	Chanteloup	FR85130	Pong	FR86030	Relais du Miel
FR74030M	Belvédère	FR85200M	Petite Boulogne	FR86090	Saint Cyr
FR74060	La Colombière	FR85210	Les Ecureuils	FR87020	Leychoisier
FR74100	Europa	FR85240M	Jarny-Ocean	FR88040	Lac de Bouzey
FR74110	Le Taillefer	FR85260	Guyonnière	FR88080	Des Bans
FR76130	La Forêt	FR85270	Oceano d'Or	FR88090	Lac de la Moselotte
FR77030M	Jablines	FR85280	Places Dorées	FR89060	Les Ceriselles
FR80010	Drancourt	FR85300	Grand' Métairie		
FR80040	Le Royon	FR85310	La Trévillière		

Fishing

We are pleased to include details of sites which provide facilities for fishing on site. Many others are near rivers or in popular fishing areas and have facilites within easy reach. Where we have been given details, we have included this information in our reports. It is always best to contact sites to check that they provide for your individual requirements.

FR01010	La Plaine Tonique	FR07090	Des Plantas	FR14060	Hautes Coutures
FR02000	Vivier aux Carpes	FR07110	Le Pommier	FR14080	Le Puits
FR02060M	Guignicourt	FR07120	Ardéchois	FR14090	Brévedent
FR03010	La Filature	FR07130	Les Coudoulets	FR14100M	Du Château
FR03050	La Petite Valette	FR07150	Domaine de Gil	FR14130M	Fanal
FR03170M	Dompierre	FR09020	Arize	FR14140	Pont Farcy
FR04010	Hippocampe	FR09030	Le Montagnou	FR15030	Le Val Saint Jean
FR04020	Verdon	FR09060	Le Pré Lombard	FR16030M	Le Champion
FR04030	Moulin de Ventre	FR09080	Du Lac	FR16050M	Cognac
FR04060	Haut-Verdon	FR11110	Val d'Aleth	FR16060	Marco de Bignac
FR05030	Les Six Stations	FR12000	Peyrelade	FR17110	Monplaisir
FR06070N	Origan	FR12020	Les Rivages	FR17200	Au Fil de l'Eau
FR06080	Les Cigales	FR12040	Les Tours	FR17220	La Brande
FR06100	Les Pinèdes	FR12050	Terrasses du Lac	FR19050	La Rivière
FR07020	Ardéchois	FR12080	Les Genêts	FR19060	Le Mialaret
FR07030	Soleil Vivarais	FR12100M	Lauradiol	FR19070	Chateau de Gibanel
FR07050	Le Ranc Davaine	FR12150	Marmotel	FR20010	Arinella Bianca
FR07070	Les Ranchisses	FR12170	Le Caussanel	FR20030	Merendella
FR07080	La Bastide	FR14030	Martragny	FR20040N	Riva Bella

Fishing

FR20220	Les Oliviers	FR35020	Des Ormes	FR64040	Les Gaves
FR21000	Lac de Panthier	FR36050M	Vieux Chênes	FR64060	Pavillon Royal
FR21040M	De Fouché	FR37030	Moulin Fort	FR64070	Le Ruisseau
FR21070	Les Grèbes	FR37050	La Citadelle	FR64090	La Chêneraie
FR22040	Le Châtelet	FR37070M	Ile Auger	FR65060	Pyrenees Natura
FR22060M	La Hallerais	FR37110M	Bord du Cher	FR66030	Cala Gogo
FR22090	Galinée	FR38060	Les Trois Lacs	FR66040	Le Soleil
FR22130	Port l'Epine	FR38110	Champ du Moulin	FR66070	Le Brasilia
FR22140	Port La Chaine	FR38120	Bontemps	FR67030	Du Ried
FR22200	Le Bocage	FR39010	Plage Blanche	FR68030M	Masevaux
FR23010	Poinsouze	FR39030	Chalain	FR70020M	Lac Vesoul
FR24000	La Tuilière	FR39040	La Pergola	FR71050	Moulin de Collonge
FR24010	Le Verdoyer	FR39050	Fayolan	FR71060	Montrouant
FR24040	Moulin du Roch	FR40040	La Paillotte	FR71070	Epervière
FR24060	Le Paradis	FR40050	Le Col-Vert	FR71090	Lac de St-Point
FR24090	Soleil Plage	FR40070	Lous Seurrots	FR71110	Du Lac
FR24100	Le Moulinal	FR40090M	Lou Broustaricq	FR72030	Chanteloup
FR24110	Aqua Viva	FR40100	La Rive	FR72060M	Val de Sarthe
FR24150	Deux Vallées	FR40120N	Arnaoutchot	FR73030	Les Lanchettes
FR24170	Port de Limeuil	FR40170	La Réserve	FR74070	Escale
FR24230	Moulin de Paulhiac	FR40190	Saint Martin	FR76040	La Source
FR24240	Les Bo-Bains	FR41030	Alicourts	FR77030M	Jablines
FR24280	Barnabé	FR41040	Des Marais	FR77080M	Les Prés
FR24290	Moulin du Bleufond	FR41060	De Dugny	FR78010	International
FR24310	La Bouquerie	FR41090	de la Varenne	FR78040M	Etang d'Or
FR24320	Les Peneyrals	FR42010M	Charlieu	FR80010	Drancourt
FR24340	Val de la Marquise	FR43030	Vaubarlet	FR80030	Port de Plaisance
FR24350	Moulin de la Pique	FR44020M	Du Moulin	FR80060	Val de Trie
FR25000	Val de Bonnal	FR44040	Sainte-Brigitte	FR81020	Moulin de Julien
FR25030	Bois de Reveuge	FR44090	Deffay	FR81040M	Auzerals
FR25050M	Saint Point-Lac	FR45010	Bois du Bardelet	FR81060	Les Clots
FR26020	De Senaud	FR46040	Moulin de Laborde	FR83070	Etoile d'Argens
FR26120	Gervanne	FR46110	Du Port	FR83080	Au Paradis
FR27020	Catinière	FR47030	Fonrives	FR83100	La Plage
FR28110M	Bonneval	FR47050	Moulin de Campech	FR83120	Domaine
FR29010	Ty-Nadan	FR49010	Etang de la Brèche	FR83170	La Bergerie
FR29020	Saint-Laurent	FR49020	Chantepie	FR83200	Les Pêcheurs
FR29030	Du Letty	FR49040	Etang	FR83240	Moulin des Iscles
FR29050	Orangerie de Lanniron	FR49070	Vallée des Vignes	FR84050	La Sorguette
FR29060	Le Pil-Koad	FR49090	Isle Verte	FR85040	La Garangeoire
FR29090	Raguénèz-Plage	FR50000	Etang des Haizes	FR85130	Pong
FR29110	La Plage	FR50030	Lez-Eaux	FR85190	Marais Braud
FR29130	Des Abers	FR50050	Le Cormoran	FR85260	Guyonnière
FR30000	Gaujac	FR50060	Le Grand Large	FR85350	La Ningle
FR30060	Fumades	FR50080	Haliotis	FR85510	Le Bois Joli
FR30070	Boisson	FR50090	La Gerfleur	FR85540	Eden
FR30100N	La Sablière	FR51020M	Châlons-sur-Marne	FR85550	Port de Moricq
FR30120	Ile des Papes	FR52020	Forge de Ste Marie	FR86030	Relais du Miel
FR30160	Le Boucanet	FR52030	Lac de la Liez	FR86040	Le Futuriste
FR30170	La Sousta	FR55010	Les Breuils	FR86080	Les Peupliers
FR30180	Mas de la Cam	FR56010	Grande Métairie	FR86090	Saint Cyr
FR33020	Fontaine-Vieille	FR56080M	Le Pâtis	FR87020	Leychoisier
FR33080	Barbanne	FR56120	Les Iles	FR88010	Deux Ballons
FR33310	Panorama	FR56130	Mané Guernehué	FR88040	Lac de Bouzey
FR33320	Talaris	FR56140M	Bas de la Lande	FR88070	Messires
FR34110	Le Club Farret	FR58030	Bezolle	FR88080	Des Bans
FR34130	Le Neptune	FR59010	La Chaumière	FR88090	Lac de la Moselotte
FR34150	Nouvelle Floride	FR59050M	Mauberge	FR89060	Les Ceriselles
FR34160	Charlemagne	FR61010M	La Campière	FR95000	Séjours Etang
FR34180	Borio de Roque	FR63040	La Grange Fort		
FR34200	Californie Plage	FR63070	Le Pré Bas		
FR35000	Vieux Chêne	FR63080	Le Moulin de Serre		

Horse Riding

We understand that the following sites offer riding on site for at least part of the year. However, we recommend that you contact the site to check that the facility meet your requirements. It is worth bearing in mind that French attitudes to safety may differ from your own (for example, you may be required to take your own hard hat).

Brittany

FR29010	Ty-Nadan
FR35000	Vieux Chêne
FR35020	Des Ormes
FR44090	Deffay
FR56120	Les Iles

Northern France

FR80010	Drancourt

Paris & Ile de France

FR77030M	Jablines

Eastern France

FR68070	Les Sources
FR88040	Lac de Bouzey
FR88080	Des Bans

Vendée & Charente

FR17140	Sequoia Parc
FR85540	Eden
FR85040	La Garangeoire

Loire Valley

FR49020	Chantepie

Burgundy

FR58030	Bezolle

Franche-Comté

FR25030	Bois de Reveuge

Savoy & Dauphiny Alps

FR38120	Bontemps

Atlantic Coast

FR33110	Côte d'Argent
FR40050	Le Col-Vert
FR40180	Le Vieux Port

Dordogne & Aveyron

FR24250	Tourterelles
FR24240	Les Bo-Bains
FR46110	Du Port

Limousin & Auvergne

FR03010	La Filature
FR63050	La Ribeyre

Rhône Valley

FR07030	Soleil Vivarais

Provence

FR04100	International
FR04020	Verdon

Midi-Pyrénées

FR09020	Arize

Mediterranean

FR11060	Arnauteille
FR34190	Champs Blancs
FR34170	Les Mimosas
FR34210	Berges du Canal
FR34180	Borio de Roque
FR34060	Oliveraie
FR66040	Le Soleil
FR66200	Les Marsouins
FR66180	Mas Llinas
FR83020	Esterel
FR83160	Les Cigales

Corsica

FR20010	Arinella Bianca
FR20050N	La Chiappa

Golf

We understand that the following sites have facilities for playing golf. However, we would recommend that you contact the site to check that the facility meets your requirements.

Brittany

FR35020	Des Ormes

Northern France

FR80010	Drancourt

Loire Valley

FR41030	Alicourts

Burgundy

FR71110	Du Lac

Atlantic Coast

FR40120N	Arnaoutchot

Limousin & Auvergne

FR15030	Le Val Saint Jean

Rhône Valley

FR07120	Ardéchois
FR26020	De Senaud

Midi-Pyrénées

FR81030M	Gourjade

Mediterranean

FR34190	Champs Blancs
FR34210	Berges du Cana

Travelling in France

The Law

You must be aged 18 or over to drive a car in France, but a UK national driving licence is sufficient – only non-EU nationals require an International Driving Permit. You should carry your Registration Document, and your Insurance (valid for use in Europe) and you must display a GB plate. You must carry a warning triangle, and a spare set of light bulbs and your headlights must be adjusted to dip to the right. A first-aid kit and fire extinguisher are recommended but not compulsory.

Drive on the right-hand-side of the road, and remember to look left when turning onto a another road.

Conditions and Conventions

'A' roads are Autoroutes, usually toll roads
'N' roads are Routes Nationale, the equivalent of our A roads
'D' roads are Routes Departemental, the equivalent of our B roads
'C' roads are Routes Communale, unclassified minor roads
'Prioité a Droite' means 'Give way to traffic coming from your right' (even if you think you are on a more main road and have the right of way – you don't, so give way.

On roundabouts (rounded anti-clockwise of course) traffic already IN the roundabout has priority.

Traffic Lights

Lights in France turn from Red to Green without going through an amber period. Flashing amber means you can proceed with caution

Most traffic lights have small repeater lights at shoulder height adjacent to the line where you must stop – these are very useful as many traffic lights don't have a set of lights on the far side of the junction.

Watch for 'right filters' – a slowly flashing amber light/arrow which allows you to filter right, with care.

Pedestrian Crossings

There are lots of pedestrian crossings, even more than in the UK, but they are more often than not ignored by motorists (except those from abroad). Don't be surprised if you're honked at for stopping for pedestrians!

Autoroutes

Mostly these are toll roads, and you must pay to use them. You will either have to pay at the toll (Péage) where you join, or you must take a ticket from the machine at the Péage and surrender this, with your money or credit card, at the Péage where you leave the Autoroute. There are service areas (Aires de Service) with full facilities every 40 km. on Autoroutes, and rest areas (Aires de Repos) also at regular intervals. Both have warning signs well in advance, indicating the facilities and even the price of fuel.

Signposting

Is better than in the past but the positioning and angling of signposts is something one just gets used to.

Navigating

Michelin Maps are the most popular, particularly the Michelin 1: 200,000 scale Atlas, but for more detailed maps you can buy IGN Maps, which are the French equivalent of our Ordnance Survey maps, but often even more expensive.

Breakdowns

You should have breakdown insurance; towing in France can involve long distances and hefty charges. If you do break down you are required to display your warning triangle 30 m. behind your car (or car and caravan) and it should be visible for at least 100 m. if possible. Don't forget to turn on hazard lights as well. There are emergency phones every two kilometres on Autoroutes.

Security

Take sensible precautions against theft of, or from, your vehicle and/or caravan – be vigilant in car parks and Aires de Service where thieves are often active.

Before you set off for a holiday abroad it's worth making yourself a checklist of things to do, and what to pack. It's not always best to rely on our memory for this, so here is a shortlist of essentials to start you off:

- ☐ Passports
- ☐ Tickets
- ☐ Motor Insurance Certificate, Green Card or Continental Cover clause
- ☐ V5 Registration Document and/or (if not your vehicle) the owners authority
- ☐ Breakdown Insurance Certificate
- ☐ Driving Licence
- ☐ Form E1-11 (to extend NHS Insurance to European destinations)
- ☐ Foreign Currency (euros) and/or Travellers Cheques
- ☐ Credit Card(s)
- ☐ Campsite and Tourist Guide(s)
- ☐ Maps/Road Atlas
- ☐ GB Stickers on car & caravan/trailer
- ☐ Beam deflectors to ensure headlights dip towards the right hand side
- ☐ Red Warning Triangle
- ☐ Spare vehicle/caravan driving light bulbs
- ☐ Torch
- ☐ First-Aid Kit (incl. mosquito repellent)
- ☐ Fire extinguisher
- ☐ Basic tool kit (eg screwdriver, pliers)
- ☐ Continental mains connector/ adaptor, and long cable
- ☐ Polarity tester
- ☐ Spare fuses for car and caravan
- ☐ Spare fan/alternator belt

Remember: it is well worth having your car and caravan serviced before you go, and do check that your outfit is properly 'trimmed'.

Travelling in France

Speed

Most of Europe has a bewildering range of speed limits, but in France it is simple and logical. One set of limits covers motor caravans, solo cars and cars towing trailers or caravans. These are the limits:

In built-up areas 50 kph (31 mph)
Outside built-up areas 90 kph (56 mph)
Motorways 130 kph (81 mph)

There is also a requirement that no vehicle may use a French motorway unless it can cruise at 80 kph (50 mph).

When it is raining the maximum speed outside built-up areas is automatically reduced to 80 kph (50 mph) and on motorways to 110 kph (68 mph). The definition of rain is any time you have to put wipers on, so reduce speed even if it has stopped raining but roads are wet.

On non-charged sections of motorway, speed limits may be reduced to 110 kph (68 mph) and there may be signs on any road reducing the maximum speed allowed because of road conditions or oher factors.

The French do not tend to use a sign on the outskirts of a town or village to tell you a speed limit applies. A name post is sufficient to indicate that built-up area limits apply. On the exit from the town you will see the name post again, but with the name crossed out. That means the built-up area speed limits no longer apply.

Speed limits are rigidly enforced: 110 kph means exactly that, not 111 kph. The French have adopted the Gatso automatic speed recording and photographing machine and holidaymakers have returned home to find a speeding summons waiting.

Under French Law the summons for speeding cannot be enforced unless the driver of the vehicle is clearly identifiable in the photograph. However the majority of speeding motorists are caught by a following Police vehicle or Police speed camera. French Police don't wear reflective jackets and do hide behind hedges.

During the summer months French magistrates escape from stuffy court rooms and set up court in a tent by the road. Motorists caught speeding are escorted there and given on-the-spot fines. In some circumstances the Police can themselves impose an on-the-spot fine. On-the-spot means just that. If you can't pay there and then they'll escort you to a cash machine or bank to draw out money.

Since 2001 laws have come into effect so that anyone caught exceeding the speed limit by more than 40kph will LOSE THEIR LICENCE ON THE SPOT – this means you won't be able to complete your journey without a substitute driver, to say nothing of the standard £900 fine! If you really cannot pay, magistrates have the power to confiscate your vehicle until you do. Anyone caught for a second offence faces a three month jail sentence plus a £2,200 fine. So although French speed limits are more generous than ours, exceeding the limit can be a seriously expensive pastime.

Insurance

There is probably no subject which causes campers, caravanners and motor-caravanners venturing abroad more worries than insurance. The problem is that there is an overlap, so that sometimes one problem is apparently covered on two insurance policies. To avoid confusion let's cut through the hype and take a clear look at insurance and what you will need.

Road traffic insurance

Under European Law your ordinary car or motorcaravan road insurance will cover you anywhere in the EU. But many policies only provide minimum cover. So if you have an accident your insurance may only cover the cost of damage to the other person's property.

To maintain the same level of cover abroad as you enjoy at home you need to tell your vehicle insurer. Some will automatically cover you abroad with no extra cost and no extra paperwork. Some will say you need a Green Card – which is neither green or on card – but won't charge for it. Some will charge extra for the green card.

Ideally you should contact your vehicle insurer 3-4 weeks before you set off, and confirm your conversation with them in writing.

A good insurance company will provide a European recognised accident report form. On this you mark details of damage to yours and the other party's property and draw a little diagram showing where the vehicles were in relation to each other. You give a copy of your form to the other motorist, he gives you a copy of his. It prevents all the shouting which often accompanies accidents in this country.

Holiday insurance

This is a multi-part insurance. One part covers your vehicles. If they breakdown or are involved in an accident they can be repaired or returned to this country. The best will even arrange to bring your vehicle home if the driver is unable to proceed.

Many new vehicles come with a free breakdown and recovery insurance which extends into Europe. Some professional motoring journalists have reported that the actual service this provides can be patchy and may not cover the recovery of a caravan or trailer. Our advice is to buy the motoring section of your holiday insurance.

The second section of holiday insurance covers people. It will include the cost of doctor, ambulance and hospital treatment if needed. If needed the better companies will even pay for English language speaking doctors and nurses and will bring a sick or injured holidaymaker home by air ambulance.

The third part of a good holiday insurance policy covers belongings. If someone breaks in to your motorhome and steals your passports and money, one phone call to the insurance company will have everything sorted out. If you manage to drive over your camera, it's covered.

One part of the insurance which is often ignored is the cancellation section. Few things are as heartbreaking as having to cancel a holiday because a member of the family falls ill. Cancellation insurance cannot take away the disappointment, but it makes sure you don't suffer financially as well.

Ideally you should arrange travel insurance when you book your ferry. If you are using the Alan Rogers' Travel Service they will be able to take care of all your travel insurance requirements.

For those travelling independently, we have arranged special terms with Insure4Europe run in association with Green Flag (and which imposes no restriction on the age of your vehicle). Full details are shown overleaf.

Insurance

Form E111

By arrangement between the British Government and rest of the European Community Governments, British holiday-makers can enjoy the same health care as that Government offers its own citizens. The form which shows you are entitled to take advantage of this arrangement is called E111.

E111 doesn't replace holiday insurance, but is in addition to. The form is available from all main UK Post Offices. Fill out one for every member of your family. Get it stamped by the counter staff and take it on holiday with you.

In theory one Form E111 lasts you for ever. But we have had reports that in some rural areas in Europe they may not understand that, so our advice is to get a new E111 every year. It is free.

And that is all you need to know about insurance. You know what they say about insurance, don't you? You'll only need it if you haven't got it.

Mike Cazalet

Public Holidays in France 2004

1 January (Thu)	New Year
9 April (Fri)	Good Friday (Moselle and Alsace)
11 April (Sun)	Easter
12 April	Easter Monday
1 May (Sat)	Labour Day
8 May (Sat)	Victory Day 1945
20 May (Thu)	Ascension
30 May (Sun)	Whitsun
31 May	Whit Monday
14 July (Wed)	Bastille Day
15 August (Sun)	Assumption
1 November (Mon)	All Saint's Day
11 November (Thu)	Armistice Day
25 December (Sat)	Christmas
26 December (Sun)	Boxing Day (Alsace and Moselle)

www.insure④europe.com

Taking your own tent, caravan or motorhome abroad?

Looking for the best cover at the best rates?

Our prices considerably undercut most high street prices and the 'in-house insurance' of many tour operators whilst offering equivalent (or higher) levels of cover.

Our annual multi-trip policies offer superb value, covering you not only for your european camping holiday but also subsequent trips abroad for the next 12 months.

Total Peace of Mind

To give you total peace of mind during your holiday our insurance policies have been specifically tailored to cover most potential eventualities on a self-drive camping holiday. Each is organised through Voyager Insurance Services Ltd who specialize in travel insurance for Europe and for camping in particular. All policies are underwritten by UK Underwriting Ltd, on behalf of a consortium of insurance companies that are members of the Association of British Insurers and the Financial Ombudsman services.

24 Hour Assistance

Our personal insurance provides access to the services of Inter Group Assistant Services (IGAS), one of the UK's largest assistance companies. European vehicle assistance cover is provided by Green Flag who provide assistance to over 3 million people each year. With a Europe-wide network of over 7,500 garages and agents you know you're in very safe hands.

Both IGAS and Green Flag are very used to looking after the needs of campsite-based holidaymakers and are very familiar with the location of most European campsites, with contacts at garages, doctors and hospitals nearby.

Save with an Annual policy

If you are likely to make more than one trip to Europe over the next 12 months then our annual multi-trip policies could save you a fortune. Personal cover for a couple starts at just £95 and the whole family can be covered for just £115. Cover for up to 17 days wintersports participation is included.

Low Cost Annual multi-trip insurance

Premier Annual Europe self-drive
including 17 days wintersports

£95.00 per couple

Premier Annual Europe self-drive
including 17 days wintersports

£115.00 per family

Low Cost Combined Personal and Vehicle Assistance Insurance

Premier Family Package
10 days cover for vehicle, 2 adults plus dependent children under 16.

£75.00*

Premier Couples Package
10 days cover for vehicle and 2 adults

£61.00*

* Motorhomes, cars towing trailers and caravans, all vehicles over 4 years old and holidays longer than 10 days attract supplements – ask us for details. See leaflet for full terms and conditions.

Saga Caravan and Motorhome Insurance

Wide-ranging cover at low prices

Saga is one of the main providers of caravan and motorhome insurance in the UK for people aged 50 and over. If you are looking for high levels of cover at low prices, it could pay to call us.

Saga Caravan and Motorhome Insurance includes:

- All year round cover throughout Europe, at no extra cost
- 'New for old' caravan or motorhome replacement - if your caravan is less than five years old or your motorhome is less than two years old and with a mileage of under 12,000, and it is either stolen or damaged beyond repair, providing you were its first owner
- Substantial cover for your personal belongings and camping equipment
- No Claim Discount available, subject to your past claims experience.

SAGA

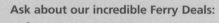
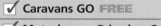

INCONITO - Photos : Dorian Shaw - Scorpius - Wallis - Hoa-Qui.

Fifty-five good reasons for coming to France

SITES & PAYSAGES of FRANCE, 55 quality campsites covering the rich diversity of the French regions.

SITES & PAYSAGES of France offers campers and caravanners a carefully chosen selection of high quality, 3- and 4-star comfortable campsites across the country. Our 55 campsites are situated in attractively landscaped, tree-shaded environments, with all the amenities for tents, caravans, camping-cars, mobile homes or chalet accommodation. All are laid out with 'room to breathe' and located in areas of great natural beauty, with masses to do and see, from on-site sport and leisure activities, to nearby heritage visits… not forgetting the sublime joys of authentic local French cuisine.

Ask us for your FREE 2004 guide

SITES & PAYSAGES
Chemin des Bosses - Orouet
85160 - St Jean de Monts - FRANCE
Fax 00 33 251 590 535

Information & reservations in English
00 33 228 114 036

www.sites-et-paysages.com
E.mail us at: **contact@sites-et-paysages.com**

Dover to Dunkerque

With up to 10 sailings a day Norfolkline is the smart way to cross the Channel.

Dunkerque is a favourite gateway into France that provides...

SPECIAL OFFERS AVAILABLE THROUGHOUT THE YEAR

...rapid access to Belgium, Holland and beyond.

Miles better for France

Wherever you live in the UK, wherever you're heading for in France, there's a Brittany Ferries route to save you miles of unnecessary driving. Sail by day or overnight from Portsmouth, Poole or Plymouth and enjoy award-winning service.

New Portsmouth - Cherbourg route for 2004

Additional weekend Portsmouth to St Malo sailings for 2004

New luxury flagship for 2004, offers the fastest UK to Spain ferry crossing

Call now to book
0870 908 1261

Paying too much

for your mobile home holiday?

Travel off peak
and Pay Just £27.50 per night
with Holiday Cheque

Holiday Cheque gives you exclusive off peak access to quality mobile homes and chalets on nearly 100 of Europe's finest campsites. You'll find superb family facilities, including sensational pools, great value restaurants, friendly bars and real hospitality. And the kids can have the time of their lives! All for just £27.50 per night.

- ✓ 100 top campsites
- ✓ All just £27.50 per night
- ✓ High quality mobile homes
- ✓ Luxury high specification chalets
- ✓ Fully equipped - down to the corkscrew!
- ✓ Plus unbeatable ferry prices

Huge savings - but hurry

HOLIDAY CHEQUES COST JUST £27.50 PER NIGHT. THAT'S A SPECIAL PROMOTIONAL RATE, SAVING UP TO 50% OFF CAMPSITE'S STANDARD PRICES. BUT IT'S FIRST COME, FIRST SERVED, SO THERE'S NO TIME TO LOSE IF YOU WANT TO BOOK THE CAMPSITE OF YOUR CHOICE.

Luxury mobile homes and chalets on Europe's finest Sites

HOLIDAY CHEQUE

Call today for your FREE brochure
0870 405 4058

it will save you £££'s on your holiday

www.holidaycheque.co.uk

Alan Rogers

Belle FRANCE

Walking & Cycling Holidays

Discover the easy going
alternative

Belle France offers cycling and walking holidays
through the most beautiful and interesting parts
of France.

Your luggage is moved for you whilst you find
your own way, at your own pace with our
detailed maps and notes.

Relax in the evening in charming family run hotels,
offering a good standard of accommodation and
a warm and friendly welcome.

Call now for a
FREE brochure
0870 405 4056

www.bellefrance.co.uk

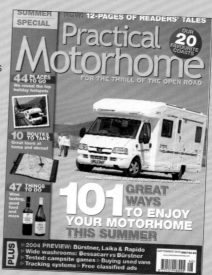

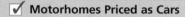

Index of Advertisers

	page		page
Alan Rogers - Mobile Homes	368	Holiday Cheque	379
Alan Rogers - Pitch and Ferries	369	Insure4Europe	367
Belle France Holidays	380	IPC Magazines	373
Brittany Ferries	377	Norfolk Line	376
British Naturism	354	Saga Insurance	370
Camping Cheque	382	Sea France	375
Camping Plus Bretagne	29	Sites et Paysages	374
Castels Camping & Caravanng	372	Vendee Travel Service	378
Haymarket Magazines	381	Warners Group	371

Campsites

FR22040	Le Châtelet	31	FR37060	L'Arada Parc	143	FR63050	La Ribeyre	253
FR29000	Les Mouettes	35	FR37030	Le Moulin Fort	144	FR63080	Moulin de Serre	255
FR29130	Des Abers	36	FR37090	La Rolandière	146	FR07020	Ardéchois	259
FR29080	Le Panoramic	37	FR41010	Val de Loire	147	FR07030	Soleil Vivarais	261
FR29060	Le Pil-Koad	39	FR41070	Grande Tortue	149	FR07070	Les Ranchisses	262
FR29050	Orangerie Lanniron	40	FR45010	Bois du Bardelet	151	FR07090	Des Plantas	263
FR29020	Saint Laurent	42	FR49010	Etang de la Brèche	153	FR07110	Le Pommier	265
FR29190	Les Prés Verts	43	FR49060	Européen	155	FR26020	De Senaud	266
FR29310	La Roche Percée	44	FR86030	Relais du Miel	157	FR69020M	Grappe Fleurie	270
FR29140	Haven de Kerlann	46	FR86040	Le Futuriste	159	FR04100	International	272
FR29090	Raguénès-Plage	47	FR86090	Parc de Saint-Cyr	160	FR04020	Camp du Verdon	272
FR29010	Ty-Nadan	48	FR21000	Lac de Panthier	163	FR04030	Moulin de Ventre	274
FR29180	Les Embruns	49	FR21040M	De Fouché	164	FR04010	Hippocampe	275
FR35000	Le Vieux Chêne	50	FR71020M	Des Meuniers	167	FR04080	Etoile des Neiges	276
FR44040	Sainte-Brigitte	52	FR71070	L'Epervière	169	FR05000	Princes d'Orange	277
FR44090	Du Deffay	54	FR71090	Lac de St Point	171	FR84090	Pont d'Avignon	280
FR44130	L'Hermitage	55	FR38010	Le Coin Tranquille	179	FR09060	Pré Lombard	285
FR44160	Armor-Héol	56	FR74100	Europa	187	FR32010	Camp de Florence	287
FR56020	La Plage	57	FR33110	Côte d'Argent	192	FR65070	Le Rioumajou	289
FR56010	La Grande Métairie	58	FR40020	Les Chênes	199	FR11060	Arnauteille	295
FR56040	Penboch	60	FR40100	La Rive	202	FR11070	Les Mimosas	297
FR56050	Kervilor	61	FR40160	Les Vignes	205	FR11080	La Nautique	298
FR56200	Lann Hoedic	62	FR40190	Saint Martin	206	FR30080	Mas de Reilhe	301
FR56120	Les Iles	63	FR40170	Haven La Réserve	207	FR30160	Le Boucanet	303
FR27020	Catinière	71	FR40180	Le Vieux Port	208	FR30190	Gorges du Gardon	304
FR50000	Etang des Haizes	73	FR64060	Pavillon Royal	209	FR34170	Les Mimosas	307
FR50070	Anse du Brick	74	FR64090	La Chêneraie	210	FR34150	Nouvelle Floride	308
FR50060	Le Grand Large	75	FR64110	Col d'Ibardin	211	FR34030	Le Napoléon	309
FR61010M	La Campière	77	FR12150	Marmotel	215	FR34140	Haven Carabasse	311
FR80030	Port de Plaisance	85	FR12050	Terrasses du Lac	217	FR34070	Sérignan Plage	312
FR80040	Le Royon	86	FR12020	Les Rivages	219	FR34060	Oliveraie	315
FR80060	Le Val de Trie	87	FR12000	Peyrelade	220	FR66170	Mar I Sol	319
FR77030M	De Jablines	91	FR12080	Les Genêts	221	FR66030	Cala Gogo	320
FR52030	Lac de la Liez	98	FR16050M	De Cognac	222	FR66040	Le Soleil	320
FR67030	Du Ried	101	FR16030M	Le Champion	223	FR66110	Le Dauphin	324
FR88070	Des Messires	104	FR16020	Gorges Chambon	224	FR06080	Les Cigales	327
FR17010	Bois Soleil	110	FR24080	Moulin de David	231	FR06050	La Vieille Ferme	328
FR17050	Orée du Bois	112	FR24030	Les Périères	232	FR06090	Gorges du Loup	329
FR17140	Sequoia Parc	113	FR24090	Soleil Plage	233	FR06030	La Bergerie	330
FR17160	Le Clos Fleuri	114	FR24150	Les Deux Vallées	234	FR83020	Esterel	332
FR17180	Haven La Pignade	115	FR24320	Les Peneyrals	235	FR83230	Colombier	334
FR17230	L'Océan	117	FR46030	Les Pins	238	FR83070	Etoile d'Argens	336
FR17190	Logis du Breuil	118	FR46010	La Paille Basse	239	FR83010	Pins Parasols	338
FR85210	Les Ecureuils	125	FR47010	Moulin du Périé	241	FR83200	Les Pêcheurs	339
FR85070	Les Biches	133	FR47030	De Fonrives	242	FR83170	La Bergerie	340
FR85300	La Grand' Métairie	135	FR03010	La Filature	245	FR83080	Au Paradis	341
FR85120	Haven Bois Masson	136	FR15030	Val Saint Jean	247	FR83220	Cros de Mouton	342
FR85150	La Yole	137	FR19060	Le Mialaret	249	FR20010	Arinella Bianca	349
FR37010	La Mignardière	142	FR23010	Poinsouze	250			

Brittany

Map 1

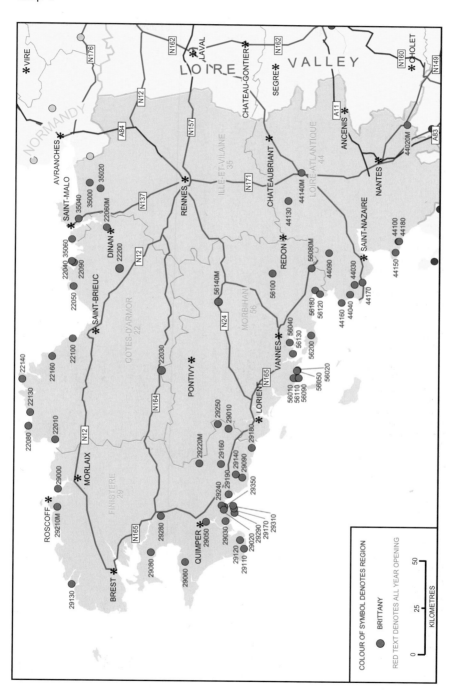

Map 2

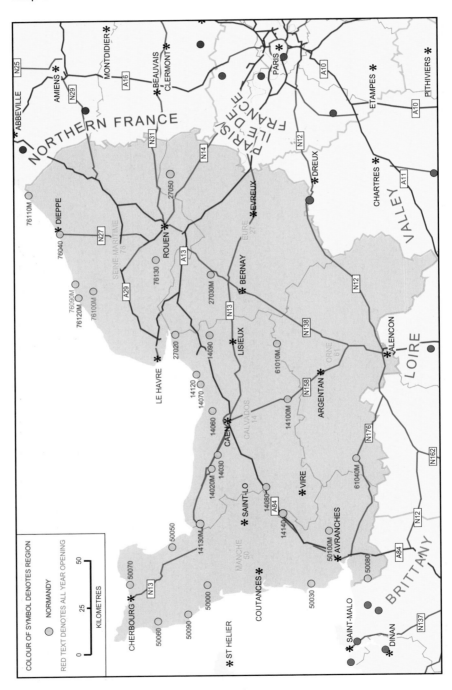

Map 3

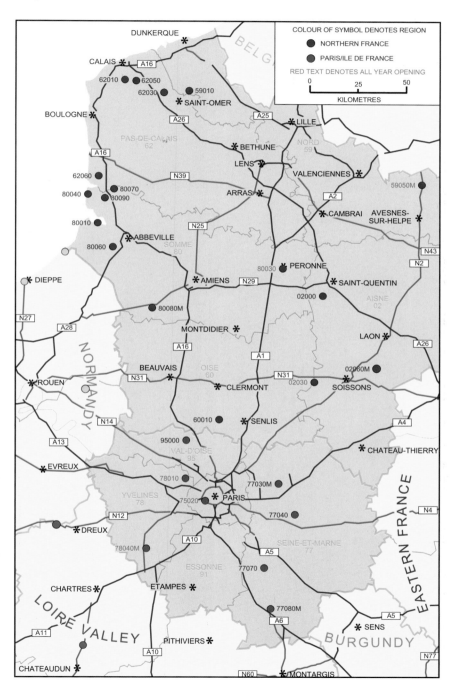

Eastern France

Map 4

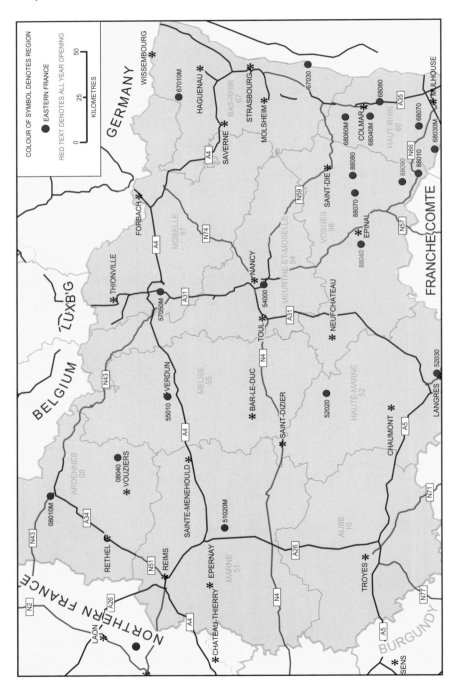

Map 5

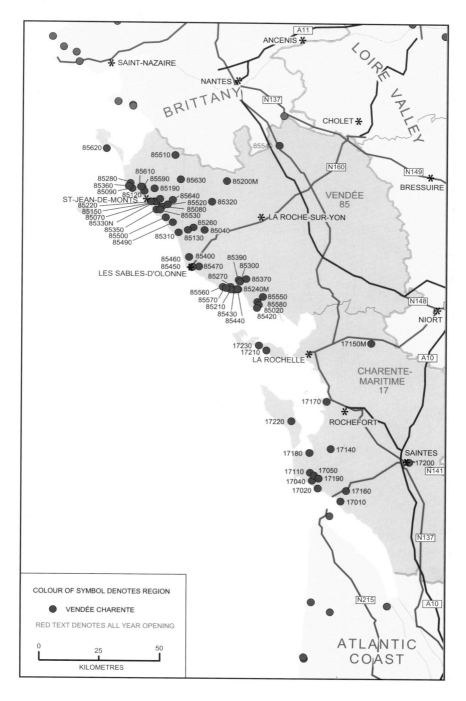

ANCENIS ✳

A11

LOIRE VALLEY

✳ SAINT-NAZAIRE

NANTES ✳

N137

BRITTANY

CHOLET ✳

85540

85620

85510

N160

N149

VENDÉE
85

BRESSUIRE ✳

85280
85360
85090

85610
85590
85120

85630
85190

85200M

ST-JEAN-DE-MONTS ✳
85220
85150
85070
85330N
85350
85500
85490

85640
85520
85080
85530
85260
85310   85040
85130

85320

✳ LA ROCHE-SUR-YON

85460
85450
LES SABLES-D'OLONNE

85400
85470
85270

85390
85300

85370

85560
85570
85210
85430
85440

85240M
85550
85580
85020
85420

N148

NIORT ✳

17230
17210

17150M

LA ROCHELLE ✳

A10

CHARENTE-
MARITIME
17

17170

17220

ROCHEFORT ✳

17180

17140

SAINTES
✳ 17200

17110
17040
17020

17050
17190

17160

N141

17010

N137

N215

A10

ATLANTIC
COAST

COLOUR OF SYMBOL DENOTES REGION

● VENDÉE CHARENTE

RED TEXT DENOTES ALL YEAR OPENING

0   25   50

KILOMETRES

Loire Valley West

Map 6

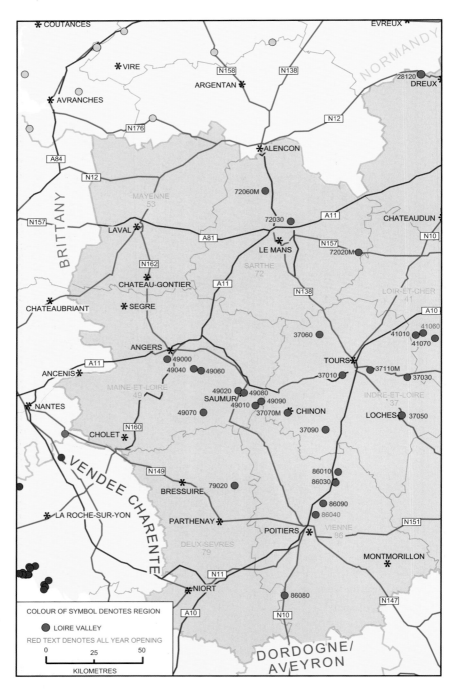

COUTANCES

EVREUX

VIRE

N158   N138

ARGENTAN

28120
DREUX

AVRANCHES

N176

N12

A84

N12

ALENCON

MAYENNE
53

72060M

N157

72030   A11

CHATEAUDUN

LAVAL

A81

N157

N10

LE MANS

72020M

N162

CHATEAU-GONTIER

A11

SARTHE
72

BRITTANY

N138

LOIR-ET-CHER
41

CHATEAUBRIANT

SEGRE

A10

37060

41060

41010

41070

ANGERS

TOURS

37110M

A11

49000

ANCENIS

49040   49060

37010

37030

MAINE-ET-LOIRE
49

49020   49080

SAUMUR

49090

49010

NANTES

49070

37070M   CHINON

INDRE-ET-LOIRE
37

LOCHES   37050

N160

CHOLET

37090

VENDEE

N149

86010

86030

BRESSUIRE

79020

86090

86040

CHARENTE

LA ROCHE-SUR-YON

PARTHENAY

POITIERS

VIENNE
86

N151

DEUX-SEVRES
79

MONTMORILLON

N11

NIORT

86080

N147

COLOUR OF SYMBOL DENOTES REGION

A10   N10

LOIRE VALLEY

RED TEXT DENOTES ALL YEAR OPENING

0   25   50

KILOMETRES

DORDOGNE/
AVEYRON

NORMANDY

N12

Map 7

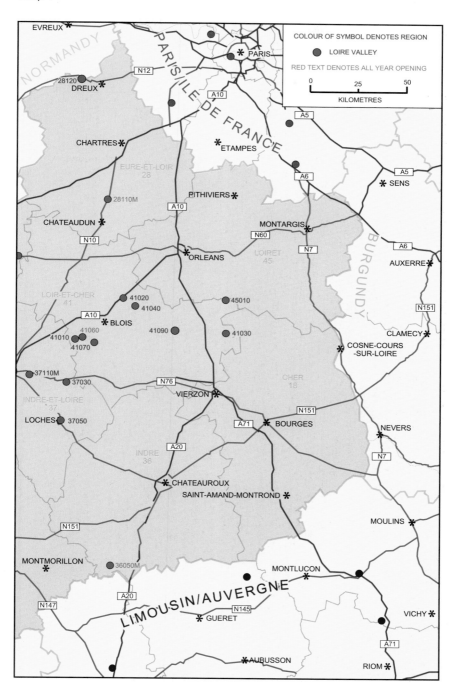

Burgundy

Map 8

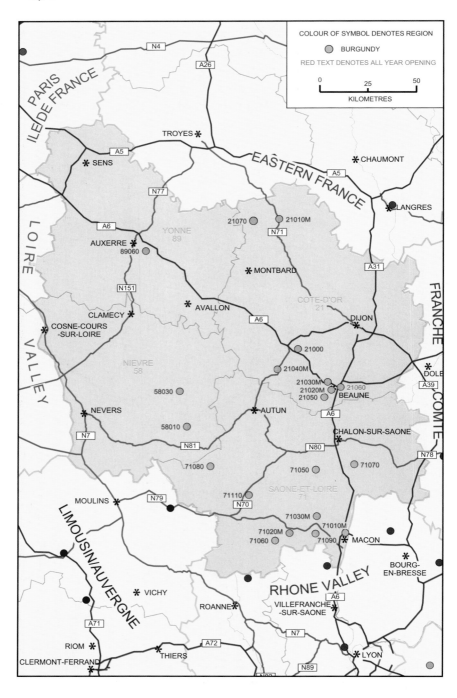

COLOUR OF SYMBOL DENOTES REGION

● BURGUNDY

RED TEXT DENOTES ALL YEAR OPENING

0   25   50

KILOMETRES

PARIS ILE DE FRANCE

N4

A26

TROYES ✳

EASTERN FRANCE

✳ CHAUMONT

A5

✳ SENS

A5

●LANGRES

N77

A5

LOIRE

A6

AUXERRE ✳
89060 ○

YONNE
89

21070 ○   ○ 21010M

N71

✳ MONTBARD

N151

A31

CLAMECY ✳

AVALLON ✳

COTE-D'OR
21

A6

DIJON
✳

✳ COSNE-COURS
-SUR-LOIRE

○ 21000

○ 21040M

NIEVRE
58

21030M ○
21020M ○   ○ 21060
21050 ○   BEAUNE

58030 ○

VALLEY

✳ NEVERS

58010 ○

✳ AUTUN

FRANCHE-COMTE

✳ DOLE

A39

A6

N7

N81

N80

CHALON-SUR-SAONE
✳

N78

71080 ○

71050 ○

○ 71070

MOULINS ✳

N79

71110 ○

N70

SAONE-ET-LOIRE
71

71030M ○

LIMOUSIN/AUVERGNE

71020M ○   ○ 71010M
71060 ○   ○ 71090 ✳ MACON

BOURG-
EN-BRESSE
✳

✳ VICHY

RHONE VALLEY

A6

ROANNE ✳

VILLEFRANCHE
-SUR-SAONE

A71

N7

RIOM ✳

A72

✳ THIERS

N89

CLERMONT-FERRAND

✳ LYON

392

Map 9

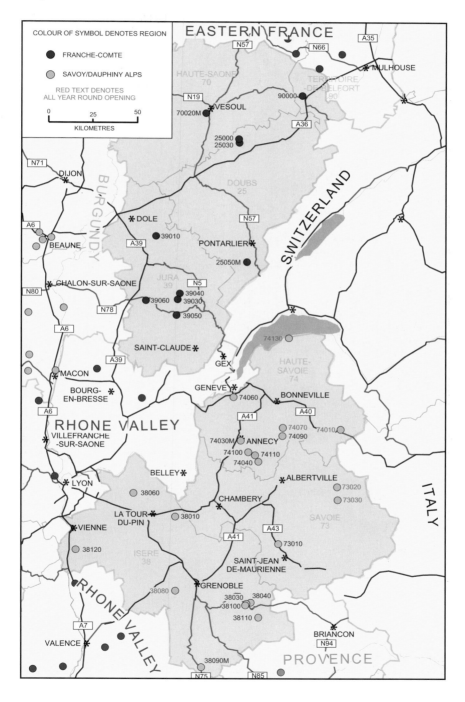

Map 10

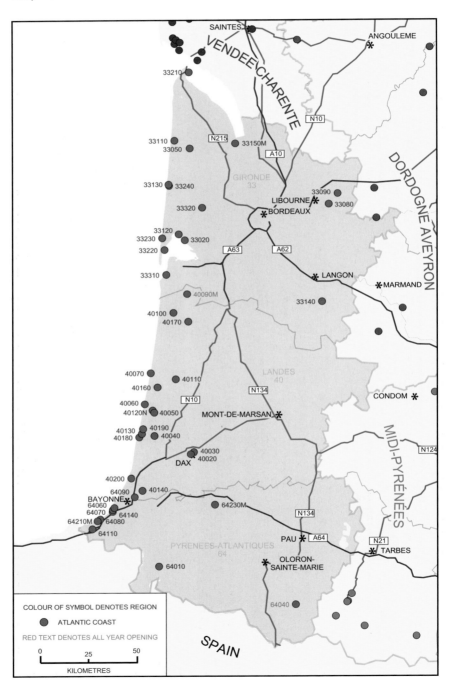

SAINTES

ANGOULEME *

VENDEE CHARENTE

33210

N10

33110
33050

N215

33150M

A10

GIRONDE
33

33130 33240

33090
33080

LIBOURNE *
* BORDEAUX

33320

33120
33230 33020
33220

A63

A62

33310

LANGON *

* MARMAND

40090M

33140

40100
40170

LANDES
40

40070

40160

40110

CONDOM *

40060
40120N 40050

N10

N134

40130 40190
40180 40040

MONT-DE-MARSAN *

40030
40020

DAX

N124

40200

64090 40140

BAYONNE *
64060
64070 64140
64210M 64080

64230M

N134

MIDI-PYRENEES

64110

PAU * A64

N21

* TARBES

64010

PYRENEES-ATLANTIQUES
64

OLORON-
* SAINTE-MARIE

64040

COLOUR OF SYMBOL DENOTES REGION

● ATLANTIC COAST

RED TEXT DENOTES ALL YEAR OPENING

0   25   50

SPAIN

KILOMETRES

Dordogne & Aveyron

Map 11

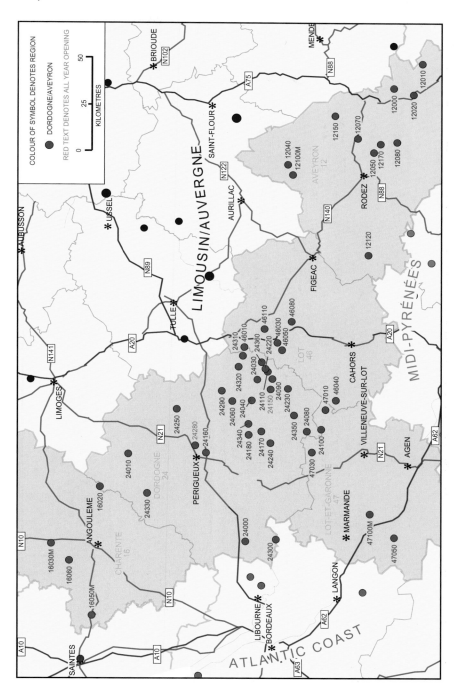

Limousin & Auvergne

Map 12

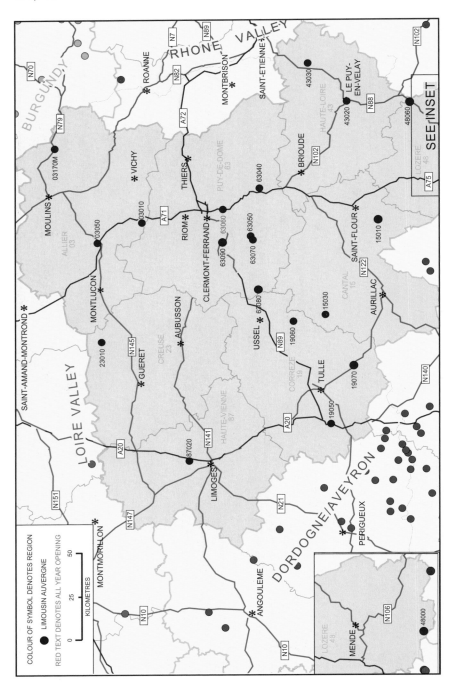

Map 13

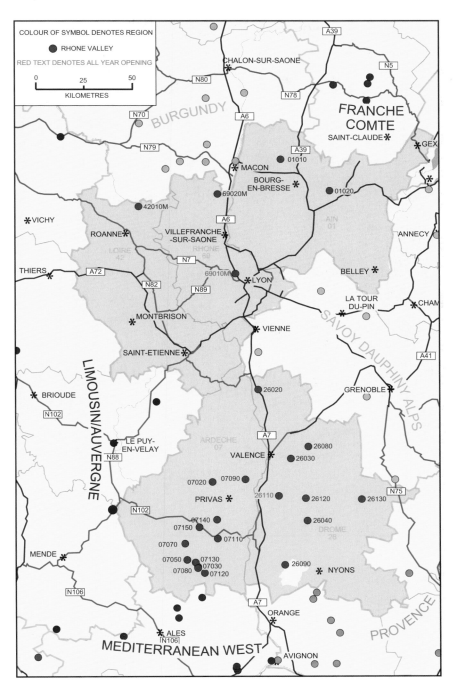

COLOUR OF SYMBOL DENOTES REGION
● RHONE VALLEY
RED TEXT DENOTES ALL YEAR OPENING

0   25   50
KILOMETRES

CHALON-SUR-SAONE

A39

N5

N80

N78

N70

BURGUNDY

A6

FRANCHE COMTE

SAINT-CLAUDE ✳

N79

A39

✳GEX

01010

✳ MACON

BOURG-EN-BRESSE ✳

✳

69020M

01020

42010M

✳VICHY

A6

AIN 01

ANNECY

ROANNE✳

VILLEFRANCHE-SUR-SAONE

LOIRE 42

RHONE 69

N7

BELLEY ✳

THIERS ✳

A72

N82

69010M

✳LYON

N89

LA TOUR DU-PIN ✳

✳CHAM

MONTBRISON ✳

✳ VIENNE

SAVOY DAUPHINY ALPS

SAINT-ETIENNE ✳

GRENOBLE ✳

A41

✳ BRIOUDE

LIMOUSIN/AUVERGNE

26020

N102

LE PUY-EN-VELAY

ARDECHE 07

A7

26080

N88

VALENCE ✳

26030

07020

07090

N75

PRIVAS ✳

26110

26120

26130

N102

07140

07150

07110

26040

DROME 26

07070

MENDE ✳

07050

07130

07030

07080

07120

26090

✳ NYONS

N106

A7

ORANGE

✳ ALES

N106

MEDITERRANEAN WEST

AVIGNON

PROVENCE

Provence

Map 14

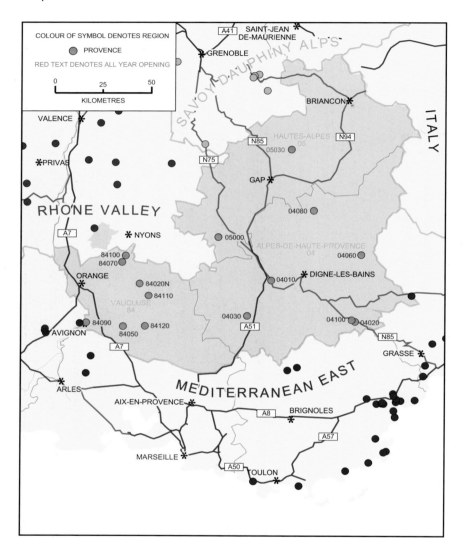

Midi-Pyrénées

Map 15

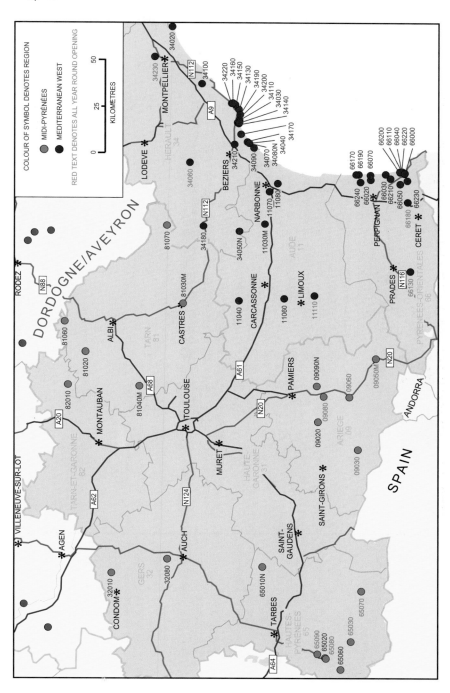

Map 16

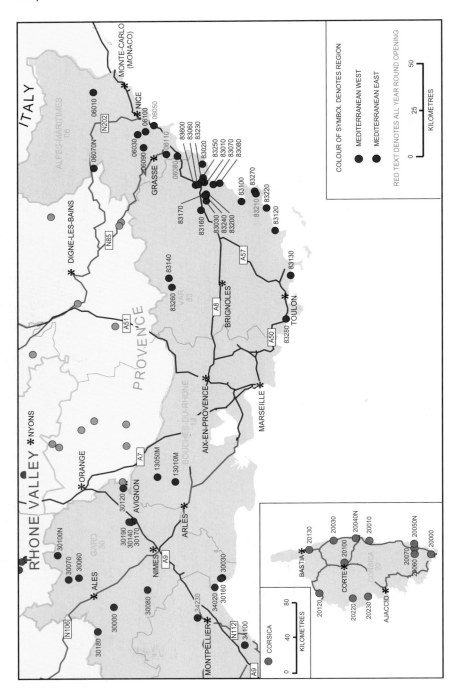

COLOUR OF SYMBOL DENOTES REGION

● MEDITERRANEAN WEST
● MEDITERRANEAN EAST

RED TEXT DENOTES ALL YEAR ROUND OPENING

KILOMETRES
0   25   50

Regions & Départements of France

For administrative purposes France is actually divided into 23 official Regions covering the 95 départements (similar to our counties).

However, theses do not always coincide with the needs of tourists (for example, the area we think of as the 'Dordogne' is split between two official regions. We have, therefore, opted to feature our campsites within unofficial 'tourist' regions.

We use the departement numbers as the first two digits of our campsite numbers so, for example, any site in the Manche departement will start with the number 50.

Town & Village Index

Agde	306	Bormes-les-Mimosas	344	Dol-de-Bretagne	50, 51
Agos Vidalos	290	Bourg-d'Oisans	180-182	Domfront	76
Airvault	157	Bourg-St Maurice	184	Dompierre-les-Ormes	167
Albon	266	Boussac-Bourg	250	Dompierre-sur-Besbre	245
Alèria	354	Brécey	76	Donzenac	248
Alet les Bains	296	Bretignolles-sur-Mer	129	Douarnenez	38
Allègre	299	Brissac	152	Doucier	175
Allegre les Fumades	301	Brousses et Villaret	296	Doussard	186, 187
Allés sur Dordogne	229	Buysscheure	81	Ebreuil	245
Amphion les Bains	188	Buzancy	96	Eguisheim	102
Andernos les Bains	191	Calvi	353	Eperlecques	83
Anduze	299	Calviac en Périgord	232	Erquy	29
Angers	151	Campagne	236	Esquieze-Sere	288
Angles	120	Campouriez	216	Estaing	290
Annecy	185	Candé-sur-Beuvron	149	Etables-sur-Mer	32
Arès	194	Canet de Salars	218	Falaise	69
Argelès-Gazost	288, 289	Canet-en-Roussillon	322, 323	Fiquefleur-Equainville	71
Argelès sur Mer	318-325	Cany-Barville	78	Fleurie	270
Argentat	248	Cap Ferret Océan	197	Foix	284
Arnay le Duc	164	Carantec	35	Forcalquier	275
Arradon	60	Careil	52	Fort-Mahon-Plage	86
Aubenas	264	Carlucet	240	Fouesnant	43-45
Autingues par Ardres	82	Carnac	58, 59	Fouras	116
Autrans	181	Carqueiranne	344	Francueil-Chenonceaux	144
Avignon	280	Carsac-Aillac	231	Fréjus	334-338
Avrillé	121	Castellane	272	Fresne-sur-Authie	84
Azur	200	Castelnau-Magnoac	286	Ghisonaccia	349
Badefoils sur Dordogne	229	Castres	291	Gibles	168
Baden	64	Caurel	30	Gien	151
Balaruc les Bains	314	Cavalaire-sur-Mer	342	Gigny-sur-Saône	169
Ballan-Miré	142	Chabeuil	267	Gordes	281
Bannalec	46	Chaillac	141	Grâne	268
Barbières	268	Châlons-en Champagne	97	Grez sur Loing	91
Barjac	300	Chamonix	185	Grignan	268
Barneville Carteret	76	Charleville-Mezieres	96	Grimaud	341
Bayeux	66	Charlieu	269	Guégon-Josselin	62
Bayonne	210	Château-d'Olonne	126	Guemene-Penfao	55
Bazas	195	Châteaulin	37	Guérande	52
Beaumont sur Sarthe	156	Châtellerault	157	Guignicourt	82
Beaune	162	Châtillon-sur-Seine	162	Guilligomarc'h	45
Bédoin	278	Chinon	142	Guines	83
Beg-Meil	44	Clairvaux-les-Lacs	176	Hautecourt	258
Belfort	177	Clapiers	316	Hautot-sur-Mer	77
Belves	236	Clisson	53	Herpelmont	104
Bénodet	41	Clohars-Carnoët	49	Houlgate	67
Benon	114	Cluny	170	Hourtin	191, 192
Bénouville	67	Cognac	222	Huanne	173
Berny-Riviere	82	Concarneau	43	Ingrandes-sur-Vienne	158
Bidart	209, 213	Concourson-sur-Layon	154	Isigny-sur-Mer	70
Bignac	222	Corcieux	106	Issoire	254
Biguglia-Bastia	353	Cordes-sur-Ciel	291	Issy-l'Évêque	179
Biron	230	Corte	352	Jablines	91
Biscarosse	202	Couhé	158	Jard-sur-Mer	124, 125
Bois de Céné	119	Coutures	155	Jugon-les Lacs	30
Boisset et Eaujac	299	Crévecoeur-en-Brie	90	Jumieges	79
Boissière de Montaigu	120	Creysse	240	La Bastide-de-Sérou	283
Bonifacio	350	Daglan	233	La Baule	56
Bonnac-la-Côte	256	Darbres	264	La Clusaz	189
Bonneval	141	Dardilly	270	La Colle-sur-Loup	331
Boofzheim	101	Dax	199		

Town & Village Index

La Couarde sur Mer	117	Mandelieu la Napoule	327	Parentis-en-Born	207
La Forêt Fouesnant	41, 42	Mansle	223	Paris	90
La Grande Motte	305	Marcenay	165	Pauillac	196
La Haye du Puits	73	Marigny	175	Payrac-en-Quercy	238
La Mothe-Achard	127	Marseillan Plage	308-311	Peisey-Nancroix	184
La Plaine-Sur-Mer	55	Martragny	66	Penestin-sur-Mer	63, 64
La Roche Bernard	60	Masevaux	101	Perigeux	226
La Romieu 287		Maubeuge	82	Péronne	85
La Roquette-sur-Siagne	330	Maupertus-sur-Mer	74	Perros Guirec	33
La Tranche-sur-Mer	121, 122	Mauriac	247	Pierrefitte-sur-Sauldre	147
La Trinité	350	Maussane	332	Piriac-sur-Mer	56
La Trinité-sur-Mer	57, 61	Médis	114	Pleubian	34
La Turballe	52	Melun	92	Plobannalec-Lesconil	39
Labenne Océan	208	Menglon	269	Plougoulm	35
Lacanau	198	Mesland	147	Poilly	151
Lacanau-Océan	195	Messanges	206, 208	Poix-de-Picardie	85
Lalley	179	Metz	100	Pont Farcy	70
Landéda	36	Meursault	164	Pont Kereon	46
Landevieille	128	Meyrueis	252	Pont-Aven	46
Langogne	252	Mézos	204	Pontchâteau	54
Langres	98	Millau	219	Pont-de-Salars	217
Lanloup	32	Mirabel et Blacons	269	Pont-l'Evêque	68
Largentière	262	Mirandol-Bourgnounac	292	Pontorson	75
Laruns	212	Moliets-Plage	207	Pornic	53, 57
Laurens	315	Monpazier	231	Port Camargue	300
Le Bar sur Loup	329	Montbron	224	Portiragnes Plage	307
Le Bec-Hellouin	72	Montcabrier	237	Porto	353
Le Bois-Plage-en-Ré	116	Montclar	276, 295	Porto-Vecchio	350, 351
Le Boulou	325	Montignac	227, 228	Poullan sur Mer	38
Le Château-d'Oléron	118	Montmarault	246	Puget-Theniers	328
Le Grand-Bornand	188	Montmeyan	345	Pyla sur Mer	197, 199
Le Grau du Roi	300, 303	Montpon Ménestérol	224	Quimper	40
Le Guilvinec	39	Montrevel-en-Bresse	258	Quissac	301
Le Muy	342	Montsoreau	155	Rabastens	291
Le Perrier	120	Mousterlin	45	Raguénéz	47
Le Poet Célard	267	Moyenneville	87	Ramatuelle	345, 346
Le Puy-en-Velay	251	Muides-sur-Loire	148	Rambouillet	93
Le Trein d'Ustou	283	Murol	253, 254	Régusse	347
Le Tréport	78	Nages	292	Remoulins	302, 305
Le Verdon-sur-Mer	196	Nampont-St Martin	84	Riquewihr	102
Le Vigan	237	Nant-d'Aveyron	218	Rivière sur Tarn	220
Lège	197	Narbonne	297, 298	Rochefort en Terre	61
Les Abrets	179	Nébouzat	256	Ronce les Bains	115
Les Issambres	341	Nesles-la-Vallée	93		
Les Mathes	109-112	Neung-sur-Beuvron	150		
Les Ollières-sur-Eyrieux	263	Neuvéglise	246		
Les Pieux	75	Neuvic	249		
Les Sables-d'Olonne	126	Névez	47		
Lézignan-Corbières	295	Neydens	186		
L'Isle sur la Sorgue	279	Notre Dame de Riez	130		
Lit-et-Mixe	205	Nozay	53		
Loches en Touraine	144	Oberbronn	100		
Locunolé	48	Olonne-sur-Mer	127		
Longeville sur Mer	123	Olonzac	317		
Lons-le-Saunier	176	Onzain	150		
Lussac	192	Orcet	254		
Lyons la Foret	71	Orpierre	277		
Maché	121	Ounans	174		
Mâcon	176	Palau del Vidre	322		
Maisons-Laffitte	92	Palinges	170		

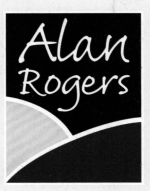

Town & Village Index

Roquebrune sur Argens 336-340
Roquelaure 286
Rougemont 173
Ruoms 258-261
Sagone 354
Sainte Mère Eglise 74
Saintes 115
Salies de Bearn 212
Salignac-Eyvigues 235
Salles Curan 221
Sampzon 260
Sanary sur Mer 346
Sanchey 105
Sanguinet 205
San-Nicolao 352
Sarlat 230-233
Sarzeau 62
Saulxures sur Moselotte 106
Saumur 152, 154
Sauveterre la Lemance 241
Savigny les Beaune 162
Scaer 42
Seraucourt le Grand 81
Sérignan 312
Séverac-l'Eglise 217
Sillé le Philippe 156
Singles 255
Sonzay 143
Sorgeat 285
Sospel 327
Souillac sur Dordogne 239
St Amans des Cots 216
St Antoine de Breuilh 227
St Antonin Noble Val 292
St Augustin sur Mer 118
St Avit de Vialard 229
St Aygulf 336
St Boil 168
St Calais 156
St Cast-le-Guildo 29, 31
St Crépin-Carlucet 235
St Croix-en-Plaine 103
St Cyprien 318
St Cyprien-Plage 320
St Cyr 160
St Emilion 194
St Etienne du Bois 119
St Geniès en Périgord 235
St Geniez-d'Olt 215
St Georges de Didonne 110
St Georges les Baillargeaux 159
St Gilles Croix de Vie 129, 130
St Hilaire de Riez 131-134
St Hilaire la Foret 133, 134
St Honoré-les-Bains 166
St Jean de Luz 210, 212
St Jean de Monts 135-139
St Jean du Gard 304
St Jean Pied de Port 209
St Jean-St Nicolas 277

St Jorioz 187
St Julien de Lampon 237
St Julien des Landes 128
St Julien-en-Born 202
St Just-Luzac 113
St Lary Soulan 289
St Leu-d'Esserent 94
St Lucieb de Porto-Vecchio 351
St Lunaire 51
St Malo 50
St Martin de Seignanx 206
St Martin des Besaces 68
St Martin sur la Chambre 183
St Maurice sur Moselle 105
St Pair sur Mer 72
St Palais sur Mer 109
St Pardoux 225
St Paul lès Dax 200
St Pereuse en Morvan 166
St Point 171
St Point-Lac 174
St Pons de Thonières 315
St Privat de Champclos 300
St Raphael 331, 335
St Reine de Bretagne 54
St Rémy de Provence 331
St Remy sur Avre 141
St Romain en Viennois 281
St Sauveur de Montagut 259
St Sigolène 251
St Symphorien le Valois 73
St Valery en Caux 78
St Valéry sur Somme 84
St Vincent sur Jard 123
Suévres 148
Taden 31
Tarascon sur Ariege 285
Telgruc sur Mer 37
Thonnance les Moulins 97
Tonneins 242
Torreilles Plage 317, 318
Torreilles 319
Tourtoirac 226
Tredrez-Locquémeau 34
Trélévern 33
Trept 180
Trogues 146
Ucel 264
Urrugne 211
Vaison la Romaine 279
Vallon-Pont d'Arc 264
Valras-Plage 314, 316
Vandenesse en Auxois 163
Varennes sur Loire 153
Varilhes 284
Vence 330
Venosc 182
Verdun 100
Veretz 143
Vernet les Bains 325

Vernioz 183
Vers-Pont-du-Gard 304
Vesoul 177
Veulettes-sur-Mer 79
Vézac 234
Vias-Plage 309, 310
Vias sur Mer 311
Vielle St Girons 201, 204
Vieux-Mareuil 225
Vignolles 165
Villars-Colmars 276
Villefranche de Queyran 243
Villefranche de Rouergue 215
Villeneuve les Avignon 302
Villeneuve de Berg 265
Villeneuve les Béziers 307
Villeneuve Loubet Plage 328
Villeréal 242
Villers les Nancy 98
Villers sur Authie 86
Villers sur Mer 69
Villes sur Auzon 278
Vimoutiers 77
Vincelles 171
Volonne 274
Wattwiller 103

Campsite Index by Number

FR01010	La Plaine Tonique	258
FR01020	Ile Chambod	258
FR02000	Vivier aux Carpes	82
FR02030	Croix du Vieux Pont	82
FR02060M	Guignicourt	81
FR03010	La Filature	245
FR03050	La Petite Valette	246
FR03170M	Dompierre	245
FR04010	Hippocampe	274
FR04020	Verdon	272
FR04030	Moulin de Ventre	275
FR04060	Haut-Verdon	276
FR04080	Etoile des Neiges	276
FR04100	International	272
FR05000	Princes d'Orange	277
FR05030	Les Six Stations	277
FR06010	Sainte Madeleine	327
FR06030	La Bergerie	330
FR06050	La Vieille Ferme	328
FR06070N	Origan	328
FR06080	Les Cigales	327
FR06090	Gorges du Loup	329
FR06100	Les Pinèdes	331
FR06110	Panoramic	330
FR07020	Ardéchois	259
FR07030	Soleil Vivarais	261
FR07050	Le Ranc Davaine	260
FR07070	Les Ranchisses	262
FR07080	La Bastide	260
FR07090	Des Plantas	263
FR07110	Le Pommier	265
FR07120	Ardéchois	264
FR07130	Les Coudoulets	258
FR07140	Les Lavandes	264
FR07150	Domaine de Gil	264
FR08010M	Mont Olympe	96
FR08040	La Samaritaine	96
FR09020	Arize	283
FR09030	Le Montagnou	283
FR09050M	La Prade	285
FR09060	Le Pré Lombard	285
FR09080	Du Lac	284
FR09090N	Millfleurs	284
FR11030M	La Pinède	295
FR11040	Le Martinet Rouge	296
FR11060	Arnauteille	295
FR11070	Les Mimosas	297
FR11080	La Nautique	298
FR11110	Val d'Aleth	296
FR12000	Peyrelade	220
FR12010	Val de Cantobre	218
FR12020	Les Rivages	219
FR12040	Les Tours	216
FR12050	Terrasses du Lac	217
FR12070	Grange de Monteillac	217
FR12080	Les Genêts	221
FR12100M	Lauradiol	216
FR12120	Rouergue	215
FR12150	Marmotel	215
FR12170	Le Caussanel	218
FR13010M	Les Romarins	332
FR13050M	Mas de Nicolas	331
FR14020M	Bayeux	66
FR14030	Martragny	66
FR14060	Hautes Coutures	67
FR14070	La Vallée	67
FR14080	Le Puits	68
FR14090	Brévedent	68
FR14100M	Du Château	69
FR14120	Les Ammonites	69
FR14130M	Fanal	70
FR14140	Pont Farcy	70
FR15010	Le Belvédère	246
FR15030	Le Val Saint Jean	247
FR16020	Gorges du Chambon	224
FR16030M	Le Champion	223
FR16050M	Cognac	222
FR16060	Marco de Bignac	222
FR17010	Bois Soleil	110
FR17020	Puits de L'Auture	109
FR17040	Bonne Anse Plage	109
FR17050	Orée du Bois	112
FR17110	Monplaisir	110
FR17140	Sequoia Parc	113
FR17150M	Château Benon	114
FR17160	Le Clos Fleuri	114
FR17170	Les Charmilles	116
FR17180	La Pignade	115
FR17190	Logis du Breuil	118
FR17200	Au Fil de l'Eau	115
FR17210	Interlude	116
FR17220	La Brande	118
FR17230	L'Océan	117
FR19050	La Rivière	248
FR19060	Le Mialaret	249
FR19070	Chateau de Gibanel	248
FR20000	U. Farniente	350
FR20010	Arinella Bianca	349
FR20030	Merendella	352
FR20040N	Riva Bella	354
FR20050N	La Chiappa	351
FR20060	La Vetta	350
FR20070	Santa Lucia	351
FR20100	Santa Barbara	352
FR20120	Le Panoramic	353
FR20130	San Damiano	353
FR20220	Les Oliviers	353
FR20230	Le Sagone	354
FR21000	Lac de Panthier	163
FR21010M	Louis Rigoly	162
FR21020M	Les Cents Vignes	162
FR21030M	Savigny-les-Beaune	162
FR21040M	De Fouché	164
FR21050	Grappe d'Or	164
FR21060	Les Bouleaux	165
FR21070	Les Grèbes	165
FR22010	Les Capucines	34
FR22030	Nautic International	30
FR22040	Le Châtelet	31
FR22050	Le Vieux Moulin	29

Campsite Index by Number

FR22060M	La Hallerais	31
FR22080	Le Ranolien	33
FR22090	Galinée	29
FR22100	Abri Côtier	32
FR22130	Port l'Epine	33
FR22140	Port La Chaine	34
FR22160	Le Neptune	32
FR22200	Le Bocage	30
FR23010	Poinsouze	250
FR24000	La Tuilière	224
FR24010	Le Verdoyer	225
FR24030	Les Périères	232
FR24040	Moulin du Roch	230
FR24060	Le Paradis	227
FR24080	Moulin de David	231
FR24090	Soleil Plage	233
FR24100	Le Moulinal	230
FR24110	Aqua Viva	231
FR24150	Deux Vallées	234
FR24160	Grand Dague	226
FR24170	Port de Limeuil	229
FR24180	Saint Avit Loisirs	229
FR24220	Chênes Verts	232
FR24230	Moulin de Paulhiac	233
FR24240	Les Bo-Bains	229
FR24250	Tourterelles	226
FR24280	Barnabé	226
FR24290	Moulin du Bleufond	228
FR24300	La Rivière Fleurie	227
FR24310	La Bouquerie	235
FR24320	Les Peneyrals	235
FR24330	Etang Bleu	225
FR24340	Val de la Marquise	236
FR24350	Moulin de la Pique	236
FR24360	Le Mondou	237
FR25000	Val de Bonnal	173
FR25030	Bois de Reveuge	173
FR25050M	Saint Point-Lac	174
FR26020	De Senaud	266
FR26030	Grand Lierne	267
FR26040	Le Couspeau	267
FR26080	Le Gallo Romain	268
FR26090	Les Truffières	268
FR26110	Les 4 Saisons	268
FR26120	Gervanne	269
FR26130	Hirondelle	269
FR27020	Catinière	71
FR27030M	Saint-Nicolas	72
FR27050	Saint-Paul	71
FR28110M	Bonneval	141
FR28120	Pré de l'Eglise	141
FR29000	Les Mouettes	35
FR29010	Ty-Nadan	48
FR29020	Saint-Laurent	42
FR29030	Du Letty	41
FR29050	Orangerie de Lanniron	40
FR29060	Le Pil-Koad	38
FR29080	Le Panoramic	37
FR29090	Raguenèz-Plage	47
FR29110	La Plage	39
FR29120	Manoir de Kerlut	39

FR29130	Des Abers	36
FR29140	Kerlann	46
FR29160	Genets d'Or	46
FR29170	La Piscine	44
FR29180	Les Embruns	49
FR29190	Les Prés Verts	43
FR29210M	Bois de la Palud	35
FR29220M	Kerisole	42
FR29240	Kéranterec	41
FR29250	Bois des Ecureuils	45
FR29280	La Pointe Superbe	37
FR29290	Grand Large	45
FR29310	Roche Percée	44
FR29350	Atlantique	43
FR30000	Gaujac	299
FR30030	Abri de Camargue	300
FR30060	Fumades	299
FR30070	Boisson	301
FR30080	Mas de Reilhe	301
FR30100N	La Sablière	300
FR30120	Ile des Papes	302
FR30140	Soubeyranne	302
FR30160	Le Boucanet	303
FR30170	La Sousta	305
FR30180	Mas de la Cam	304
FR30190	Gorges du Gardon	304
FR32010	Florence	287
FR32080	Le Talouch	286
FR33020	Fontaine-Vieille	191
FR33050	Les Ourmes	191
FR33080	Barbanne	194
FR33090	Le Pressoir	192
FR33110	Côte d'Argent	192
FR33120	La Cigale	194
FR33130	Les Grands Pins	195
FR33140	Le Grand Pré	195
FR33150M	Les Gabarreys	196
FR33210	Pointe du Medoc	196
FR33220	Petit Nice	197
FR33230	Le Truc Vert	197
FR33240	L'Océan	198
FR33310	Panorama	199
FR33320	Talaris	198
FR34020	Le Garden	305
FR34030	Le Napoléon	310
FR34040	Lou Village	314
FR34050N	Mas de Lignières	317
FR34060	Oliveraie	315
FR34070	Sérignan Plage	312
FR34080N	Sérignan Plage Nature	312
FR34090	La Yole	316
FR34100	Mas du Padre	314
FR34110	Le Club Farret	309
FR34130	Le Neptune	306
FR34140	La Carabasse	311
FR34150	Nouvelle Floride	308
FR34160	Charlemagne	309
FR34170	Les Mimosas	307
FR34180	Borio de Roque	315
FR34190	Champs Blancs	306

Campsite Index by Number

FR34200	Californie Plage	310	FR44090	Deffay	54
FR34210	Berges du Canal	307	FR44100	Le Patisseau	53
FR34220	La Creole	311	FR44130	Hermitage	55
FR34230	De Chênes	316	FR44140M	Henri Dubourg	53
FR35000	Vieux Chêne	50	FR44150	La Tabardière	55
FR35020	Des Ormes	51	FR44160	Armor-Héol	56
FR35040	P'tit Bois	50	FR44170	Ajoncs d'Or	56
FR35060	La Touesse	51	FR44180	Boutinardière	57
FR36050M	Vieux Chênes	141	FR45010	Bois du Bardelet	151
FR37010	Mignardière	142	FR46010	Paille Basse	239
FR37030	Moulin Fort	144	FR46030	Les Pins	238
FR37050	La Citadelle	144	FR46040	Moulin de Laborde	237
FR37060	Arada Parc	143	FR46050	Le Rêve	237
FR37070M	Ile Auger	142	FR46080	Lacomté	240
FR37090	La Rolandière	146	FR46110	Du Port	240
FR37110M	Bord du Cher	143	FR47010	Moulin du Périé	241
FR38010	Coin Tranquille	179	FR47030	Fonrives	242
FR38030	La Cascade	180	FR47050	Moulin de Campech	243
FR38040	Rencontre du Soleil	181	FR47100M	Tonneins	242
FR38060	Les Trois Lacs	180	FR48000	Champ d'Ayres	252
FR38080	Au Joyeux Réveil	181	FR48060	Les Terraces du Lac	252
FR38090M	Belle Roche	179	FR49000	Lac de Maine	151
FR38100	Belledonne	182	FR49010	Etang de la Brèche	153
FR38110	Champ du Moulin	182	FR49020	Chantepie	152
FR38120	Bontemps	183	FR49040	Etang	152
FR39010	Plage Blanche	174	FR49060	Montsabert	155
FR39030	Chalain	175	FR49070	Vallée des Vignes	154
FR39040	La Pergola	175	FR49080	Ile d'Offard	154
FR39050	Fayolan	176	FR49090	Isle Verte	155
FR39060	La Marjorie	176	FR50000	Etang des Haizes	73
FR40020	Les Chênes	199	FR50030	Lez-Eaux	72
FR40030	Pins du Soleil	200	FR50050	Le Cormoran	74
FR40040	La Paillotte	200	FR50060	Le Grand Large	75
FR40050	Le Col-Vert	201	FR50070	Anse du Brick	74
FR40060	Eurosol	201	FR50080	Haliotis	75
FR40070	Lous Seurrots	202	FR50090	La Gerfleur	76
FR40090M	Lou Broustaricq	205	FR50100N	Le Pont-Roulland	76
FR40100	La Rive	202	FR51020M	Châlons-sur-Marne	97
FR40110	Sen Yan	204	FR52020	Forge de Ste Marie	97
FR40120N	Arnaoutchot	204	FR52030	Lac de la Liez	98
FR40130	La Côte	206	FR54000	Le Brabois	98
FR40140	Lou P'tit Poun	207	FR55010	Les Breuils	100
FR40160	Les Vignes	205	FR56010	Grande Métairie	58
FR40170	La Réserve	207	FR56020	La Plage	57
FR40180	Le Vieux Port	208	FR56040	Penboch	60
FR40190	Saint Martin	206	FR56050	Kervilor	61
FR40200	Sylvamar	208	FR56080M	Le Pâtis	60
FR41010	Val de Loire	147	FR56090	Moulin de Kermaux	59
FR41020	Grenouillière	148	FR56100	Moulin Neuf	61
FR41030	Alicourts	147	FR56110	Moustoir	59
FR41040	Des Marais	148	FR56120	Les Iles	63
FR41060	De Dugny	150	FR56130	Mané Guernehué	64
FR41070	Grande Tortue	149	FR56140M	Bas de la Lande	62
FR41090	de la Varenne	150	FR56180	Le Cénic	64
FR42010M	Charlieu	269	FR56200	Lann Hoedic	62
FR43020	Puy-en-Velay	251	FR57050M	Metz-Plage	100
FR43030	Vaubarlet	251	FR58010	Des Bains	166
FR44020M	Du Moulin	53	FR58030	Bezolle	166
FR44030	Château de Careil	52	FR59010	La Chaumière	82
FR44040	Sainte-Brigitte	52	FR59050M	Mauberge	83

Campsite Index by Number

FR60010	Campix	94	FR71060	Montrouant	168
FR61010M	La Campière	77	FR71070	Epervière	169
FR61040M	Champ Passais	76	FR71080	Etang Neuf	179
FR62010	La Bien-Assise	84	FR71090	Lac de St-Point	171
FR62030	Château de Gandspette	83	FR71110	Du Lac	170
FR62050	St Louis	83	FR72020M	Du Lac	156
FR62060	L'Oree du Bois	84	FR72030	Chanteloup	156
FR63040	La Grange Fort	254	FR72060M	Val de Sarthe	156
FR63050	La Ribeyre	253	FR73010	Le Bois Joli	183
FR63060	Le Clos Auroy	255	FR73020	Le Versoyen	184
FR63070	Le Pré Bas	254	FR73030	Les Lanchettes	184
FR63080	Le Moulin de Serre	255	FR74010	Deux Glaciers	185
FR63090	les Domes	256	FR74030M	Belvédère	185
FR64010	Europ	209	FR74040	La Ravoire	186
FR64040	Les Gaves	212	FR74060	La Colombière	186
FR64060	Pavillon Royal	209	FR74070	Escale	188
FR64070	Le Ruisseau	213	FR74090	Plan du Fernuy	189
FR64080	Tamaris Plage	210	FR74100	Europa	187
FR64090	La Chêneraie	210	FR74110	Le Taillefer	187
FR64110	Col d'Ibardin	211	FR74130	La Plage	188
FR64140	Bérrua	213	FR75020	Bois de Boulogne	90
FR64210M	Chibaou-Berria	212	FR76040	La Source	77
FR64230M	Mosqueros	212	FR76090M	Etennemare	78
FR65010N	Eglantière	286	FR76100M	Cany-Barville	78
FR65020	Trois Vallées	288	FR76110M	Les Boucaniers	78
FR65030	Pyrénées	288	FR76120M	Veulettes-seu-Mer	79
FR65060	Pyrenees Natura	290	FR76130	La Forêt	79
FR65070	Le Rioumajou	289	FR77030M	Jablines	91
FR65080	Le Lavedan	289	FR77040	Des 4 Vents	90
FR65090	Soleil du Pibeste	290	FR77070	Belle Etoile	92
FR66000	Le Pujol	323	FR77080M	Les Prés	91
FR66020	Ma Prairie	322	FR78010	International	92
FR66030	Cala Gogo	320	FR78040M	Etang d'Or	93
FR66040	Le Soleil	320	FR79020	Courte Vallée	157
FR66050	Le Haras	322	FR80010	Drancourt	86
FR66070	Le Brasilia	323	FR80030	Port de Plaisance	87
FR66110	Le Dauphin	324	FR80040	Le Royon	85
FR66130	Eau Vive	325	FR80060	Val de Trie	88
FR66170	Mar I Sol	319	FR80070	Ferme des Aulnes	86
FR66180	Mas Llinas	325	FR80080M	Bois des Pêcheurs	87
FR66190	Les Tropiques	317	FR80090	Val d'Authie	85
FR66200	Les Marsouins	324	FR81020	Moulin de Julien	291
FR66210	Le Roussillon	318	FR81030M	Gourjade	291
FR66220	Du Stade	318	FR81040M	Auzerals	291
FR66230	Le Romarin	325	FR81060	Les Clots	292
FR66240	Le Trivoly	318	FR81070	Rieu Montagné	292
FR67010M	Eichelgarten	100	FR82010	Trois Cantons	292
FR67030	Du Ried	101	FR83010	Pins Parasol	338
FR68030M	Masevaux	101	FR83020	Esterel	331
FR68040M	Trois Châteaux	102	FR83030	Leï Suves	338
FR68060M	Riquewihr	102	FR83060	La Baume	335
FR68070	Les Sources	103	FR83070	Etoile d'Argens	336
FR68080	Clair Vacances	103	FR83080	Au Paradis	341
FR69010M	Porte de Lyon	270	FR83100	La Plage	341
FR69020M	Grappe Fleurie	270	FR83120	Domaine	342
FR70020M	Lac Vesoul	177	FR83130	Le Beau Vezé	344
FR71010M	Mâcon	176	FR83140	Lacs du Verdon	345
FR71020M	Meuniers	167	FR83160	Les Cigales	342
FR71030M	St Vital	170	FR83170	La Bergerie	340
FR71050	Moulin de Collonge	168	FR83200	Les Pêcheurs	339

Campsite Index by Number

FR83210	Les Tournels	345	FR85370	Mancellières	121
FR83220	Cros de Mouton	343	FR85390	Batardières	134
FR83230	Colombier	334	FR85400	Bois Soleil	127
FR83240	Moulin des Iscles	336	FR85420	Bel	122
FR83250	Douce Quiétude	335	FR85430	Bolée D'Air	123
FR83260	Eouvière	345	FR85440	Les Brunelles	123
FR83270	La Cigale	346	FR85450	Les Roses	126
FR83280	Mas de Pierredon	346	FR85460	Dune des Sables	126
FR83600	Holiday Green	334	FR85470	Les Pirons	126
FR84020N	Bélézy	278	FR85490	Beaulieu	130
FR84050	La Sorguette	279	FR85500	Bahamas Beach	129
FR84070	Carpe Diem	279	FR85510	Le Bois Joli	119
FR84090	Pont d'Avignon	280	FR85520	Renardieres	130
FR84100	Soleil de	281	FR85530	Parée Préneau	131
FR84110	Les Verguettes	278	FR85540	Eden	120
FR84120	Des Sources	281	FR85550	Port de Moricq	120
FR85020	Du Jard	122	FR85560	Le Curtys	124
FR85040	La Garangeoire	127	FR85570	Le Pomme de Pin	124
FR85070	Les Biches	133	FR85580	Les Blancs Chenes	121
FR85080	Puerta del Sol	132	FR85590	Plein Sud	135
FR85090	Abri des Pins	138	FR85610	Calypso	135
FR85120	Le Bois Masson	136	FR85620	Le Caravan'ile	139
FR85130	Pong	128	FR85630	Maison Blanche	120
FR85150	La Yole	137	FR85640	Les Chouans	130
FR85190	Marais Braud	132	FR86010	Petit Trianon	158
FR85200M	Petite Boulogne	119	FR86030	Relais du Miel	157
FR85210	Les Ecureuils	125	FR86040	Le Futuriste	159
FR85220	Acapulco	136	FR86080	Les Peupliers	158
FR85240M	Jarny-Ocean	123	FR86090	Saint Cyr	160
FR85260	Guyonnière	128	FR87020	Leychoisier	256
FR85270	Oceano d'Or	124	FR88010	Deux Ballons	105
FR85280	Places Dorées	138	FR88040	Lac de Bouzey	105
FR85300	Grand' Métairie	133	FR88070	Messires	104
FR85310	La Trévillière	129	FR88080	Des Bans	106
FR85320	Val de Vie	121	FR88090	Lac de la Moselotte	106
FR85330N	Cap Natur'	134	FR89060	Les Ceriselles	171
FR85350	La Ningle	131	FR90000	Etang des Forges	177
FR85360	La Forêt	139	FR95000	Séjours Etang	93

Campsite Index by Region

Brittany

FR22090	Galinée	29
FR22050	Le Vieux Moulin	29
FR22200	Le Bocage	30
FR22030	Nautic International	30
FR22060M	La Hallerais	31
FR22040	Le Châtelet	31
FR22160	Le Neptune	32
FR22100	Abri Côtier	32
FR22130	Port l'Epine	33
FR22080	Le Ranolien	33
FR22010	Les Capucines	34
FR22140	Port La Chaine	34
FR29000	Les Mouettes	35
FR29210M	Bois de la Palud	35
FR29130	Des Abers	36
FR29080	Le Panoramic	37
FR29280	La Pointe Superbe	37
FR29060	Le Pil-Koad	38
FR29110	La Plage	39
FR29120	Manoir de Kerlut	39
FR29050	Orangerie de Lanniron	40
FR29030	Du Letty	41
FR29240	Kéranterec	41
FR29220M	Kerisole	42
FR29020	Saint-Laurent	42
FR29190	Les Prés Verts	43
FR29350	Atlantique	43
FR29170	La Piscine	44
FR29310	Roche Percée	44
FR29250	Bois des Ecureuils	45
FR29290	Grand Large	45
FR29140	Kerlann	46
FR29160	Genets d'Or	46
FR29090	Raguénèz-Plage	47
FR29010	Ty-Nadan	48
FR29180	Les Embruns	49
FR35000	Vieux Chêne	50
FR35040	P'tit Bois	50
FR35060	La Touesse	51
FR35020	Des Ormes	51
FR44030	Château de Careil	52
FR44040	Sainte-Brigitte	52
FR44140M	Henri Dubourg	53
FR44100	Le Patisseau	53
FR44020M	Du Moulin	53
FR44090	Deffay	54
FR44150	La Tabardière	55
FR44130	Hermitage	55
FR44170	Ajoncs d'Or	56
FR44160	Armor-Héol	56
FR44180	Boutinardière	57
FR56020	La Plage	57
FR56010	Grande Métairie	58
FR56090	Moulin de Kermaux	59
FR56110	Moustoir	59
FR56040	Penboch	60
FR56080M	Le Pâtis	60
FR56100	Moulin Neuf	61
FR56050	Kervilor	61

FR56140M	Bas de la Lande	62
FR56200	Lann Hoedic	62
FR56120	Les Iles	63
FR56130	Mané Guernehué	64
FR56180	Le Cénic	64

Normandy

FR14020M	Bayeux	66
FR14030	Martragny	66
FR14060	Hautes Coutures	67
FR14070	La Vallée	67
FR14080	Le Puits	68
FR14090	Brévedent	68
FR14100M	Du Château	69
FR14120	Les Ammonites	69
FR14130M	Fanal	70
FR14140	Pont Farcy	70
FR27050	Saint-Paul	71
FR27020	Catinière	71
FR50030	Lez-Eaux	72
FR27030M	Saint-Nicolas	72
FR50000	Etang des Haizes	73
FR50050	Le Cormoran	74
FR50070	Anse du Brick	74
FR50080	Haliotis	75
FR50060	Le Grand Large	75
FR50090	La Gerfleur	76
FR61040M	Champ Passais	76
FR50100M	Le Pont-Roulland	76
FR61010M	La Campière	77
FR76040	La Source	77
FR76110M	Les Boucaniers	78
FR76100M	Cany-Barville	78
FR76090M	Etennemare	78
FR76120M	Veulettes-seu-Mer	79
FR76130	La Forêt	79

Northern France

FR02000	Vivier aux Carpes	81
FR02060M	Guignicourt	81
FR59010	La Chaumière	82
FR02030	Croix du Vieux Pont	82
FR59050M	Mauberge	83
FR62050	St Louis	83
FR62030	Château de Gandspette	83
FR62010	La Bien-Assise	84
FR62060	L'Oree du Bois	84
FR80040	Le Royon	85
FR80090	Val d'Authie	85
FR80010	Drancourt	86
FR80070	Ferme des Aulnes	86
FR80030	Port de Plaisance	87
FR80080M	Bois des Pêcheurs	87
FR80060	Val de Trie	88

Paris & Ile de France

FR75020	Bois de Boulogne	90
FR77040	Des 4 Vents	90
FR77030M	Jablines	91
FR77080M	Les Prés	91
FR77070	Belle Etoile	92
FR78010	International	92

Campsite Index by Region

FR95000	Séjours Etang	93
FR78040M	Etang d'Or	93
FR60010	Campix	94

Eastern France

FR08040	La Samaritaine	96
FR08010M	Mont Olympe	96
FR51020M	Châlons-sur-Marne	97
FR52020	Forge de Ste Marie	97
FR52030	Lac de la Liez	98
FR54000	Le Brabois	98
FR57050M	Metz-Plage	100
FR55010	Les Breuils	100
FR67010M	Eichelgarten	100
FR68030M	Masevaux	101
FR67030	Du Ried	101
FR68040M	Trois Châteaux	102
FR68060M	Riquewihr	102
FR68070	Les Sources	103
FR68080	Clair Vacances	103
FR88070	Messires	104
FR88040	Lac de Bouzey	105
FR88010	Deux Ballons	105
FR88090	Lac de la Moselotte	106
FR88080	Des Bans	106

Vendée & Charente

FR17040	Bonne Anse Plage	109
FR17020	Puits de L'Auture	109
FR17110	Monplaisir	110
FR17010	Bois Soleil	110
FR17050	Orée du Bois	112
FR17140	Sequoia Parc	113
FR17160	Le Clos Fleuri	114
FR17150M	Château Benon	114
FR17200	Au Fil de l'Eau	115
FR17180	La Pignade	115
FR17170	Les Charmilles	116
FR17210	Interlude	116
FR17230	L'Océan	117
FR17190	Logis du Breuil	118
FR17220	La Brande	118
FR85200M	Petite Boulogne	119
FR85510	Le Bois Joli	119
FR85550	Port de Moricq	120
FR85630	Maison Blanche	120
FR85540	Eden	120
FR85580	Les Blancs Chenes	121
FR85370	Mancellières	121
FR85320	Val de Vie	121
FR85420	Bel	122
FR85020	Du Jard	122
FR85430	Bolée D'Air	123
FR85440	Les Brunelles	123
FR85240M	Jarny-Ocean	123
FR85560	Le Curtys	124
FR85570	Le Pomme de Pin	124
FR85270	Oceano d'Or	124
FR85210	Les Ecureuils	125
FR85460	Dune des Sables	126
FR85470	Les Pirons	126
FR85450	Les Roses	126

FR85040	La Garangeoire	127
FR85400	Bois Soleil	127
FR85260	Guyonnière	128
FR85130	Pong	128
FR85310	La Trévillière	129
FR85500	Bahamas Beach	129
FR85520	Renardieres	130
FR85490	Beaulieu	130
FR85640	Les Chouans	130
FR85350	La Ningle	131
FR85530	Parée Préneau	131
FR85190	Marais Braud	132
FR85080	Puerta del Sol	132
FR85070	Les Biches	133
FR85300	Grand' Métairie	133
FR85330N	Cap Natur'	134
FR85390	Batardières	134
FR85590	Plein Sud	135
FR85610	Calypso	135
FR85120	Le Bois Masson	136
FR85220	Acapulco	136
FR85150	La Yole	137
FR85090	Abri des Pins	138
FR85280	Places Dorées	138
FR85360	La Forêt	139
FR85620	Le Caravan'ile	139

Loire Valley

FR36050M	Vieux Chênes	141
FR28120	Pré de l'Eglise	141
FR28110M	Bonneval	141
FR37070M	Ile Auger	142
FR37010	Mignardière	142
FR37110M	Bord du Cher	143
FR37060	Arada Parc	143
FR37030	Moulin Fort	144
FR37050	La Citadelle	144
FR37090	La Rolandière	146
FR41030	Alicourts	147
FR41010	Val de Loire	147
FR41020	Grenouillière	148
FR41040	Des Marais	148
FR41070	Grande Tortue	149
FR41060	De Dugny	150
FR41090	de la Varenne	150
FR49000	Lac de Maine	151
FR45010	Bois du Bardelet	151
FR49020	Chantepie	152
FR49040	Etang	152
FR49010	Etang de la Brèche	153
FR49080	Ile d'Offard	154
FR49070	Vallée des Vignes	154
FR49060	Montsabert	155
FR49090	Isle Verte	155
FR72060M	Val de Sarthe	156
FR72020M	Du Lac	156
FR72030	Chanteloup	156
FR86030	Relais du Miel	157
FR79020	Courte Vallée	157
FR86010	Petit Trianon	158
FR86080	Les Peupliers	158
FR86040	Le Futuriste	159

Campsite Index by Region

Burgundy

FR21020M	Les Cents Vignes	162
FR21030M	Savigny-les-Beaune	162
FR21010M	Louis Rigoly	162
FR21000	Lac de Panthier	163
FR21040M	De Fouché	164
FR21050	Grappe d'Or	164
FR21060	Les Bouleaux	165
FR21070	Les Grèbes	165
FR58010	Des Bains	166
FR58030	Bezolle	166
FR71020M	Meuniers	167
FR71060	Montrouant	168
FR71050	Moulin de Collonge	168
FR71070	Epervière	169
FR71030M	St Vital	170
FR71110	Du Lac	170
FR89060	Les Ceriselles	171
FR71090	Lac de St-Point	171

Franche-Comté

FR25030	Bois de Reveuge	173
FR25000	Val de Bonnal	173
FR25050M	Saint Point-Lac	174
FR39010	Plage Blanche	174
FR39030	Chalain	175
FR39040	La Pergola	175
FR39050	Fayolan	176
FR39060	La Marjorie	176
FR71010M	Mâcon	176
FR70020M	Lac Vesoul	177
FR90000	Etang des Forges	177

Savoy & Dauphiny Alps

FR38090M	Belle Roche	179
FR38010	Coin Tranquille	179
FR71080	Etang Neuf	179
FR38030	La Cascade	180
FR38060	Les Trois Lacs	180
FR38080	Au Joyeux Réveil	181
FR38040	Rencontre du Soleil	181
FR38110	Champ du Moulin	182
FR38100	Belledonne	182
FR38120	Bontemps	183

FR73010	Le Bois Joli	183
FR73020	Le Versoyen	184
FR73030	Les Lanchettes	184
FR74010	Deux Glaciers	185
FR74030M	Belvédère	185
FR74060	La Colombière	186
FR74040	La Ravoire	186
FR74110	Le Taillefer	187
FR74100	Europa	187
FR74070	Escale	188
FR74130	La Plage	188
FR74090	Plan du Fernuy	189

Atlantic Coast

FR33020	Fontaine-Vieille	191
FR33050	Les Ourmes	191
FR33110	Côte d'Argent	192
FR33090	Le Pressoir	192
FR33080	Barbanne	194
FR33120	La Cigale	194
FR33130	Les Grands Pins	195
FR33140	Le Grand Pré	195
FR33150M	Les Gabarreys	196
FR33210	Pointe du Medoc	196
FR33230	Le Truc Vert	197
FR33220	Petit Nice	197
FR33320	Talaris	198
FR33240	L'Océan	198
FR40020	Les Chênes	199
FR33310	Panorama	199
FR40040	La Paillotte	200
FR40030	Pins du Soleil	200
FR40060	Eurosol	201
FR40050	Le Col-Vert	201
FR40070	Lous Seurrots	202
FR40100	La Rive	202
FR40110	Sen Yan	204
FR40120N	Arnaoutchot	204
FR40160	Les Vignes	205
FR40090M	Lou Broustaricq	205
FR40130	La Côte	206
FR40190	Saint Martin	206
FR40140	Lou P'tit Poun	207
FR40170	La Réserve	207
FR40180	Le Vieux Port	208
FR40200	Sylvamar	208
FR64010	Europ	209
FR64060	Pavillon Royal	209
FR64080	Tamaris Plage	210
FR64090	La Chêneraie	210
FR64110	Col d'Ibardin	211
FR64230M	Mosqueros	212
FR64040	Les Gaves	212
FR64210M	Chibaou-Berria	212
FR64070	Le Ruisseau	213
FR64140	Bérrua	213

Dordogne & Averyron

FR12150	Marmotel	215
FR12120	Rouergue	215
FR12100M	Lauradiol	216
FR12040	Les Tours	216

INSPECTED CAMPSITES & SELECTED

Campsite Index by Region

FR12050	Terrasses du Lac	217
FR12070	Grange de Monteillac	217
FR12010	Val de Cantobre	218
FR12170	Le Caussanel	218
FR12020	Les Rivages	219
FR12000	Peyrelade	220
FR12080	Les Genêts	221
FR16050M	Cognac	222
FR16060	Marco de Bignac	222
FR16030M	Le Champion	223
FR24000	La Tuilière	224
FR16020	Gorges du Chambon	224
FR24330	Etang Bleu	225
FR24010	Le Verdoyer	225
FR24160	Grand Dague	226
FR24250	Tourterelles	226
FR24280	Barnabé	226
FR24300	La Rivière Fleurie	227
FR24060	Le Paradis	227
FR24290	Moulin du Bleufond	228
FR24240	Les Bo-Bains	229
FR24180	Saint Avit Loisirs	229
FR24170	Port de Limeuil	229
FR24040	Moulin du Roch	230
FR24100	Le Moulinal	230
FR24080	Moulin de David	231
FR24110	Aqua Viva	231
FR24220	Chênes Verts	232
FR24030	Les Périères	232
FR24230	Moulin de Paulhiac	233
FR24090	Soleil Plage	233
FR24150	Deux Vallées	234
FR24310	La Bouquerie	235
FR24320	Les Peneyrals	235
FR24340	Val de la Marquise	236
FR24350	Moulin de la Pique	236
FR46040	Moulin de Laborde	237
FR46050	Le Rêve	237
FR24360	Le Mondou	237
FR46030	Les Pins	238
FR46010	Paille Basse	239
FR46110	Du Port	240
FR46080	Lacomté	240
FR47010	Moulin du Périé	241
FR47100M	Tonneins	242
FR47030	Fonrives	242
FR47050	Moulin de Campech	243

Limousin & Auvergne

FR03010	La Filature	245
FR03170M	Dompierre	245
FR15010	Le Belvédère	246
FR03050	La Petite Valette	246
FR15030	Le Val Saint Jean	247
FR19070	Chateau de Gibanel	248
FR19050	La Rivière	248
FR19060	Le Mialaret	249
FR23010	Poinsouze	250
FR43020	Puy-en-Velay	251
FR43030	Vaubarlet	251
FR48060	Les Terraces du Lac Naussac	252

FR48000	Champ d'Ayres	252
FR63050	La Ribeyre	253
FR63040	La Grange Fort	254
FR63070	Le Pré Bas	254
FR63080	Le Moulin de Serre	255
FR63060	Le Clos Auroy	255
FR63090	Les Domes	256
FR87020	Leychoisier	256

Rhône Valley

FR01010	La Plaine Tonique	258
FR07130	Les Coudoulets	258
FR01020	Ile Chambod	258
FR07020	Ardéchois	259
FR07080	La Bastide	260
FR07050	Le Ranc Davaine	260
FR07030	Soleil Vivarais	261
FR07070	Les Ranchisses	262
FR07090	Des Plantas	263
FR07150	Domaine de Gil	264
FR07120	Ardéchois	264
FR07140	Les Lavandes	264
FR07110	Le Pommier	265
FR26020	De Senaud	266
FR26040	Le Couspeau	267
FR26030	Grand Lierne	267
FR26090	Les Truffières	268
FR26110	Les 4 Saisons	268
FR26080	Le Gallo Romain	268
FR42010M	Charlieu	269
FR26130	Hirondelle	269
FR26120	Gervanne	269
FR69010M	Porte de Lyon	270
FR69020M	Grappe Fleurie	270

Provence

FR04020	Verdon	272
FR04100	International	272
FR04010	Hippocampe	274
FR04030	Moulin de Ventre	275
FR04060	Haut-Verdon	276
FR04080	Etoile des Neiges	276
FR05030	Les Six Stations	277
FR05000	Princes d'Orange	277
FR84110	Les Verguettes	278
FR84020N	Bélézy	278
FR84070	Carpe Diem	279
FR84050	La Sorguette	279
FR84090	Pont d'Avignon	280
FR84100	Soleil de 281	
FR84120	Des Sources	281

Midi-Pyrénées

FR09020	Arize	283
FR09030	Le Montagnou	283
FR09080	Du Lac	284
FR09090N	Millfleurs	284
FR09050M	La Prade	285
FR09060	Le Pré Lombard	285
FR32080	Le Talouch	286
FR65010N	Eglantière	286
FR32010	Florence	287

Campsite Index by Region

FR65020	Trois Vallées	288
FR65030	Pyrénées	288
FR65080	Le Lavedan	289
FR65070	Le Rioumajou	289
FR65090	Soleil du Pibeste	290
FR65060	Pyrenees Natura	290
FR81040M	Auzerals	291
FR81020	Moulin de Julien	291
FR81030M	Gourjade	291
FR82010	Trois Cantons	292
FR81070	Rieu Montagné	292
FR81060	Les Clots	292

Mediterranean West

FR11060	Arnauteille	295
FR11030M	La Pinède	295
FR11040	Le Martinet Rouge	296
FR11110	Val d'Aleth	296
FR11070	Les Mimosas	297
FR11080	La Nautique	298
FR30000	Gaujac	299
FR30060	Fumades	299
FR30100N	La Sablière	300
FR30030	Abri de Camargue	300
FR30080	Mas de Reilhe	301
FR30070	Boisson	301
FR30140	Soubeyranne	302
FR30120	Ile des Papes	302
FR30160	Le Boucanet	303
FR30190	Gorges du Gardon	304
FR30180	Mas de la Cam	304
FR34020	Le Garden	305
FR30170	La Sousta	305
FR34130	Le Neptune	306
FR34190	Champs Blancs	306
FR34170	Les Mimosas	307
FR34210	Berges du Canal	307
FR34150	Nouvelle Floride	308
FR34160	Charlemagne	309
FR34110	Le Club Farret	309
FR34030	Le Napoléon	310
FR34200	Californie Plage	310
FR34220	La Creole	311
FR34140	La Carabasse	311
FR34070	Sérignan Plage	312
FR34080N	Sérignan Plage Nature	312
FR34040	Lou Village	314
FR34100	Mas du Padre	314
FR34180	Borio de Roque	315
FR34060	Oliveraie	315
FR34090	La Yole	316
FR34230	De Chênes	316
FR34050N	Mas de Lignières	317
FR66190	Les Tropiques	317
FR66210	Le Roussillon	318
FR66220	Du Stade	318
FR66240	Le Trivoly	318
FR66170	Mar I Sol	319
FR66030	Cala Gogo	320
FR66040	Le Soleil	320
FR66050	Le Haras	322

FR66020	Ma Prairie	322
FR66000	Le Pujol	323
FR66070	Le Brasilia	323
FR66200	Les Marsouins	324
FR66110	Le Dauphin	324
FR66180	Mas Llinas	325
FR66130	Eau Vive	325
FR66230	Le Romarin	325

Mediterranean East

FR06010	Sainte Madeleine	327
FR06080	Les Cigales	327
FR06050	La Vieille Ferme	328
FR06070N	Origan	328
FR06090	Gorges du Loup	329
FR06030	La Bergerie	330
FR06110	Panoramic	330
FR13050M	Mas de Nicolas	331
FR06100	Les Pinèdes	331
FR83020	Esterel	331
FR13010M	Les Romarins	332
FR83600	Holiday Green	334
FR83230	Colombier	334
FR83250	Douce Quiétude	335
FR83060	La Baume	335
FR83240	Moulin des Iscles	336
FR83070	Etoile d'Argens	336
FR83030	Leï Suves	338
FR83010	Pins Parasol	338
FR83200	Les Pêcheurs	339
FR83170	La Bergerie	340
FR83100	La Plage	341
FR83080	Au Paradis	341
FR83160	Les Cigales	342
FR83120	Domaine	342
FR83220	Cros de Mouton	343
FR83130	Le Beau Vezé	344
FR83260	Eouvière	344
FR83210	Les Tournels	345
FR83140	Lacs du Verdon	345
FR83280	Mas de Pierredon	346
FR83270	La Cigale	346

Corsica

FR20010	Arinella Bianca	349
FR20000	U. Farniente	350
FR20060	La Vetta	350
FR20050N	La Chiappa	351
FR20070	Santa Lucia	351
FR20100	Santa Barbara	352
FR20030	Merendella	352
FR20120	Le Panoramic	353
FR20220	Les Oliviers	353
FR20130	San Damiano	353
FR20040N	Riva Bella	354
FR20230	Le Sagone	354

THIS FORM WILL
save you money

TO QUALIFY FOR SOME MONEY SAVING OFFERS, AND USE-
FUL INFORMATION, SIMPLY RETURN THE COUPON.
NO STAMP REQUIRED.

Register me for savings - today

Ferry savings
Please keep me posted with the latest ferry savings,
special offers and up to date news

Discounts on Alan Rogers Guides
Please offer me discounts on future editions of the
Alan Rogers' Guides plus other camping and caravan-
ning publications

www.alanrogers.com

INSPECTED
CAMPSITES
& SELECTED

Register me for: (Please tick)
❑ Ferry Savings ❑ Discounts on Alan Rogers guides

Mr/Mrs/Ms ____ Initial ____ Surname ____

Address ____

Postcode ____

Telephone ____ Email ____

Brickbats and Bouquets
Tell us what you think of the Alan Rogers Guides
____
____
____

Priority Subscription 2005
**Want a brand new copy of the 2005 Alan Rogers Guides hot
off the press?** If so we'll rush you a priority copy - and guarantee you'll
pay no more than this year's prices. Of course postage and packaging will
be completely free.

❑ BRITAIN & IRELAND ❑ FRANCE ❑ EUROPE
❑ SPAIN & PORTUGAL ❑ ITALY ❑ MOBILE HOMES & CHALETS

Credit card number ☐☐☐☐ ☐☐☐☐ ☐☐☐☐ ☐☐☐☐

Expiry date __/__ Issue no. (switch) ____

*No funds will be taken before 1st January 2005, or publication,
whichever is soonest. Alternatively enclose a cheque (post-dated to
1st January 2005).*

Return in an envelope to address overleaf - **NO STAMP REQUIRED!**

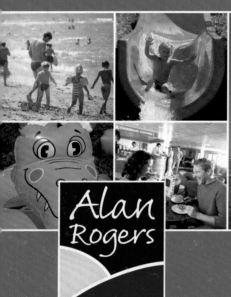